D0319595

.(4.10)

Anatomy
of Agriculture

Anatomy of Agriculture

A study of Britain's greatest industry

Peter Wormell

HARRAP LONDON
and
KLUWER PUBLISHING LONDON

First published in Great Britain 1978
by GEORGE G. HARRAP & CO LTD
182–184 High Holborn, London WC1V 7AX
and KLUWER PUBLISHING LTD
Harlequin Avenue, Brentford, Middlesex

ISBN 0 245 53302 8

Filmsetting by Woolaston Parker Ltd, Leicester
Printed in Great Britain by offset lithography
by Billing and Sons Ltd, Guildford, London and Worcester

Dedicated to FARMERS the world o'er

'*If there is positively something I know nothing about—it is agriculture.*'

First Duke of Wellington

'*Farming is easy if your ploughshare is a pen, and a cornfield is a thousand miles away.*'

Dwight D. Eisenhower

'*Fifty millions, all dwelling in a small island, growing enough food for only, shall we say, thirty millions . . . is a spectacle of . . . insecurity which history has not often seen before.*'

Sir Winston Churchill

Preface

This is an attempt to record and analyse the structure, forces and pressures that lie behind British farming. To the man who milks his cows in the early hours it is obvious that Farming Begins Here, but for every person engaged in the pursuit of farming, from the wealthy landed aristocrat to the lowly shepherd on a distant hill, there are three times as many people engaged in the ancillary industries. Depending upon which attitude you take, they are either backing up the farmer with service and research or milking him for the potential market that farming presents.

In all, over 12 per cent of the working population in Britain today is directly dependent upon a healthy and prosperous agriculture, and the import-saving role of the industry may become more vital as world food-supplies shrink. Yet Britain is not considered an agricultural nation in the same category as Australia, New Zealand, Canada or even many European countries. The vast continent of Australia and the prairies of Canada conjure up visions of the grain basket of the world. In Europe the actual working population engaged in the oldest occupation of mankind is on average four times greater than in the UK. It is as high as 50 per cent in Yugoslavia.

From the paddy fields of Burma to the misty heather of Scotland, the ancient craft of husbandry is to be found. You may see motor-cars being built in the English Midlands, uranium being mined in Western Australia and gold in South Africa, but while such activities are of greater or lesser importance to national economies the world over, the overriding importance of farming everywhere is not to be denied.

Farmers may live in the countryside, wear old clothes, and only invade the local town on market day, either to be treated with reverence for the sales potential they represent, or with disgust for snarling the traffic. Farmers have a way of being arrogant, never having recovered from their historic role in filling the nation's larder when Hitler was menacing the White Cliffs, yet the affluence of a town-bred population is enabling many more people to use the countryside as a dormitory, a week-end retreat from the pressures of city life, or to invade the country lanes on Sunday afternoons. Against this, the farmer is no longer insular either. He has realized that farming is an industry, not just a way of life; that to be accorded his place in the business world he must integrate with non-farming people, and take his place within the confines of modern society. The agrobusinessman has arrived.

This is not to suggest that the hatchets have been buried, and the peace pipes smoked; there is still a wide gulf in outlook, in purpose, and in environment. In any tightly populated island like Britain, there must be more understanding between the 'townee' and his country cousin; after all, it was only 150 years ago that nine out of ten people lived in the countryside. Today nine out of ten live in urban conurbations, but the movement has commenced back to the countryside from whence our great-grandfathers once came. There is an hereditary yearning to follow the plough, to savour the morning mists, and smell the hay. That this may in reality result in smelling the slurry, the diesel fumes of modern machinery, and be awoken by racing tractors, illustrates how the countryside has changed since we last saw it 150 years ago.

If the townsman finds it difficult to understand the modern farmer, then the farmer is baffled too. Ministerial committees, marketing boards, proliferate; there is a never-ceasing supply of White Papers, Acts of Parliament, Official Reports, Commercial Surveys, Statistical Reports, and Experimental Results. Even in farming, amid the stability of the countryside the rules change almost daily.

It is the structure behind the industry that provides its fascination. It is a complex and multifarious structure, that has very largely originated since farming came out of the 1939–45 War, having undergone a revolution that had changed a thousand years of practice. In the last three decades a vast supporting structure has grown up to sustain the edifice.

This 'Anatomy of Agriculture' seeks to probe the structural background and explore the myriad complexities. Farming is the largest single industry in the UK today, and despite its 'muck and mystery' image, is proving an efficient brother to the remainder of British industry.

It has been decided to use the metric system for measurements, as that is the official system in this country, and one becoming daily more familiar. It has seemed to the author—and his publishers—unnecessary to detail the more common conversions, but it might be useful to give the ratio that is probably the most intimately associated with farming, that between acres and hectares. One acre is almost exactly 0·4 hectares; and conversely, 1 hectare = some 2½ acres (2·471 to be more precise).

P.W.

Acknowledgments

I must record my thanks to the following for kindly reading and commenting upon various sections of this work, while in no way holding them responsible for the views expressed, which are my own:
Lord Netherthorpe, past President, NFU.
Past Ministers of Agriculture: Lord Peart and Rt Hon. James Prior MP.
Sir Henry Plumb, President NFU.
Sir Richard Trehane, past Chairman MMB.
Col. G. R. Judd of Strutt & Parker.
Lt. Col. C. A. Brooks, past Master Worshipful Company of Farmers.
Anthony Rosen, Managing Director, Fountain Farming Ltd.
Eric Maddison, Principal, Writtle Agricultural College.
Charles Harwood, Editor, Agritrade (UKASTA).
Dean Swift, Director–General, AEA.
Jonathan Swift, Director–General, BAGMA.
Philip Hassall, Editor–in–Chief, *Big Farm Management*.

I must also thank countless others, who through the years of research have been most helpful and co-operative, in particular Sir Nigel Strutt, who took on the monumental task of reading the entire MS, for his helpful corrections and advice; Roy Minton of Harrap for his diligent assistance; and Carole Dandy, my patient secretary, who typed it all over a period of three years.

Contents

Illustrations

Farming Parlance

Covent Garden is not an Opera House, it's a vegetable market, and in any case has now become Nine Elms.

Smithfield Market is near Bart's Hospital and sells meat.
Smithfield Show is at Earl's Court and sells farm machinery.

Paris is not a city in France, it is a show that embraces The Ideal Home, Crufts, The Horse of the Year, The Boat Show, and The Smithfield Show—all rolled into one.

BSC does not stand for the British Steel Corporation: it is the British Sugar Corporation.

Leyland is not a large car company with labour problems—it is a make of tractors.

Ford is an easy place to cross a river.

An ADHAC is not a make of calculating machine—it is a committee set up to sort out the muddles resulting from the abolition of tied cottages.

The 'Royal' is a show held in Warwickshire.

The 'Royal' is also the Royal Agricultural Society of England, which runs this show.

The other 'Royal' is the Royal Agricultural College at Cirencester.

Knightsbridge is not a traffic-congested part of London; it is where both the NFU and CLA live.

'The Ministry' is not a religious vocation—it is the father of UK farming.

Its mother is the RASE.

The 'Weekly' does not mean bath night—it is a farming magazine.

SMMB is not a private enterprise railway line—it is the Scottish Milk Marketing Board.

Ny AB is not an Indian prince—it is the National Institute of Agricultural Botany.

Abacus is not a Japanese counting board—it is a variety of spring barley.

Julia is not a leggy blonde; she is another barley that grows in the springtime.

Wild oats are not a sign of male virility; they are weeds that grow all the year round.

Eastwood is not a point on the compass—it is the name of a poultry tycoon.

Luing is not a dreaded lung disease; it is a breed of cattle.

The 'City' is not the financial heart of London; it is the place whence the institutional farm owners come.

AMC is not the Associated Mineral Corporation—it is the Agricultural Mortgage Corporation.

Bank managers do not live in cupboards; they like a day shooting pheasants.

Concorde is not an aeroplane—it is the name that no one has yet thought of as the fastest-growing wheat variety.

Chicago is not the place where gangsters come from—it is the place where grain prices are 'rigged'.

Hereford is not a town near Wales—it is a breed of cattle, largely found in the Argentine.

A 'large black' is not an oversized coloured immigrant—it is a breed of pig.

Ransomes is not a firm who make lawnmowers—it is a make of plough.

Plumb is not a fruit that comes from a tree—it is a farmer who comes from Warwickshire.

Strutt is not something that holds an aeroplane together—it is an Inquiry into modern farming.

Albright & Wilson is not the title of Sir Harold's autobiography—it is a company who make chemicals.

Woolley is not a jumper you wear in the winter—it is a man who led the NFU.

'The President' is not a peanut farmer from Georgia—he is the chap who runs the NFU, the CLA and the NUAAW.

Stoneleigh is not near Coventry where the NAC resides, it is in Northampton where Lord Netherthorpe was born.

Fountain Farming is not a farm with lions in Trafalgar Square—it is a very, very, very large farming outfit.

'In the Club' does not mean an unexpected pregnancy, but being in the Farmers Club in Whitehall Court.

'Strip and park her' does not refer to dismantling an old banger—but a firm of estate agents.

Knight, Frank and Rutley is often confused with Frank Wright and Nutley, or Nightly, Nightly and Nightly.

Savills is not a shipping line, it is another firm of estate agents.

Wye is not a river, it is where the centre for European Farm Studies resides.

Cambridge is not a university city—it is the home of the NIAB, PBI, NSDO and Professor Denman.

Oxford is a Farming Conference and the home of Mike Soper.

Farmscan is not looking at the farm through rose-coloured spectacles—it is a competition.

The Farmer's Bank is: Barclays, Midland, National Westminster, Lloyds and anyone else who can get in on the act.

ARC is not the Amalgamated Roadstone Company who make ready-mixed, it is the Agricultural Research Council, who are also mixed.

Direct-drilling is not a farmer planting seeds, it is something ICI thought of to sell more chemicals.

Neddy is not a horse, it is a committee.

Little Neddy is a smaller committee.

ACT is not what Max Bygraves does—it stands for Agricultural Central Trading.

Game Fair is not a score in tennis, it's a show the CLA run.

Swan is not a bird owned by the Queen—it is a report on the use of antibiotics in animal husbandry.

RABI is not a Jewish priest—it is the Royal Agricultural Benevolent Institution.

'Food from our own Resources' does not mean what it says.

Neither does Rape—it's a new-fangled farm crop.

Rhode Island is not near New York—it's a hen.

New York dressed does not mean a bow tie and tuxedo, it means naked, gutted poultry meat.

Milk really does not come from bottles.

The BAA is not a breed of sheep—it's the British Agrochemicals Association.

Murphy is not a voluble Irishman—it's a company who make chemicals for farmers owned by Dalgety, who come from Australia.

Cherry-Valley is not a haven for geriatrics in the USA, it's a duck company owned by Joe Nickerson.

Claas is not something to keep children in—it's a combine harvester.

A combine harvester is something the Wurzels invented.

Methabenzthiazuron is a chemical—what else could it be?

Part 1
The Land

1 The Stampede from the Farms

'As Napoleon's decrees had done a century before, the Kaiser's submarines now provoked a complete change in official policy towards farming.'
'The British Genius' (Grosvenor and McMillan).

Rags to riches, and back again in three generations, is a truism when applied to individual families; it is also the story of farming, which went from prosperity to poverty, and is now back again. Whatever the future swings may be, the lessons of the past have created a period of prosperity and stability since 1945.

Today's agro-politico jungle is the culmination of a period of evolution in English social history. It is a current situation that is in tune with the current political climate, and is acceptable to farmers, politicians and the public at large. It has evolved in conjunction with the changing pattern of contemporary life and living standards in the UK, and with due deference to world population and feeding trends. But its origins go back to Napoleon.

In 1800, when Napoleon was knocking on the door, and before Nelson had risen to the heights of his fame, 90 per cent of the population lived in the countryside, and during the Napoleonic Wars British agriculture flourished to a remarkable extent. It was a period of high prosperity, although at that time the revolution in methods had not yet commenced. Neither had the Industrial Revolution, the dawning of the Victorian Age, and the massive shift of public opinion towards Britain's role as an industrial instead of an agricultural nation.

The Repeal of the Corn Laws in 1846 was only carried by Peel through the House of Commons because of the waning political power of land; nevertheless, despite its description in some history books as a death blow to agricultural superiority in the UK, this is not true. British agriculture continued to prosper for another thirty years after the Corn Laws had been repealed. The Industrial Revolution was in full swing, and Britain's population was expanding rapidly with the larger families which were commonplace at that period; but the villages were becoming denuded as the workers moved from rural deprivation to the greater security of factory jobs.

The real death-knell to British agriculture was the inauguration of the Canadian Pacific Railway, which opened up the newly discovered virgin lands of Canada, and enabled mass importation of cheap grain from the prairies in North America. The arrival of refrigerated ships from the Antipodes and Argentina opened the door to other massive competitors from abroad, in respect of meat and dairy products. It was these twin developments, plus the withdrawal of protection against imports, which hit British farming and sent it into a long period of poverty.

Politically the importation of cheap food from the newly developed countries made good sense. It enabled the British public to be fed more cheaply, it kept down the cost of living, and thus made our goods even more competitive on world markets. Only Germany was a serious threat; Japan was not to become an industrialized giant until after the Second World War. This policy was orientated towards food for the masses, and instituted into British life the philosophy of 'cheap food'. Even today food is cheaper in Britain than anywhere else in the EEC, or the rest of Europe, possibly excluding Spain. It has been this century-old facet of British political policy for cheap food which has bedevilled farmers' incomes and the whole support system for British farmers trying to produce food at constant prices, when costs have escalated.

The decline of British agriculture after 1875 was severe. In 1871 agriculture produced 20 per cent of the national income from 19 per cent of the working population. Today, 2·7 per cent produce about 3 per cent of what we now call the Gross National Product (GNP). The decline after the 1870s did not matter to the urban population, or to the politicians, although occasional tepid measures were passed to alleviate the deprivation of the agricultural community, such as the concession on the assessment for local rates in 1896, but farmers were unable to pay their rents and were leaving their farms overnight. On the Terling estate of Lord Rayleigh, it is recorded:[1] 'Tenants everywhere were surrendering their leases and in some cases abandoning their farms overnight. The countryside was going derelict.'

The political power of the farmers was rapidly declining, and it was only the war clouds which started to gather as the Victorian era died with its Queen that provoked a reluctant interest in the countryside and its affairs. As Lord Fisher was bringing the British Navy out of the era of Nelson—who had been dead almost a century—British agriculture was also being dragged reluctantly into the twentieth century. The First World War brought a period of prosperity back to the countryside as the nation fought for survival at home as abroad. Henry Ford established his factory for producing tractors at Cork in 1917, and the Government started to exploit land resources to the full.

Guaranteed prices were introduced, and compulsory cropping, and all seemed set fair for another boom reminiscent of that following the Napoleonic Wars, a boom lasting some sixty years. In the aftermath the 1920 Agriculture Act guaranteed farmers' prices, but with national depression round the corner, this Act was repealed after only a year, and payments on an acreage basis were given for only the 1921 harvest. In the intense political upheavals of the inter-war years up to 1939, farming was once again thrown to the wolves, although successive Governments—Tories, Labour and Coalition—toyed with various ideas to

[1] Sir William Gavin, *Ninety Years of Family Farming* (Hutchinson, 1967).

relieve the extreme agricultural distress. They did nothing of any positive use.

Although the depression in the last quarter of the nineteenth century had indeed been acute, the inter-war depression was also severe. Lord Murray wrote:[2]

> The fall ... between 1929 and 1932, which was almost unparalleled in its severity, caused acute agricultural depression; the industry became increasingly under-capitalised in relation to the total agriculture area under crops and grass.

Another chronicler,[3] Stanley Baker, says:

> A sense of betrayal pervaded the farming scene during the 1920s and early 1930s arising from the failure of the Government immediately after World War 1 to redeem many of the promises it had held out as an inducement to farmers to come to the nation's rescue when food shortage threatened. Successive Governments showed a callous indifference to the plight of British agriculture.

But this period laid the foundations for the 1947 Agriculture Act, and its thirty-year run of stability. Politicians were being converted gradually to the philosophy that food supplies were important, and that British farming could not exist in a completely free trading situation. In the 1920s complete de-rating was applied to farming, ahead of its application to other industries, and the Government was realizing that coal, steel and textiles, as well as farming, could not exist without some form of protection from the foreigners. The most important legislation for farmers was the Agricultural Marketing Acts of 1931 and 1933, though the Agricultural Mortgage Corporation had already been created, in 1928. The Marketing Acts helped to produce stability, and farmers who had been pouring their milk down the drains because it was unsaleable found salvation in the newly created Milk Marketing Board. It was not tariffs but import quotas which the politicians used to bolster up a depressed industry; agreements with overseas suppliers and experiments in international agreements; and finally price subsidies introduced for some of the staple farm products such as wheat, barley, oats, sugar beet and fat cattle. Government was still reluctant to spend its own money, and the wheat subsidy was financed by a levy on imported flour. Horticulture also received some assistance, but—as farmers will readily tell you—it has always been the more prosperous arable farmers of eastern England who have benefited the most. 'To the rich shall it be given.'

It was this background which enabled the massive Socialist majority in the 1945 Parliament to enact its famous 1947 Agriculture Act, which put on a permanent footing the security and stability of British farmers. But it was also passed at a time when ration books and scarcity of food, both in Britain and in the rest of the world, were paramount factors in any political action. In this situation the farmers had an easy task in getting virtually all they wanted, and a near-starved nation still had cause to be grateful to the farming industry for its salvation. A few lone voices were raised against agricultural prosperity, such as

---

[2] Keith Murray, *Agriculture—History of the Second World War* (HMSO, 1955).
[3] Stanley Baker, *Milk to Market* (Heinemann, 1973).

that of Stanley Evans, MP for Wednesbury, who in an infamous speech declared 'Farmers are living on feather beds, and carrying their money to the bank in pillowcases.' He earned the nickname 'Feather-bed Evans', and there was envy that during the public's exigencies and deprivations farmers never went hungry.

Whether from envy, sympathy, gratitude, or practical politics, it seemed a vital part of the post-War plan to set farming on a stable course for the future.

The Labour Government got the credit for this support, and Tom Williams, the Minister, became the idol of the farming community for the next quarter of a century. But the outlines of this legislative measure were already formulated when Clement Attlee came to power, and with only minor amendments it was passed. The principles were supported by all political parties, and have been enacted, with varying degrees of success, by both Socialist and Tory Governments since that day.

It may seem strange that a Labour Government, with little or no agricultural roots, or sympathy, should have enacted the most important piece of legislation affecting farmers in this century, but the ideology of planned markets and Government participation appealed to the Socialist mind. However, although State planning was enshrined within the Act, the Labour Governments have in fact never even threatened to crack this particular whip. The major innovation was the system of annual Price Reviews, which became identified in the public mind as the 'Annual Farmers' Wage Increase', a popular misconception whipped up by headlines of monotonous regularity. Although some Price Reviews were disallowed by the NFU and Government of the day, new schemes have been introduced, such as an idea for financing the amalgamation of farms, capital grants for the erection of permanent buildings, and other smaller sectionalized payments; nevertheless, the bedrock was in the system of deficiency payments which made up the difference between the actual market price and that price guaranteed under the Annual Review. It was a Tory Minister, Christopher Soames, in 1961–2, who found that the escalating cost of farm support was unacceptable. He put a dent in the principles of the Act by limiting the increases which farmers could expect in future Reviews. But if some Reviews have been 'disagreed' between Government and farmers, the Government has not seemed unduly worried.

After the Tory win at the General Election in 1970, there was a major shift away from deficiency payments, and a change-over towards the Common Agricultural Policy, the cornerstone of the EEC. Jim Prior stamped the country, softening farmers' attitudes, and weaning them away from a system which had worked more or less satisfactorily as a form of protection for agricultural prosperity for nearly a quarter of a century. The changed system of the CAP meant that levies would be employed, and subsidies phased out. In the event more momentous world food problems were to negate the actual effects of much of this on the farm, but it marked a departure from a well-tried system. Had the system worked itself out? Were we now living in a different world? And how best could the demands for cheap food be met when world prices were escalating violently? In modifying the policy to keep in tune with the times, insecurity and muddle over less efficient policies in force in such a varied agricultural area as the Nine renders matters much more difficult, but UK farmers had by this time achieved a new stake in the economy of the country.

While in the past it has been possible to jettison farming interests with only minor repercussions on the remainder of the nation—and at some stages in the last century positively to benefit those other sections—farming today is no longer in isolation from the nation. Not only have the urban masses who fled to the towns a century ago now returned to repopulate the villages—though as dormitories for commuting to their work-place in the nearest town—but the 2½ per cent of the population actually engaged in farming is supplemented in voting terms by another 10 per cent who now rely upon the farmers' custom.

The reduction of labour on the farms, and the movement into the technological age, has made the farmer a big customer for the multi-million-pound agro-chemicals industry and for the tractor and farm machinery manufacturers, and with farming prosperity at a useful level the farmer and his family can be good customers for farmhouse furniture and motor-cars.

Thus the isolationism of the farming community has disappeared with the mobility of the nation and the integration of one industry with another. It is a political strength which has aided the farmers' leaders in their arguments with Government.

2 The Land

'Land, they ain't making it any more.'
Mark Twain

So much from so little for so many

The first instinct of both man and animal is the power of self-preservation by eating; the newly born calf instinctively finds its mother's teat, and the mother instinct nourishes and feeds its offspring. And so, if the acquisition of food to fill an empty belly was the first industry of man, he nurtured his instinct for self-preservation by hunting. Shortly afterwards he began to grow his own food, and thus farming began.

Farming can truly be said to be the oldest industry in the world, and also the most widespread. In our urbanized and sophisticated plastic world today we can pinpoint the centres of the motor-car industry, of the uranium mines, or of the centres of academic learning. Yet in every country except the polar regions, farming to a greater or lesser extent, and in many varied forms, is carried out. The day has long gone when individual men grew sufficient for their own needs. The day has passed when individual countries grow primarily for their own needs. Food-production is a world-wide industry, and is of world concern. It can upset the economic balance of nations, and shortages in one part of the world are often to be put against surpluses in others.

For twenty-five years there were massive grain stocks in the world, and despite the fact that two-thirds of the world's population is supposedly living on a diet that is below the normally accepted nutritional standards of the sophisticated third, those food stocks were maintained in the lands of plenty by the forces of politics and the lack of economic resources of the poorer nations.

As food is essential for survival, the quantity of land available in the world must be balanced with the potential productivity of that land to the number of mouths to feed.

Within the world, oceans cover over 70 per cent of the earth's surface. The potential agricultural output of any nation is determined not by its territorial limits—which wars have continually changed—but by the actual amount of the cultivable land in an equable climatic region. It is symbolic of the emphasis placed upon land that it has been the excuse for the majority of history's wars. In earlier times the territorial gains were made largely to satisfy egotistical whims. As civilization progressed, this became more a matter of acquiring additional people, from whom both work and taxes could be gathered.

When one studies the geography of world production, it appears immediately that vast regions have little agricultural potential.

Distribution of the world's land areas

	%
Polar Regions	22
Arid Desert	16
Semi-Arid	17
Useful for crop and livestock production for part of the year, with inconsistent rainfall	26
Good in temperate latitudes, less good in tropics	19
	100

It will be seen that only a small fraction of the world's land surface is available for food-production, and although this would appear to be one hectare in every five, many of these land areas do not have the consistency of climate to yield well every year. The most favoured estimate of first-class food-producing land is only one useful hectare for every eleven that are useless. The land actually used for farming purposes with any degree of success is usually estimated to be one-tenth, and since such crops as rubber may involve farming in the widest sense, they do not necessarily provide nutrition for the world's inhabitants.

The most concentrated area of population density is in fact the geographically small continent of Europe. It is the equable climate of this part of Europe that has produced a healthier environment that has stimulated the survival of mankind.

It follows that the best lands have been taken for living space, despite their need for food-production. The United Kingdom, like much of Europe, has a geographical position highly conducive to land use for agriculture. Nevertheless, the UK has the world's fifth highest density of population. The Benelux countries, with a virtual lack of mountainous regions and a generally equable climate, have the highest densities, with the Netherlands quite remarkably ahead of Belgium, followed in the league table by Japan, Germany and the United Kingdom. The following table (1975 figures) shows the population densities by the International Measurement Scale per square kilometre.

Netherlands	352
Belgium	316
Japan	277
Germany	245
United Kingdom	228
Italy	180
France	91
USA	22
Canada	2

While this table demonstrates the average densities of population, the more sophisitcated countries have tended to amass vast numbers in large cities.

This table is calculated on the square kilometre for international comparative purposes, but in international land-mass measurements the more normal measurement is by square miles, and thus the United Kingdom with a total of 94,216 square miles is the seventy-second in size among the countries of the world. Compared with other European countries, we approximate the closest with West Germany, which has 95,900 square miles and a similar population. Yugoslavia, with 99,000 square miles, but a population one-third of our size and many mountainous regions, compares only in geographical terms but not in economic. Australia, which is nearly thirty times larger than the United Kingdom, has a population of just over thirteen million, less than a quarter of the United Kingdom population. Each inhabitant has on average 104 acres (42 hectares), although much of this is arid, while the United Kingdom population has the pleasure of just under half a hectare for every man, woman and child for living space, and it is estimated that it requires one hectare to produce sufficient food for each person annually. Although on the land surface of the world there are one and a half hectares of cultivable land in equable climates, this does not imply that they are in fact being cultivated, but it holds out a hope for the survival of mankind. In recent years the annual increase in agricultural production has been 3 per cent, while the world population has increased at only 2 per cent. Although in the United Kingdom we have half a hectare each, many of these are non-farmable, Britain has traditionally been a large food-importing nation. International trade has been of great importance for the maintenance of the country's standard of living. We provide just over half our total food needs, or about two-thirds of those items which will grow in our climate. Oranges and bananas, in fact most fruits, must be imported.

The average American visitor to the United Kingdom expresses surprise that with such a teeming population there are any green fields left at all, and particularly that within a short distance of Eros in Piccadilly Circus there is quiet, unspoilt farmland, producing heavy crops. One notable example is the highly productive brick earth soils near Southend-on-Sea on the projected site of the ill-fated third London Airport at Maplin Sands, but since nearly one-third of our total population live in seven great conurbations, of which six are in England and one in Scotland, it leaves more rural charm and open spaces than the tourist could envisage.

The measurement of the complete land mass of the British Isles is entrusted to the Ordnance Survey Department, which is based in Southampton. The total land area has varied very little since the last marshland embankments were erected in the early years of the nineteenth century. Broadly speaking, the British Isles are slipping slowly into the sea from the south-east, while the north-west is slowly rising. Despite immense public pressure, the reclaimable Wash has never become a reality, although the Dutch example of the Zuider Zee (or IJsselmeer) is there for all to see. Small areas have been won from the sea by individual farmers with coastline holdings. These have been on the east coast; around the Romney Marsh area on the south coast; and in the Solway Firth, but erosion still takes place, although the River Authorities have expended many millions in coastal defences by raising the embankments. Thus, even though there is a continual battle to withstand the ravages of the ocean, the general land mass throughout the last hundred years has been almost perfectly inelastic.

Agricultural measurement has been calculated in acres, but will gradually be adopting the European hectare (2·471 acres = 1 hectare). The accepted measurement for national purposes in square miles reveals that the mainland of Britain has 88,764 square miles, with an additional 5,452 square miles in Northern Ireland. Land mass is not solely a measurement of dry land within a country, as it includes the areas covered by inland water, and in the United Kingdom there are 1,191 square miles of inland water, with almost twice as much of this in Scotland as in England and Wales. The latter country has only 49 square miles of inland water, but Northern Ireland has nearly 5 per cent of its total mass covered by inland water. Even the Scottish lochs only occupy 2 per cent of the land, and the total for England and Wales is under ½ per cent.

Although the United Kingdom provides half a hectare for each of its population, this varies from only a quarter hectare in England to one and a half hectares per head in Scotland and 1 hectare in Wales and Northern Ireland. In the United Kingdom one-third of the whole country is land over 240 metres and classed as mountain/moorland. It produces only 4 per cent of our agricultural output, and varies from two sheep per hectare on the best areas to one sheep for every six hectares on the bad. Attempts have been made to re-seed some of these upland pastures by plane-borne seed and fertilizer applications, and by using modern chemicals to kill the weeds, but the effects have made little significant difference to the total viability of the agricultural industry. In Israel pioneering irrigation methods have turned the desert green, and the upland improvement schemes in the UK have proved themselves possible, if not economically viable. The Highlands of Scotland occupy about one-fifth of the whole land mass of Britain—hundreds of square miles of mountains where agriculture is negligible, and it is estimated that only 10 per cent has any potential for forestry. Much of this land produces very little for the United Kingdom farming economy. In Britain as a whole, about one-third of the agricultural area is hill land, and of this only one-seventh is enclosed and cultivated with either arable crops or grass. Thus the area of highly productive farming is considerably restricted. This has its repercussions in trying to equate and evaluate the income levels of farmers as a whole, and in any treatise on United Kingdom farming the comparatively short geographical distances throw up considerable variations. Even summer thunderstorms affect one village, but miss its neighbour. It is a problem that has plagued governments in trying to assess a fair level for farmers' incomes, which inevitably must try to balance the so-called barley barons of East Anglia with the peasant existence of the Celtic fringe farmers. But inasmuch as the cropping and production in different parts of Britain will vary, there has been a political attempt to balance up geographical and climatic regions with special hill-farmer subsidies. Despite the high density of population of the United Kingdom in world comparative terms, the concentration in the large cities means that as a whole 82·45 per cent of the total land surface is still agricultural land. This varies from a high of 87·3 per cent in Scotland, but is still at 78·3 per cent in England and Wales. Urban land only accounts for 11 per cent in England and Wales, and the remainder is attributed to forestry, the communications network and industrial factory areas. Apart from the area of Greater London, the area of farmed land exceeds 90 per cent of the total land area in the intensively farmed Holland division of Lincolnshire and in Radnor and Westmorland, as well as seven Scottish counties, but five of them have a high proportion of mountainous areas where the agricultural return is small. If we exclude the lower-grade agricultural land classified by the Ministry as rough grazing, we find that in the eastern and midland counties 95 per cent of the total agricultural land is used for crops and grass, whereas the figure drops to only 10 per cent in the Scottish Highlands. The best agricultural land in Scotland is found on the east coast in Fife, between the Firth of Forth and the Firth of Tay.

Farming land classification survey

It took seven years for the first agricultural land classification survey of England and Wales to be completed, from 1967 to 1974. The net result is a set of 113 coloured maps to a scale of one inch to one mile, and it graded agricultural land in five classifications.

The survey was carried out by a Research Group of the Land Service of ADAS, and each map was accompanied by additional background information, including some justification for the gradings adopted. It revealed that only 2·8 per cent of the agricultural land was in Grade 1, but the absence of any real grading system was shown when nearly 50 per cent of all land was lumped together in Grade 3. The survey only classed individually areas of 200 acres (80 hectares), and its purpose was to conserve the best agricultural land when non-agricultural applications for use were being made. Even the best grades of land only covered 14 per cent of the total land area of England and Wales, or 17·4 per cent of the farmland.

These gaily coloured maps are an extension of the normal Ordnance Survey, which has been in existence for well over a hundred years, but they paid only lip service to the real problem of classifying land. In Scotland, which was not covered by this survey, they have a system of A, B, C, with sub-divisions of six in each of these groups, giving in total eighteen differing levels of soil-grade, but they are confined to the Lowlands. Thus even today there is a very incomplete knowledge of the soil-nature and classification in the United Kingdom.

With Teutonic thoroughness, the Germans instituted a comprehensive method of classifying farmland as early as 1934, in which instead of 200-acre blocks every hectare of non-urban land was classified. The German system distinguishes certain soil-types, and is also used in planning applications, in land taxation and in assessment for mortgage-potential of the owner. It also determines the purchase price of farmland and farm rents. The German system works on a 100-point scale according to an agreed schedule of soil types, weighted by such ancillary factors as climate, rainfall, relief, communications, proximity to markets and tendencies to natural climatic disasters, such as frost, flood and wind-blow. Prior to 1939, the 100-points top grade was situated near Magdeburg, and other soils shown as a percentage of this or related regional standards. Today the Federal German Republic has now established a new 100 per cent centre near Braunschweig (Brunswick).

The five ADAS grades were:

Grade 1   Land with very minor or no physical limitations to agricultural use. Yields are consistently high, and cropping highly flexible, since most crops could be grown, not excepting the more pernickety horticultural crops.

Grade 2   Land with some minor limitation which excludes it from Grade 1. A wide range of both agricultural and horticultural crops can usually be grown, although there may be some restrictions in the range of horticultural crops and arable root crops.

Grade 3   Land with moderate limitations due to the soil, relief or climate, or some combination of these factors. The range of cropping is comparatively restricted on land in this grade. Very few horticultural crops could be grown, and towards the bottom of the grade arable root crops are limited to forage crops. The principal use of this grade of land would be for cereals and grass.

Grade 4   Land with severe limitations due to adverse soil, relief or climate, or a combination of these. This land will contain a largely grass area with only occasional fields of oats, barley or forage crops, and probably little wheat.

Grade 5   This land, like category 5 housing, is pretty poor, and would generally be found to be under grass or rough grazing and totally unploughable, with the possible exception of an occasional pioneer forage crop

	Percentage of total land area, England and Wales	Percentage of total farmland, England and Wales
Grade 1	2·3	2·8
Grade 2	11·8	14·6
Grade 3	39·6	48·9
Grade 4	16·0	19·7
Grade 5	11·3	14·0
Urban	8·5	—
Other non-agricultural	10·5	—
	100·0	100·0

To most farmers there are but three soil-types: light, medium, heavy. The lighter soils are easier cultivated, have free natural drainage, can grow a variety of crops, but rely upon a wet summer to sustain high yields. On certain parts, particularly in East Anglia, this light soil with its sandy content has been known to blow away in a dust-bowl fashion; but there have been outstanding examples (such as the estates of the Earl of Iveagh at Elvedon Hall in Norfolk) where they have created a system of farming that produces useful crops.

The medium soils have a far greater range potential in cropping and present few problems to farmers. The possibility of stones and flints in the soil does entail more expenditure upon the working tines of cultivating implements, but the compensations in steady yields through a variety of summers, plus the ease and economy of working, makes this soil-type highly desirable.

The heavy soils with a clay content provide an intractable solid weight of clay that requires expertise to farm it successfully. In many of these areas, while grass farming may predominate, the out-wintering of stock requires a more freer-draining soil than the heavy lands provide. On the boulder-clays root crops such as sugar beet and potatoes do well, providing operations are timed correctly, but on the London Clay soils along the Thames Estuary the grass farming of yesteryear has yielded to an all-cereal rotation, facilitated by the advent of new and more powerful machinery. Today crawler tractors have given way to the heavier-horsepower wheeled versions, and arable farming on a restricted crop cycle has become successfully established.

Between these soil-type variations lie many other factors that determine the nature of the farming. The rainfall which may vary from over 150 inches (3,811 millimetres) in some of the Hebridean Isles can drop to as little as under 20 inches (508 millimetres) in parts of East Anglia. Generally speaking, the rainfall and the amount of evaporation can determine the management problems of a cropping sequence, and farmers tend to gravitate towards that sort of land which they presumably feel they can farm successfully.

The basic land structure of Britain was created by the glacial deposits that remained after the retreating ice-cap which swept across the British Isles at least three times during the prehistoric period in Britain. It swept across England from Liverpool to Ipswich, and deposited the best soils in abundance. Thousands of years of wind and rain have softened that lunar landscape into Shakespeare's green and pleasant isle. The North Sea was dry land eight thousand years ago, and today silt deposits have built up in many areas around our coasts. The average depth throughout the English Channel and North Sea is only some 15 metres, and indeed very large areas of England particularly are only 15 metres above the present high-water mark of the tide (HWT).

A few farmers have attempted to change the nature of their soils. Marling is the process of transferring heavy soil from one area and spreading it on lighter land, and marling and claying has been the subject of a grant by the Ministry as a soil-improvement technique. While most farms have some variation of soils even within individual fields, it is obviously a very expensive operation to transport one type of soil to another area, and even within farms the detriment of removing fertile topsoil has been a drawback. By normal reckonings, two centimetres of soil represents some 270 tonnes per hectare. In an opposite direction, the Ministry have paid out substantial grants for the cost of laying clay tiles and mole drains to facilitate better cropping on the heavier intractable soils, and while some farms may be described as 'farming on the chalk', where white granules may be observed, particularly after a rain, other areas have an acidity problem, and chalk or ground lime is applied to neutralize the acidity. This practice again has been Government-aided.

In an attempt to balance farming incomes, Government subsidies are increased for those farmers on hill land.

Climatic disasters

British farmers have little to fear from the climatic disasters which befall many other farming areas in the world. In fact, they seldom suffer from the climatic extremes, a fact which has helped both their own prosperity and the steady progress of British farming. A nation where one section of the community is struggling for existence one year, and keeping chickens in its Rolls-Royce the following, cannot sustain a steady rate of progress with any degree of security, so that this is invaluable.

Against this, it is often said that in Britain we do not have a climate, we just have weather, and the inconsistencies and unpredictability of British weather patterns have often made the long-range forecasters into a laughing-stock. True, the day-to-day pattern is mainly controlled by a succession of depressions from the Atlantic which move in a generally easterly or north-easterly direction towards the British Isles, but the variations of rainfall and sunshine in one year as opposed to another do not significantly affect the farming pattern. It is said that the difference between a hot summer and a coolish summer in Britain is a mere average of two degrees. Farmers throughout the world suffer considerably from violently changing weather patterns. In 1965 there was a general drought in several continents, and in New York restaurants were liable to a $50 fine if water was supplied when not ordered. That year sheep were sold at a shilling a head in parts of Australia. Either drought or floods do affect farmers throughout the world, although on balance the effects of drought are more catastrophic. The 1972 Report of the Australian Agricultural Company stated that in New South Wales 'Summer crops were disappointing, and at the end of the year wheat crop prospects were almost negligible following the extremely dry winter.' In 1970 a drought throughout the central states of the USA reduced the maize crop by 13 per cent, but in total tonnage it amounted to as much as the total normal UK harvest. New Zealand suffers similarly from droughts, whereas Bangladesh and the Indian sub-continent suffer from excessive monsoons.

As an illustration of the effects of drought, the Australian wheat crop in 1972 was 8·6 million tonnes. It dropped to 6 million tonnes in a year of drought, and rose again in 1974 to 11·9 million tonnes. Such declines in crop-growing and crop-production have serious effects upon farmers' prosperity.

In the UK the sight of helicopters dropping pathetic bales of hay to stranded animals in a flooded meadow makes headlines, but is in fact a rare occurrence.

Hailstones in selected areas have been known to strip a whole crop of corn, and British farmers can insure against this sort of loss, but the insurance companies have the most susceptible villages plotted in advance. In the Fens soil blows have been known to sweep away the top layers of soil, taking the sugar-beet seeds with them into the nearest hedgerow. Certainly, British harvests are affected by dry summers, and losses do occur from inclement August weather, but the fluctuation of average yields does not normally vary by more than 40 to 80 kilos per hectare. An official drought of twenty-one days without measurable rainfall is not an uncommon occurrence, but it usually rains on the twenty-second day. Since the last War there have been only four major disasters to British farming.

The 1947 winter caused an immense loss of cattle and sheep on the hills, when a prolonged period of snowfall lasted for nearly three months, and it was impossible to find many buried animals. The second occasion was in 1953, when gale-force winds and an exceptional high tide coming from the north-east raised the North Sea (which was contained by the narrow opening of the English Channel) to unprecedented heights. On 31 January 1953 it burst the embankments along the east coast and inundated great quantities of low-lying land. One form of Government assistance was the free supply of gypsum, which was applied to neutralize the salt deposits from the covered farmland, but in many instances only low-lying marshes were flooded, and the water that rushed in rushed out again on the next tide.

The next natural disaster which hit UK farmers was the drought of 1976, when at Stow-in-the-Wold only 11·4 millimetres of rain fell from January to harvest, and in Wiltshire a normal annual rainfall of 1,076 millimetres was reduced to only 355 millimetres; accompanied by the 'summer of the century', when day after day it beat unrelentingly down, and forest fires became an everyday occurrence in Britain, the drought caused severe problems to farmers. It also created problems in other directions. Beer-consumption shot up, but with stand-pipes in the streets, unprecedented water-rationing in modern Britain, a full meeting of the Cabinet to discuss the latest developments, and the appointment of a 'Minister for the Drought', Dennis Howell, it was a traumatic time in UK annals.

It hit milk-producers, and production in August 1976 was the lowest for eight years in that month. The sugar-beet crop, estimated to produce nearly one million tonnes of white sugar, dropped to just over 600,000 tonnes. The potato crop was ravaged, and prices shot up; vegetables became as expensive as caviare; and the UK cereal crop dropped by three million tonnes from its peak two years earlier. The Country Landowners Association, on its everlasting hobby-horse, asked for tax relief, and the NFU estimated that farm incomes would drop by up to 40 per cent.

The drought extended over Northern Europe, and French and German farmers received the benefit of special schemes from their Governments. In the UK it became the first problem of the new Minister of Agriculture, John Silkin, who increased the fat sheep guarantees, also the milk price by 2p per gallon,

The network of motorways transgressing good British farmland at Hemel Hempstead
Photo 'Big Farm Management'

Farming within the urban fringe. Grove Farm, Tring, one of the *Farmers Weekly's* ring of farms   *Photo 'The Farmers Weekly'*

One-third of Britain is among the hills. Goed Y Brenin (The King's Forest),
Merionethshire *Photo 'Big Farm Management'*

extended the beef subsidy, and fixed a new special rate of grant for the installation of farm storage reservoirs.

The winter of 1977–8 was also a catastrophic one for UK farmers. In January breaches in the sea walls flooded valuable farmland in Kent and Norfolk. With inundation from salt water, it was estimated that much of this would be sterile for three years. It was estimated that 3,600 hectares were affected in Kent, and 200 hectares in Norfolk.

The following month a blizzard hit the Scottish Highlands, and livestock losses were high. Helicopters were used to transport badly needed fodder to stranded sheep and other livestock, and the President of the Scottish NFU put in a plea to the Government for special financial relief. The following week it was the turn of the South-West, and a freak blizzard hit Cornwall, Devon and parts of South Wales. Cattle and sheep disappeared under 6-metre-high snow-drifts piled up by a howling south-easterly that brought down power lines and created complete chaos in those areas. Sheep and cattle were lost, and milk-producers suffered without electricity to milk their cows; the Government appointed the erstwhile Minister of Drought, Denis Howell, 'Minister for Snow'.

Although the Government provided assistance through the Royal Navy and the RAF, to transport feeding stuffs to beleaguered farmsteads, and the general public were treated to scenes of dramatic disaster, the thaw soon followed, but in its wake came serious flooding, and Sir Henry Plumb toured the area. Noises were made about Government assistance, which in reality only amounted to pointing out the legitimate relief from income tax which would be normal in any loss-making situation.

It is symbolic of farmers' disregard for the weather pattern that the NFU never asked for any allowance in its price review negotiations for the vagaries of the weather. The Union and the farmers accept that it is one of their natural adversaries and ask no favours when it goes against them. An estimate of farming losses, mainly on the arable crop-growing side, suggested that only 30 per cent of those losses were due to inclement weather conditions.

Nevertheless, farmers in Britain have tried hard to insulate themselves from even these mild climatic fluctuations. The essence of arable farming is to keep the feet of the plants dry enough to stop them rotting—unlike the growing of rice in paddy fields—and man-made land drainage has been perfected throughout the years, though, like painting the Forth Bridge, the job is never finished. On more than half the agricultural land in England and Wales field drainage is a fundamental necessity for efficient farming. A national survey revealed that farm production on 2·9 m hectares of agricultural land is limited by the absence of efficient draining systems, while another similar area depends upon the maintenance of existing systems. This reveals the extent of the problem. Against this, the irrigation of many crops is carried out either from near-by streams and rivers, from springs and boreholes, or from man-made reservoirs which tap the winter flow from ditches and provide a storage for summer application.

Although in the arable east of England oil-fired driers have been installed on every major cereal farm, and most farmers have at least access to a corn-drier, the method and technology of drying hay by blasting volumes of air through the loose matted material is not universally adopted. The British climate will not allow most horticultural crops to compete with the earlier-maturing foreigners unless glasshouses are provided, and particularly in the Lea Valley on the Essex/Hertfordshire borders a vast glasshouse industry has grown up. Although in most parts of Britain the winters are not severe enough to necessitate bringing livestock under cover, nevertheless there has been a movement towards in-wintering of the hardier sheep, and many an air-conditioned pig and poultry palace would do justice to a millionaire's mansion. On the other hand, crop-losses are insufficient to warrant covering the fields against rainfall!

The net result must be that, despite the day-to-day unpredictability which hampers farming operations, the general annual pattern in this country does not produce violent disasters such as the seven years' drought that created the Canadian Dust Bowl in the 1880s.

The wastage of land

'Is then no nook of English ground
Secure from rash assault?'

Wordsworth

In the United Kingdom the food-productive areas are the important raw materials of British agriculture. This is a declining asset, which has meant that British farming has been steadily contracting with respect to hectarage. Happily for the national economic balance sheet, this diminution has been coupled with increased productivity, and the net result has been that farming has still contrived to expand its tonnage production.

As the population rises the living-space per capita decreases, and similarly the agricultural area diminishes with the sheer weight of population, plus the more highly sophisticated standards of living, which are in themselves space-wasting. Thus land left for farming becomes more out of balance with the density of population.

British farming is contracting at a rate of approximately 260 square kilometres each year, and the rate is not diminishing, but the picture of a Britain covered by concrete is far from the truth, and the image is not as bleak as the figures suggest. Both the National Farmers Union and the Country Landowners Association make great play whenever good agricultural land is threatened. They make a patriotic plea on the grounds of national food-production, but as a general rule few landowners would turn down the opportunity for gaining vast sums of money for land to be developed other than for farming.

The recorded land lost by farmers, and withdrawn from the Ministry Total Returns, is divided into urban for private or council housing estates, industrial development for factories and recreational development, which has been increasing as weekly hours of work diminish and the State has provided land for leisure. These uses—which are probably irrevocable—have been taking 18,000 hectares annually. In total, however, the more commonly quoted figures of land-losses average 23,000–25,000 hectares annually. The remaining (average 5,400 hectares) is transferred from general agriculture to forestry purposes. This latter amount is classed in the Ministry mind as being withdrawn from farming and food-production potential, but in fact it always comprises the lowest-grade farmable land in the wetter counties, and the probable food-loss is negligible. Additionally, from an aesthetic viewpoint, the appearance of a tree-filled landscape must be more enjoyable than the ragged skyline of an industrial skyscape, and the eventual productivity in national terms from timber-production is not inconsequential.

In terms of national output per hectare, there can be little doubt that the contribution to the gross national product from a factory is far greater than from that same site under agriculture. Similarly, in any debate on people versus pigs, the undoubted verdict would be in favour of providing council houses rather than pig palaces. The needs of human beings for a roof under which to raise their families takes priority over the requirements of pigs rearing their litters, and the ancillary need of a population to transport itself along a ribbon of concrete from home to workplace is an obvious priority.

While the dictates of an expanding population, ever seeking higher housing standards, will always prevail, there is little doubt that land and its annual production of food is an ever-continuing raw material, so that the importance of designating and protecting the best productive farmland should be an absolute priority. Despite political lip-service to the creed of agricultural conservation, and the workings of the Planning Acts, there has since 1947 been little real attempt to safeguard the agricultural interests, and there has been no real resistance from the farming community itself.

Public inquiries and a ham-fisted system of County Planning Departments and Planning Acts have not mitigated the steady drain of farmland. Moreover, besides better climate and employment prospects, the south-eastern quarter of England has also the best farmland, and it must be remembered that it is the most productive land that often tends to be lost to agriculture.

If the urbanization of British land continues at its present rate, it would take 670 years before the last blade of grass was finally covered. Despite its obsession for collecting and publishing statistics, the Ministry of Agriculture, after a hundred years at the same job, is still rectifying and correcting the total amount of farmland. The figures below show the annual changes, which are explained as: corrections to returns, unexplained differences and land not previously recorded.

Ministry of Agriculture Land Total Changes

1963–4	2,416 hectares gained	1963–8	Net increase of agricultural
1964–5	2,625 ,, gained		area 4,416 hectares
1965–6	4,208 ,, lost		
1966–7	9,291 ,, gained		
1967–8	5,708 ,, lost		

It is a salutary thought that, despite the emphasis upon statutory form-filling and statistical computer analysis, there is still no exact measurement of the agricultural area. The major stumbling block is probably the element of human error in farmers' returns.

From 1900 onwards the total agricultural land area showed little change, although the area of crops and grass continued to decline annually. This decline was halted, and expansion set in, during the period of import constraints between 1914 and 1921. However, the inter-War depression in agriculture again produced undrilled and uncultivated land; farmers contracting their businesses in an effort for survival decided it was cheaper to leave land to grow weeds, scrub and eventually bushes, rather than to expend time and money growing unprofitable crops. This inter-War period also saw a steady population and housing expansion. It was accompanied by a lack of planning controls which enabled housing development to be continued without restraint. The result was 'ribbon development', which stretched along existing roads as speculative builders advanced into open country on village and town perimeters to set out new housing estates. The Second World War restricted this development and again put a greater emphasis upon food-production, with the 'Dig for Victory' campaign which emphasized the value of home-grown food. The immediate post-War period saw again an expansion of housing targets by rival governments, using their building figures as a mark of their success in governing. Quite remarkably, the post-War averages have remained constant within their five-year brackets, although the annual housing targets have fluctuated (primarily caused by mortgage restraints). The 1947 Planning Act has been strengthened many times, but in essence it provides for Britain a guard against indiscriminate, haphazard, un-co-ordinated, housing development in areas where the cost of servicing (i.e., public roads, schools, electricity, gas and telephone services, and lastly sewage-disposal schemes) has been minimized as factors of irresponsibility.

Average area taken from agriculture for urban, industrial and recreational development

Five-Year Periods		
1926/7–1930/1	21,750	hectares
1931/2–1935/6	25,833	„
1936/7–1940/1	15,916	„
1941/2–1945/6	10,666	„
Post-War Averages		
1946/7–1950/1	16,458	hectares
1951/2–1955/6	17,000	„
1956/7–1960/1	14,625	„
1961/2–1965/6	15,790	„

It is a conjectural point that since a housing plot is only occupied partially by the dwelling itself, there could still be some food-productive capacity from the horticultural or floral production from those gardens, some of which at least would have been otherwise produced by the horticultural industry from British commercial farmland. This argument was deployed by R. H. Best and J. T. Ward in *The Garden Controversy*, in which they demonstrated that in terms of national resources the products of a vegetable garden, managed by the householder, were greater than the productivity of the land-growing farm crops. Allowing for the total national resources involved in the growing, harvesting, packaging, transport and distribution, the eventual journey of vegetable produce from a farmer's field looks a bad bet when compared to the simplicity of picking vegetables from the urban garden. Inasmuch that as a nation we expend a vast amount of human sweat pushing lawn-mowers, and of imported fuel for the larger machines, we can be considered not so much a nation of gardeners as a nation of lawn-cutters, and the grass area in the average garden is normally 50 per cent of the total. The value of vegetable-production at home can never be proved, but it does point the object lesson that land going out of agricultural ownership does not necessarily go out of food-production. It does, of course, still mean that it is lost from the agricultural industry, and since on average three thousand farms per year are removed from the total statistics, the industry as a whole is having to produce its profitability from a smaller rural workshop.

Britain is not alone in this annual loss of farmland. Throughout Europe every nation is building housing estates and factories to keep pace with its expanding population. The problems are similar to those in the United Kingdom. Even in the United States the land used for farming purposes rose steadily from 1850 (when it represented only 15 per cent of the total land mass), to a peak in the early 1950s, when 61 per cent of the total land mass was recorded as productive farmland. This figure is now being reduced at an annual rate of nearly (1·25 million hectares) which is approximately 1 per cent of the total farmed area. In British terms such an annual land loss would wipe out farming completely in just eight years. In a broader context, the annual drop of 1 per cent in the United States can be compared with the annual British loss of less than ·02 per cent. The lack of planning controls in the United States, the feeling of spaciousness and a population density that is ten times lower than in Britain, gives a considerably lower priority to any study of the conservation of land for farming purposes. The sprawl of American cities seems amazing to British eyes, and in countries like Australia there is little regard to either the productivity for farming purposes or even the ownership of land.

Even in tightly controlled Britain, there is still some substance in the notice declaring 'Ancient Lights', which in law guards the owner's right to daylight. The full problems of land-ownership and land-owners are dealt with more fully in a later chapter. Suffice to say that in Britain every inch of land is regarded as sacrosanct; yet there is still a steady transference away from farming.

People need land

The population of Britain was estimated at the time of the Domesday Survey to be approximately a million, although this figure cannot be too accurate. By 1696 there had been a fivefold increase in approximately six hundred years. That same fivefold increase was achieved again by the mid-nineteenth century in approximately 150 years, and it has approximately doubled since that time. As the first 600 years added 4½ million people, the second similar increase was added in about 100 years, but the next 100 years (1801–1901) added 22 million people. In seventy-one years of this century the official figures recorded an increase of some 17 million, which is about the same rate as for the nineteenth century, and despite the Registrar-General's forecasts of massive population increases, the last quarter of the twentieth century looks like slowing down that projection.

Population Graph

	UK	England and Wales	Scotland	Northern Ireland
1696		5·5 m		
1760		6·5 m		
1792		8·75 m		
1801		8·872 m		
1811		10·150 m		
1901	38·237 m	32·528 m	4·472 m	1·237 m
1911	42·082 m	36·070 m	4·761 m	1·251 m
1921	44·027 m	37·887 m	4·882 m	1·258 m
1931	46·038 m	39·952 m	4·843 m	1·243 m
1951	50·225 m	43·758 m	5·096 m	1·371 m
1961	52·709 m	46·105 m	5·179 m	1·425 m
1971	55·515 m	48·750 m	5·229 m	1·536 m

In 1964 the number of births registered exceeded deaths by 339,430, which was the highest natural increase since 1947 (369,205), and until the early 1970s the forecasts of a continually rising graph were continuing, but the pill had been introduced in 1963 and the Abortion Act was passed in 1968. It is symbolic of the reliance upon the pill as a controllable method of levelling off birth rates that in 1971, when there was a pill scare, the population of live births in the UK shot up dramatically, but it now continues to fall. The original forecast for the year 2013 was for a UK population of 64 million, but the Report by the Population Panel which was set up in November 1971 to assess the significance of population growth, and which predicted this figure, also conceded that Britain should be able to find means of accommodating such an increase. However, by 1974 the birth-rate had fallen to the lowest level on record, with long-term population growth at a standstill for the first time. The replacement level for population requires that each married couple should have 2·1 children, and until the 1970s a figure of 2·4 children would have increased the population. Predictably, comparative affluence has not in fact produced families of the size predominant in the second half of the nineteenth century. Much of the population increase has in fact been accomplished by increased life expectancy, through medical advances. Similarly, although fears are expressed that immigration will boost the population, the numbers emigrating seem to balance out, and have little effect upon the overall population levels.

Bread or water: mainly water

'You spend half a pint and flush two gallons'
HRH Prince Philip, 1969.

Water is vital for agriculture, and the quantity of it available throughout the relevant growing months of the season determines the agricultural potential of the various countries of the world. The arid areas and the desert regions obviously cannot support agriculture. In Britain, however, there is a dichotomy in water problems. The influence of the Gulf Stream and the prevailing south-west winds bring rainfall from the Atlantic, which basically makes Ireland its traditional emerald green, but on the mainland of Britain the volume of rainfall declines towards the east, the mountains of Wales and the Scottish Highlands increasing rainfall amounts. In reality, only marginal areas in isolated pockets along the extreme east coast have insufficient rainfall for normal agriculture.

This sharp variation in water-supplies has been accentuated by the rapidly rising population, but perhaps disproportionately by the introduction of more modern standards of living. In Britain as a whole there is an incomprehensible muddle over water-supplies. Farmers need sufficient quantities to sustain crop-growth without the tragedy of flooding. The affluent urban population needs more and more water, and industrial concerns employ this commodity in ever-increasing volume. Water as a commodity is considered the property of the State. It is directed (or misdirected) through various official bodies, through publicly owned rivers and watercourses, and is used by the population. Farmers upon whose land the water originally falls are only entitled to this amount without charge. Even in the eastern regions where irrigation reservoirs have been constructed to catch the winter rainfall on private farms, the farmers require licences, and payment charges are levied for this water, although much of it is only temporarily diverted on its route towards the sea.

Water from underground springs is also only allowable to farmers by licence and payment, and extraction from rivers during those months when it may be required for the crops can only be done on a registered meter, in accordance with the issued allowances. Work has been done on transpiration, and farmers have tried to prove that a vast quantity of the water artificially irrigated passes through the soil and back into the subterranean passages, into the rivers again.

The vast increases in domestic water-consumption have resulted from the greater percentage of houses on the main sewer, the advent of more household lavatories, twin bathrooms and car-washing, which has become a regular and normal usage of tap-water.

In the early 1970s the demand for water was such that schemes were under consideration which would have involved the flooding of over 12,000 hectares in the south-east of England alone. Since the demand had doubled in a quarter of a century, and was expected to double again in the next twenty-five years, the British Waterworks Association and the Water Resources Board foresaw a vast land grab for public reservoirs to fulfil this demand. The proposed reservoirs were broadly in three groups: a triangle in the East Anglian area, an area in Wales and another further north between Leeds and Carlisle; included in these schemes under discussion were two areas on the coast where barrages could have restricted the tidal area and flooded it with retained fresh water. They were around the Wash in small lagoons on the southern side, and the Morecambe Bay barrage, which has been planned in at least three different schemes. Another possibility is a similar area at the estuary of the river Dee.

Daily water consumption per head

	litres
Flushing lavatory	54½
Washing and baths	64
Laundry	18
Washing-up	14
Car and garden	9
Drinking and cooking	4½
Total	164

Other uses and consumption of water for industry

	litres
1 pint of beer	14
1 bag of cement	182
1 daily newspaper	191
4½ litres of petrol	182
51 kilos of coke	14,000
1 tonne of steel	63,000
1 four-door family car	450,000
1 tonne of aluminium	1,350,000

The plans for packing many areas of Britain with reservoirs is costly in land-use, removing the potential agricultural production, although the municipal reservoirs have become focal points for visitors as attractive areas in the countryside. The land lost to farming has become a haven for wildlife and bird-ringers, while in other instances sailing clubs have sprung up like mushrooms. Balancing the land-loss in food-production terms is out of the question, but even as the production of vegetables from household gardens must count against the farming loss, the adequate water-supplies can also sometimes be of benefit to farmers; and a new water area may provide a picnic or caravan site near-by, from which some farmer may enhance his income.

The schemes for reservoirs have in the past been given an absolute priority, and despite the fact that evaporation counterbalances the actual rainfall which may fall into an open lake, the need to fill these reservoirs from a more distant point means that they are simply, in the true meaning of the word, a holding basin near a centre of consumption.

The largest scheme undertaken in the UK is at Empingham, in Rutland, which was completed in the mid-1970s, and is roughly the size of Lake Windermere. It is the largest man-made lake in the country, and has flooded about 5 per cent of the old county of Rutland, taking 1,700 hectares from fifty-nine farmers, roughly half of whom have suffered a loss of their farmable area which makes the remainder no longer economical. One farmer at Lyndon Hall, Oakham, lost 90 of his 150 hectares, which had been farmed by his family (the Conants) since 1634. Only the Jacobean farmhouse and one hectare were left of one of the farms. Even a church was lost in the Empingham project, which was described by the NFU as a national disaster, but which the Welland and Nene River Authority said was desperately needed for the planned urban development of the Daventry/Wellingborough/Northampton and Peterborough areas, where a 1968 population of 673,000 was expected to double by the year 2000.

Although there is an international grid system for electricity on the Continent of Europe, and a national grid system in the UK, there is little attempt to create a national water grid. However, the 1970s are seeing some more imaginative schemes for transporting water from the areas of over-sufficiency to those of urban consumption. Perhaps the most imaginative is the Clywedog Reservoir, which is situated near Llanidloes in the mountains of Wales, where a dam which was built in 1967 has created a vital artery for a future national water grid. Clywedog can hold 50,000,000 tonnes of water which, collected in winter, can be released during the summer along the river Severn (which rises near-by), and by tapping this flow at Bridgenorth for Wolverhampton, Kidderminster for Birmingham, and Ripple for Coventry, considerable and reliable water-supply sources have been created. Additionally, the water is returned after use, excepting from Birmingham and south Staffordshire, while even this water is now proposed to be expensively repumped. Lower down at Gloucester, a new line over the Cotswolds from Gloucester to Cirencester can feed the river Thames into the Metropolitan Water Board's Hampton Station, to eventually finish up in the Lea Valley Reservoirs and to be sent to dry Essex. Also completed in 1972 was a 48-kilometre pipeline from the Ouse near Ely towards the headwaters of the Essex rivers near Saffron Walden. Thus by cleaning out existing watercourses and building a new reservoir at Ardleigh, near Colchester, the extremely dry area of the south-east, with an expanding commuter population and a rainfall of some 500 millimetres, can be supplied from the Welsh mountains. Very little of this imaginative and expensive type of operation has become a reality. It is the water crisis which faces half of Britain that is prompting action of this nature.

The filching of vast areas for reservoirs continues unabated: 650 hectares at Grafham Water in Huntingdonshire and 420 hectares at Derwent in Northumberland have gone in recent years. There are, however, many ways in which land could be saved. The Water Resources Board has estimated that in the North of England seven new reservoirs will be needed by the year 2000. These will require 5,000 hectares of farmland. The alternative is to develop the Morecambe Bay, Dee and Solway barrages, so that approximately 3,130 hectares would remain undisturbed. In Wales and the Midlands the area for flooding has been assessed at 4,000 hectares, but the Dee Scheme would save 1,930 hectares of this. In the south-east, where the largest amount of land is required—assessed at 6,000 hectares, for the building of seven large reservoirs—4,200 hectares of this could be saved if the Wash Lagoons Scheme was put into operation. Thus the answers to land conservation in UK water-supply problems are not difficult to find.

Surrounded as Britain is with umpteen millions of litres of seawater, the obvious solution to the water problems would seem to be in the desalinization process, by which water can be de-salted by distillation or by freezing. The process is well known and well tried in other parts of the world, but although it was once the great white hope for boosting our supplies, it now looks more like a dead duck. It has always been said that the excessive cost of erecting desalinization plants would result in normal household water costing six times as much. Obviously, the land-loss lobby has never yet persuaded governments that the cost of desalinization plant should be subsidized. A pilot plant to be erected near Ipswich was mooted in the late 1960s, but it was axed a few years later, before it had ever got off the drawing-board.

Desalinization plants are in operation in the world today in Hong Kong, Gibraltar and Jersey. This last plant was built in 1970 at a cost of £1·25 million, and it is used as a regular means of topping up the island's reservoirs, producing around 225 million litres per year. Neighbouring Guernsey installed a £250,000 plant in 1958 as an insurance against drought problems in the vital horticultural industry. In the event, however, it has been a white elephant, and has only been used a few times, and only on one occasion was it of assistance in saving the Guernsey tomato crop.

The real long-term solutions to water-storage are not unknown to engineers. Instead of vast areas of open reservoirs on the ground surface, it is feasible to construct natural underground reservoirs which can be recharged with winter rainfall. The chalk strata will hold water, and no vast underground cavern is required. The process consists of pumping water from the areas of run-off to the deficit regions, and letting it soak into large saucer-shaped areas. These natural underground reservoirs constitute a technique that is widely used in the United States, Sweden, Holland and Germany. In West Germany, for instance, over one-third of the water-supply is provided in this way.

The new Water Authorities

At any election meeting in the sixties a politician would have been stunned to silence by a questioner inquiring about his party's water or population policies.

In fact, no party had any policies. Times, however, are changing, and in the seventies it was recognized that this was indeed a future problem. Although there had been incidents of water-shortages entailing restraints upon consumption, and regulations forbidding car-washing and garden hoses, the backroom boys with commendable foresight saw that water-supply problems allied to an increasing population were going to require some considerable planning. The result was the 1973 Water Act, which abolished the previous Water Authorities and the jumble of 1,528 separate bodies dealing with Britain's water-supply and disposal and streamlined this aqueous anarchy into ten regional Water Authorities related more logically to water catchment areas and transcending Local Authority boundaries. The new bodies are related to natural resources and hydrological factors. They are charged with controlling river-pollution, enlarging reservoir space and water supplies, and improving sewage treatment.

Agriculture lost out in its battle for control of the Water Authorities. Instead of remaining under the control of the Ministry of Agriculture, the National Water Council and the Regional Authorities came under the powers of the Department of the Environment with minuscule agricultural representation. In 1971 the NFU in its Annual Report of the Parliamentary Committee said:

> The Union will continue to press for the solution most acceptable to agriculture, and will stress the importance of adequate agricultural representation and local knowledge. The Union has urged strongly throughout that drainage should continue to be the responsibility of the Minister of Agriculture.

and the following year in its Annual Report again the NFU stated:

> The Union, not being convinced that vast authorities are necessarily synonymous with improved efficiency had pressed strongly for single purpose authorities under which there would be considerable amalgamation of sewage authorities and water undertakings, but with the number of river authorities being reduced only minimally.

The President of the Country Landowners Association, Charles Graham—who later became a member of the National Water Council himself, as one of the two appointments by the Minister of Agriculture against the eight appointments by the Secretaries of State for the Environment— said, 'We regret the passing of the Water Resources Board, which we feel will not be adequately substituted by any other body.'

The ten Regional Water Authorities were set up, and took over on 1 April 1974, but underneath this tier were set up local Land Drainage Committees which continued many of the activities of the previous River Authorities. The Chairman of the National Water Council was Lord Nugent of Guildford, MP for that town 1950–66, Parliamentary Secretary at the Ministry of Agriculture for six years from 1951, but a water-conservation expert in his role as Chairman of the Thames Conservancy and President of the Association of River Authorities. Although these appointments were made during a Conservative administration, the political balance was achieved by the further appointment of another Life

Peer, Lord Cooper of Stockton Heath, who was Socialist MP for Deptford, 1950–1, and a former Secretary of the National Union of General and Municipal Workers. Like his Chairman, he was also previously a member of the Thames Conservancy. Of the remaining members of the Water Council, two were ladies, a Director of the Imperial Group, Ltd, and some economic advisers and municipal representatives, and only one, Francis Pemberton, senior partner of Cambridge land agents Bidwells and power behind the throne in the establishment of the National Agricultural Centre at Stoneleigh, had any real agricultural connection. Pemberton, a well-known figure in agricultural circles, was President of RASE in 1975. Nevertheless, out of the ten Regional Chairmen appointed by the DoE, five turned out to be members of the Country Landowners Association, and the CLA claimed a signal triumph by securing that land-drainage should be administered by separate statutory regional and local committees. The tug-of-war was over, and farming interests as usual were not entirely neglected.

In January 1974 the defunct Water Resources Board published its last National Report, which was a collation of the data and experience gained by the Board during its latter years. It was in fact as a final death-wish document the most useful thing it had ever done, and set out the projected water demands with the suggestion that there was little immediate worry until 1981, but thereafter more critical decisions on national water-planning would be required. It also drew attention to the desired combination of estuarial as well as inland reservoir sources, and the balance between inter-regional transfers of water, as opposed to regional self-sufficiency. Finally the message had got home that water-supplies was a national problem that should transcend local boundaries.

The position today is the culmination of several half-hearted attempts to rationalize the water problem, though that solution has been to nationalize it. The 1930 Land Drainage Act gave powers to the Catchment Committee to maintain works existing at that time and to watch the situation. Their role then was one of getting rid of potential urban and agricultural flooding problems. Today the water-supplies for drinking, coupled with the careful disposal of sewage, have brought the 1930 situation from one of constipation to conservation. The 1948 Rivers Act set up the local River Boards for England and Wales. The 1961 Act dealt with the financial side, and tried to cover that vital area of no-man's land between the jurisdiction of the River Boards in main watercourses and the farmer's responsibilities, which ceased at the ditches around his own fields. It has always been maintained that along highways the water running from the impervious surface may flood farmers' adjoining fields, even though in most cases the ownership of the ditches remains with the owner of the land. It is another point of common acceptance in Britain that any landowner at the bottom of the hill must accept the water from his neighbours higher up, even if this involves additional expenditure by the man at the bottom of the flow. The 1963 Water Resources Act resulted in a difference of emphasis since it laid down that besides getting rid of water as quickly as possible one must also try to conserve it. Nevertheless, in 1965 the *Farmers Weekly* was pointing out that a patchwork of unrelated schemes would never make a national plan with local authorities squabbling over available resources. It concluded its leading article (19.2.1965): 'The Government is pledged to harness all the technology it can in carrying out national policies. It must fulfil this pledge in a plan for water. The great thirst can be satisfied—without taking any more land out of food production.'

3 The Pressure

'We have somehow to reconcile the claims of history and of beauty and of peace with the surging pressures of an age dedicated to movement. . . . The price of that movement is the provision of roads'.
John Peyton, MP, Minister for Transport Industries, 1971

'Roads are our economic lifelines.'
Rt Hon. Peter Walker

In Britain in 1972 there were about 336,000 kilometres of roads. During the decade from 1960 to 1970, 21,920 additional kilometres of roads were built. The motorway system, with its original target of 1,600 kilometres of motorways, was achieved by January 1972, although in 1960 there were only 152 kilometres. The Department of the Environment has made a plan for 5,600 kilometres of what it terms 'high-standard strategic routes', to be completed in England by the early 1980s, and doubling the motorways to 3,200 km, and an annual completion rate of 240 kilometres per year. Needless to say, this target is not being achieved. Urban roads servicing the needs of conurbations and cities are estimated to require an additional 1,600 kilometres. Such is the pressure upon land-usage for the mobility of private individuals and for the distribution of industrial goods.

The land-loss to roads is sometimes difficult to quantify. Widening roads by cutting into existing verges makes no impact upon agricultural usage, and the minimal effects of a few square metres in straightening out country lanes is again irrelevant; but just as the railways carved their way across Britain during the nineteenth century, creating a total extent of approximately 18,000 miles (28,000 kilometres) during that time, the Beeching axe reduced this by about one-third. Even allowing for cuttings and embankments, the average width of railways is approximately a quarter of that of normal roads, and an even smaller proportion of giant motorways. Moreover, whereas the railways in their construction were prepared for steep banks, the grass cutting of verges by machinery and tractors means that modern motorways require a lower angle of embankment. This means deeper incursions into the surrounding farmland. Since railway traffic is continuallly declining (freight levels 1960, 249 million tonnes, 1972, 170 million tonnes) and the weight of transport is being placed upon the road system, even a new era in oil-supplies will hardly change the pattern of transportation.

In Britain roadside verges cover more than 200,000 hectares, which is more than twice the area of 128 nature reserves. A survey of the M1 revealed that there was an average of six hectares of grassland per kilometre, and throughout the thousand-plus kilometres of motorway system there are between 4,000 and 6,000 hectares of wasted verge grassland. A normal three-lane dual motorway requires

2¼ hectares per kilometre of impervious hard surface, added to an average of 3 hectares for grassland, and we can see that the motorway system alone, which has been largely carved through virgin farmland, has destroyed 9,000 hectares in its first decade of construction. That figure will double by 1990. The M1 Survey revealed a vast range of flora and fauna, and 384 species were counted, while in total the roadside verges of the nation have recorded over 600 species of flowering plants out of the 2,000 which occur in this country. Although this wide range has found a permanent habitat, the roaring of traffic is hardly conducive to much botanical examination. According to the Nature Conservancy, the animal species surveyed on verges include 20 species of mammals, 40 birds, 6 reptiles, 25 butterflies, and even 6 species of bumble bee. But the agricultural and food-producing potential is lost for ever. A typical example is the Spaghetti Junction where the M1 and M6 motorways converge just east of Birmingham, which in itself occupies over 60 hectares against the average British farm size of 40 hectares.

With a total length of public roads in Great Britain that is continually increasing, and an estimated traffic which in thousand million vehicle-kilometres doubled itself in the decade to 1970, there is an immense pressure for new roads which completely destroy many farms. The policy in Britain is in strict contrast to those countries like the USA, where without any land problems and an even greater car population per head, the road system consists of wider numbers of traffic lanes and complete disregard for the area which they occupy. Official inquiries devoted to examining proposed route alignments have very rarely changed the designated and preferred route. It is perhaps symbolic that when the oak-trees of Epping Forest were threatened by the M11/M16 (London Outer Ring Road) there was more opposition than has ever been mustered in defence of food-production. In most cases the roads will always win in any battle for land-conservation, but while complete areas of farmland designated for urban development do at least take away a complete block, the construction of a ribbon of concrete across the countryside often divides a farm into two parts.

Generally the official attitude and the expenditure criteria allows for tunnels or bridges to pass farm traffic and cattle from one side of the road to the other. In some instances farmers faced with a busy main road, needing to be crossed by livestock or wide machinery in the early hours before dawn, have now found that a bridge or tunnel has made their further fields more accessible, despite the loss of land that has occurred.

A policy of roofs over heads

'*A bin of wine, a spice of wit,*
A house with lawns enclosing it.'
        R. L. Stevenson

It is not necessarily the weight of population increases which determine the amount of land required for houses, but the location of those houses and the affluence of the inhabitants. In the nineteenth century the population fled from the depressed rural areas into the gold-paved pavements of the nearest town. It was infra dig to live 'in the country', and as rural depopulation and financial depression saw the countryside become a jungle, the townsman knew little of what was going on, and cared less.

Two World Wars chipped away at the image of straw-sucking rural peasants, and the necessity to feed the urban masses put farmers on to a new pedestal. It is perhaps ironic that it took the Kaiser and Hitler to popularize the British farmer, but the prospects of starvation from the U-Boat menace certainly helped. Then the prospect of hungry people gave an impetus to land conservation for food-production purposes. It was, however, the motor-car that by the 1960s once again made a reality of country living, with its rural thatched cottage and rose-covered gate. Side by side with this was the fact that many towns had come to the limits of their natural expansion. The rigidity of the Green Belt areas surrounding towns finally led to a vast growth of new housing estates superimposed upon the villages.

Even in 1965, Leslie B. Ginsburg, Head of the Birmingham School of Planning, suggested that the demand for housing in the rural areas would continue to grow—'Whether because the Englishman is at heart a countryman and only regards towns as evil necessities in which to make money, or whether it is escapism from our congested cities.' He suggested that a million more people would wish to move out during the last twenty years of the century. In 1911 the percentage of urban dwellers had risen to 80 per cent of the total population. By 1950, 90 per cent were urban dwellers, but that figure is now going sharply into reverse. City centres are becoming places of daily work, and not of permanent habitation. The effect on villages has been to create rural dormitories, desolate during working hours. The net result is that although a greater percentage of the population now live in rural areas, there is little understanding or affinity to the farmers' problems, and in many cases conflicts have arisen.

Within the UK the ½ hectare of overall land space which each member of the population shares brings an approximate 1,660 persons per square kilometre. At current building levels of 24–29 houses per hectare, it produces an average density of 100 people per hectare by normal modern housing standards, although in municipal tower flats it is possible to house up to 960 persons per hectare. Since the urban population is contained within 11 per cent of the total land area of England and Wales, densities in the older housing estates are far greater than modern planning dictates will allow. Although by 1970 the planners were designating 35 hectares per thousand head of population on new estates—which figure had been only 23 hectares half a century before—the rate of expanding garden and habitation areas is slowing down rapidly.

1920	23 hectares per 1,000 head of population
1940	30 hectares per 1,000 head of population
1950	32 hectares per 1,000 head of population
1970	35 hectares per 1,000 head of population

Despite the appearance of these figures, the pre-War decades recorded an increase of spaciousness standards of 3·6 hectares per 1,000 population in each decade, whereas the post-War period has shown an increase of only 1·4 hectares per 1,000 head in each decade. The rate of acceleration is slowing down, even if the demands for increasing land space appear to be insatiable.

With a population that has increased by almost 4 millions in the past twenty-five years, the necessity for roofs over heads has been paramount. In 1970 there were 18·7 million houses in Great Britain; this was 2·3 million more than ten years earlier, and although the annual rate of building has varied around a third of a million houses per annum in the early 1960s, the two-year period 1967–8 saw a massive 840,000 new houses completed. The mid-1970s have seen a recession, and the annual rate of building must be equated with the demolition of slums, etc. In total, some 110,000 dwellings are demolished annually, and although some sites are used again, many are not. By the standards of housing development, it must be assumed that out of the 16,000 hectares average land losses to urban industrial and recreational uses in the 1966–70 period, almost 14,000 hectares of this was for housing developments. The impact of this upon the overall farming area is not as important as the geographical location of those sites. For instance, village infilling where little real food-production was apparent may deplete the agricultural area without severely adversely affecting the agricultural production.

New day, new faces . . . new town

The New Towns Act 1946 heralded the concept of creating new centres of population in architectural dream palaces. It was an early post-War symbol of the brave new world emanating from the 1945–50 Labour Government under Clement Attlee. Thirty years later the New Town concept is becoming tarnished. Few of the early examples have yet been completed; even Harlow, one of the very first, is still undecided about where its boundaries should be; and there have been continual reappraisals of optimum population levels. From an agricultural viewpoint, this has cast a shadow over large co-ordinated areas of land. As opposed to smaller parcels spread in different corners.

The only pre-War example of a New Town, Welwyn Garden City, Hertfordshire, has now been followed by a long list. Although inevitably this pattern of development originated around the London conurbation, the Cumbernauld New Town in Scotland, set among rolling countryside, has achieved a great deal in town planning, but since the main objective was (and still is) to provide a brand-new town, and to balance the interests, ages and occupations of the inhabitants, as well as providing near-by employment in its self-contained industrial estates, the concept of new towns is something of which Britain may be proud.

Not all the New Towns have been sited on good agricultural land. Basildon, for instance, was originally a shanty town where the agricultural output was very low, and pre-1939 a vast proportion was unproductive and completely derelict. Telford New Town sits on land originally ravaged by industry. Stevenage, Crawley, Bracknell and Hemel Hempstead were products of the early era, but Milton Keynes in Buckinghamshire presents the largest and latest New Town concept. It occupies some 8,900 hectares, of which 7,300 was agricultural land. It extinguished 96 farm holdings, 51 tenanted, and 56 owner-occupied. Parts of an additional ten farms lost some land. By the Ministry of Agriculture Classification, this land was mainly in the third or 'average' grade, but there were two areas in the Stony Stratford–Wolverton district and a third near the village of Milton Keynes which were in the second grade. It is, perhaps, symbolic of the general agricultural attitude that despite opposition from the NFU the main points of argument were not as to the concept of covering farmland with bricks and roads, but as to how much money the farmers should have.

The problems of land assembly for co-ordinated planning objectives anywhere in the UK are fraught with immense difficulties by virtue of the complete fragmentation of ownership. Thus the New Towns Act 1946, and the later 1965 Act, gave powers of acquisition by compulsory purchase to the newly created New Town Authority. Compensation is allowable for freehold value plus an element for disturbance, but at Milton Keynes negotiations for land began in 1968, and purchase was not completed until mid-1971. Since values had risen considerably regarding agricultural land, as well as housing land, many farmers described the operation as a 'confidence trick'. The Act allows market value to be paid on land purchased, but does not interpret future values where development may occur. Normal development values can accrue to farmers after planning permission has been granted, but the variation in the New Towns Act does not permit any of the benefits to accrue to the original landowners; thus, not unexpectedly, farmers have fought against these Compulsory Purchase Orders.

In the 1970s Compulsory Purchase Orders have been served for the take-over of 1,538 hectares of productive farmland near Preston, Lancashire. This marks only the start of a massive land assembly project by which up to 6,070 hectares will be absorbed, by either voluntary or compulsory purchase, before 1980. This New Town will eventually cover an area of 14,000 hectares in the Preston–Leyland area of Central Lancashire. In Scotland also, 2,832 hectares near Lesmahago, occupied by about forty farmers, is proposed by the Scottish Development Department to house a 35,000 overspill population from Glasgow.

In *The South East Study, 1961/1981*[1] the whole problem of housing the bursting population of London was given a microscopic investigation. It set out the need for the expansion of several new towns, the enlargement of existing towns as far away as Ipswich, and the land requirements of the south-east corner for a twenty-year period. It found that nearly 2½ million of the anticipated 3½ million population increase up to 1981 will be excess of births over deaths, and

[1] Published by the Ministry of Housing and Local Government (HMSO, 1964).

just over 1 million net inward migration of people from the remoter areas, seeking to discover if the pavements of London are really paved with gold. The development programmes for north-east England and central Scotland, coupled with the later designation of development areas where industrialists could receive heavy subsidies to establish their factories, have been attempts to control the migration away from London, but with little avail.

This report, while emphasizing the nature of the problem, paid scant regard to farmland. Admittedly it did state that high-quality agricultural land should not be taken for urban development 'wherever there is a practical alternative', which in essence left the door open to almost anything. It was symbolic that the proposed Ipswich expansion—which in reality did not materialize—was deliberately planned on the western side in the best agricultural land, whereas the eastern side of that town is covered by heathland and little real agricultural productivity. Although the public inquiry established this point, it is dubious if the farming lobby would have won the day if the expansion had progressed.

> The south east has an unusually large proportion of good agricultural land, but in many parts of the region the areas most desirable for development are those of particularly high agricultural quality. Good farmland can often be saved by diverting expansion to one side of a town rather than another, but sometimes there is no easy way of reconciling agricultural and other planning interests, and it may then be necessary to avoid or defer large scale growth, if the programme can be made up elsewhere.

Thus the official view in 1964 did not pay regard to the food-producing interests. Ten years later, however, in view of the changing world of food shortages, there was a greater consciousness of the need.

The irreconcilable differences between the planners' concepts and the farming interests have been and will be a national problem in conserving our heritage. Since farmers have accepted vast sums of money and welcomed the planning permissions for residential development, the planners often appear to be satisfying their own whims: there would appear to be little chance of achieving a national land policy.

The total population living in New Towns in Britain today is 1·8 million, but the central Lancashire area alone holds just over 13 per cent in one large conurbation of nearly a quarter of a million people. The total population housed in these 231,000 houses on 110,000 hectares in Britain is little more than 2½ houses to the hectare, or in population terms just under 17 persons per hectare. This low density is explained by the large, well-planned open spaces, adequate road systems, shopping and amenity areas, industrial estates, and schools. Thus the complete land space requirements for the population are contained within these areas.

Translated into national terms, this reveals that the total population of England and Wales at 47·136 million people should occupy 2·8 million hectares if the standards of the new towns are to be maintained. Since the non-agricultural area is 2·5 million hectares—which includes forests—the new towns can be proved to be less crowded than the more ancient centres of population. Discounting the forest areas, they are almost twice as generous in land space as other areas. But land-conservation was never a dictum of the New Town Authorities.

New towns in Britain

New town	Date of designation	Population 31/12/1974	Designated hectarage
England			
Stevenage	11.11.46	74,500	2,504
Crawley	9. 1.47	71,000	2,420
Hemel Hempstead	4. 2.47	74,500	2,392
Harlow	25. 3.47	81,500	2,560
Aycliffe	19. 4.47	24,725	1,221
Peterlee	10. 3.48	25,750	1,116
Hatfield	20. 5.48	26,000	940
Welwyn Garden City	20. 5.48	40,000	1,728
Basildon	4. 1.49	84,900	3,128
Bracknell	17. 6.49	41,150	1,320
Corby	1. 4.50	52,500	1,772
Skelmersdale	9.10.61	39,200	1,652
Redditch	10. 4.64	47,000	2,872
Runcorn	10. 4.64	49,600	2,896
Washington	24. 7.64	39,000	2,236
Milton Keynes	23. 1.67	64,000	8,760
Peterborough	21. 7.67	97,800	6,376
Northampton	14. 2.68	145,500	7,984
Warrington	26. 4.68	134,000	7,460
Telford	13.12.68	94,500	7,700
Central Lancashire	26. 3.70	242,500	14,092
		1,549,625	83,129
Wales			
Cwmbran	4.11.49	43,500	1,264
Newton	18.12.67	6,700	600
		50,200	1,864
Scotland			
East Kilbride	6. 5.47	71,430	4,100
Glenrothes	30. 6.48	31,500	2,292
Cumbernauld	9.12.55	38,425	3,116
Livingston	16. 4.62	22,300	2,680
Irvine	9.11.66	48,500	4,976
Stonehouse	14. 8.73		2,708
		212,155	19,872
Total UK		1,811,980	104,865

There are twenty-nine designated New Towns in Britain. Fourteen emerged between 1946 and 1950, in the mad rush of post-War housing problems. During the Tory Administration of 1950–64 only three new towns were agreed, although three were actually designated in 1964, just before Sir Alec Douglas-Home went out of office. Eight new towns were designated between 1964 and 1970, and only one (Stonehouse) in the 1970s. This does not preclude the fact that most of the new towns have expanded beyond the original area as the problems of second-generation families have arisen.

In retrospect, the face of Britain today represents the results of three decades of rigid planning controls, although these master plans have been stretched to meet an expanding population; but the overall picture has been one of concentrating urban communities, by restricting town sprawl and by the preservation of Green Belts. Village development has been concentrated around the centre by the addition of urban-style estates with pavements and street lighting. The end result has been to leave many more undisturbed blocks of farmland, as well as undisturbed viewpoints. The net policy result must safeguard the agricultural potential of the nation, even though the main considerations were social ones, and the more practical aspects of providing sewage and general services where housing is concentrated.

The leisure boom

The vast increase in the leisure time of the working-man has created a problem of utilizing these holidays to the best advantage. The five-day week is now almost universal, and whereas only 2 per cent of the population enjoyed more than two weeks paid holiday annually in 1950, now 65 per cent have that holiday by statutory right. Similarly, the car population in 1950 of 2·3 million private cars had increased to 11·5 million twenty years later, and a forecast figure of 20 million private cars has been suggested by the year 2000.

The time, and mobility, coupled with a degree of affluence and greater education, have combined to produce a rocketing interest in enjoying the countryside. Participation in natural history, field and water sports, rambling and camping have all increased. The Camping Club of Great Britain had a membership in 1951 of only 8,000, but 55,000 members by 1971, and the Caravan Club rose even more dramatically from 7,000 to 104,000 during the same period. It is estimated that over 3 million people take part in angling as a hobby. Additionally, the pressures on the countryside come from overseas visitors. In 1950 some 600,000 overseas visitors came to Britain, but in twenty years this figure has multipled tenfold to over 6 million.

During the past quarter of a century several new attractions in the countryside have evolved. Chief among these is the Stately Homes Business, and vast numbers visit annually such places as Woburn Abbey in Bedfordshire, Lord Montagu's Motor Museum at Beaulieu in Hampshire, the Lions at Longleat, or the magnificence of the Duke of Devonshire's Chatsworth home in Derbyshire. The average American tourist, however, still does the usual rounds of standing at the railings of Buckingham Palace, admiring the grandeur of King's College, Cambridge, making a pilgrimage to the Memorial Theatre at Stratford-upon-Avon, taking a quick look at the Lake District, and concluding around the Scottish lochs. The antiquity of Hadrian's Wall is left for the British to admire, Stonehenge and the Cheddar Gorge are one-day trips for Britons, while the vast, mobile urban mass makes a dash for the beaches at Blackpool or Southend. In fact, over three-quarters of all holidays taken in Britain are at the seaside.

It is the short forays into the neighbouring countryside that are the most popular events for the typical urban family at weekends, and since the average man barely travels away from his parked car, the deep intrusion into the countryside or the destruction of farmers' crops is minimal, although it may be annoying and costly in specific areas.

Since the land area utilized by the day trippers is very largely that which was uncultivated anyway, the vast increase of casual tourism into the countryside has had little effect upon food-production. If anything it has brought more benefits to farmers than the reverse. Only a very few farms have set themselves up in business as a show-place for paying visitors; overnight caravan sites, of which many are situated on farmland, do bring a revenue to the agricultural community, and in certain more difficult farming areas such as Cornwall and Wales the advent of tourism, properly controlled, has been the salvation of many farming families. Similarly, in the Uplands of Scotland the farmer's wife has supplemented the farm income from residential guests.

It is fair to say that the British countryside and the farm structure lends itself quite well to the absorption of tourists. Even the forest areas are now being transformed by an open invitation to visitors rather than closed gates, and owners are discovering that the financial return from recreation can exceed that of the timber-growing business. A combination of the two seems an ideal exploitation of the potential. If the townsman is prepared to pay for the views and fresh air which the farmer and landowner take for granted, then the farmer is fast realizing that this can be capitalized into hard cash. It is impossible to quantify the actual area now being used for recreational needs on private farms, although the official country parks under the control of the County Councils do occupy 11,700 hectares. This figure arises from the objectives of the 1968 Countryside Act which created country parks for the purpose of 'providing, or improving, opportunities for the enjoyment of the countryside by the public'.

Of far greater importance in land-use has been the increasing popularity of golf in Britain. It is estimated today that over three-quarters of a million people play this game. Its obvious advantages of fresh air and exercise to a claustrophobic office-bound population has instituted its increasing popularity. At the present time there are approximately 1,120 golf courses in this country, which at an average hectarage of 50 each amounts to 56,650 hectares, but the projection that something between 400 and 500 new courses will be required by 1980 will absorb an additional 20,000–30,000 hectares. Since many of these are the brain-child of a farmer wishing to utilize part of his land for greater income, they are in fact in direct conflict to food-production from this land, although again the financial rewards to the agricultural community should fully compensate. Golf courses vary in size from between 40 to 60 hectares for 18 holes. On clear, open ground the lower figure is acceptable, but on more undulating country, where spinneys, steep slopes or rock have to be avoided, the larger area is required. Building a golf course is a very expensive item; with land conversion, clearance of fairways and laying of greens, plus the maintenance of a watering system and the inevitable Nineteenth Hole, the investment starts at a figure of £100,000 and continues upward.

Too many derelict hectares

It may seem incredible in tiny Britain, with every square metre of land counted and jealously guarded by its owner, that there should be any derelict land at all. Efforts at conservation, an emphasis upon land utilization, housing and agricultural land interests perpetually conflicting, and a bursting population in an inelastic island; and yet there are probably 122,000 hectares of derelict land.

The actual figure is disputed according to the criteria used. For instance, in 1964 the Ministry of Housing and Local Government estimated that there were 40,000 derelict hectares. Ten years later the succeeding Ministry (now known as the Department of the Environment) put the figure at 53,000, but a report by the Professional Institutions Council for Conservation (a body representing eighteen professional groups, including chartered surveyors, planning institutes and local authorities) suggested that the true figure of dereliction is nearer 122,000 hectares. The difference is accounted for in the definition. Basically, the official definition of derelict land 'land so damaged by industrial or other development that it is incapable of beneficial use without treatment'—is a sound and comprehensive definition, but the interpretation of that criterion makes the end result vastly different. There are a number of significant exemptions.

Land in active use, irrespective of its condition, is excluded; thus on a working mineral site, although part may be completed, part being worked, and part for future workings, that which has been completed and is in all senses derelict is not classified as such. The anomalies are illustrated vividly by the fact that in Bedfordshire, where brick clay, sand, gravel and chalk are all mined and dug extensively, the official figures reveal only 121 hectares of derelict land, whereas the County Planning Department estimate that 1,200 hectares are in a derelict or despoiled condition. In the former West Riding of Yorkshire, where one-quarter of the UK collieries are situated, and where one-third of the national coal-output is mined, the official derelict area in 1966 was 2,538 hectares, against the County Planning Department's figure of 9,733 hectares. In so far as farming is concerned, land which is being under-farmed, badly farmed, weed-infested, or even marginal areas on erstwhile productive farms that have been neglected, does not count. In this respect, the Ministry of Agriculture has calculated that on a normal farm up to 10 per cent of the area is non-productive for crop-growing purposes, consisting as it does of the homestead and its surrounding buildings, transport arteries to the fields and hedges and ditches, the latter occupying a considerable area in those counties where lush growth is possible and where hedges are retained for livestock-protection purposes; or even pheasant-shooting.

That the rate and area of the total despoliation of Britain is increasing can be seen by the following table.

Year	Total	Net increase or decrease	Area reclaimed
	Ha	Ha	Ha
1964	34,364	—	839
1965	36,800	+2,465	833
1966	37,554	+763	666
1967	37,460	−94	665
1968	37,972	+515	854
1969	38,692	+729	1,012
1970	39,182	+394	1,478
1971	39,336	+159	1,937

Although the rate of reclamation is increasing significantly, and in 1972 reached a figure of 2,164 hectares—which was 12 per cent over the 1971 figure, and nearly 50 per cent over the 1970 figure—the total area considered derelict still increases significantly. England and Scotland still counts its dereliction annually (the Scottish Office records some 6,070 hectares, but Wales, with a suggested figure of some 8,100 hectares, ceased to take an annual count after 1969. With its proliferation of slagheaps, one wonders if the result of an annual survey would have been too embarrassing).

Government Grants of up to 85 per cent have been available to local authorities in the development areas for land-reclamation schemes, but since the greatest problem is probably in those areas with the lowest rateable value, the 15 per cent that must be found locally is a great burden. The Government Grants are one reason for the DoE's reluctance to reclassify too many derelict areas. Once classified they could be the subject of a Grant Application, and indeed part of the discrepancy in the total dereliction figures is the deletion of those lands owned by the National Coal Board, British Rail and the Department of Defence. These Government-owned lands do not qualify for grants, and the Coal Board and British Rail are supposedly operating on commercial lines. In another context, the various Electricity Boards are spending token amounts to underground their cables in selected beauty spots; these are more usually short lengths in picturesque, attractive villages. Whilst this is not dereliction in the normal sense, it does affect views of the countryside.

If finance is a problem, there are others just as great; little is known of the cost of restoration, and even less of what to do with the reclaimed or realigned landscape. In 1965 Study Group No. 12 of the 'Countryside in 1970' Conference estimated that with an annual expenditure of £5 million, the hard-core derelict land could be redeemed in ten years, but by 1970 the Countryside Conference concluded that in the interim the magnitude of the problem had multiplied, as well as the costs of reclamation, with the result that a ten-year programme would now be costing in the order of £19 million annually. In its Report[2] the PICC suggested that there were four main aims of derelict land reclamation:

(a) Return to economic use by agriculture or forestry;
(b) Development of facilities for outdoor recreation;
(c) Enhancement of amenity and conversation value;
(d) Provision of land for housing, industry, roads, etc.

This Study Group, having crystallized the principal objectives into four categories, then suggested that the first three needed ecological research, and that there were wide gaps in the knowledge of what would happen after reclamation. Only in the provision of land for housing, industry and roads did they consider that the technology already existed to meet the structural and hydrological considerations. For any return to agriculture they suggested that a research programme was necessary because of a lack of specific knowledge of the growth responses of farm or forestry crops to site conditions, and the long-term prospects of soil stability and water purity. The same basic problems of ignorance were attributed to land which might be used for outdoor recreation or for amenity and conservation value.

The problem of derelict land is increasing, and the 15 per cent to be found locally is considered a burden. The fact remains that this reclaimed land does have a value greater than before reclamation, and the vested body would reap some benefits from its enhanced value. The same PICC Report came out in favour of grants for professional fees for feasibility studies in advance of the approval of actual projects. Certainly a feasibility study would illuminate the problems of reclamation, but would inevitably eat up the grant allocations at a faster rate than any government is ever prepared to facilitate. Slagheaps seem to be the primary offenders in the dereliction in Britain, but the problems of moving them are immense, and natural vegetation or animal habitats are slow to evolve. It takes up to a hundred years for the heaps to become covered with vegetation again. The impoverished nature of these man-made mountains precludes almost all forms of life.

The problem of derelict land is not large in the context of land-usage in Britain, but it seems regrettable that this area should be increasing. Since reclaimed land that is useful for food-production is a national asset, as well as improving the general environment of those who live near by, it is to be hoped that before the turn of the century we shall have mastered this ever-encroaching problem and

[2] *Dereliction of Land* (Professional Institutions Council for Conservation, 1974).

reduced the area. Certainly at the suggested 120,000 hectares it is a blot upon the British countryside that is quite inexcusable.

Beneath the soil

'Some brittle sticks of thorn or briar
Make me a fire,
Close by whose living coal I sit
And glow like it.'
             Robert Herrick

'The rugged miners poured to war from Mendip's sunless caves'
             Macaulay

The land of Britain represents a natural resource that is self-replenishing. Properly cultivated and fertilized, it will produce crops virtually for ever, but the mineral resources are non-renewable, and it is a salutary thought that the metals derived from minerals, although not ultimately destroyable, are very largely wasted. It is furthermore a fact that during the last fifty years we have consumed more of the world's mineral resources than in the whole of previous history. World demand continues to expand, and as the richer deposits become exhausted the pressures on the lower-grade ores become apparent. The more readily assessable and easier-developed mineral wealth will have to be extracted from the remoter areas, and in particular (expensive though it may be) from beneath the world's oceans.

In Britain the ancient Cornish tin-mines, although less important than formerly, still exist, and production of metalliferous minerals—iron ore, tin and lead—is running at ten million tonnes per year. However, the production of iron ore is declining, while that of tin and lead, although small, is expanding. Far in excess of the production of metalliferous minerals is the production of sedimentaries such as chalk, limestone, clay, sand and gravel, which together comprise an annual production of over three hundred million tonnes annually. The fossil fuels extracted from the soil, such as coal and petroleum products, assume far more massive figures, although coal-production itself declined between 1960 and 1970, from 198 million tonnes to 142 million tonnes.

Extracting minerals from the soil leaves a hole in the ground or a cavity beneath it, and removal of these ugly blots on the landscape involves the loss of productive land. This is no new factor. The Norfolk Broads, for instance, were largely created by the extraction of peat for fuel during the Middle Ages, and many other ancient quarries and chalk pits are accepted as natural features of the landscape, but the needs of the twentieth century are using up the soil beneath our feet at a faster rate than ever before. Mineral production in the UK, excluding coal, accounts for just over $\frac{1}{2}$ per cent of the gross national product, but it is vital for sustaining the raw material needs of modern industry. Chalk deposits are extensively quarried, and applications of finely ground chalk are used by farmers on acid soils to neutralize that acidity. It must be noted that in many areas, particularly south of the Thames, there are chalk outcrops, and the phrase 'farming on the chalk' is commonplace. But the chalk requirements for farming are largely achieved from a static area of chalk quarries, the mining operations merely going deeper, while the much vaster annual requirements for chalk in the manufacture of cement is embracing a steadily increasing area. Clay pits are also being dug for similar use in the manufacture of cement.

Brick-making requires a vast bulk of natural raw materials dug from the soil, and the London Brick Company's concentration of the Fletton brick industry on the belt of Oxford clay in the Bedford-Peterborough area provides sufficient bricks to build over 200,000 houses per year. This represents just over half the present housing achievements, and is produced from an annual consumption of about 40 hectares of clay-bearing land.

Far greater is the need for aggregates, and the sand and gravel industry estimates an annual requirement of 1,600 hectares to meet Britain's current needs, half being for the Government's motorway programme. Limestone is used for innumerable products, ranging from smelting to road stone to cosmetics, with an increasing demand for both. Fluorspar and limestone are being worked in the Peak District National Park, and in the 1973 Report of the Sheffield and Peak District Branch of the Council for the Protection of the Environment it was stated that a section of the Peak National Park three kilometres long was being eroded each year. 'Assuming that the present annual production is five million tons this represents the removal every year of a chunk of the Peak Park two miles long by one hundred feet high and sixty-six feet wide, and this chunk will increase in size each year as demand continues to grow. If the past rate of increase continues, this annual chunk will be double its present size in ten years time.'

Farmers and landowners do not have complete ownership of all minerals beneath their soil. The Crown is deemed the owner of gold, silver, petroleum and other hydrocarbons beneath our feet, and coal is the property of the NCB, but farmers do have possession of clay, chalk and other strata beneath their soil. While the sky above a farm is the property of the landowner (subject to the aircraft traffic routes and the passage of light aircraft—for instance, electricity cables that hang over a farmer's land without the actual pylons being situated upon it do attract a small annual way-leave payment for this assumed ownership), beneath the soil there is no limit to the depths to which a chalk or gravel pit may extend, and in most cases mining is restricted by water flooding or other more practical aspects. The quarrying of gravel and sand brings to landowners a considerable annual sum, and in many cases the land is later reinstated with little ill effects, apart from a lowering of the landscape.

The extraction of all forms of minerals is strictly controlled by the original 1947 Town and Country Planning Act and by successive adjustments and strengthening in later Acts. This contrasts vividly with the pre-1939 era, when extractors could happily dig holes in the countryside, despoil the landscape, and walk away, leaving their mess behind them. Not only is the extraction strictly controlled, but subsequent restoration of the site is often made a condition of the original consent. While this is working effectively with those permissions given in more recent years, there have been considerable difficulties in the past in enforcing the regulations. Sir Ralph Verney[3] remarked, 'The evidence suggested that the reduction in environmental disturbance and dereliction since the advent of Planning Control had been notable.' He continued that there had been failures in enforcing adequate restoration conditions on mineral operators, and noted the slowness and pettiness of some Local Planning Procedures. Particular criticism was levelled at the DoE for the slow and cumbersome way in which Appeals were sometimes handled.

Pipes, pipes and more pipes

The *Third Man* was inspired by the sewers of Vienna—The Pied Piper piped the rats from the underground network of Hamelin. London has so many underground passages that no one has yet been able to map them correctly or measure them. PLUTO, which stood for Pipe Line Under The Ocean, was a prefabricated supply line that serviced the fuel needs of the Allied Forces at the Normandy beach-head after D-Day in June 1944. The fascination with underground exploration continues with those enthusiasts who spend their week-ends potholing in the crevices and cracks of the mountainous regions in several parts of Britain. This preoccupation with undergrounding is now resulting in a new map of Britain which contains literally thousands of kilometres of underground gas and oil pipelines.

Although the initial impetus for these pipelines originated in the early post-War period as a bomb-proof method of transportation, they have grown at a staggering rate, and with the advent of North Sea Gas there are four long-distance radiating lines emanating from the Norfolk coastline. Major water pipelines have been mentioned earlier in the chapter on the water-conservation problems of Britain. On the whole they tend to be shorter sections, linking rivers which are then used as the water-carrier, but both gas and oil pipelines need to be continuous to the ultimate destination. Electricity is more expensive to underground, and the National Grid circumnavigates Britain on the giant pylons and sweeping cables, with new lines having been constructed in more recent years to take the electrical output of the nuclear-power stations. The pipeline problem is greater in Scotland than in England, with the natural route for southbound lines from the North Sea oil reserves constricted along an arable strip on the east coast bounded by mountains and sea, while an oil line from Peterhead to

[3] Chairman of the Working Party Report on the Management of Natural Resources *Sinews for Survival*, a study of public opinion taken at the request of the Secretary of State for the Environment (Rt Hon. Peter Walker, MP) and presented to the United Nations Conference on the Human Environment held at Stockholm, July 1972.

Grangemouth and two gas lines along the same route have played havoc, with their disturbance of farm soil-structure and cropping.

Bottlenecks are already occurring near Perth and east of Aberdeen, where river-crossing situations make the closer proximity of the pipelines inevitable. In other parts of Britain there are converging areas in the Midlands where an underground Spaghetti Junction already exists. While the water pipes which catered for local needs were relatively small in diameter, many of these new pipelines are two metres wide, and in the construction the machinery for excavation and insertion of the pipes requires a vast swarth across fertile farmland. The pipes themselves after burial should be deep enough not to hinder cultivations or fertility, but the stirring up of topsoil and subsoil together makes many of these pipelines visible from the air in the crops for several years afterwards. Land drainage is visibly affected also.

The Statutory Undertakers, such as the Gas Corporation and the privately owned oil companies, pay for the land needed on a reasonably generous scale to a set of conditions covering compensation for immediate and subsequent damage, but this code of conduct does not apply to the water and sewage authorities, who are empowered with rights of entry denied to the gas and oil consortia, and are less liable for damage. In most instances the Authority owning the pipeline does not buy the land, but pays an Easement Fee. This can amount to a figure that works out at approximately the value of the land itself, and is normally scaled to existing land values in the requisite locality. The farmer still has his land left, but the disruptive effects are considerable, and most landowners would happily be without a pipeline under their farms.

Although coal is being discovered under the seabed, oil is also being drilled under farmland, and licences for prospecting for oil cover a big area of the South of England, excluding London, as well as parts of Lincolnshire, Lancashire and Cheshire. Already British land-based wells are producing 88,000 tonnes a year, which although small in terms of the UK total consumption of 109 million tonnes, does represent an expanding figure. Present predictions suggest that 200,000 tonnes, or more than double the present output, could be easily and inexpensively produced.

Since oil and gas discovered underground are the property of the Crown, the only deal the farmer can make is for compensation or loss or damage caused, and for leasing the land requirements for the actual drilling operations, which could be as small as eight hectares.

Open-cast mining operations

In the vast wastelands of Australia mineral deposits including coal are literally scooped up from the open countryside. The draglines, bulldozers and earth-scrapers move in, extract the valuable minerals, and move on. Coal is produced from the fossilized and compressed remains of forest regions of millions of years past. Although the deposits are sometimes extremely deep in the soil, there are many areas in Britain where the reserves are only covered by the soil of the last glacial age, and the system of open-cast coal-mining can take place.

Although coal-mining is an ancient occupation, it was only in 1942, when the pressure of wartime emergencies were upon us, that open-cast coal-mining came into any prominence. An initial output in 1942 of 1·3 million tonnes quickly rose to about 8 million tonnes by 1945. It was just after that when Earl Fitzwilliam put in a poignant plea to Prime Minister Attlee that his Wentworth estate near Peterborough should not be destroyed by open-cast operations from the Ministry of Fuel and Power. He failed in his visit to No. 10, but restoration has since taken place. After 1952 open-cast operations were handed over to the National Coal Board, and by 1958 an annual production of 14 million tonnes was reported. During this period operations were embarked upon under the Defence Regulations still surviving from wartime Britain, which established compulsory rights to enter land and extract coal by open-cast methods.

In 1958 the Open Cast Coal Act was passed, and it still provides the guideline for controlling open-cast operations. The 14 million tonnes of 1958 has been rapidly reduced to an average during the last decade of around 7 million tonnes, with the emphasis on anthracite and other scarce smokeless fuels. Open-cast operations have been restricted partly by the NCB policy, but also to help employment in the industry. The job of coal-mining from open-cast operations is done entirely by mechanical diggers, and mechanized machinery. The total output from open-cast methods amounts to roughly 5 per cent of the total British coal-production, but between 1952 and 1970, 107 million tonnes of coal were produced in this way, at a profit to the Board of over £100 million, after allowing for all costs, including full restoration, agricultural treatment and land drainage. Opening a new park project at Stoke-on-Trent, the NCB Chairman, Derek Ezra, said that since 1942 the Board has restored 46,500 hectares of land for farming after open-cast operations, inferring (not always correctly) that the land acquired for open-cast operations was in poor shape before the coal was extracted. Today the NCB Open Cast Executive hold nearly 14,000 hectares (total NCB holdings 97,000 hectares) for operational purposes, and in Scotland at the present time about 1,150 hectares of farmland is being used for open-cast mining. Scotland produces about 20 per cent of the open-cast tonnage, and calculated on that basis the national hectarage in use at any one time for open-cast operations looks like around 6,000 hectares.

Of the total NCB land holdings, some 40,000 hectares are being used at the present time for underground operations, and although the pit-head sites are small in themselves, the spoil does deface the landscape (besides being a potential menace). Undergrounding operations do, however, affect farmers, and subsidence of field levels, with consequent drainage problems, is not unusual. There have, however, been great technical advances in predicting and measuring the subsidence anticipations, and slopes towards rivers can now be fully controlled. Aerial surveys are used to produce plans showing contours every 23 centimetres across the land, and the Institute of Geological Sciences has been called in with its experts on water-bearing strata to help organize the mining operations below the surface. There is in existence a 1957 Coal Mining (Subsidence) Act, but the NFU regards the compensation it allows as totally inadequate in most cases.

The Selby Project

In 1974 it was decided to go ahead with a new vast coalfield beneath the quiet, flat farmland between Selby and York, an area of over 390 square kilometres which contains rich coal deposits, although the main site for the drift head is only 32 hectares. The importance of the Selby find means that 10 million tonnes of coal a year can be extracted from this area for at least the next fifty years, and with fully automated and computer-controlled operational equipment it will be the most up to date, and indeed the largest, single coal-mine in Europe. The typical reaction of the local traders is summed up in the statement that a coal-mine will become a gold-mine, but for the farmers the prospect of their land being lowered by subsidence, or taken altogether, was very different. In national terms, a mine of this capacity operated on the 'drift' system means a gently sloping cavity is cut into the ground, dropping about 270 metres in just over 8 kilometres. In an effort to protect overhead properties, only a 3-metre seam at about 270 metres below ground-level is being taken out, by leaving pillars of coal immediately below such historic buildings as Selby Abbey, which rests its foundations in water. In total, only 60 per cent of the available deposits may be eventually extracted. Much of this area on the Plain of York is already low-lying and highly productive farmland. Some is barely six metres above sea-level, and subject to flooding from tidal rivers. Driving from Hambleton to Ryther, and from Selby eastward, is not unlike driving across the Fens, with raised roads, drainage ditches and posts to mark out the road should it be flooded. Although subsidence can take place unexpectedly, the NCB has pointed out that the whole of Coventry, with its Cathedral and precision industries, has been hollowed out by coal-extraction.

There is, however, argument. The high-water table in this area is not always to the farmer's advantage, and some have suggested that instead of the Plain of York being turned into a lake, it could be that better drainage would considerably improve much of it. The siting of the mine head is in close proximity to the Bishop Wood Forestry Commission Plantation—not one of the best plantations of the Commission, where an instant screening of the buildings required could have considerable savings on the landscaping costs. The naturalists have lodged a claim on behalf of the rare plants to be found in this wood, but since there will be no winding gear and few tall buildings, the NCB anticipate it may resemble the Longannet drift mine in Fife—which, however, does have undulating hills to assist its blending into the landscape.

After Cromwell. . . came the restoration

Although the total area of derelict land in the UK at 121,000 hectares is a national scandal, the annual area of restoration has doubled in recent years, and much greater impetus is given today to the restoration and beautification of our landscape after mining operations have been completed. The Civic Trust annually makes awards for restoration projects, and even the Sand and Gravel Association (SAGA), which has been the greatest despoiler in the past, has now instituted a series of awards for restoration. SAGA started this movement in 1970 by awarding plaques each year for the best examples of restoration of worked-out gravel pits.

The 1972 Award was typical. It went to the Cory Sand and Ballast, which is an operating company in the William Cory & Son Division of Ocean Transport & Trading. It was for an area of 8 hectares at South Ockendon, in pit-marked Essex, where more than 40 hectares were restored by that company to a superior standard of environmental landscaping that would have warmed Capability Brown or Humphrey Repton's hearts. In his speech at the ceremony, the General Manager, A. G. Ellis, said:

> We well know that as gravel operators our activities bear heavily on the quality of the environment. However, sand and gravel is needed for the houses, schools, hospitals and roads in the area, and I think that at this pit we have achieved almost the impossible, for we have opened up agricultural land, taken out the gravel, in-filled and restored the land for further use, and actually been complimented by somebody in the process.

Although the slag-heaps of yesteryear belonging to the NCB are being only slowly and expensively removed, the Board must be complimented upon its rigid adherence to the principles of restoration from its open-cast activities. Most sites are worked for between five and ten years, and wherever possible the rehabilitation of agriculture is accomplished as certain sections become redundant for mining operations. Most sites have only removed coal to a depth of three to four metres. The topsoil down to thirty centimetres, and the subsoil down another sixty, is carefully removed and stacked up in preparation for re-spreading over the area after the lumbering machinery has passed on. It provides an ideal solution for restoring and retaining that area for food-production purposes. Many of the earlier rehabilitation schemes were poorly carried out, and too thin a layer of topsoil covering a mixed burden of clay, shale, rocks and boulders prevented proper cultivation, or the installation of permanent underground drainage systems. Today, however, there is greater expertise, and the Ministry of Agriculture supervises the renovation. In most cases the period before crop-production is restored does not exceed eighteen months, but in Yorkshire, where arable rotations have been adopted on many restoration sites, a five-year period of careful management has been found to be necessary.

The NCB has shown considerable imagination in restoration works, and has several outstanding examples where the effects of open-cast mining are

Park House, Derbyshire, showing the ravages to the landscape of open-cast coal-mining
Photo National Coal Board

Park House, after clearing up the mess   *Photo National Coal Board*

A typical open-cast coal-mining site in the course of operations   *Photo National Coal Board*

difficult to detect. In Scotland it set aside 30p per tonne for land-restoration, and has in recent years been spending around half a million pounds annually. The open-cast site at Greensyke Avonbridge, Stirling, had 80,000 tonnes of coal with a volume of 1,639,535 cubic metres which was all removed in sixteen months. Today that land is growing excellent crops, and has blended into the landscape again. The Cannock Project in Staffordshire and the Polesworth Project on the Staffordshire/Warwickshire border are two outstanding examples near the West Midland conurbation where the NCB has achieved splendid results from an imaginative plan. The Cannock area covered 26 square kilometres (2,590 hectares). The Polesworth Project is an imaginative scheme to supply a regional outdoor sports centre and aquatic nature reserve and field study centre, marine facilities for enthusiasts and farmland restored to a high level of production. This area shows the scars of nineteenth-century dereliction, with the historic centre around Polesworth Abbey in the middle. It suffered a century and a quarter of pit-working in rich, shallow deposits, some of which is still being carried on, but the entire Polesworth Project will cover up the Victorian scars.

Restoration of mining devastation is not entirely the prerogative of the NCB or of official bodies. At the village of Leycett in Staffordshire, where the pock-marked landscape appears at its worst, and where the NCB demolished the village in 1969, leaving only the school, schoolhouse and a cricket club for its ghostly villagers, an example of local squirearchy is taking place. Originally the Crewe family had an estate which covered 12,000 hectares. Today this is reduced to 600 hectares, and Lady Crewe bequeathed the estate to Staffordshire farmer and journalist Quintin Crewe and his brother Colin.

The Leycett site covers over 120 hectares, but a new village is planned by the Crewes to cover 10 hectares, and to re-create a village of over a thousand people. There will be 111 hectares available for public parkland, and an emphasis on 'horsey' activities is planned. The equestrian complex with a leather works, pottery, smithy, hotel and related amenities could provide two hundred jobs for Leycett people.

Mining for the wealth beneath our soil will always absorb land, and although the damage inherited from our forefathers will take a long time to clear, it is felt that this must be done. Despite the greater demands for all mineral wealth, we do live, for the first time, in an age when giant mechanical earth-movers have the horsepower and ability to move mountains. If world food-production problems or, indeed, the environmental lobby grows louder, we may see a real attempt to clear the backlog of those blots upon our landscape.

Protection and reclamation

The countryside is the farmer's workshop, in which he grows his crops, grazes his cattle and rears his family. It is fast becoming the nation's playground also. Although the farmer may hold title deeds to the land of his farm, the urban visitor is entitled to the view, and continual controls are being placed upon farmers to preserve that view.

The essential underlying philosophy of the last quarter of the twentieth century is that the countryside of Britain should be retained in its natural state. This poses the question of what is its natural state. Without the hand of man, the countryside would rapidly become an overgrown jungle, and one account of the aftermath of a nuclear explosion suggests that within forty years an uninhabited Britain would be completely covered with grass. Even the widest motorways would become grass-covered once traffic ceased to flow, and without the feet of mankind a luxuriant growth would creep over every building. Man has made the countryside what it is today. There is nothing natural about it, and the vistas created by Capability Brown are minuscule in relation to the vista of Britain that has been created by the farmer, particularly in the more southern counties. The Grand Canyon, or the sandstone hills of Nevada, seems to be totally unshaped by man, but in tiny Britain it is the farmer who has created the landscape as we know it.

Farmers have been castigated for hedgerow eradication, and it was the pressure of the environmental lobby which resulted in the withdrawal of the Government Grants for bulldozing hedgerows, applicable under the Farm Improvement Scheme superseded by the Capital Grants Scheme in 1971. But the eradication of hedgerows has added an estimated 2,000 hectares per annum to the national farm, without undue harm to the patchwork quilt of British landscape (which is picturesque only from an aerial view, but totally impractical for the larger and wider modern farm machinery). It is to be noted in studying the hedgerow pattern on ancient farm maps that the field boundaries in 1700 resemble those today after the bulldozers have pushed away the Victorian hedge plantings, resulting from the aftermath of the Enclosure Acts. Ancient hedges can be recognized by the number of species of plant in each 100-metre stretch. For every different species—oak, ash, elm, quickthorn, etc.—the inquiring historian should count a century, and thus a hedgerow with five tree species can be dated as 500 years old. Similarly, the Victorian hedgerows were usually straighter. The more twisted and shapeless a hedgerow, the greater its probable antiquity.

Since our ancestors changed the shape of the countryside as often as they changed their shirts, the lobbyists today are only trying nostalgically to preserve something from the recent past, while ignoring the more distant. Conflicts that arise between farmers and the public simmer gently beneath the surface most of the time, but such bodies as the Ramblers' Association can often upset the farming community by their insistence on retaining the countless public footpaths of ancient vintage, many of which are no more than lines on a map. Originally designed to provide access to the church across fields, or other communications, the footpath system dates from medieval times, and puts a serious constraint upon farming today.

While the farmer is allowed to plough up a grass-covered footpath, he is required to smooth down the line of the path within six weeks, and cannot, of course, prevent the general public from using it. Moving footpaths even a short distance can be a protracted business, and in many instances they pass right through houses and farm buildings. At least one is known that, on the map, enters a cowshed at one end and comes out at the other through a solid brick wall. The complexities of moving footpaths, and the indignation aroused, make it indeed a daunting prospect.

If land-protection has now become synonymous with the times in which we live, the question must be asked: from whom and for whom are we protecting it? Now, in the 1970s, with European Conservation Year and the creation of a Department of the Environment (a word which most people would have required a dictionary to understand a few years before), people have come to realize that affluence and washing machines do not constitute all that life can offer. Greater leisure, and an awareness that farmers were changing the countryside (which urban people regard as their heritage), has resulted often in a tightening of controls and a hardening of attitudes. The non-farmer seeks to protect the countryside from the so-called ravages of modern farming, and through various Government edicts, and in the swelling ranks of the National Trust, the CPRE and other bodies, the forces are consolidating in the cause of preservation and protection. It is symbolic, though, that the CPRE, whose initials once stood for the Council for the Preservation of Rural England, has since changed its name to the Council for the Protection of Rural England—a subtle change of emphasis to remove from it the stigma of old-fashionedness, but which also emphasizes a feeling that the need is one for protection rather than preservation. The Government, meanwhile, through the Green Belts and Tree Preservation Orders, are seeking to placate both sides.

While Green Belts surrounding major towns form a barrier containing urban sprawl, Tree Preservation Orders seek to maintain the beauty of the existing landscape. All such controversies, however, have been made more urgent by the realization that the world is heading for greater starvation problems. The Rome Conference in November 1974 highlighted for the first time the need for a world strategy to assure food-supplies and harness the available resources. That it achieved little was perhaps not unexpected, but it brought the problem into focus.

How green is a Green Belt?

A Green Belt is not necessarily composed of grazing cows and rustic scenery. It was not an attempt to preserve farmland, but much more one to provide clean, fresh air for the city-dwellers. London's Green Belt stems from as long ago as 1931, and was formalized by the 1938 Green Belt Act, which was directed towards providing recreational facilities as much as it was for securing the continuance of farming in those areas.

Green Belts exist around every town of any consequence. The essence of post-War planning has been to contain the development within defined limits, and to provide a countryside area between these towns and cities and the next centre of occupation. In a reply in the House of Commons on 16 January 1974, Geoffrey Rippon (then in charge of the former Ministry of Housing and Local Government) stated that at that time 2,100 square miles (5,440 square kilometres) of land in England had the status of Green Belt, but a further 3,500 square miles had either been given interim protection or had been proposed for inclusion by Local Authorities. To suggest that a Green Belt is farmable is laughable. Many Green Belts embrace existing towns, and farming beside large centres of population can be difficult for the farmer because of the trespass and damage which occurs. Just as a dividing line separates housing development from open countryside, a dividing line exists between farming in the proper areas where it can carry on without major vandalism, and those areas where it cannot.

The London Green Belt was until 1972 the only statutory Green Belt in Britain. It had its inception in a *Report on Open Spaces*, by Raymond Unwin, issued by the Greater London Regional Planning Committee prior to 1931, and originally fostered by the London Society. Various Acts of Parliament promoted by the LCC and by the adjoining County Councils set up the principle, which included the provision of buying farms and holding them as County Council property to ensure that development did not take place. In this instance, a county like Essex has 2,011 hectares of Green Belt farms on the eastern side of London. The Green Belt is a strip of open land roughly 264 kilometres long, extending in a circle around the outer limits of the London conurbation. It varies in width from 8 to 16 kilometres, and there have been attempts to extend this as well as to nibble away at it. It has not remained inviolate, and development construction has taken place after appeal to the responsible Minister. This magnificent stretch of countryside has a profusion of views and a variation of scenery. It includes part of the Chilterns, the Surrey hills and the Thames Valley, and has in many instances provided surprising farming communities very close to London itself.

However, the thought that the London Green Belt is an unspoilt piece of countryside surrounding the City would be erroneous. The London Green Belt extends beyond the limits of such outer London towns as Watford in the north and Redhill in the south. Its exact limits are unclear, but its effects have been generally beneficial in containing London within roughly its pre-War geographical limits. But it is continually being attacked. Motorways that must reach the metropolis have at some stage to traverse across its open countryside; and in 1965 Richard Crossman, Minister of Housing, was assailed for permitting a new village on proposed Green Belt land at Hartley, Kent, while defending the Belt concept against the swelling tide of pressure for housing. Again, in 1974 the Minister, Geoffrey Rippon, in another desperate attempt to provide housing land, asked for over 800 hectares of the Metropolitan Green Belt for housing developments. Thus even those in charge of defending the Belt have been guilty of destroying it. There has been a suggestion that the perimeter should be pushed back a kilometre all the way round, and another which allowed wedge-shaped incursions to be made with green areas between them. Both ideas were unacceptable, and although in theory Green Belt inviolability is supported, there has been a continual revision of boundaries. On balance, the idea has worked, and since changing circumstances and differing pressures demand changing decisions, the perpetual rethinking and examination of the Green Belt limits has not been a bad thing. Certainly many other cities have been unable to achieve such constraint upon the natural demands for expansion, with the inevitable sprawl.

Woodman, spare that tree!

In the visual amenities of the countryside trees play an important part. It is perhaps particularly English that our trees are protected by three Acts of Parliament, and three official Statutory Instruments, and that there are three circulars from Government Departments setting out guidelines for Tree Preservation Orders (T.P.O.s). Farmers may not fell trees without a timber licence, and although for normal forestry operations this licence is not withheld, the T.P.O.s which list individual and outstanding trees in both the countryside and in urban surroundings do have an effect upon farming operations. Section 60 of the Town and Country Planning Act 1971 says:

> If it appears to a Local Planning Authority that it is expedient IN THE INTERESTS OF AMENITY to make provision for the preservation of trees or woodlands in their area they may for that purpose make an Order with respect to such trees, groups of trees or woodlands as may be specified.

The definition of 'amenity' is simply pleasantness, and the preconditions for making such an Order are therefore unlimited. In a further paragraph the concept of amenity is defined as being something which should be enjoyed by the public at large, and here again the circumstances for creating a T.P.O. are limitless.

T.P.O.s have been strongly criticized by farmers and foresters as perpetuating in a vertical position a piece of wood that has outlived its use and should be laid horizontal. They have pointed out that in many instances a new planting of young trees would make more sense, but there is much emotion generated concerning specific fellings. The Tree Preservation Orders have not greatly affected serious arable farming, and since the owners of land are very conscious of tree-planting as an amenity to their holdings, the T.P.O. has probably achieved very little, because incentives to preserve trees already exist.

4 Protecting the Countryside

The National Trust

'Trust on, and think tomorrow will repay'
Dryden

'The National Trust... it's a form of creeping socialism, nearly'
Brian Parkyn, MP.

There are three outstanding features about the National Trust; there is nothing national about it, it is unique and it has vast, uncountable wealth.

It is called a National Trust, which suggests either that it is comprehensively national in its operations (which it isn't), or that it is national in the sense of enjoying Government instigation or support (which isn't true either). The National Trust covers England, Wales and Northern Ireland, but ironically does not cover Scotland, which has its own National Trust. For many years both the Chairman and the Deputy Chairman of this rather English body were Irish peers. The Earl of Antrim was Chairman from 1965 to 1976, while the Irish Earl of Rosse, with his home in Birr Castle, County Offaly, Eire, was Deputy Chairman until 1975, and had been an active member of the National Trust for thirty years. A previous Chairman was a Scottish peer, the Earl of Crawford and Balcarres, a 28th Earl to boot, the Premier Earl of Scotland. He had his home in Fife, and was Chairman of the National Trust for twenty years, from 1945 to 1965. He died in 1976.

This galaxy of aristocratic talent from the fringes of Britain was succeeded by two Old Etonians: newspaper magnate Lord Gibson became Chairman in 1976. He was Chairman of the Financial Times Ltd (part of the Cowdray empire, the family name being Pearson, and Gibson having married into the family) and the new Deputy Chairman was Mark Norman, merchant banker and managing director of Lazards for fifteen years, from 1960 to 1975.

The label 'National' has at times worked to the Trust's detriment, in that potential donors, and certainly foreigners, believe it to be an adjunct of a Government Department.

The Trust's uniqueness is evidenced by the fact that there is nothing to protect the châteaux of the Loire or the castles of the Rhine against penal taxation or other ravages. The Trust operates as the owner of properties, to preserve them for ever for national enjoyment. It has achieved a remarkable success, and as a charity organization it is safeguarding the more vulnerable stretches of countryside and coastline, historic houses and landscaped gardens that private individuals can no longer afford to maintain. However, while it has acquired vast properties, it has by no means a large percentage of the great estates. In Britain today the largest percentage still remain in private hands, but the Trust exists as a powerful and immensely wealthy body whose role will undoubtedly increase, and whose power is immense. While not a Department of Government, it is nevertheless protected by Acts of Parliament.

The Trust itself says, in its 1973 Annual Report, 'No value is put in the books on the many properties and chattels held by the Trust for preservation'. The uncharitable might say it was trying to hide away its salted wealth, but in fact no value *can* be put upon the many ancient archaeological sites or the historic country houses, many packed with antique furniture and magnificent oil paintings.

The Trust boasts that it is the third largest landowner in the United Kingdom, with 152,560 hectares of land, and protective covenants over a further 31,560 hectares; as such, with its total now approaching 200,000 hectares, it has outstripped the Church and the Colleges as Britain's largest private land-holder (though the definition of 'private' may lead to some debate). It owns, and opens to the public, over 150 important country houses, many valued for their fabric alone at over £1 million. There are 100 large landscaped gardens. It protects 19 churches and chapels, 8 deer parks, 15 wind and water mills, 9 medieval barns, 10 archaeological sites of Roman vintage, 45 prehistoric sites, 9 industrial monuments; it has 2,000 farms, and even owns 17 whole villages. If this seems a vast accumulation of properties, the Trust also has capital endowment funds amounting to over £17 million. Against this it costs over £8 million annually to administer the Trust, and in many years it has a deficit. Income comes from farm rents, and from the income gained by opening properties to the public. It draws nearly £¾ million as income from visitors; £½ million in grants for maintenance and improvements from Government Agencies. Its strength lies in its rapidly expanding personal membership, and this figure is now over half a million fee-paying members, each contributing £5 per year, with family membership at £10. For this money the members are entitled to free entry to any of the Trust's properties that are open to the public, and to its publications. One suspects that a vast proportion of the membership is motivated chiefly by the free passes.

The National Trust was founded as long ago as 1895. Its three founders foresaw that industrialism would be an increasing threat to the countryside and ancient buildings of England, Wales and Northern Ireland; they did not include Scotland even then. These three founders were Miss Octavia Hill, a social worker whose pioneer achievements in the realm of housing reform had made her as well known as Mary Whitehouse today. Second was Sir Robert Hunter, a solicitor by profession, with a special regard for the open spaces in Surrey; and Canon Hardwicke Rawnsley, a man of letters who loved the Lake District. They formed the National Trust as a public company, with power to acquire and preserve for the nation places of historic interest or natural beauty, but with the stipulation that it was not a company trading for profit. The first property to be acquired was 1¾ hectares of cliff land overlooking the Barmouth Estuary in North Wales. In complete contrast, the second purchase was of a fourteenth-century timber-framed Clergy House at Alfriston in Sussex. Twelve years later, in 1907, the Trust was given the accolade of responsibility in an Act of Parliament which gave it its mandate 'To promote the permanent preservation for the benefit of the nation of land and buildings of beauty or historic interest'.

By 1930 the three founders would have seen an organization grown to 2,000 members, and by 1945 the membership was 8,500. The 1973 *Annual Report* puts the total membership at 428,000, which was in itself a dramatic increase of over 72,000 in one year, as against the 56,000 in the previous year. These vast increases in membership derive from visitors to the Trust's various properties.

Owners of historic houses have often thought that their descendants could live for ever in the ancestral home if they transferred it to the National Trust, but giving an expensive white elephant to the Trust and hoping for family occupation in perpetuity is not acceptable, and it often takes years of negotiation actually to give a very large house away. Although some properties have come into the Trust's possession in lieu of death duties to the State, the Trust will not accept anything unless it is suitably endowed, and this means that handing over the ancient castle in return for retention of a small flat, with the inconvenience of visitors trampling the flower-beds and floors in summer-time, is not enough. Invariably the Trust requires that the estate must provide the dowry, so that it can continue the expensive business of keeping the roof of the mansion watertight. Nevertheless, when the proper negotiations and appropriate endowments have been arranged to provide for a self-supporting entity, then the Trust will accept. The list of properties acquired annually makes impressive reading. These legacies form a valuable source of income, and amount sometimes (as in 1973), to a value of over £2 million (in 1972, incidentally, it was less than £½ million). The Trust itself buys properties, and has often been unable to purchase certain tracts of landscape because the auctioned prices in a free market were beyond its resources. Some legacies do not always work out in the way that the donor envisaged. Such was the case of Mrs Gubbay, who died in 1968, when the tax rules were different from those pertaining today. What she left the Trust as the residual part of her estate should have been worth £1·6 million, with a priceless collection of English furniture and porcelain, but because duty was paid at the highest rate on her whole estate, the actual residual amount was under £200,000. The changed status of the Trust came from a provision of the 1972 Finance Act which gave special concessions free of duty, free of aggregation with the remainder of the estate, and free of Capital Gains Tax. Such was the Government's sympathy towards preserving the heritage of the nation in a manner which costs the State coffers relatively little.

Enterprise Neptune was an imaginative appeal launched in 1965 as an urgent measure to raise £2 million to buy stretches of unspoilt coastline before the despoilers could get to work. The Trust prior to 1965 already owned 280 kilometres of coastline, but in raising the £2 million by November 1973, 286 more kilometres were added to that figure. As soon as the £2 million was raised, a new appeal was immediately launched for another 160 kilometres of coastline. The support from such a large appeal came from many official bodies, such as local authorities: £100,000 from the Government-sponsored Countryside Commission; and £50,000 from the Pilgrim Trust, as well as over £75,000 from major oil companies. Such is the emotional attraction of the work of the National Trust and its impartiality in administering its affairs that it can attract this sort of support. It puts the Trust in open competition with private buyers of farmland if that farmland happens to have an unspoilt view. It is adding to the Trust's considerable status in the League Table of rich landowners.

The properties of the National Trust are a formidable list, representative of the history of England. The former homes of Wordsworth, Kipling, Sir Winston Churchill, Beatrix Potter and Ellen Terry are numbered among its 150 country houses. It owns a 400-hectare estate around Stonehenge, acquired to preserve the beautiful surroundings of the ancient site; although Stonehenge itself is in the charge of the Department of the Environment which, by a happy partnership, allows National Trust members free admission. The Trust's 2,000 farms cover a vast percentage of its 212,000 hectares, but there are some restrictions on the farming activities. The Trust seeks to preserve the way of life of an agriculture that has sometimes passed by, but it is an active force in farming, as its own sheep-farming operations in the Lake District prove.

The Trust owns 150,000 head of sheep on farms near Keswick. Its objective was to preserve the character of an area where farmers were drifting away and villages becoming moribund as sheep-farming became uneconomic. This was a threat not only to the character of the communities, but to the appearance of the hills, now growing ragged grass which has been short-cropped by sheep for centuries. The Trust built model barns and pens on one of its farms as a showplace to encourage farm efficiency. The tenants in the area were subsidized with low rents, and every encouragement has been given to retain these marginal farms as viable propositions, providing a livelihood for the local farmers.

The Trust operates with a staff of seventy at its head office in Queen Anne's Gate, London, and at sixteen regional offices throughout the area of its jurisdiction. Apart from the permanent staff, there is a council of which half is elected from the general membership, the other half appointed by national institutions such as the British Museum, the National Gallery, the Royal Horticultural Society and the Ramblers' Association. By 1967 the organization had grown so fast that an independent advisory committee was set up under the chairmanship of Sir Henry Benson to review the management organization and responsibilities. He streamlined the whole operation on a more business-like footing, and it presents today quite a smooth operation.

An American staff reporter of the *Wall Street Journal*, Neil Ulman, wrote

'Despite its aristocratic patrons and policy makers, and the obvious benefits it provides to wealthy donors of homes, the Trust gets very little criticism ... considering its tax free status.' It has also benefited from several helpful legislative Acts of Parliament, and apart from the question of tax status, the Acquisition of Land (Authorisation Procedure) Act of 1946 gave the Trust the right of appealing to a joint committee of both Houses of Parliament if ever a Public Authority proposed to take any of its land by the use of compulsory powers—a right that has been granted to no other private landowner.

Cosseted and protected, the National Trust makes its contribution to the balance of the countryside, and if its objectives of presenting a working countryside, rather than a museum, can be achieved it will have a worthy place in the annals of British agriculture. It encourages aristocratic owners to remain in residence, though some call them anachronisms. It banned otter-hunting from all its water (prior to general protection of the animal), banned stag-hunting where the original donors showed disapproval, but allows the continuance of fox-hunting where it is part of the traditional English pattern.

The National Trust for Scotland

The Scottish equivalent of the National Trust was formed on 1 May 1931, thirty-six years after the National Trust for England, Wales and Northern Ireland was formed. It was created as a conservation body at a time when the pre-War depression period was at its height, and on Clyde Bank in Berth No. 534 stood an abandoned, partly built ship that was ultimately to be launched as the *Queen Mary*. The National Trust for Scotland is younger, smaller, less wealthy than its counterpart south of the border, and it is more deeply involved with Government, on whom it has had greater reliance from its inception. Although the National Trust declines to disclose its wealth, the Scottish Trust puts an insurance value of £5 million on its eighty properties. This, however, must be a modest figure, and does not include its rolling stretches of magnificent scenery.

It owns 33,000 hectares (the NT has 200,000), and its membership stands at 64,000 (NT 500,000). The increase of the National Trust between 1972 and 1973 of 72,000 members was greater than the Scottish total. But its membership has risen rapidly, and particularly in the 1970s has escalated phenomenally. Starting with only 64 members in 1932—at which time the National Trust had over 2,000 members—it has reached 1,300 by 1939. By 1950 that figure had almost doubled and in the decade to 1960 it went up sevenfold.

1950	2,400
1960	17,500
1970	34,250
1974	64,000

Over a million visitors per annum are counted through the gates of the Scottish National Trust properties, and although there are only 14 properties which gross over 20,000 visitors per annum as against 67 properties of the National Trust, the most popular, Culzean Castle and Country Park with a total of 248,384 (1973 figures), compares with the top of the National Trust League Table, Tatton Park in Cheshire, which had 274,000 visitors in 1973. These figures are calculated by including both house and gardens; it is Housesteads Roman Fort in Northumberland which draws the most visitors as a single attraction.

Although the National Trust was formed in 1895, and the Council for the Protection of Rural England in 1926, it was also in 1926 that the Scottish equivalent, the Association for the Protection of Rural Scotland, saw the magnificent work that the National Trust was doing, and set about creating an equivalent body for Scotland. Why the land of heather and tartan had been excluded originally seems obscure, but despite the depressed times the National Trust for Scotland was created, sponsored by such people as the Duke of Atholl (known as 'Bardie') eighth Duke, ADC to King George V, Knight of the Thistle, three times Lord High Commissioner to the General Assembly of the Church of Scotland, and a soldier who had seen service with the Nile Expedition in 1898, as well as a pioneer in early aeronautics with experiments in man-carrying kites. This remarkable man inspired the National Trust for Scotland to try to rival its elder sister south of the border.

The Trust started with a cash balance of £100, but the merits of its objectives inspired gifts, and with considerable aristocratic background it gained in prestige. However, even in the first *Annual Report*, for the year ending 30 April 1932, it extended an invitation to the Council of 'One Arm of Government'—the Forestry Commission. From the outset its objectives were unblushingly conservationist, and it was essentially pragmatic in its approach to any proposition or situation. Just as the Pilgrim Trust contributed £50,000 to Enterprise Neptune in 1965, its assistance in a grant of £500 a year for three years took the immediate anxiety of administrative costs from the newly formed body. As early as 1932 the Scottish Office was inviting its comment upon a new Town and Country Planning Bill, and it has throughout the years had a much closer liaison with Government Departments through the more regionalized system pertaining north of the border.

The Housing (Scotland) Act 1935 unintentionally put a premium on the destruction of old property, but its potential effects gave the new Trust a fighting campaign. The list of properties it now owns is impressive. Culzean Castle, in Ayrshire, was offered to it by the fifth Marquess of Ailsa in 1945, and although there was no endowment, the Council accepted this gift. It is a vast castellated house exuding the work of Robert Adam in its elegant rooms, and there are 230 hectares of gardens, woodlands and parks. In 1945 the property became a memorial to the War with some form of ex-Servicemen's housing, and funds were raised for adaption and construction of cottages. The top floor of the castle has been transformed into Scotland's National Guest House, and it gave rise to the story that General (later President) Eisenhower owned a Scottish castle. He was in fact the first life tenant of this part of the castle, as a recognition of his efforts as Supreme Commander of the Allied Forces in Europe.

Although the National Trust in England rates very highly among the list of landowners, the Scottish Trust has as its primary purpose the promotion of conservation, and this does not always involve ownership. A typical example is the custodianship of the remote island of Fair Isle, which is assured for ever as a permanent base for the Fair Isle Bird Observatory Trust. The St Kilda group of islands was bequeathed in 1957 by the fifth Marquess of Bute (a family that has been closely associated with the Trust from its early days). This group of islands had been bought by Lord Bute in 1931, and at the first Ordinary General Meeting the Duke of Atholl hinted that this would be an acceptable gift. It took twenty-six years to materialize, and was immediately passed by lease to the Government-sponsored Nature Conservancy.

Inevitably, the work of the Scottish National Trust differs from that of its English equivalent. It is concerned with large mountainous areas with little income potential, but vast beauty; such areas as Glencoe and the battlefield of Bannockburn inaugurated by the Queen on the 650th Anniversary in 1964. However, there are many large private houses and estates in Scotland that are now protected by the Trust. The second Annual Report (1933) recorded the progress in Culross where the Palace (built 1597–1611 for Sir George Bruce from the revenue of his collieries and other enterprises north of the Forth) was purchased by the Trust in 1932 at a price of only £700 from the Earl of Dundonald. Small though this amount seems, it was nearly half the first legacy which the Trust received. Through financial stringency, the Palace of Culross was immediately placed under the guardianship of the Office of Works, which removed the whole expense from voluntary to Government funds.

The Trust's entry into agriculture is minimal, but at the Burg, on Mull, in conjunction with the West of Scotland College it carried out a project to eradicate bracken and to improve the soil. This was a wartime experiment to increase the stock-carrying capacity of the farm. Today, despite its late arrival on the scene, the Scottish Trust plays a useful if different role in preserving the heritage of Scotland. It runs on a deficit and has many difficulties, but undoubtedly it has saved and preserved many fine houses and conserved many wild and rural areas.

The Nature Conservancy

> *'Pollution is a sign of our failure to conserve properly. When we produce waste beyond the capacity of nature to render it harmless.'*
>
> 'Twenty-one Years of Conservation'
> (The Nature Conservancy, 1970)

The Nature Conservancy is a wholly owned adjunct of a Government Department, and its role is threefold: to offer advice on conservancy policies and problems; to maintain and expand nature reserves, both publicly and privately owned; and lastly to embark upon serious research on the possible ecological damage to the environment, and particularly wildlife habitats, from the pressures of modern society. It was formed in 1949, the same year as the National Parks Commission. The Conservancy, however, lasted in its original format for twenty-four years until the new Nature Conservancy Council Act of 1973, while the National Parks Commission was absorbed into the Countryside Commission in 1968.

Both those bodies date back beyond their official inception. As the build-up and sophistication of Government Departments continues, there sometimes arises a need to reassess the conservation problem, and to rehash the method of tackling it. The fact that there is a need for conservancy is more apparent at the present time than it has ever been in the past. It seems to be fighting a rearguard action in a polluted plastic world. Despite these pressures, the Conservancy's successes have been considerable.

The Conservancy, as it is today, is a Government body that shows that peculiar British combination of mixing State and private interests in a glorious hotchpotch. Of the 121,000 hectares which the Conservancy administers, in fact only 32,500 (27 per cent) is actually owned by the State. Sixty per cent of its land is held under agreements with owners and occupiers, and 13 per cent is held by leases from private owners. The vast bulk of the Conservancy land was purchased in its first ten years up to 1959, and by that date it had bought 27,875 hectares at a total cost of £112,000, or just over £4 per hectare. The land held under Nature Reserve Agreements was leased to it at ludicrous rents of only 17d a hectare, and even at that time it was receiving £3,000 as income from properties. It follows from these figures that a vast percentage of the Nature Conservancy land is in the remoter areas of Britain, and it is in Scotland where its major work is carried out. Its Scottish holdings represent an area three times greater than that in England, and nine times greater than its Welsh Reserve Areas. Whereas the average Welsh Nature Reserve is of under 360 hectares, the English Reserve approximately 400 hectares, the average Scottish Nature Reserve is of 2,000 hectares.

It is impossible to add together the land area administered by the Nature Conservancy, the National Trust and the Countryside Commission with its National Parks, and form a composite calculation of the total impact of these three bodies upon the British heritage. The Nature Conservancy looks for areas of ecological, even geological, value, whereas the National Trust (apart from its coastline acquisitions under the 'Operation Neptune' plan) has only gone where it was invited, and the Countryside Commission, with its emphasis upon the recreational potential and aesthetic beauty of its holdings, has a different outlook on life. There are Nature Reserves administered by the Nature Conservancy Council that exist inside National Parks designated by the Countryside Commission, and the Conservancy also leases Nature Reserve sites from land in the possession of the National Trust. Such complicated overlapping precludes any balance sheet of the total holdings.

If the situation is complicated by the convergence with the two other major national bodies, then the work of nature conservancy in Britain today is further complicated by another nation-wide tier of local reserves, existing below the level of the National Conservancy Council. It was as early as 1926 that the Norfolk Naturalists Trust was created, yet by 1960 there were less than eight County Trusts in existence. Today there is a Local Naturalists Trust for every county in the country, although with the redistribution of local-authority boundaries, some of these transcend demarcation lines. Some of the County Naturalists Trusts are embodied in limited companies; others are registered as charities, but in total they now manage more than 800 Nature Reserves in the UK, with a total area of approximately 24,000 hectares of which they actually own about 5,000. Like the national parent body, they either lease or manage by agreement their remaining hectarage. The rate of acceleration and expansion of the Conservation Trusts has been phenomenal. In fifteen years from 1960 to 1975, the number of Reserves has risen from 50 to 800, and the area from 1,600 hectares to its present 24,000. The rate of acquisition slowed to a trickle after the land-price boom in 1972, but after the Trusts reorganized their methods of appeal for financial support the impetus was regained in 1974. There is even a society for the Promotion of Nature Reserves (SPNR) based at Nettleham, Lincoln, and its assessment of the cost of acquiring reserves in the period 1964–74 was £400,000. This is twice the figure spent in land acquisitions by the official Government-sponsored parent body, although the Local County Trusts are in no sense subordinate to the Government.

The financial sums flowing into the Naturalists Trusts throughout the country come from the annual subscriptions of well-wishers and enthusiasts, but additionally in the purchase of Nature Reserves the World Wildlife Fund has often contributed 25 per cent of the cost. The Pilgrim Trust has generously advanced massive sums. The Nuffield Trust lent the SPNR £25,000 as a revolving loan fund in 1961, which has been turned over at least six times in interest-free bridging loans to Local Trusts to enable a purchase to be made, with the appeal for the cost launched afterwards. It is therefore difficult to pinpoint the Nature Reserves in this country, and to know which belong to the Local Trusts and which to the National Conservancy Council. In essence, it is usually the smaller areas that are locally owned, and the Local Trusts restrict their work to administering their reserves. Where the national body differs is in its work as an advisory body and in the research area of wildlife and its habitats.

On yet another tier are the Sites of Special Scientific Interest (S.S.S.I.). There are today around 3,500 S.S.S.I.s; 2,300 in England, 800 in Scotland and 400 in Wales, and they have been so designated by the Conservancy Officers, and their locations notified to the Local Planning Authorities, who are charged with ensuring that nature-conservation factors are taken into account before any Planning Permission is granted that may affect these sites. While the Conservancy evidence is considered and given due weight, it does not have any statutory powers; these remain with the Local Planning Authorities. The designation of an area as an S.S.S.I. can often be accomplished without the owner's knowledge, and it does not in any way alter his rights or the freehold legality. It does not give the Conservancy Officers, or anyone else, any rights of access, and even when common land is involved, the common rights remain unaffected. It does, however, constrain somewhat farmers who might wish to plough up or remove hedgerows on one of these areas, but the powers are weak, and the Conservancy itself admits that the protection of an S.S.S.I. depends very largely on the support and goodwill of the landowner. The Conservancy gets a great deal of co-operation through its policy of establishing cordial relationships with owners, and encouraging them to take an interest in protecting any scientific interest of a section of their land.

Designation of such an area does not imply that large numbers of people will come to visit the site. The Conservancy is in fact at pains to treat the location of these sites with great discretion, and if the existence of any very rare species is discovered the location of an S.S.S.I. is kept strictly confidential.

This rapid expansion in demand for field facilities has had an adverse effect on many S.S.S.I.s. The main problem is the noise caused by hammers on small outcrops where rock formations are being examined by hordes of students. Access to its Reserves has been a bone of contention for the Conservancy. There is pressure that publicly owned land is often more restricted as to public access than is privately owned property. In its early days the Conservancy, with its emphasis upon research, was deeply involved in the need for keeping out the public, but in more recent years a change of heart has occurred, although there are grave dangers that in allowing even restricted access the original aims of preservation will be set at nought. An example of this is the story of the military orchid, which was discovered at the Rex Graham Nature Reserve near Mildenhall in Suffolk, now opened to the public.

The military orchid is one of Britain's rarest plants, and this colony was discovered in an old chalk-pit on Forestry Commission land in 1955. There is only one other known site in Britain, and attempts were made to keep the location of the Mildenhall colony secret. The pit was fenced off, and guarded by the Forestry Commission, but in spite of these precautions the find soon became common knowledge in the botanical world, and over-enthusiastic visitors tramped over the site, creating considerable damage. By 1972 the site was also becoming overgrown with sycamore and wild privet, and this was blotting out the military orchid. The solution was to declare the pit a Nature Reserve under a joint management agreement with the Suffolk Trust. The sycamores were carefully removed by the Forestry Commission, and voluntary work-parties organized by the Local Trust cleared the privet and made steps on the steep path into the pit. A raised path has been erected over the critical area, and now botanical enthusiasts can view the military orchid without fear of extinguishing the colony.

The Queen, the Prime Minister and a Hebridean island

The Royal Charter which set up the Nature Conservancy was signed by King George VI in 1949, and just over two years later the first National Nature Reserve was declared at Beinn Eighe, Ross. Seven months later came the first Local Nature Reserve at Aberlady Bay in East Lothian; the same year Gibraltar Point in Lincolnshire was the first in England. In 1954 the Conservancy leased from the National Trust the Scolt Head National Nature Reserve, and a succession of important sites were created, yet after ten years the Conservancy was writing:[1]

> It is in some ways disappointing that after ten years only approximately half the number of Nature Reserves in the entire programme should yet have been established, and some of those only in part. Yet on average every hour since the Conservancy first began has seen about an acre and a half added to the National Nature Reserves.

But some important acquisitions have been made. It was as recently as 1974 that two new important additions were made; one came from the Queen's private Balmoral estate and the other on the Chequers estate, traditionally the country 'tied cottage' of incumbents of No 10 Downing Street.

The Balmoral Wildlife Reserve is known as the Glen Muick and Lochnager Wildlife Reserve. It comprises an area of 2,570 hectares, and is the largest managed by any of the Local Trusts, and was acquired on the tenth anniversary of the Scottish Wildlife Trust. It ranges in height from 396 metres in Glen Muick to the 1,158-metre peak of Lochnager Mountain, red deer being easier to see in the open at Glen Muick than at any other place in the Highlands. The Reserve includes highland country and wild life which have not previously been well represented in the Reserves of the Scottish Trust. Blue hare, red deer, ptarmigan and red grouse feed on the heather and other moorland plants, while such predators as the golden eagle can be frequently seen. In his message on the tenth anniversary of the Scottish Wildlife Trust, Prince Philip said that the new Reserve has been established to keep the difficult balance between the protection of wild animals and plants and the granting of public access.

The appropriately named Happy Valley above Great Kimble, and not far from Chequers Knap (all part of the Prime Minister's official residence), is now a nature reserve administered by the Berkshire, Buckinghamshire, and Oxfordshire Naturalists Trust. The Coombes on the Chequers Estate support some of the finest stands of box in Britain, and the steep chalk screes with their specialized plants provide a unique ecological hunting-ground. The box-woods at Chequers are only repeated naturally in Britain at Box Hill in Surrey and at Boxwell in Gloucestershire. The Chequers Reserve extends to only 48 hectares, but it nevertheless represents a unique opportunity for proper conservation. However, if the ignorant assume that conservation means letting nature run amuck, they are mistaken. At Happy Valley much of the area was overgrown, and the Trust

[1] *The Nature Conservancy: The first ten years.* (HMSO, 1959).

immediately installed cattle to reintroduce the proper balance of farming and the balance of nature.

Although the third largest in Britain, the Rhum Nature Conservancy property does present a unique research station for wildlife and botanical study in the isolation of an unspoilt Scottish island.

Rhum (or Rum) is situated in the Inner Hebrides, with the surrounding islands of Eigg, Muck and Canna. To the north-east the Cuillins of Skye rise from the silver sea eleven kilometres away, but on the south-west side of this grim island the wild Atlantic storms lash against the volcanic cliffs, with their unique layers of ultra-basic rocks. The Conservancy purchased Rhum and opened it for research work in 1959. It is 10,500 hectares in size, which puts it almost on a parity with Jersey. It is a diamond-shaped island, with little cover and only one landing-place. The Scandinavian names of the mountains ring beautifully in this wild and exciting place: Askival, Halival, Barkaval, Trallival and Ainshaval, the highest of which is Askival, rising to 810 metres (though this is lower than the highest point of the Cuillins on Skye). It was here in 1845 that the second Marquess of Salisbury reintroduced the native red deer, and the Rhum ponies are reputed to be descendants of horses that swam ashore from the Spanish Armada. It was Sir George Bullough who built Kinloch Castle of Arran sandstone, a castle of the twentieth century which was supposed to resemble in its façade his own private yacht (the central tower is off-centre to represent the funnel). The architect is reputed to have made the castle too short, and so the covered terrace, arched and castellated, was added to bring the silhouette to the required length. Sir George is buried in a mausoleum at Papidil, on a well-cropped area of flat grassland facing the wildest part of the Atlantic seaboard, and from this spot the gales lash the open columns of what must be the most unique resting-place in the British Isles. Lady Bullough, who lived to be well over ninety, was brought from her home near Newmarket to be buried beside him, and the wagons carried her across eleven kilometres of rough track from the landing-place at Kinloch on Loch Scresort.

Rhum has presented an exciting challenge to the Conservancy. There are goats running fleet-footed along the cliffs. The islanders have their own self-supporting herd of cows. The Rhum ponies graze the more sheltered meadows, and an area has been reserved for afforestation, but it is the Manx Shearwater and the golden eagle that provide the excitement of Rhum. Its privacy allows the red deer to flourish, but culling must be carried out, and venison is exported, mainly to Germany. In one year alone they sold 952½ kilos at a price of £2,400. The flora of Rhum includes such rarities as the Norwegian sandwort and Alpine penny cress. Moss campion, purple saxifrage and mossy cyphel are mountain plants which grow plentifully, but surprisingly bog myrtle is very rare. The moorland vegetation is dominated by the blue moor grass, bents and fescues. Heather has been reduced by burning, and the high mountain-tops are peopled by Alpine flora. Over 1,800 kinds of plants have been recorded on Rhum, including over 800 species of fungi.

The invertebrates that inhabit Rhum have been studied and recorded by the Chief Warden, and about 2,000 kinds of insects have been discovered. Uncommon species such as the transparent burnet moth and several attractive butterflies such as the large heath, the dark green and the small pearl-bordered fritillaries, and in the sheltered trees around the village of Kinloch the speckled wood butterfly, have been seen. There are cliff-breeding colonies of guillemots, puffins, razorbills, fulmars and kittiwakes, but the Manx shearwater predominate, and three pairs of golden eagle usually breed in their cliff-side.

The island provides a weather station, and in parts has a rainfall of 3,810 millimetres. It is a self-contained community which is wholly employed and supported by the Conservancy, with the exception of the schoolmistress, who is employed by the Invernesshire County Council. The population is only forty strong, and the children go to school at Fort William after the age of eleven. As an example of community living, the Conservancy has re-created an echo from the past. Today it has built a village hall of prefabricated timber sections for the benefit of the community and for visitors to the island. The castle has a caretaker and is beautifully warm; it is used as a hostel for visiting scientists. The white-walled cottages cluster around the shores of Loch Scresort, and there is even a post-office. As a complete experiment in the preservation of unique species of wildlife, flora and fauna, and as an example of maintaining a balanced nature, Rhum is the outstanding example (perhaps due to its island location) of the work of the Nature Conservancy.

The future

The Nature Conservancy Council Act 1973 established a new role for conservancy in Britain. Despite its preoccupation with administering its nature reserves, the Conservancy has always been deeply involved with research. The original task of protecting wildlife and establishing reserves now takes second place to its function within its parent body, the National Environment Research Council (NERC), under whose wing it was placed in June 1965, having previously been administered by the Privy Council Department. The research aspect is now coming to the fore. Originally the Royal Charter of 1949 stemmed from a wartime report on Nature Conservation published in 1943, and it was in 1915, during another World War, that submissions for public responsibility for conservation were made by the Society for the Promotion of Nature Reserves, which had itself been founded in 1912. The 'Dower' Report to the Ministry of Town and Country Planning in 1945 firmly recommended a Wildlife Conservation Council as a permanent organ of Government, but it still took four years before the Royal Charter was granted.

As part of the NERC, the Conservancy has gone into action over such matters as the death of sea-birds by oil-pollution. The *Torrey Canyon* disaster in 1967 afforded a dramatic example of this, and the Conservancy Recommendations on pesticides and other toxic chemicals were accepted by the Government in 1969. The Conservancy emphasizes that its job is not so much to do the conservation itself as to encourage and demonstrate to others how it should be done. In some respects it has completed many of the original tasks, while in its Statement of Policy, 1974, the Conservancy Council stated that it was 'appraising the research already commissioned to ensure its relevance to our nature conservation objectives'—surely a statement which implies that a change of direction is imminent. There is little dispute by farmers as to the need for a balanced countryside, but such changes as the use of chemicals, the eradication of hedges to accommodate larger machinery and the lack of livestock in some areas has changed the pattern of the countryside. Farmers, though, are not the main target of the Conservation Authorities. They are studying the implications of recreational activities, of industrial spoilage and of new coniferous forestry.

> The spread of conifer forests across many of our uplands is causing profound changes in the wildlife, not only on the planted ground, but also on that adjoining the forests. The opening up of the Marine Oilfields around our northern shores is likely to have important consequences for the coastal areas nearby[2]

Thus the challenges of the future may well be far greater than those since 1949. The Conservancy has built up an expert staff of just over 500 people, and has its Advisory Committees for England, Scotland and Wales. It has a background of solid achievement that may well be needed even more in the future. Its nature-reserve expansion may well slow down as it identifies itself to a greater degree with the research into wildlife and its mysteries, and in persuading Governments that they must act upon the fruits of this work.

[2] Nature Conservancy Council Statement of Policies, November 1974.

5 Opening the Countryside

The Countryside Commission

'Within these private Elysiums were a diversity of walks and rides, across pasture unbroken by fences or hedges, with cattle, sheep or deer free to roam at will.'

Marcus Binney
'The Destruction of the Country House.'

'The Commission—re-named the Countryside Commission in 1968—is in Advisory Body'

'The AA Book of the British Countryside' (1973).

While the National Trust can provide a lifeline for impoverished aristocrats, and the Nature Conservancy acts as the conscience to modern mechanically minded farmers, the Countryside Commission, with its primary job of encouraging hordes of visitors to tramp the British countryside in the summer months, is regarded by farmers and landowners with great suspicion. The Trust buys its properties, even the Conservancy does most of its operations on its own land, but the Countryside Commission designates large areas of Britain as National Parks, or areas of outstanding beauty, and effectively blocks much agricultural progress while giving very little financial compensation. In an explanatory booklet, it states, 'When the Secretary of State has confirmed designation by the Commission of a National Park, no change occurs in ownership of land. There is no question of nationalization of the land as public property.' Admittedly, designation as a National Park does not violate the sanctity of freehold ownership, and the rights of privacy which that embodies. It is in the constraints which it places upon the farming activities, and the additional expenditure which it forces farmers into incurring through its stringent planning controls, that makes it an object of considerable suspicion, and of little love. The feeling goes deeper with respect to the Commission's objectives of opening up the British countryside to the non-farming community.

As the successor body to the National Parks Commission (which deceased in 1968, aged nineteen), the Countryside Commission is a sub-department of a sub-department of Government, and ultimately comes under the wing of the

Department of the Environment. Its National Parks Policy having been completed, its new role is that of a Government vehicle for the distribution of finance to County Councils in their policies of establishing country parks (11,700 hectares by 1975) and the lesser picnic areas, and in administering those National Parks, long-distance footpaths and areas of outstanding beauty of which the National Parks Commission laid the foundations in its formative years. The Countryside Commission has even been expelled from its elegant Regent's Park Headquarters in London at No. 1 Cambridge Gate (now occupied by the Nature Conservancy Council as its HQ for England).[1] It is now housed in a disused police station in Cheltenham, far removed from the seat of power and centre of government. This does not mean that it is losing importance in governmental eyes, but its role has changed radically, and in the rejection of its proposed Eleventh National Park in the Cambrian Mountains, it looks as if the end of the road has arrived.

The Countryside Commission and its predecessor have in fact designated 18·6 per cent of the total land area of England and Wales as either National Parks or area of outstanding natural beauty. The National Parks area covers 9 per cent of the total of 58,340 square miles of England and Wales, and the A.O.N.B.s cover 9·6 per cent of the total area. There are no National Parks in Scotland; the Countryside Commission only has jurisdiction over England and Wales. It differs in this from the Nature Conservancy, which covers all three countries and finds its major work in Scotland, and the National Trust, when there is a separate body for Scotland. In terms of the multitude of administrative bodies for farming and the British countryside, it is usually Scotland that has its own organization.

National Parks

The National Parks of England and Wales were the primary objective of the National Parks Commission when it was originally set up in 1949. This policy evolved from a recommendation of the 'Dower' Report in 1945, and the National Parks and Access to the Countryside Act 1949 set the wheels in motion. National Parks are designated areas of outstanding grandeur. The policy has been one of preservation in its natural form, and although for a quarter of a century this protection has been backed by legislative teeth, there have been some infringements. These have arisen not from modern agriculture, but more from mineral-extraction, which ironically seems to find the greatest reserves in the more beautiful areas. The preservation of a fine landscape and the ensuring of public access is a contradiction in terms. In reality, the main work has been to exercise stringent planning controls on the erection of new buildings. The Commission is empowered to pay grants to mitigate the additional costs, and it

[1] The NCC has its National Headquarters in even more elegant Belgrave Square, and an office for Scotland in Edinburgh, and for Wales in Bangor.

has finance for removing eyesores, clearing derelict sites, preserving and planting trees, laying out footpaths and nature trails, providing parking places, providing camping and caravan sites and even holiday accommodation. The main restrictions have been constraints upon the farming activities in these areas.

National Parks

National Park	Area		Designation Date	Population
	sq. kilometres	hectares		
Peak District	1,409	138,752	17 April 1951	38,370
Lake District	2,252	221,696	9 May 1951	46,000
Snowdonia	2,197	205,824	18 Oct. 1951	34,762
Dartmoor	949	93,440	30 Oct. 1951	31,000
Pembrokeshire Coast	585	57,600	29 Feb. 1952	21,025
North York Moors	1,438	141,568	28 Nov. 1952	22,350
Yorkshire Dales	1,768	179,808	12 Oct. 1954	18,580
Exmoor	689	65,024	19 Oct. 1954	11,300
Northumberland	1,035	101,888	6 April 1956	2,600
Brecon Beacons	1,349	132,824	17 April 1957	33,560
	13,671	1,338,424		259,547

This illustrates that the whole of the National Park programme was worked out in the short space of six years, 1951–57, with half the total area being designated between April and October, 1951. The Peak District National Park (1,409 square kilometres) can claim to be the first such area designated in Britain, although in the United States the Yellowstone National Park of over 260,000 square kilometres was opened in 1872. The Peak Park ranks fifth in size, and contains that incomparable area of Derbyshire that attracts many hundreds of thousands of visitors annually. At Bakewell the Countryside Commission opened a valuable Information Centre within the old Market Hall in the town square, although the solid Market Hall façade contrasts strangely with this metal and glass 'box' which the Countryside Commission has installed within the ancient fabric. Near by is the Duke of Devonshire's magnificent Chatsworth, a public-access park with the attraction of a stately home, but all privately owned. The Lake District and Snowdonia are the largest two National Parks, and as such are part of our national heritage. The burning question must be whether these areas would have been submerged by modern man to any greater degree if the National Parks Commission had not existed. In many respects sheer grandeur and size would have made it difficult for man to have completely ruined the landscape. Nevertheless, on balance, the Countryside Commission has probably assisted in maintaining their beauty.

Within these parks (vast as they appear) the Countryside Commission does in fact acquire ownership of only relatively small areas. In the Lake District, for instance, it acquired, in 1968 on a ninety-nine year lease from the Crown Estate Commissioners, a part of the northern boundary of Coniston Water, and in 1970 it bought 747 hectares of Blawith Fell, on the western shore of Coniston Water. In the Peak District it acquired 18½ kilometres of the disused Buxton-

Ashbourne railway line, and this is open as a scenic route for walking and pony trekking. Altogether it now owns there a strip of land more than 48 km long.

In Snowdonia the Secretary of State for Wales purchased in 1968 some 5,000 hectares, formerly part of the Vaynol estate. Although it is not, and never has been, the policy of any Government, either Socialist or Tory, to purchase normal farmland, this sale and purchase in 1968 was heralded as only a short-term holding before disposal to the tenants, or to the Caernarvonshire County Council. In the event much of the land has been disposed of, but the summit of Snowdon has been retained in the ownership of the State.

Areas of Outstanding Natural Beauty

The A.O.N.B.s extend over 11,911 square kilometres, about 1,820 less than the National Parks themselves. They are designated areas which impose considerable planning restrictions upon the erection of farm buildings. There are only three sites in East Anglia, such as the Norfolk coast, the Suffolk coast and 57 square kilometres of Dedham Vale which Constable perpetuated on canvas in his incomparable style. Dedham Vale is the smallest, and at that size is manageable for a small local inter-county administrative committee, but the 1,513 square kilometres of the Cotswolds present a far larger operation.

The National Parks' general administration has now devolved on to local administrative committees, and the areas of outstanding natural beauty have a lesser managerial problem. This has left the Countryside Commission itself in a truly advisory capacity, helping to pull all the strings and co-ordinate the general policies, but has drawn much of its teeth. While it is right to preserve our British heritage, even the Countryside Commission itself admits that there are serious conflicts of interest. While the areas designated as National Parks have become static, there is still a movement towards discovering and designating A.O.N.B.s, and it seems that one day these smaller areas of landscape will outnumber the major National Parks. The impetus for designation comes from the County Councils, with whom the Countryside Commission does most of its work. Since the early 1970s the County Councils have been rapidly examining their own areas of jurisdiction, to help the greater forces for preservation. (It is of interest, however, that in its Sixth Report (1972 73) the Countryside Commission rejected seventeen areas that had been suggested to it.) While the reorganization in local government boundaries which came into operation 1 April 1974 rationalized many of the Country Parks, it fragmented many of the A.O.N.B.s, due to the diversion of major planning functions from the wider County Councils to the smaller District Councils. Two of the multi-county Parks, Yorkshire Dales and Snowdonia, became single-county Parks, and the whole of the Lake District now comes within the new county of Cumbria. But the A.O.N.B.s fared differently; all but five of the areas became divided between two or even more District Councils, and several lie either side of the new county boundaries.

The advent of Country Parks

The 1970 Act set up the Country Parks, whereby the Commission would grant 75 per cent of the total expenditure, and a similar amount for the wardening service to be provided. They have been slow to start, but in more recent years the County Councils, private landowners and even the National Trust have redesignated parkland areas which were already open to the public, and can now collect a 75 per cent grant annually for their operational costs. Additionally, a good deal more land has been purchased outright for the purpose of laying out these new leisure parks. It was of importance that the Fourth Report of the Countryside Commission (year ending 30 September 1968) recorded:

> There has been a welcome growth of interest among the non public bodies, and among landowners and others in the opportunities afforded by the Act ot obtain grant for recognised schemes . . . Although the response has been good in some counties, the fact remains that three years after the Act came into force, 17 out of 58 administrative counties in England and Wales had failed to produce a single scheme for a Country Park or picnic site on which the Commission could recommend grant aid.

At that time there were, however, 45 approved Country Parks and 53 picnic sites, and during that year 27 of the 45 Country Parks had been accepted. A further 22 were agreed in principle, 58 were withdrawn or rejected and 122 were under consideration. Of picnic sites, 30 were approved in 1970–71, 33 more agreed in principle, 76 were under consideration and 30 were withdrawn or rejected.

By the following year the Countryside Commission was able to report that there were now 84 Country Parks covering an area of 10,000 hectares (nearly a quarter of the size of the Isle of Wight), and approved expenditure by the Countryside Commission on Local Authority Country Parks had just topped the £2 million mark. Eighty-six picnic sites had been approved; the average area of a Country Park was given as 111 hectares, and of a picnic site 5½. By 1973 there was 99 Country Parks covering 11,740 hectares, at a cost of £2·5 million. Besides existing parks, new ones were being acquired, and some interesting projects were arising.

The City of Coventry climbed on the bandwagon by designating its Coombe Park of 117 hectares under the Act. This park had been opened in 1966, and consists of woodland, grassland and 37 hectares of water. The advent of a Countryside Commission grant enabled the installation of lavatories, the laying of a nature trail and the restoration of woodland all to be removed from the local rates to the national Exchequer. Of greater interest, and more within the spirit of the Act, has been the development by Nottinghamshire County Council of 97 hectares of disused gravel pits at Holme Pierrepont, opened by Prime Minister Heath in July 1972. At this Country Park, with the co-operation of the DoE, the Sports Council, County Council and the Countryside Commission, the unsightly gravel pits were transformed into a stretch of parkland which includes a 2,000-

metre rowing course built to international standards. The Countryside Commission contribution came to £120,000.

The Park that never was: the Cambrian fiasco

Since National Parks are neither national nor parks in the generally accepted sense of the word, the proposal to expand the ten parks created in the euphoria of the birth of the National Parks Commission came to a full stop after Brecon Beacons was designated in 1957. Twelve years elapsed before a movement began to utilize 1,494 square kilometres of the Cambrian mountain area of Wales as the Eleventh National Park.

The proposal would have given Wales 5,610 square kilometres of National Park, and its boundaries would have embraced the whole of the Central Wales Massif, stretching 144 kilometres from south to north, and 32 kilometres at its widest point. This sparsely inhabited area, with an annual rainfall never less than 1,270 millimetres, reaching a maximum of 2,540 millimetres (ten-year average of the whole area, 1500–1800 millimetres), and a complete absence of a roadway network was in fact an area of unspoilt rural wildness that would have been destroyed by the invasion of massive numbers of tourists. The original scheme was talked about from 1969 onward, and in April 1971 the Countryside Commission reduced the originally proposed area by 285 square kilometres, down to a figure of 1,209 square kilometres. In August 1972 they deposited this proposal with the DoE for designation as a National Park. The battle which ensued took no one by surprise, except perhaps the Countryside Commission itself, and a year later, in July 1973, the then Secretary of State at the DoE, Geoffrey Rippon, finally closed the file by refusing to designate the area, or even to hold a public inquiry, such had been the violent weight of public opinion against the plan.

It was not only farmers and landowners who sought to annul this proposal. Every local authority in the area was against it as well, and the anger engendered among all sections of the community makes it doubtful whether another Country Park will be designated in Britain. The Norfolk Broads came under scrutiny in 1976–77, but opposition from many directions soon transpired. The efforts of the Countryside Commission to promote this project were embodied in its Statement in the 1971–72 Annual Report, where it stated:

> Although this beautiful area is sensitive to change, the Commission continue to believe that carefully planned provision for recreation could contribute to the economy of this seriously depopulated part of mid-Wales, when properly linked with farming and forestry, and that the creation of a National Park would ensure planned conservation of its lovely moorland and gorges.

It was suggested that the designation would bring revival in the form of additional sources of income to an impoverished area, but the record of the previous National Parks, and their interference with local industries and farming, was not a good recommendation for the Commission's plans. The *Farmers Weekly*[2] stated:

> The greatest disservice the Government can do is to persist in putting a 'National Park' label on areas it especially wishes to preserve . . . We should drop the name and stop interpreting conservation as the 'freezing' of countryside carved out fifty or one hundred years ago.

The same leader stated unequivocally that the designation of a National Park put a burden on those whose lives and livelihood were bound up within it.

While the NFU and the rebel Farmers Union of Wales have rarely seen eye to eye over anything, this particular project united them, and the Chairman of the NFU Parliamentary Committee, Ernest Richards, pointed out that the Commission was aware that farmer opposition would be considerable. He said, 'This designation will be seen as an imposition which, if confirmed, could disturb the day-to-day farming operations on thousands of productive holdings', and he added for good measure that previous experience in other National Parks had hardened farmers' feelings against them. It was unfortunate that the Countryside Commission laid its application before the Secretary of State while the Lord Sandford Committee was in the process of reviewing the whole policy of National Parks.[3]

The CLA unanimously from its five affected County Branches—Merioneth, Cardigan, Brecon and Radnor, and Caermarthen—said that the whole project would do nothing to enhance the beauty of the hills and gorges, and that since it contained no noteworthy features such as Snowdon in the North Wales Park, there was little likelihood of creating tourist attractions away from the coast, where there was already abundant accommodation, caravan sites and other amenities. It pointed out that there would be no benefits to the inhabitants, the tighter planning restrictions would constrain landowners and occupiers, and that they would suffer the extra cost of administering the area. Perhaps its strongest line was in the final paragraph: 'The undoubted natural beauty of the Cambrian Mountains is not threatened, or likely to be threatened, by alien development. That natural beauty will not be preserved or enhanced by designation.'

In his rejection Rippon went against his own statement that a public inquiry would be held; he had found the weight of public opposition, as received by the Welsh Office, too strong. In a fit of pique, the Countryside Commission maintained:

> The objections showed a lack of understanding of the significance of designation which demonstrated the need for full public discussion of the issues. The effect of recent and proposed legislative changes affecting the administration and financing of National Parks appears to have been ignored.

---

[2] 25 August 1972.
[3] The Sandford Committee's *National Parks Policies Review* was published in April 1974, and suggested that the design and siting of farm buildings in National Parks should be brought under planning control, and that more stringent conditions should apply within these areas.

It continued that it was being misunderstood, and that the Cambrian area was gravely threatened by the extension of commercial forestry, water schemes and a revival of extractive industry.

Despite the campaign mounted by the farming organizations, it is notable that only the concerted opposition of all interests combined served to defeat the Eleventh National Park.

John Cripps

Chairman of the Countryside Commission is John Cripps, only son of the iron Chancellor of the Exchequer, Sir Stafford Cripps, during the first post-war Labour Government under Attlee. He is a well-known figure in agricultural circles, speaking at conferences or contributing at meetings, and his love of the countryside and his knowledge of its activities is as wide as anyone's. He has been Chairman since 1970, he was on the Executive Committee of the CPRE and a member of the Nature Conservancy, but it was his 24-year stint as Editor of *The Countryman* from 1947 to 1971 that fully exploited his talents.

This soft-spoken, bespectacled man, with a large frame, has a dry but compelling voice. He has not the austere looks of his father; a more rotund figure gives him the look of a farmer himself. He has a magnificent administrative brain, and although the body he controls has often appeared anti-agriculture, he emphasizes that this is far from its objectives or ambitions. In fact, his uncompromising attitude says that the Commission does not want to discourage visitors to farms. Neither, for that matter, do farmers. It is essential that the non-farming public have a greater appreciation of what farming is all about. The Commission can hardly be said to have an agricultural bias. It represents a cross-section of interests, with many members drawn from other walks of life.

Scotland

The National Parks Commission for England and Wales (1949–68) laid the foundations of the Countryside Commission by acquiring and setting up the National Parks system. Since it did not apply to Scotland, the successor body—The Countryside Commission—similarly did not embrace the land north of the Tweed. A separate Countryside Commission for Scotland was, however, created at that time; it stems from the Countryside (Scotland) Act 1967. It is with some surprise that one learns that Scotland, with its vast region of unspoilt beauty and incomparable wild charm, has no National Parks at all. One of the first reports issued by the new Countryside Commission was an examination of this problem, and a vigorous defence of the status quo. The answer lies in the overall picture of conservancy, conservation and the nature of the Scottish landscape. In fact, 98 per cent of the 77,700 square kilometres of land, fresh-water lochs and rivers could be termed 'countryside'. This description covers the whole of Scotland, except towns with a population of over 5,000. As in the case throughout the British Isles, the vast majority of the population are contained in a surprisingly small land area.

Since the work of the Countryside Commission consists largely of its National Parks operations, the Countryside Commission for Scotland has a smaller job to do than has its sister organization; in fact, the Nature Conservancy, whose title seems to embrace the whole of Britain, does the major part of its work in Scotland. Why are there no National Parks in Scotland? We have already given the answer: when the National Parks and Access to the Countryside Act was passed in 1949 Scotland was omitted, due to the fact that access to open country had always been easier there. There was no significant pressure from landowners, seeking to control and restrict access to the countryside, or from the town-based public agitating for greater recreational areas and access to the countryside. The anomaly created in 1949 exists today, and while there is no legislation for National Parks in Scotland, there is no move to seek it either.

As early as 1884 a Bill was promoted called the Access to the Mountains (Scotland) Bill, but this proposed legislation did not reach the Statute Book, although it marked the beginning of an interest in public recreation and countryside conservation. Since the pressures on the Scottish countryside in the early part of the twentieth century were vastly less than those in England, the need for laws was not evident.

Without any official National Parks, Scotland, however, has a series of forest parks created by the Forestry Commission, the first in 1935, some fifteen years ahead of the first National Park in England. The Forestry Commission created its forest parks—now extending in five parks to cover 120,000 hectares—in the belief that where land was publicly owned in connection with new forest plantings, it should remain open for public enjoyment. Those areas where tree-planting, for a variety of reasons, will never be accomplished have been opened to the public. Restrictions of private cars to those forest roads that only lead to recreational facilities has localized the pressure, and the main area of the parks remains peaceful for the pedestrian.

When the Ramsay Committee[4] was preparing its report on the creation of National Parks it designated five areas in Scotland extending to a total of 4,940 square km, or 6 per cent of Scotland's land surface. The areas designated were:

	Square kilometres
Loch Lomond/Trossachs	832
Glen Affric/Glen Cannich/Strathfarrar	676
Ben Nevis/Glencoe/Black Mount	1,664
The Cairngorms	468
Loch Torridon/Loch Muree/ Little Loch Broom	1,300

[4] 1945 *Report on National Parks* under the chairmanship of Sir J. Douglas Ramsay.

A further three areas were recommended to be placed on a reserve list for later consideration:

	Square kilometres
Moidart/Morar/Knoydart	1,066
Glen Lyon/Ben Lawers/Schiehallion	364
St Mary's Loch	468

The Ramsay Committee defined a National Park in Scotland as

An extensive tract of country of outstanding natural beauty, preferably also of scientific, cultural or historic interest, owned or controlled by the nation, accessible to all as a matter of right under suitable regulations, and administered by or on behalf of the nation to the end that its distinctive values may be preserved unimpaired for the enjoyment and recreation of this and future generations.

Since the National Trust for Scotland already held extensive mountain properties (some of which were contained in the Ramsay Recommendations) it would seem that a large part of those ideals have been accomplished, albeit in a different manner to that originally envisaged.

Without any National Parks to administer, the Countryside Commission for Scotland has become primarily an advisory body for the selection of sites for country parks. By 1974 there were 99 (over 10 hectares) designated in England and Wales, but only 4 such parks in Scotland.

On a larger scale, Renfrew County Council has pioneered a Regional Park of 116 square kilometres with recreational provisions and a policy of maintaining landscape character. Not all the land is available for public access, and the project resembles a miniature National Park in its methods of control. Another similar development is under consideration for the Pentland Hills.

Thus the Scottish counterpart of the Countryside Commission has very largely found that its work is already being done by other bodies which have been established for many years. It is symbolic that the greater scenic magnificence of Scotland is in no way being eroded or despoiled at a greater rate than in England, and although the pressures of tourism are greater, it has been possible to continue leisure and conservation without the need for laws.

National Parks — the world situation

1972 was National Parks Centenary Year. It was the anniversary of the opening of the Yellowstone National Park in the USA, where the policy of conservation and recreation has been apparent from a much earlier stage than in most other countries. The lessons of the USA during the last century have spotlighted the problems, and since the population, and its mobility, has increased far beyond expectations, the demand for facilities such as roads, accommodation and campsites within the National Parks has been at variance with preservation of a 'wild and natural' character, even to the extent of creating irreparable damage to some of the most important natural and historic sites.

The conflicts that have arisen from such unrestricted public travel has caused a rethinking of National Parks policies, and during the National Parks Centenary Year it was internationally agreed that a system of zoning was required. This would ensure that the usage of any area was related to the capacity of that area to withstand visitor pressure, but it entailed a vast operation of surveying National Parks to assess the differing landscape and vegetation types, and to plan the developments of traffic so that as far as was possible wild life and foot traffic could survive.

The second edition of the UN *World List of National Parks and Reserves* lists only those designated areas which satisfy the general definition approved by the 10th General Assembly of IUCN in New Delhi in 1969. A National Park was described as being:

> a relatively large area where one or several eco systems are not materially altered by human exploitation and occupation, where plant and animal species geomorphological sites and habitats are of special scientific, educative and recreative interest, or which contain a natural landscape of great beauty.

The UK section of the UN List comprises 74 areas—56 National Nature Reserves and 18 other Reserves. The 10 National Parks in England and Wales are not on the official list because they do not qualify under the foregoing definition. This must underline the difficulties of establishing National Parks which already have a considerable population living within their boundaries: the fact that over a quarter of a million people live within the ten National Parks can hardly keep them free from the polution which Homo sapiens always leaves behind. If it is any consolation, the 35 *Naturparke* of the German Federal Republic are similarly excluded from the Official UN World List. To qualify for inclusion in the UN List, a National Park must include at least 2,400 acres (1,000 hectares) of fully protected area falling within wilderness, strict natural or managed natural zones. To find such an unspoilt area, where tarmac roads or human habitations are non-existent, in closely crowded Britain is a difficult proposition. The mountainous regions do provide this, but since man's influence reaches to most parts of Britain, it is not surprising that our National Parks do not qualify.

From preservation to protection: the work of the CPRE

The Council for the Protection of Rural England is a pressure group of considerable influence, integrity and independence, if not too much original initiative. It is a pin-pricking group of affiliated organizations that acts as the conscience of England. It is an independent organization, with 41 branches and over 27,000 individual members, but it acts as the mouthpiece of the 54 constituent bodies which are its main part. It was founded in 1926, and in half a century has widened its sphere of influence; even if its major role seems to be destructive rather than constructive, it curbs the wildest excesses of Government Departments.

The CPRE has a distinguished place in the protection of the countryside, and its strictures (usually voiced at public inquiries or through its aristocratic friends in the Lords) have gained it a quite remarkable degree of influence.

This power may stem in part from the patronage bestowed upon it by the Queen, and her father before her. The Duke of Norfolk, Earl Marshal of England, was President of the CPRE for twenty-five years, 1946–71, and he succeeded the Earl of Crawford, who had occupied the presidential chair for twenty years from the Council's inception in 1926. The Duke was succeeded by Lord Molson of High Peak (a constituency of Derbyshire that he represented as a Tory MP for 22 years, until his retirement in 1961). As a former Minister of Works, Molson became Chairman for three years, 1968–71, and this type of succession has given the CPRE an eminence and a degree of respectability, when it might have been a noisy and in effectual pressure group. Its strength also lies in its constituent bodies, which embrace such respectable members as the Royal Society of Arts, the Royal Institute of British Architects, the Ancient Monuments Society, and also the AA and RAC, the Ramblers' Association and the Youth Hostels Association. Both the Scouts and the Women's Institutes are also represented, and the farming interest and support comes from the National Farmers Union and the Country Landowners Association. The third important body in any agricultural triumvirate, the Farm Workers Union, is not a constituent body of the CPRE.

The Council does not receive any financial assistance from Central Government. Perhaps it is too often a thorn in the side of Government Departments. It keeps going on its own financial income, and in fact lives on a shoestring. The national headquarters in less fashionable Hobart Place, London, is sustained on a budget of less than £50,000 per annum, although the local counties look after themselves. The CPRE has solid cash investments of a quarter of a million pounds salted away. These have largely been built up by a wise spread in their share portfolio throughout the years, and indeed their investment in the shares of British American Tobacco Ltd, and in Whitbreads 'A' Shares, reveals lack of inhibition. One cannot imagine the Temperance Society investing in this particular type of holding, but Whitbreads have demonstrated their concern for the British countryside in the film *Who Cares For England?* first screened on BBC 2 in colour, 1968.

The lack of Government support for voluntary bodies is not unusual, and the CPRE has been running at a deficit for several years. In 1972 it raided its own coffers to the extent of £10,459, and in the following year by the sum of £14,440. Even as far back as 1967, the annual deficit was nearly £14,000, and £9,000 in 1968. In 1971 Heath mentioned a sum of £3 million as a form of Government assistance to voluntary bodies. This was seen by the CPRE as a lifeline to sustain its work, but in the event only £40,000 was made available for the environmental sector of the voluntary organizations, and this was earmarked for specific purposes. Despite protests by the Council, it did not succeed in attracting any Government funds. In view of its successes in curtailing the many projects for new roads, electricity pylons, gas installations, Water Authorities reservoirs (and above all in the successful quashing of many housing proposals) the CPRE could hardly expect Government finance to enable it to continue its harassment of Government Departments.

Planning in Britain today is as pervasive as anywhere in the world—it is a British characteristic to abide by the rules, and we seem to love red tape—but the sheer physical difficulties remain of inhabiting these islands to so high a density, whilst still preserving a vast percentage of virtually unspoilt countryside. Even with varied legislation, stemming from the Town and Country Planning Act 1946, the ever-vigilant CPRE and its kindred societies still find plenty of work to do. In his 25-year review of the CPRE at the 1951 AGM, the then Chairman, Professor Sir Patrick Abercrombie, the eminent town-planner, stated that continual vigilance was needed, and he exploded the mistaken idea prevalent at that time that the aims of the CPRE and others had finally been achieved by the recent legislation, observing, 'Nothing is further from the truth. The CPRE and the other voluntary bodies associated with it are needed now more than ever to represent the public interest in these matters.' Twenty-five years later the CPRE stated, 'Trees come down and hedges are grubbed up, and little is done to replace the vital cover thus lost; and smiling valleys disappear for ever under reservoirs, or are removed by mineral workings, while our rivers are so polluted that the creatures in them are dying.' This is possibly an overstatement, but the CPRE continued in this vein:

> The powers are there; the strong and growing public unease is there; and C.P.R.E. exists to make sure that the powers are properly exercised, and the public unease translated into articulate, united and efficiently organised public opinion. Only if these things are done shall we save and revitalise our towns and villages, replant our trees, guide our motorways gently into the landscape, subordinate the vehicle to the countryside and the demands of the gravel extractor to the beauty he is destroying, and produce a proper attitude to water conservation.

From its Hobart Place headquarters the CPRE finds itself three or four times a year opposing private Parliamentary Bills, but enthusiasm often has to take the place of money. The preliminary Parliamentary procedure for opposing Private Bills costs in the region of £200 each time, and if counsel is briefed and complications arise, then the costs spiral. It cost the CPRE over £6,000 to oppose the Plymouth and South West Devon Water Bill, which sought to inundate over 300 hectares on the river Swincombe in the heart of the Dartmoor National Park, but it won its case. In many examples it has opposed the early stages of a Bill, and although funds ran out after the first reading, the case had been put with sufficient force for members of the House of Commons to realize the full implications of the proposed legislation. In the case of the Calderdale Water Bill, and of the Yorkshire Derwent Bill which threatened Farndale, the Bill was thrown out.

During the 42-month period up to May 1967 the CPRE successfully fought 30 major cases against various Ministers. There were four cases for re-routing electricity lines where expensive undergrounding or a changed route was the outcome. There were six cases where mineral undertakings sought to expand, and the CPRE claims the credit for the Minister dismissing their Appeals. On major roads there were three cases where proposals were rejected. Sixteen proposals for housing or industrial development were refused after CPRE intervention, including the proposal for a World Exhibition Centre at Osterley Park. In many other ways objection to the siting of development was sustained after CPRE Appeals. The Third London Airport fiasco after the Roskill Commission Report was the subject of much pressurizing by many bodies including the CPRE, and in 1969 it bitterly opposed the inland site at Great Shishal, near Cambridge. Although it did not oppose the concept of the Channel Tunnel, it did concern itself with the proposed approach roads for this defunct project. In 1971 the CPRE made history by persuading the Ministry of Town and Country Planning (now part of the DoE) against exploratory borings for natural gas at Stoney Ridge, in the North Yorkshire Moors National Park. This was the first known case in which permission for exploratory borings was ever refused on appeal. This formidable list of objections makes the CPRE into a body that envisages its primary role as 'protecting' rural England: in 1971 it cunningly kept the same initials, but dropped the word Preservation in favour of Protection. The CPRE claims that its work is not exclusively defensive. It hopes to make positive contributions towards improving the environment, and the National Parks system under the wing of the Countryside Commission was first suggested by the CPRE in 1929. It campaigned for twenty years in conjunction with such bodies as the Ramblers' Association to make the dream into a reality. Today some of the major work of the Council is concerned with the agitation against juggernaut lorries ruining our towns and villages.

Respected though unbeloved by Government Departments, the CPRE is regarded with considerable suspicion by farmers and landowners, although by including their names among the constituent bodies that make up the Council, the NFU and the CLA have given it their support. Nevertheless, the inclusion of such other bodies as the Ramblers' Association does not enhance the Council's standing in farmers' eyes, and its predictable campaign for greater control over the design and siting of farm buildings, plus its interest in greater access to the countryside (which is still largely private property) all give rise to suspicion in farmers' minds. Among its 27,000 members there are few farmers. Nevertheless, in its policy of closely examining governmental as well as private planning proposals, the CPRE could well rename itself the Conscience and Protestations for Remote Environments.

Scotland

The Association for the Protection of Rural Scotland (APRS) was formed in

1926, the same year as the CPRE. It has followed the pattern of its English equivalent, but has on the whole made less impact. This might be taken to mean that there is not the urgent need to agitate against despoilers in Scotland: the pressures upon the countryside are less urgent. In any event, the APRS is smaller than its Welsh equivalent, and even its total assets of £10,000 are only half those of the Council which protects the Principality.

There has never been a satisfactory rapport with the CPRE, and the coldness between the two bodies can be judged from this quote from the 1975 Annual Report:

> There has been a great improvement in our relations with the CPRE. Its wide ranging interests and activities, also its expertise in the handling of environmental issues have been of great value throughout the year. Every effort will be made to maintain and improve our liaison with this most useful, helpful and knowledgeable body.

The last comment, after forty-nine years of existence for both bodies, hardly shows a union of wedded bliss. However, the APRS can claim a unique distinction in that for these forty-nine years its subscription rates remained unchanged; surely in any inflationary period a reason for pride. However, the lack of finance combined with a general lack of direction has not given it the influence of the CPRE.

Predictably, in the 1970s the major preoccupation of the APRS has been with the North Sea oil developments. It was Britain's need for quick results that prompted Edward Heath to appoint Lord Carrington in 1972 to cut all red tape and to obtain the maximum amount of oil flowing ashore in the shortest possible time. Laudable though this was from an economic point of view, a howl of protest went up from such bodies as the APRS and the other conservationist societies.

The APRS takes the view that Scotland should not be desecrated for the prosperity of England. In 1974 it successfully opposed the construction of three oil refineries, and the 1975 Annual Report states, 'It is arguable that Britain's oil needs for the foreseeable future could adequately be achieved with the expansion of existing refineries at Grangemouth, Teesside and Milford Haven.' Obviously a case of building oil refineries anywhere but in Scotland! A reasonable increase in oil rigs is accepted, but the APRS remains opposed to a proliferation of oil bases around Scotland's coastline. The pipe-laying activities for North Sea Gas from St Fergus, Aberdeenshire, to Carlisle, and the rapidly increasing number of transportation pipelines on the east coast of Scotland have been causes for the APRS to fight.

Like the CPRE, it is a body that co-ordinates the efforts of a vast number of constituent bodies, and indeed nearly all the County Councils of Scotland support it, although with some donations such as the Perth and Kinross Joint County Council of £2.10, it hardly seems worth writing the cheque. The CPRE subsists on an annual administrative income of under £4,000, and the employment in 1974 of a poorly paid full-time secretary could not disguise the fact that the APRS (despite its claim to be the oldest amenity and environmental association in Scotland) is hardly a major fighting force. Its low-key image is sustained by the low-key support which it gains in Scotland.

Wales

Although nominally formed in 1928, two years after the CPRE, the Council for the Protection of Rural Wales has only had an independent existence since 1960. Prior to that it depended on the CPRE for support. Today, however, it is a fully independent body with its own membership, secretariat and financial independence.

Membership by 1974 was 4,209, and the CPRW has 13 branches covering the whole of the Principality. Its aims are to secure the protection and improvement of rural scenery and amenities in the Welsh countryside. It keeps its members in touch by means of news-letters, and holds an Annual Study Conference.

It is symbolic of the lack of urgent work that the regular news-letters are concerned with national rather than local affairs, and comments upon the Channel Tunnel seem remote from Snowdonia and the Cambrian Mountains.

The CPRW is viewed with some misgivings in Wales itself, as may be judged from the following comment in the *News Letter* of Autumn 1974. 'The Eisteddfod is a significant and important event in Welsh national life, but the tendency has been to view CPRW as a limited and indeed an alien organization.' An annual budget of £5,243 compares unfavourably with that of the CPRE, whose headquarters expenses annually are £50,000.

6 Reclamation of Land

'This precious stone, set in the silver sea,
Which serves it in the office of a wall
Or as a moat defensive to a house
Against the envy of less happier lands.
This blessed plot, this earth, this realm, this England'
                                              Shakespeare

Three exciting major engineering projects in this century withered in the event
from timidity. As a generation we can count our failure to build the Channel
Tunnel and the Maplin Airport, or to reclaim the Wash, as significant examples
of our lack of courage. In each case the requisite finance has been the stumbling-
block, and while it is not my purpose here to discuss the implications of the
Tunnel or the Airport, the failure to build the Wash Barrage has been a crucial
disaster in land conservation.

Other nations have recognized their need to create farming land where there
was none before. Although the nineteenth century saw the opening up of the
Canadian Prairies, the Australian hinterland and vast tracks of superb grazing
in the Argentine, the potential areas in the world today that are ripe for
reclamation are probably smaller. The efforts to increase the world's food
supplies are minuscule in relation to the problem, so within this context the
reclamation of every British hectare assumes a greater significance than it did a
hundred years ago. While the various bodies that are set up for the protection of
the British countryside fulfil their roles in an effective manner, the CPRE is only
concerned with protecting the amenities and charm of the English countryside,
the Countryside Commission with preserving the balance of nature in a vast
botanical museum, and the National Trust in preserving Britain's heritage of
stately homes and unspoilt coastline. Nobody is concerned with reclaiming land
that is lost to farming, or indeed for the possible reclamation from the sea of
those many areas around our coasts where this is possible.

Our attitude compares unfavourably with that of the Dutch, who completed
the 30-kilometre Zuider Zee dam as long ago as 1932. The pressing needs for land
in Holland, when coupled with a sensible long-term plan, resulted in a dam that
created a brackish lake of over 3,600 square kilometres, which was freed from
tidal effects, and which protected much of the low-lying land of the Netherlands
from its periodic devastating floods.

The project is of world-wide significance: many of the sea-walls that shield the
low-lying areas of Britain were themselves conceived by Dutch engineers. The
procedure in Holland has been to divide the land saved into six compartments.

Of these, the Wieringermeer Polder (193 square kilometres), the Noordoost Polder (469 square kilometres), the Oost Flevoland Polder (528 square kilometres) and the Zuid Flevoland Polder (430 square kilometres) have all been completely reclaimed. The Markerwaard Polder of some 678 square kilometres is under process of draining and reclamation, a process which may be completed by 1980. The Dutch pattern of winning land from the sea consists of drying it out and providing dykes, sluice-gates and pumping-houses to hold the water-levels at bay. Within this region the largest area (roughly 20 per cent of the whole) is the IJsselmeer (1,449 square kilometres), which will be retained as a freshwater lake to meet Holland's growing water requirements. It also provides a vast inland yachting haven for the Dutchmen in search of leisure pursuits. While the whole operation is not primarily designed for agriculture, it does provide large new tracts of land for a small nation. There are now new towns, industries, arterial roads and adjacent recreation areas to serve a nation with one of the world's highest population densities. It has added perhaps 10 per cent to the original area of Holland.

There have been many attempts by private landowners to reclaim the lower-lying semi-marshland around our coasts. Romney Marsh, famous for its sheep breed and some of the finest pasture-land in Britain, was once inundated, and around the East Anglian coast far-sighted landowners such as Sir Peter Greenwell at Butley Abbey have drained their marshes and created rich arable land capable of growing heavy crops of wheat. But these efforts have been small and fragmented; often the land enclosed by the embankments required levelling and draining, even though it was already saved from the sea, and in many cases had been for centuries.

The Wash Study

Research into the possibilities of raising a dyke across the head of the Wash has been talked about for many years. It was here that rumour has it that King John lost his jewels, and certainly this shallow area lends itself to a feat of reclamation that in engineering terms is no more difficult than the reclamation in Holland. In the 1960s a study was made of the possibilities, but successive Ministers vacillated; there was no definite commitment to the work, the only progress being the allocation of sufficient finance for a study project. The results of this feasibility study arrived in 1974. A complete barrage would have made the port of Kings Lynn an inland town more than thirty kilometres from the coast, and there were problems of the outflow of water from the river Nene and the Great Ouse, but in any event the Study Group only recommended some quite minor lagoons that fall far short of reclamation first envisaged.

Land around this area of Britain has, however, been reclaimed in small blocks, and the continual silting up of the Wash will mean that further nibbles can be made in the course of time. The Crown Estate Commissioners have drained 1,000 hectares in various parts along the Norfolk coastline adjacent to the Queen's Sandringham estate. Other reclamations in the area of the Humber estuary have been carried out. Since the Crown Commissioners own *all* the land below mean high-water level, sadly there has probably been less reclamation than there would have been had private landowners been allowed to exercise neighbouring rights. Reclamation in this area has been progressing in easy stages. Fertile heavy silt within sight of Hunstanton Pier was reclaimed in 1965 (130 hectares), and the following year another 145 hectares. Within six years this land was yielding up to 5 tonnes per hectare of wheat, and the cost of reclamation (assessed in 1973 at £2,000 per hectare) still represents a figure below the normal cost of buying farmland.

On the Sandringham estate the Crown Commissioners decided in 1965 that 280 hectares of saltings, of which 48 hectares were owned by the Queen, were to be reclaimed. This was achieved, and the estate has since bought 93 hectares from the Crown Commissioners. It now has 140 hectares of land that only became dry in 1965. The Queen's Agent, Julian Loyd, estimates that in about forty years' time another area of saltings will probably be suitable for reclamation with a tidal protection embankment. The land to be reclaimed by the turn of the century is already silting up, and is covered with a salt-encrusted vegetation. In many areas on these smooth saltings a foot does not sink. The process of neutralizing the salt content of the reclaimed land is often achieved by the addition of gypsum[1], but at Sandringham the low salt content of the Wash has made it possible to achieve an acceptable saline content merely by the installation of an underground tile drainage system and the normal leaching of the soil by annual rainfall. This washes the salt through the layers and into ditches. The cost of this project, including the erection of the embankment, came to about £310 per enclosed hectare.

The innovation made at Sandringham was direct entry into arable cropping, starting with winter wheat, although unfortunately a wet autumn necessitated sowing spring barley the following year. The important lesson was learned that although this newly reclaimed land can produce heavy crops, it is nevertheless an area of the farm that must be treated and cultivated in priority to the remainder, due to the lack of soil-structure. It was symbolic of Prince Philip's interest in the balance of nature that he suggested, during the reclamation of the Wolferton Saltings, that 16 hectares, well behind the sea wall, should be left in their original condition to provide an attractive nature reserve. Later detailed observations have shown that the pattern of this area is changing from that of a sea-bird salt-water sanctuary to that of a land-bird fresh-water sanctuary.

Across the Wash from Sandringham the stump of Boston, in faraway Lincolnshire, can be seen, and the extraordinary levelness of the whole area is

---

[1] After the 1953 East Coast floods the Government made free deliveries of gypsum to affected farmers to reclaim their land which had been inundated. Otherwise submersion under salt water for only twenty-four hours (which happened then) is sufficient to kill the crop-growing potential.

unbelievable. But there are other areas in Britain. Pagham Harbour in Sussex, a nature reserve today, has been silting up for centuries, and is now little more than a mere surrounded by undrained marsh. The first suggestions for reclaiming this area date from three centuries ago, but eventually, 126 hectares were enclosed. Later neglect led to abandonment, and they soon reverted to a waterlogged marsh again. Today modern engineering techniques and powerful machinery could easily once more reclaim this area, but nothing is being done.

The Fens were reclaimed over three hundred years ago, but little is actively under consideration today. Nevertheless, there are some other schemes. An area of over 20,000 hectares on the Solway Estuary has been suggested as a possible target for a major drainage and reclamation project. Basic information has been assembled, and although this may bring results one day, impetus seem lacking, even though there are grants available from EEC funds.

Reclamation: the world solution

'And he gave it for his opinion, that whosoever could make 2 ears of corn or 2 blades of grass to grow upon a spot of ground where only 1 grew before, would deserve better of mankind, and do more essential service to his country than the whole race of politicians put together.'

Jonathan Swift

The need to expand food-production is recognized by most world governments, though progress is minimal, and these isolated test-cases have adequately demonstrated agricultural potential, but since such demonstration is expensive, and the world is not yet dying of starvation, government financial assistance is relatively minute.

The food-producing areas today do not coincide with those of ancient times, and the agricultural production from such countries as Egypt was probably greater two millennia ago than today. Certainly around the Mediterranean region, and particularly at the eastern end, there is a vast potential for making the desert green. Further east, in ancient Persia (Iran), the Romans set up a vast system of irrigation through ducts and water channels, but for twenty centuries these have been neglected, and only in this century has much been done to rehabilitate and resurrect these ancient examples. For twenty years now there have been attempts in Iran to stimulate crop-production, and in the 1970s the Iranian Government sought British help in these endeavours. The overall success has yet to be measured.

Just after the 1939–45 War, when Lord Boyd-Orr was making impassioned speeches about impending world food disasters, and the British public was still being severely rationed, the Labour Government launched the ill-fated African Groundnuts Scheme. It was an imaginative idea to bulldoze flat vast areas of what was then called British East Africa (now Tanzania) and to plant oil-bearing groundnuts for a world that was barely emerging from wartime shortages. In charge of the scheme was Leslie Plummer (knighted in 1949), as Chairman of the Overseas Food Corporation. He later became MP for Deptford, in 1951. Wilson appointed his wife, another Labour stalwart, a Life Peeress after Plummer's death. The Overseas Food Corporation lasted from 1947 to 1950, and it cost the British taxpayer tens of millions of pounds in a fiasco that did not produce any groundnuts. There were few lessons learnt from this affair, but in retrospect it represented a bold attempt to create food-production in a new area in the world, and was set against a background of panic. The venture was ill-fated because of maladministration, muddle and lack of expertise. Such a scheme without Government interference might have had better chance of success.

World solutions lie chiefly in improving the productivity of the land, whereas the UK solutions, like the Dutch, are allied to attempting to increase the land surface by gains from the sea. In the eastern Mediterranean Jordan and Egypt are attempting agricultural improvement today. In the three years 1970–74, Jordan's contribution to this concept has turned an area of impoverished desert into a gigantic and prosperous 1,200-hectare farm, where new crops are being cultivated and experimental sheep-breeding is carried out.

The Jordanian experiment is being conducted by private enterprise, and not by a Government Agency. The farm is owned by Sherif Nasser bin Jamil, former Commander-in-Chief of the Jordanian armed forces and uncle of King Hussein. On this virgin soil Sherif Nasser called in squads of army bulldozers to clear the surface of boulders, which he utilized as the foundations for roads and building materials for the six hundred houses now on the Qasr Halabat, some fifty kilometres north-east of Amman. After clearing the boulders the task was to utilize the underground water resources, and following the creation of an adequate water-supply the desert has blossomed; a system of irrigation by canals and sprinkler systems, depending upon the contours of the land, and the production from 8 wells which can produce 2,400 cubic metres of water per hour, has only been restricted by the capacity of the pumping equipment that Sherif Nasser was able to obtain in the Middle East. The water—which appears to be unlimited—comes from underground streams originating in the Euphrates river area in North Syria. It is fresh running water in great quantities, and used with discretion could transform a very large area of the Jordanian desert.

Farming in this sort of climate can bring remarkable results. On this farm alfalfa produces a crop once every twenty-five days, with a limit of eleven crops per year. This production compares with the highest European cultivation of alfalfa, which is in the plain of the Po in Northern Italy. This area produces five crops per year, and needs advanced fertilizer treatments to achieve even this. In Jordan cotton may become the principal crop when the techniques of cultivation have been successfully mastered.

The Jordanian sheep breeds which produce wool, meat and dairy produce are becoming a feature of this new experiment, and crosses between the white mountain and black desert breeds of the Jordanian Hawaseh sheep are proving of value. The desert sheep can endure thirst for four days, and crosses with the mountain breeds have now produced a new breed which can go without water for 2 days and produce 3 kilograms of milk daily, and with lambs which can weigh up to 110 kilos. Fleece weight is 80 per cent higher than with previous breeds, and the wool quality is improved. It is symbolic of all farming practice that once the initial obstacles have been overcome experimentation, which leads to greater advances, takes place.

The cost of this remarkable project (which has brought graceful lines of poplar-trees and flourishing grape-vines to the heart of the impoverished desert), was nearly two million dollars in the first three years, but it has proved an outstanding success which will enhance the economic stability of Jordan, and undoubtedly a healthy capital return.

Not far away in Egypt there is considerable pressure to expand home food-production to combat an increasing population and to satisfy a rising standard of living. These twin pressures are producing agricultural development, which has been assisted by the construction of the high dam south of Aswan.

The Egyptian land-reclamation programme started in 1967, and in the first seven years nearly 400,000 hectares of desert had been reclaimed, of which approximately a quarter had been handed over to settlers. The Egyptian project is to desalinate soils by flooding and deep drainage to wash the salts from the soil. Initial crops of lucerne are planted, which are left for five to seven years as a base for a stronger soil structure, which is later intended to produce fruit and vegetable crops in the new lands adjoining the Nile Delta, and sugar cane in Upper Egypt. The main fruit crops are grapes, oranges, almonds and olives.

In Egypt, even with this expansion, the cultivated area only amounts to some 4 per cent of the total land area, or a twelfth of a hectare per head of population.

Since 1970 the United Nations World Food Programme has been assisting in this reclamation scheme, and its help has taken the form of providing food for the migratory labourers employed doing the actual reclamation and development, although the new settlers get some assistance for their initial three years. The Egyptian Government has been donating an equivalent value for financing the building of houses, schools, handicraft centres, medical and veterinary units, assistance for farmers' co-operatives and other village amenities. The Egyptian Land Reclamation Programme falls into two categories; there are those lands from which it is now possible to crop by reason of the irrigation facilities made possible by the Aswan High Dam. The other scheme is concerned with draining those marshy areas in the Delta, replacing the traditional open drains by underground tile systems. So in one instance they are combating a lack of water, and in the other an excess of it.

The rice area has doubled to 400,000 hectares, and cotton is now being substituted for wheat. Soya beans have appeared as a new crop, and an initial hectarage of 3,200 is expected to expand tenfold. Such projects require allied developments, soya-bean crushing plants have been planned, while the Americans have been looking at this increase as an expanding market for their own products.

India

India, with its teeming population (many on the starvation level), presents a food-supply problem to the whole world. That other vast nation, China, has in its own communistic way organized a vast agricultural redevelopment scheme. But in the non-communist countries, with greater freedom of action, the only major support comes from the UN World Food Programme, yet there is little co-ordination of effort.

The UN has as its objective the expansion of world food-production, but the means to this end are fragmentary and uncoordinated; there are, of course, difficulties. Many areas of the world's land surface are unsuitable for agricultural food-production, but nevertheless can still be productive in other directions. Rubber and timber, for example, are products of the land but are hardly edible, and in India, despite the need for food, the major projects have been concerned with timber-production. The Indian Forest Development Corporation in Maharashtra has cleared 100,000 hectares of uneconomic forest every year since 1969. The operation consists of cutting out the less productive areas and replanting with teak. In India 22·7 per cent of the land area is covered by forests, but this only produces just over 2 per cent of the national income, and the uneconomic value of this 'national asset' has at last been realized. Traditionally the forests were managed under a selection system whereby one-twentieth of the forest area was worked each year, taking the mature timber and allowing about 80 per cent of standing growth to remain, while regeneration was left to its own devices. Now the new programme embraces planting from teak nurseries in proper orders and spacings.

There is an object lesson here that the Forestry Commission in the UK might copy, for the Maharashtra Forest Development Corporation has been so successful that the State Government has seen its initial financial support repaid within four years. Income comes from the existing low-grade timber and bamboo, and the area between the teak is being used for growing cash crops in the early years of a plantation, with strips just over a metre wide being sown with either sesame or kenaf. In this mainly humid climate, the first income from planted teak can arise in only eight years when the first thinnings are sold, against the normal thinnings from a UK forest, which would hardly start before the fifteenth year.

As in Egypt, the support of the UN World Food Programme consists of food-supplies to the workers engaged in the project, but apart from stabilizing a rural community, these agricultural programmes bring in their wake proper housing, and medical and school programmes.

South America

While the Mediterranean examples of turning the desert green have been largely successful, they can in no way compare with the vast development that is taking place in South America, where thousands of hectares of jungle are being cut down and replaced by lush pasture-land as the Amazon regions head towards their new destiny as leading world beef-suppliers. The Argentine was exploited in the last century by British business-men, who realized the beef-producing potential and on the vast ranches imported the white-faced Hereford cattle which fattened remarkably and were re-exported back to their homeland in the UK. In the immediate post-War period the annual Perth sales were marked by record prices paid for pedigree stock by the Argentinian entrepreneurs who sought out the best stock to replenish their herds and sustain their beef-producing capacity. Argentinian beef suffered a severe setback in the UK after the disastrous 1957 foot-and-mouth outbreak which was largely blamed upon the virus being imported into the UK in the bones of carcasses. The resultant regulation which permitted only boned meat to be imported into Britain severely cut back South American supplies, but not unpredictably was welcomed by UK farmers who had seen their own prospects jeopardized by this vastly growing trade. Political insecurity and instability in some South American countries has not helped either. These developments have not added significantly to the UK farmer's beef-producing capacity; the only result has been for beef animals from South America to find other markets. The impetus and development of new productive areas is gaining impetus again in the 1970s.

In Brazil 315 new cattle ranches, covering nearly 78,000 square kilometres collectively, have been set up. This area (which translates into over 7 million hectares) is almost one-third of the total agricultural area of Britain, and with an average farm size of nearly 22,400 hectares each it is difficult for Britons to realize the full extent of these vast, newly opened tracts of virgin land. The 315 ranches represent an area above the size of Ireland, and such is the extent of the ranches that the oldest, established in 1967, only discovered in 1974 that it had a tribe of Indians living within its boundaries.

The Federal Government is encouraging these developments with tax incentives to sustain investment, and income-tax rebates of up to 50 per cent can be obtained, provided that the money is invested in one of the priority regions or economic sectors. The Amazon Development Board (SUDAN) estimates that £300 million will be invested in cattle projects before 1980. The Brazilian private enterprise cattle-ranching projects are producing vast quantities of beef, but without any impact as yet on world markets. Since a proportion of such increases always contributes to the rising standard of living of the home population, such impact is long-term.

In Ecuador the Amazon region is almost entirely undeveloped, and sponsored schemes have only penetrated small areas in the central and southern zones. Here it is tea plantations that form the basis of agricultural production, but the farming is at a subsistence level, and although the increasing tonnages are significant, there is evidence that the future may lie more in cattle-production than in crops.

Ecuador's traditional agricultural exports—bananas, cocoa, coffee and sugar—increased dramatically in the 1970s, although much of this resulted from higher market prices rather than a greater production. There are, however, a number of ambitious regional development projects based on the use of water resources in the main river basins, the largest being the Guayas Basin Scheme. It includes some of the best agricultural potential in Ecuador, but today less than one-third of the land is adequately cultivated. The annual rainfall is erratic, and falls over a short period, resulting in floods, followed by droughts. The need here is for a pilot project for irrigation to cover the drought periods, and the comprehensiveness of such a scheme is shown by the fact that it would cover nearly 12,000 hectares, the agricultural production would increase tenfold, the rice production be doubled by the achieving of two annual harvests; and the population is also expected to double.

In world terms, these examples of the agricultural expansion in the second half of the twentieth century are the equivalent of the opening up of the Australian and Canadian hinterlands in the nineteenth century. They form a pattern, uncoordinated as it may seem, of attempts to make the desert bloom. With greater scientific knowledge, agricultural expertise and power of bulldozers this expansion should be sustained into the twenty-first century, but whether it does will be the responsibility of individual governments and political pressures, rather than humanitarian ethics. It is said today that one-third of the world's population is undernourished, and another one-third is near starvation, but then one must remember—it is a truism, after all—that many people (and pets!) in the West eat far too much.

The UK solution

After this brief description of the pressures upon land in Britain we see that the fundamental problem remains that Britain is too small, with too large a population, and can no longer rely upon trading industrial goods to pay for food imports. There is an overall pressure upon world food-supplies, adding problems of availability to those of cost.

At the present time there is no coherent policy for land utilization. The environmental lobby and the protest groups who have saved so much land from the concrete-mixer have not done so with the interests of farming at heart. The spin-off may have saved British farming potential, however. In any event, in so tightly packed an island the overriding need must be for houses. Solutions and answers are complex. There must be more care to site new development upon the poorer agricultural regions, although even the new survey maps of Britain are not as comprehensive as the German equivalent[2]. Thus although lip service is paid towards the protection of farmland, even with our complex administration there is insufficient information available.

There is a differing emphasis in the statements of the CPRE: 'There are 170,000 acres of road and railway verge in England and Wales. ON THE CREDIT SIDE

[2]See page 28.

of motorways is that for every mile of new motorway, 13 acres of verge are also created. Of the 1,700 species of wild flowers in the country, 700 occur on verges.' Thus the CPRE call it creditable that the 170,000 acres—or 68,000 hectares—of Britain comprising roadside verges help to perpetuate wild flowers, whereas that area is in fact a vast loss to potential food-production. Farmers are blamed for the eradication of hedgerows, which have been disappearing at a rate of nearly 8,000 kilometres per year, but within Britain there remain still 960,000 kilometres of hedgerow, which is the equivalent of twenty-four times around the Equator. These hedgerows, at an average width of only 2 metres (which may be a modest estimate) cover a land area of 176,000 hectares, which is twice the total of the national nature reserves. While an ecological, biological and human balance must be retained, the potential within Britain is hardly being exploited to its full.

Areas of England where land reclamation is feasible

North-west Coast		
Esk Estuary and Morecambe	2,700 hectares	
Ravenglass	100	
Dudden Sands	500	
Morecambe Bay	1,000	
Lune Estuary	600	
Ribble Estuary	40	
Mersey Estuary	100	
Dee Estuary	600	5,640
Humber and North Lincs Coast		800
Norfolk		
The Wash	3,300	
North Norfolk	2,300	5,600
Suffolk		
Oxley Marshes		100
Essex		
Hamford Water	1,200	
Blackwater and Colne	1,000	
Dengie	500	
Crouch and Roach Estuaries	200	
Maplin	200	3,100
North-west Kent		1,300
South Coast		
Langstone, Chichester and Pagham Harbours	300	
Southampton Water and South-west Coast	1,700	2,000
		18,540

We come back again to the possibility of expanding the actual size of Britain. There are many areas of low-lying and shallow marshland or seabed where protective embankments could follow the Dutch pattern, and increase our geographical area.

The table demonstrates the areas around Britain where there exists some possibility of reclamation from the sea. In total, the 18,540 hectares only represent one year's loss from agriculture for industrial and urban development, but since land is a commodity with limitless potential, then this could be a permanent addition to the productivity of British farming, and since there is a considerable difference between the productive capacity of, say, the fertile Fen soils, and the sheep grazing of hill farms, then the area in question is disproportionate to its true value to the nation. It could provide the solution to the UK problem. Other less developed nations have embarked upon an ambitious food programme, and although there is some financial encouragement for the redeployment of industry to the less attractive areas of Britain under special Government grants for development areas, the main attitude is simply one of giving sufficient aid to ensure that the areas do not become depopulated and stagnant. There is no encouragement towards increasing the value of these areas.

7 Nationalization and Freedom

The laws of land

'Is it not lawful for me to do what I will with mine own?'
St Matthew 20:15

'Moses said: pick up your tools, saddle your asses and come with me to the promised land.
The Trade Unionist said: throw down your shovels, sit on your asses. This is the promised land.'
Source unknown. Probably the Stock Exchange

Said one distraught belted Earl on his Somersetshire estate, 'I came here in 1935, but it took thirty years to get possession of that farm. I wanted to farm it myself after the War, and although I gained possession of several farms it has taken me thirty years to get the one I wanted first. It is the nearest to the home farm, and was for many years an isolated oasis surrounded by my own farming enterprises.' This landowner had followed the pattern of many others in taking into his own possession every tenanted farm that became vacant on the decease of the occupier. He had been delayed in building up his farming by the security of tenure given to tenants by the Agricultural Holdings Act 1948, which has shaped the pattern and structure of British farming for nearly a third of a century.

Conversely, it could be said that tenants have lived with the protection of the 1948 Act without fear of eviction from unscrupulous landlords, and since a farm tenancy embraces a house and home, this protection is little different from that accorded to any tenant householder in Britain today. The farmhouse is, however, only a part of a business, thus the protection is greater than that afforded to shopkeepers, whose lease expires, and who are forced to vacate their business premises.

The Act gives complete security of tenure during the lifetime of the tenant, with certain qualifications (such as bad husbandry, which is difficult to prove), and arrears in the rent. Although rents may be increased at three-year revisal dates, they are subject to appeal if excessive, and the tenant is assured of his lifetime security. He may go to arbitration in any rent dispute. The 1976 Inheritance of Tenancies Act extended the protection to other heirs, and in effect gave a security of tenure for two generations, including other relatives besides children.

The net result has been that farms, once vacated, have been taken in hand by impoverished landlords, hit not only by rents which represented a return of only 1 per cent on the capital value of the farm, but also because despite the fact that running a large estate with many tenants is a full-time occupation, the tax laws have determined that rents constitute 'unearned income' and are more severely taxed. These twin pressures have turned the landed gentry back into the practical farmers that they were during the seventeenth and eighteenth centuries. Since farms re-let might not come back into vacant possession again for another fifty to seventy years, the protection afforded by the security from eviction under the Act has created a situation where less land is available for letting. The changing ratio of owner/occupier to tenanted land in England and Wales has swung from 60 per cent tenanted in 1945 to less than 40 per cent today, and in some of the eastern counties the tenanted area is less than 10 per cent of the whole. This fact is often used to demonstrate the changing ownership of farmland in Britain, but the changed status as tenants die and landlords become farmers has disguised the fact that many of the larger landowners still hold substantial parts of their original estates.[1]

Ironically, although tenants cannot be dispossessed by their landlords, the State can compulsorily purchase farmland for designated purposes. The New Towns are an example where complete farms have been taken. Tenants do become dispossessed of their land under the C.P.O.s, but this similarly can apply to owner/occupiers, the principal objection being that whereas the owner, with funds from his land, can repurchase another farm, the tenant without capital is unlikely to find another tenancy.

The 1948 Act passed during Tom Williams's tenure at the Ministry has been followed by John Hare's 1958 Act and Cledwyn Hughes's 1968 Act. The 1958 provisions tidied up some aspects of the Act of ten years previously. It added the provision of rent-revisions at three-yearly intervals, varied the terms of the permanent area of pasture on a farm, dealt with heather and grass burning, allowed a greater freedom of cropping from the rigidity of traditional rotations, and allowed rent increases to cover the interest charges on new capital improvements incurred on the farm by the landlord. Ten years later another Act tinkered about with payments to tenants forced to surrender their land, but only to the extent where that land was being taken out of farming. The philosophy of a massive security of tenure remains inviolate to this day.

The ethics and philosophy of the 1948 Act has manifested itself in many unexpected ways. The impossibility of evicting a tenant, and the lower financial return from rent as opposed to farming the land personally, has been used as an instrument in the reduction of the value of the land for Death Duty, later Estate Duty, later Capital Transfer Tax. Since tenanted land is usually valued at 40 per cent lower than that with vacant possession, this has been a useful means for claiming a lower probate value. Even within families of the nouveaux-riche

---

[1] The changing role of ownership is dealt with in Chapter 9, p. 153.

owner/occupiers, it has been used to advantage for creating a tenancy of a farming partnership leasing the land from the farmer/owner, thus classifying the land as tenanted.

Inasmuch as British farmland is a free market, and the land and property in the ownership of the holder is his kingdom, it is speculative just how far this possession of title extends, and how farming activity is affected by the laws of the land. The Agricultural Holdings Act has had a profound effect upon the structure of British farming during the past three decades. It has been the bedrock of stability, but has slowed down the rate of amalgamations. These have taken place despite the Act, and since the policy the world over has been to enlarge businesses, the greatest comparison with British farming must be with our neighbours on the Continent. Since we started from a higher base line than generally found in Europe, the dire need to change a peasant farming population into a thriving race of agrobusinessmen has been less pressing. Perhaps the most surprising feature of the 1948 Act is that there was little movement to change it, neither from the NFU (who might reasonably have been expected to campaign for its extension) nor from the CLA for its abolition; the subject was scarcely whispered throughout the years.

The 1976 extension was the result of an amendment by three Labour MPs of an additional clause to the Agriculture (Miscellaneous Provisions) Bill—but an amendment that was instantly embraced by the Government, and added into the draft of the Bill before it was debated in the Commons. Similarly, the number of judicial cases that have occurred annually is minute. There have been a small number where a tenant farmer has been dispossessed, after legal action, by the owner of the land whose son wished to farm, but real proof of that urge has to be justified before the courts. Bad husbandry, too, has been proved in a few cases, but since the farm must be polluted by weeds and impoverished before such action can be substantiated, the tenant has probably been near bankruptcy by that time anyway.

One particular case in 1973 spotlights the possibilities for unscrupulous landlords, but it was a rare event. The Farmers Union of Wales alleged that undue harassment was putting pressure upon tenants to vacate their holdings. A number of complaints were made that the landlords were listing 200 to 300 minor points of irritation. The objective was for the landlord to obtain vacant possession and cash in on the enhanced values. In this case the company concerned was Llanover Holdings Ltd, in Monmouthshire, owned by Robin Herbert, himself Vice-Chairman of the Countryside Commission, Chairman of the National Trust for Wales and a Director of the National Westminster Bank Ltd, but the FUW also claimed that the arbitration arrangements were unsatisfactory, since the Land Tribunal System had been abolished in 1963, and cases were now heard by a single arbitrator, usually a qualified Land Agent. The Union complained that the new system was 'without the flexibility of a larger body of men which the Land Tribunals had been composed of'. The FUW Secretary for Glamorgan complained that in the previous few years there had been eight similar cases, of which he had only won five.

The major method of rectifying past misdeeds in farming is through assessment of dilapidations when the tenant finally departs. It is at this stage that bad cropping, dirty, weed-infested fields, and dilapidated buildings are assessed, but conversely improvements during the tenancy may also be counter-claimed. It is not entirely a one-way operation. In the case of farm buildings, the modernization programme has often been slowed down by the cash difficulties of the landlord, and with many tenants clamouring low rents have made it difficult to provide capital sums without borrowing. Some landlords have borrowed, and charged the interest. In other cases tenants have erected their own buildings, with permission, and have recovered any outstanding sums on the cessation of their tenancy.

Sacrosanct and inviolate?

During the War it was possible through emergency powers compulsorily to take over badly farmed land to improve the food-producing capacity. The operation of farming was carried out by the much-maligned War Agricultural Executive Committees, composed of local large farmers, who set up a system of men and machines to do the farming themselves. Today a farmer may farm his land as badly as he pleases, although there is legal remedy if weed seeds from a dirty farm are seen to be polluting neighbouring properties. A landowner may not impede the flow of water from higher land to lower, and there are restrictions on the area of various crops which may be grown: for instance, potatoes are severely rationed, a ruling which can be enforced by fines from the Potato Marketing Board. So, how sacrosanct is the true ownership of land today?

Since the countryside is an open area, access to privately owned land is impossible to control. Although trespass occurs, the only claim is for the damage that can be proved, and is claimable by the plaintiff. Public footpaths extend to thousands of kilometres. They are a traditional right of the general public, and often cut across large arable areas. While the farmer has the right to plough these footpath areas in open country, he is bound to re-level the footpath area within six weeks. Electricity pylons can be erected, and areas of land are occupied for the purpose; underground sewers, pipelines, and other works by Statutory Undertakers can be carried out, even though the owner's permission is required, and compensation or easements are paid, but there is little chance of diverting or stopping the progress of such works through private land. After construction, access for inspection or repairs is a natural part of such agreements.

Thus with the State and Local Authorities invested with powers to take away private land when the public interests are at stake the true privacy of farmland is a myth, yet the garden of a house is no more sacrosanct, and a stranger sitting on the lawn is not committing a criminal offence. It is only breaking or entering where the owners enjoy full privacy of right.

The lack of backing in law has unfortunate effects on farmland adjoining housing areas, where children and dogs do spoil many crops. Apart from proving damage, the farmer has little redress in these matters.

Overall nationalization of the land has not taken place in Britain, and Compulsory Purchase Orders (C.P.O.s) must at least be justified before a court of law, although in the event local authorities usually win any such case. While the level of compensation, or the outright purchase value, may be a bone of contention, in a procedure whereby hundreds of landowners may be affected, such as the construction of a motorway, access is often granted, and the road constructed, before the terms of sale are agreed, or the owner compensated.

1973 Compensation Act

In the USA the prospect of a new motorway, or any development that requires land from farmers, is generally welcomed by the owners, primarily because the amounts paid are very attractive, and also because they move more readily. This is true of farmers in most of the newer countries. The fact that only 1–2 per cent of the farmland is sold annually points to a period of occupation of fifty to seventy years, generally considered to be two generations. Thus the problem of the farmer's tenacity exacerbates that of the niggardly methods and scales of compensation relating to the compulsory acquisition of land by official bodies. All this delays the 'march of progress' across the face of Britain; perhaps not a bad thing, though such delays may be more costly than the construction works themselves.

It was in an effort to streamline procedures that the 'No lame ducks: stand on your own two feet' Heath Tory administration which found itself in office in June 1970 set out to modernize the Land Compensation Act. The Queen's Speech in October 1972 was a warning of the White Paper to follow, and the end-result of the Parliamentary wrangles became the Land Compensation Act 1973, passed on 23 May that year. The original proposals were for one year's net income to be paid to owner/occupiers who within three years set up business in another farm. It also proposed that such annoyances as the noise of a new motorway would attract compensation, and gave a new deal for land-grab victims.

One stumbling-block during the various stages of the Bill through the Houses of Parliament was the interpretation of the amount of security of tenure that the Agricultural Holdings Act 1948 afforded. It took persuasion in both the Commons and Lords to convince Government Ministers that although a tenant farmer was nominally on a yearly lease, this was in fact, and for all practical purposes, a life tenancy. Said Eldon Griffiths, Under-Secretary of State for the Environment, in the Commons debate: 'Although in law holding a tenancy only on a year-to-year basis, [they] were for all practical purposes life tenants. Account ought to be taken of the fact that he can expect to conduct his business for the rest of his life.' This was done by amending a section of the 1968 Act. Since the original Act was at that time twenty-five years old, it seemed that the day of dawning was slow to come, but having established that point, the terms of compensation were extended to three years' profit as against four years' rent payable under the 1968 Act. Since the original proposal for one year's net income was hardly an improvement on four years' rent, the combined pressure from their lordships and the NFU persuaded the Government to make a more equable assessment.

In the end it was tenant farmers in particular who received the greater benefit, although all farmers with land affected by official authorities for road and redevelopment schemes benefited. Home-loss payments, which also applied to farmhouses, losses for the disruption of a business and the time lag in re-establishing themselves on a new farm (even if this were possible) were allowed under the new Act, and in net terms the rates of compensation just about doubled.

At the publication of the White Paper the NFU had said:[2]

> The long awaited White Paper on compensation for the dispossessed is a distinct advance, but falls short of equity so far as agriculture is concerned.

It continued that since 1960 the NFU had been pressing that where a farm was severed by a motorway, for instance, the owner should demand by right that the whole of his land be taken. It scored a success, and this eventually became law. After the Act was passed, the CLA said:

> This long awaited Act was passed on 23 May. In many respects, it is disappointing, but it contains some useful provisions, and remedies some injustices. The price payable for land which is compulsorily acquired is still its market value. The Government has not accepted proposals for adding a percentage to take account of the compulsory sale.

The *Farmers Weekly*[3] hailed the Act in these words:

> Tenant farmers in particular are expected to benefit from a new Act of Parliament which should help all farmers with land affected by the Authorities, road and re-development schemes. The Land Compensation Act, which received Royal assent on 23 May is hailed by the Department of the Environment as marking a fresh approach to public development.

Thus the 1973 Act rationalized the procedure of land-purchase by the Authorities, and supposedly ensured a fair deal for those dispossessed and deprived of their land. However, all was not honey, and within eight months farmers being dispossessed by the Brenig Reservoir of 920 hectares to supply water for parts of North Wales and North-West England were in conflict with the Dee and Clwyd River Authority on the terms of compensation for the eight tenants involved. Unanimity was eventually reached, but only after the River Authority had accepted that statutory compensation for dispossessed tenant farmers was inadequate. They were, however, able to invoke a section of the 1968 Act which covered hardship cases at terms much higher than the statutory compensation.

[2] *British Farmer and Stockbreeder*, 28 October 1972.
[3] 29 June 1973.

The nationalization of land

'Ownership of land spells power, and power must reside with the people.'
Resolution at 1973 Labour Party Conference

'The Labour Party, it is reliably reported, is preparing to restage one of the longest-running dramas in the history of political thought ... It proposes, once more, that age-old panacea, the Nationalization of the Land.'
Peter Wilsher
'Sunday Times', 21 May 1972.

It is doubtful if anyone has seriously worked out the implications of land nationalization. State take-over of British farmland has been no more than a battle-cry for a fringe element in the Labour party for many decades. Such a policy would need a far greater 'grass-roots' support than has been in evidence in the past.

Nationalization, of many aspects of British life, has been a dogma of the Left since time immemorial, and has even embraced the public ownership of all farmland. During the 1945 50 Labour Government there was a great move forward on many fronts, and much nationalization. The National Health Service was created. Pre-War anomalies and injustices were hunted out and abolished. The old railway companies were brought together, and emerged as British Railways. Road haulage was nationalized, and British Road Services (BRS) was created. Steel was taken over by the State, and has been a shuttlecock between the Socialists and Tories over the years, being later largely denationalized and then nationalized again. The individual, and wealthy, coal-owners lost their mines (at a price) and the NCB was born. Electricity, gas and other service industries were taken into public ownership; but land, in spite of an emotional outcry for nationalization, remained virtually unscathed.

The 1945–50 Government tinkered with some aspects of farming and land-owning through the Agricultural Holdings Act 1948, described in the previous chapter, which took away certain rights of landowners, and the 1947 Agriculture Act was to become the bedrock of farming for a quarter of a century. It did not nationalize land, but it virtually nationalized farming, and was accepted by the farming community as a bulwark against the vicissitudes of unpredictable markets through its guaranteed prices system, and was thus successfully administered by both Labour and Tory Ministers of Agriculture. Nationalization of the land proved more difficult than a taking over of the coal-mines or the railways.

The fact remains that for farmland to be held by private individuals still rankles with a section of the Labour Party and those still further left. It has been a plank of policy, although the National Executive has paid it lip-service without taking any real action to further it. Yet insidiously the State has become the owner of vast areas of British soil, if one counts the land acquisitions of various Departments of Government, the nationalized industries, local councils and a multitude of other public bodies. They have all paid the original owners the proper market price, and there has been no hint of official nationalization. The rights of owners regarding the privacy, protection and possession of land have been accepted, even if the Compulsory Purchase Orders have in fact purchased land against the owner's wishes.

In spite of all this, farming production has been successfully manipulated under the 1947 Agriculture Act, and the desire to nationalize the land has remained an undercover element of official Labour policy. During the period out of office, 1951–64, the Labour Party continued with the dogma of nationalization, though as a minor part of its general policy. During that period the value of development land escalated, while in the 1970s the movement towards nationalization came from a desire for State reward, for the planning permissions had become a licence to print money. This new aspect of the nationalizing of land contrasts with the emotive thinking in the post-War period. Since all political policies rely upon grass-roots support, it is almost ironic that one salvation for the continued private ownership of British farmland has been the opening of the stately homes—an object-lesson in the trials of landowning.

For thirteen years of Tory power, 1951–64, the Socialists could provide no teeth for their demands, and even when Wilson came into power it was the profits from development land that were an obvious target. The Capital Gains Tax was introduced in 1965, and a short-lived Ministry of Land and National Resources was created, to which an assortment of existing bodies was annexed. The Forestry Commission came under this new Ministry, but was returned to the Ministry of Agriculture two years later.

The Land Commission

The Wilsonian attempt to harness the profits of development land did not stretch as far as outright nationalization. It produced the Land Commission, created in 1965, and abolished by the Tories in 1971. This left a vacuum after its decease, and the rampant profiteering of property developers certainly contributed to the downfall of the Heath administration in 1974.

Since violently escalating property values were hitting at home-ownership and the cost of building houses, it was suggested that if a reduction in the land-value could be accomplished, it would have great vote-catching potential. Thus the Land Commission.

This body was given wide powers to purchase by compulsory acquisition, to acquire, manage, dispose and generally deal in land required for development or redevelopment. Although its teeth were considerable, it was in many ways only a sharpening of the powers already vested in many local authorities. However, it became too hidebound, despite the width of its objectives.

A levy at the rate of 40 per cent of the development value—the difference between the land's value in its current use and its value after development—was proposed. This new tax, which was designed to reduce land values, had the instant result of jumping values by 40 per cent to meet it. The Land Commission Bill also proposed a system of 'Crownholds' under which the Land Commission could dispose of land on long tenure for, say, 999 years, with certain restrictions providing control of assignment and recovery of the concessions.

In introducing this measure Fred Willey, a Minister of Land and Natural Resources, said, 'It is clear we need a better means for bringing land forward for development. Most people have been disturbed about the extent of land speculation, and it is generally accepted that the community should take a share of the value.' The Shadow Minister, Boyd-Carpenter, said, 'These proposals will interfere with the flow of land for building. They will put up the price of houses, and are a substantial measure of land nationalization.' In the event, he was substantially correct. Lord Cohen, Chairman of the Alliance Building Society, welcomed the new proposals, which he thought would prevent much of the land speculation that had taken place in the past, and would slow down the astronomical rise in land prices.

The Town and Country Planning Association thought that the new proposals were workable, and added, 'It is also fair to landowners and the public.' Prime Minister Wilson himself, in a political broadcast, called the Land Proposals 'new and radical plans for dealing with land speculation and racketeering'. The NFU in its traditional non-partisan role did not oppose the principle of recouping for the community some of the value which community expenditure created in land ripe for development, and reserved its criticisms for the non-fulfilment of a pre-election pledge to improve compensation for farmers displaced by such public works as New Towns and reservoir schemes. This, it concluded, would snarl up the national building programme, and there would be delays arising from the grievances of farmers who were being displaced without fair recompense. Another plea was added: it hoped the Land Commission would recognize the need to preserve the better farmland when designating development areas.

The CLA stated that the proposed 40 per cent levy was more likely to reduce, rather than increase, the amount of land coming on to the market, and the proposals could do little or nothing to solve the immediate shortage of land for housing. The Incorporated Association of Architects and Surveyors was more blunt, and thought the proposals 'arrant rubbish'. Thus in such uneasy circumstances the Land Commission was created. Its prime target was the entrepreneurial property developers.

In every generation opportunities for creating substantial wealth have occurred, and always the first objective has been to acquire an English country estate. The new class of property-development millionaires has been no exception, and people like Clore led the field. The examples of private family fortunes being created in the twentieth century ranks with the cotton mills and the coal-mines of the nineteenth century, or even with the slave traders and entrepreneurs of the eighteenth century, who invested their loot in solid English acres. The Land Commission, and even the subsequent Land Act (1975), have been attempts to curb the acquisition of those fortunes.

Although the Land Commission was able to harness the results of gold-plated planning permissions, it did not have the power to grant those permissions; often one public authority was battling against another. The Walker Local Government Re-Organisation Act (which set up the new County and District Councils on 1 April 1974) removed from Central Government real planning autocracy by its downgrading from county to district level of the job of passing planning applications. This reduced the State's chances of cashing in on the bonanza.

Land-ownership generates envy. The private ownership of houses is politically palatable, since so many own houses and the safety of the farming community against land nationalization may similarly be contained in the large number of individual owners that have arisen as the larger estates have become fragmented. The dangers were more inherent after the 1972 Land Boom, when £2,470 per hectare was a normal valuation. Since over 90 per cent of the value of the farming industry, including the land, is still undisputedly in private hands, the redistribution of that wealth (often inherited) makes farming an obvious target. It is true that the call has been in favour of taxing private wealth—including that of farmers and landowners—out of existence, without nationalizing the land. The method though, may be one of back-door nationalization.

The Campaign for Nationalizing Land

The CNL was launched in September 1973. Its objectives were to force the Labour Party to adopt and implement a policy of nationalizing all land. This included farmland in a broad sense, with the objective of catching the property-developers and speculators.

> The five originators of the CNL were:
> Jack Brocklebank, CBE, a member of the National Executive of the Labour Party;
> Joan Maynard, stalwart and *enfant terrible* of the NUAAW, a member of the National Executive, and to become MP for Sheffield (Brightside) just over one year later;
> Nicholas Kaldor, Professor of Economics at Cambridge University, a refugee from Budapest, who had acted as a tax adviser to the Indian Government (1956) and afterwards in the same role in no less than Chile, Ceylon, Mexico, Ghana, Turkey, Iran and British Guinea. Kaldor's main claim to fame was as a special adviser to the Chancellor of the Exchequer during the first four years of the Labour Administration from 1964. He was one of the whizz-kids, along with Balogh. The latter was brought in as an economics adviser to the Cabinet in the same period, was later consultant to Prime Minister Wilson, and was created a Life Peer in 1968. They were both born in Budapest.
> Robert Meild, another Cambridge Economics Professor, who served in the RAF from 1943 to 1945, and had also worked as a tax adviser in New Delhi and Stockholm. Meild was economic adviser to HM Treasury, 1964–7.
> Oliver Stutchbury, an Alderman of the GLC and a solicitor. He took the part as National Organiser for the CNL.

This campaign was engendered by some sharp criticisms that the previous Labour policy had been ineffective on the key issue of land nationalization. Said

Stutchbury in introducing the campaign booklet: 'Labour would stand a better chance of victory at the next election if it concentrated exclusively on this issue, as it is the greatest source of power and undeserved gains, of ill-directed enterprise and undesirable social pressures, rather than nationalizing bits of the industry.' The group states unequivocally that the next Labour Government should settle for nothing less than comprehensive nationalization. It was manifest from the statement that the ambition was to nationalize ALL the land.

> We favour a policy of land reform based on a proposal which seems to have first been aired in *Socialist Commentary* in 1961, although germs of it are to be found in the discussions of the Uthwatt Committee in 1942. We recommend that legislation be introduced by the next Labour Government which would have the effect of bringing the system of land tenure in this country back to a situation similar to what it was before the Law of Property Act, 1924. WE PROPOSE THAT FROM 'THE APPOINTED DAY' ALL FREEHOLDS SHOULD BE NATIONALIZED, AND EVERYONE WHO BEFORE THE APPOINTED DAY OWNED A FREEHOLD WOULD BE DEEMED TO BE A LEASEHOLDER ON THE TERMS OF A STATUTORY LEASE FROM THE CROWN.
> WE THINK THERE SHOULD BE NO EXCEPTIONS WHATEVER TO THIS LEGISLATION, IT SHOULD EMBRACE THE LAND CURRENTLY OWNED BY PUBLIC CORPORATIONS, CHARITIES, THE NATIONAL TRUST, THE CHURCHES, AND THE QUEEN HERSELF.

This group in fact suggested a plan for takeover of all land that might, in a more sympathetic atmosphere, have been accepted. It suggested that all land should be transferred to a 99-year period lease, and that after that period had elapsed it would be in the freehold possession of the State. Transactions by normal sale could and would take place, and the run-down in land values would presumably be at 1/99th per annum. Farmers would not pay rent, and any new buildings could be financed either by themselves or by a new body which would charge interest on the capital involved. This plan, although it was adopted by the Labour Party, had the merits that the current generation of landowners could hardly object, as it would not even affect their immediate heirs.

A new body called the Public Land Management Authority (PLMA) was advocated. It would have vested in it the functions of a National Land Agency, and would manage the land during the take-over period.

It stated, 'The ultimate objective in this plan is that at the end of the 99-year period, all land would be owned and managed by the State on annual (or longer) leaseholds.' Despite its advocacy of filching land without compunction, the booklet did discuss two possible exceptions; that of private houses and of farmland owned by 'working farmers'. It rejected both.

In debating the possibility of relief to 'working farmers' it stated:

> We have no hesitation in saying that we would much rather see the idea abandoned entirely (until the Labour Party can stiffen its backbone) than have it rotted up with a 'working farmers' exception which would make the implementation of a nationalization plan a farce.

This was not taken seriously by the Labour Party when it came into office in 1974, yet it was another stage in the movement towards nationalization. In commenting upon the proposals, the NFU—somewhat inadequately—said that it would be looking into the proposals in detail, and would be issuing a statement. It then added that if the scheme were accepted it would revolutionize the whole of Britain's farming system! The CLA, however, was more realistic: 'We don't see the scheme as a serious threat, as the Labour Party has already refused similar such systems in the past.'

The Walston Plan

Exactly one week after Harold Wilson knocked Edward Heath from his Premiership on 28 February 1974, Harry Walston got up at the Third Annual Farmland Finance Conference organized by the Country Landowners Association at the elegant Russell Hotel Ballroom in Russell Square. He expounded the 'Walston Plan' for land nationalization to an audience of two hundred of the bluest-blooded landowners in the country. The speech was received in silence, and politely applauded when he sat down.

This millionaire Socialist Life Peer, with a background of Eton and King's, is a short, broad-shouldered man with a rugged John Bull figure; a rotund, countryside, farmer-like man, with a soft voice, he expounded a logical case for the take-over of agricultural land. Harry Walston, son of Sir Charles Walstein (although he does not admit his Continental ancestry in *Who's Who*; his father changed the family name to a more English-sounding Walston), after five unsuccessful attempts to get into the Commons entered the Lords as a Life Peer in 1961 during a Tory administration. His published tracts include such titles as *Land Nationalization* (for and against), 1958, and *Agriculture under Communism*, 1961. He was a member of fashionable Brooks, the MCC, and the House of Lords Yacht Club, and a junior Parliamentary Secretary at the Foreign Office from 1964–7 under Wilson, but it was as a landowner that he addressed the CLA. His 1,200 hectares in and around Cambridgeshire and his vast estates in St Lucia made him a good choice to discuss 'Inflation and how it affects agriculture'. Walston's ancestral home, Newton Hall, just south of Cambridge, is now the home of the National Seed Development Organization.

What was the plan that Walston unveiled? It was to suggest that since high land-values were taxing landowners out of existence, they should voluntarily give up their land and become yeoman farmers. He said:

> I would seriously suggest, that it would be in the long-term interests of agriculture, and not against the interests of owner-occupiers or other members of this Association, if there were to be set up some form of Land Commission which would be empowered, in competition with other buyers, to buy agricultural land throughout the country; but which would not be allowed to invest in anything other than agricultural land. IT COULD BE SAID THAT THIS IS LAND NATIONALIZATION BY THE BACK DOOR. In a manner of speaking that is true. But it would be entirely voluntary nationalization in that no landowner would be forced to sell against his will.

Walston, in suggesting that the best cure for inflation was to give up the ghost and sell the land, was insidiously following the ancient Socialist dogma of public ownership of British farmland. He saw no hope for the owner-occupier. 'The days of the owner-occupier are clearly numbered, and we are now moving towards the system, prevalent at the beginning of the century, of landlord and tenant.' To his landed audience this might not have been too revolutionary, had he not added that he saw private ownership on the decline and the company structure ascending. Land prices had at that time been considerably worrying many landowners[4], and in a devious way this Labour peer was pushing the case for land-ownership to be vested in the public.

Other men were indeed seriously thinking that some form of nationalization would be the only salvation for the continuance of family farming in the future; high land prices and crippling taxation were letting in the institutional farmland buyers, and people like John Cherrington[5] were saying:

> The present high cost of land, coupled with the incidence of Death Duties and Capital Gains Tax, will I am certain, wipe out most farming families within a generation or so. Opinions differ as to whether that would be a good or bad thing for the country as a whole. For myself, I would sooner farm a nationalised leasehold farm than none at all.

The world situation

Macro-landlordism of Tsarist Russia was largely responsible for the Red Revolution (1917) and the Marxist State that exists today. Feudal landlords, absentee landowners and an impoverished peasantry are the ripe ingredients for any insurgence, and throughout the developing nations it has been the first act after the Revolution to take away the land from the larger owners and divide it among the proletariat.

In Turkey in 1974, 543,000 peasants were given over 3·7 million hectares of land in a fifteen-year programme. This agrarian reform brought through nationalization the redistribution of vast areas of land that had been a subject of controversy during the first fifty years of the Turkish Republic. In 1945 a Land Reform Act was passed, but this only achieved the distribution of State property. The 1974 action, however, gave away over 400,000 hectares of private property which was nationalized for free distribution. It had been a long and hard battle through the Turkish Parliament, where right-wing parties dominated the scene.

In Ethiopia demonstrations marked the peaceful support for the military regime's nationalization of rural lands. Such cries were heard as 'The tiller now owns the land', and 'Down with the oppressive landlords', followed by 'The world belongs to Socialism'. This land-reform was a radical piece of legislation, devised by a military Government which struck at the centuries-old tenant-landlord relationship, whose feudal aspects had created a wide gulf in wealth

---

[4]See following chapter on the Land Market.
[5]*Financial Times*, 19 October 1973.

between the farmer and his landlord. There was no payment for land that was filched away.

In Portugal the Government has passed legislation that enables it to take over unutilized land, and either to exploit it directly under a State farming system or to hand it over to a co-operative venture. Landowners were ordered to farm their fields or to rent them to tenant farmers. Very little land was taken from its owners, but ambitious and sweeping reforms ended Portugal's feudal tenant farming system. The objective was more in the nature of exploiting the food-producing capacity of the land rather than in any Socialistic high-sounding principles.

In Ecuador agricultural reform under the 'Agricultural Reform and Colonisation Policy' has similarly been invoked to increase the farming productivity. The impetus to tidy up an untidy system started in 1964, and was designed to abolish feudal tenancy.

8 The Price of a Farm

The land market

'A cynic is a man who knows the price of everything and the value of nothing.'
Oscar Wilde

'There is nothing wrong when an acre of good English soil is worth more than an acre of linoleum, but something very wrong with the heart of England when it is worth less.'

Source unknown

The difficulties of assessing the land market are manifold; statistics are both belated and coy. Only 1–2 per cent of the farmland is sold during any year, and the variation between farms makes nonsense of average figures. Nevertheless, there have been significant trends throughout recent history, and the 1972 Land Boom was as dramatic as the Yukon Gold Rush in the 1880s.

Since land is the first basic requirement for farming, its price is a matter of considerable importance, but it is the probate value for penal taxation that has stimulated a greater, almost obsessive, interest in the subject by landowners faced with the problems of loss of their ancestral acres. The intrusion of non-farming corporate bodies using farmland as a speculative commodity has engendered much hostility.

The landed gentry have grappled their estates to them. The possession of complete villages, including the shop, post-office and pub, a donation of land for the village school, the patronage of the living and the final accolade of appointment to the Bench, has been a way of life.

Such power derived from the mystique of land-ownership, creating determination; you do not sell the land. This has been instilled into countless generations, and persists today.

Thus the subject of the land market was definitely infra dig. A closed subject of conversation, and even among the yeomen farmers the loyal adherence to the retention of the farm goes as far as disdaining the man who sells a field. Better to plunge into debt, to borrow, or cut down on private expenditure, but never to diminish by a field the land which is the foundation of the family living.

Standards have, however, fallen. The shooting has been let to syndicates of city gents; the hounds have gone; the big house has been pulled down, and the in-filling plots in the village street sold for new housing—all in an effort to retain the greater area of the main estate and its farms. The ownership of land has changed hands more rapidly in this century than ever before, but still only a minuscule amount is sold annually. Even this figure has shown a dramatic downturn in the 1970s.

Sales of agricultural land in England
and Wales of 4 hectares and over

Hectares sold in five-year periods	
1950–4	1,596 (000s)
1955–9	1,463
1960–4	1,460
1965–9	1,144
1970–4	908

Superimposed on these figures, the ten-year averages further illustrate the reducing number of hectares sold annually.

1950s	301,600 hectares per annum
1960s	259,200 hectares per annum
1970s	181,600 hectares per annum

The last figure is calculated from the first five years of the decade. Thus during the 1950s and 1960s approximately 2 per cent of the 16 million hectares of farmland in England and Wales was sold annually, but in the 1970s only 1·5 per cent appears to be changing hands. The average length of tenure has therefore risen from fifty years per family to sixty-six years.

The price of farmland has never been used as a topic of conversation. The larger owner is more concerned with the ability of his tenants to pay their rent, and the shooting prospects, while the owner-occupier farmer is more interested in the welfare of his animals, and the progress of his crops. Not only was the subject of little interest because there was no intention of cashing in on the capital values, but because the business of farming or estate management is a much more absorbing way of life. It still takes a generation to become fully knowledgeable about the reactions of a farm to differing seasons. It takes about a hundred years in the same village to lose the stigma of 'newcomer'. The countryside still loves a gentleman, and under the system of squirearchy will disdain the upstart for the first couple of generations. Even in modern trade-unionist-dominated Britain, the countryside rules and codes have persisted with a remarkable tenacity.

It is not uncommon to hear that the present squire ONLY came here in 1910, but the REAL squires were here for five hundred years before that. One Devonian family sadly view their exile from East Anglia (which they left around 1820), since they have hardly been accepted in their new domicile, although six generations have now lived and died in the same house. On another estate in Suffolk (Sotterley Hall) there have been only three families in occupation since

William the Conqueror. The first lasted until about 1650, followed by a short-lived family who were there for a hundred years, while the present owners (the Barne family) have been in residence for nearly 250 years. A descendant from the original family (the Saturdays), who left over three hundred years ago, still comes over from the States to visit her ancestral family home.

This stoic immobility in the farming world is a counter-balance in a period when there is less significance in 'having roots', and when people are becoming more itinerant than ever before. Yet, surprisingly, the stability of the rural population has not led to sterility.

Until the 1970s it was unusual to find an article in the farming press on the subject of land values. The price of farmland, and any trends that it might have taken, was completely a non-event. There had certainly been trends, which in essence amounted to a regular appreciation at a steady rate that was making the acquisition of farmland a better investment than the Stock Exchange, but even with the option of a free house, some shooting and the joys of country living, it was not considered a 'blue chip' type of investment. The annual return from the rent, or even direct participation in the farming through a firm of Land Management Agents specializing in these things, would return to the investor a derisory 2 per cent, and even by direct farming the annual return has never compared with other forms of investment. The steady capital appreciation has far outnumbered that to be gained from the FT Index, although some individual shares may have streaked ahead of solid farmland.

Until 1965 the capital appreciation on farmland was untaxed, but the same rules applied to shares, and the purchase of farmland often followed the acquiring of fortune in a very different business arena. Intrusions into the market by outsiders bent on purchasing farms were, therefore, on a modest scale that kept pace with the number of farms being offered by the estate agents. The steady increase in value, of about 9 per cent per annum, could be equated to an inflation rate during the 1960s starting at 3 per cent and rising gradually to 6 per cent. An FT Index which hardly moved at all made the ownership of a farm a much more solid guarantee of security and capital appreciation, with the concomitant problem that its disposal or fragmentation was ten times more difficult than the telephone call required to sell shares.

In 1960 the FT Index stood at 309, and in 1970 at 349; adjusted for the changing value of the £, it had actually fallen from 130 to 100. On the same basis of calculation, allowing for a falling £, the value of farms in 1960 was indexed at 122, and by 1970 had risen to 177. A concurrent exercise in the valuation of established house properties in the south and east of England reveals that a figure of 112 in 1960 becomes 170 ten years later. Private houses appreciated by 58 points and farms by 55, which were advances in real money terms, having adjusted for the changing value of sterling.

The problems of valuation

In a logical world the value of farmland should bear some relationship at least to the potential earning capacity of the farm as a business. The factors determining farm profitability can be divided between the amount of arable land, the grassland (if of a permanent unploughable character such as hills, river meadows or marsh grazing), and lastly the stock-carrying capacity and general degree of modernization of the farm buildings. The number and condition of workers' cottages, plus the degree of modernization in the farmhouse itself, are further items.

A farm in a grassland county with a dairying potential should have an adequately modernized milking parlour. A mixed farm could have an up-to-date piggery or poultry unit as an appendage to sustain the income level, and an arable farm in the eastern counties would need a grain store. Some farm buildings are complementary to the cropping, including such innovations as concrete aprons now found in field gateways, and used for tipping sugar beet prior to delivery to the factory. Other buildings can be independent of the land itself, such as a pig enterprise that is wholly unrelated to the amount of land, but which may utilize straw and return the muck, although many such enterprises are now operated without either. The addition and condition of such appendages obviously affects the potential earning capacity of the farm, although such is the intricate nature of the business that the guiding hand of the farmer himself can produce widely varying results in the annual balance-sheet.

All these factors do have some bearing upon the price, but since the auctioneer's dictum of value is what one man can persuade another to give him for it, the forces that determine values are more complex than the mere potential profitability of the farm as a property. The swings in farmland prices have to some small degree followed farming fortunes, but not entirely. Profitability is not the paramount factor, and the real profits of a farming business bear little relation to the capital investment involved when the land itself is taken into account. In working out profitability levels as a percentage on the capital involved farmers do not take the land into consideration, but work on the basis of 'tenant's capital', being the amount invested in running the business, even if they are additionally the owner of the farm.

The scarcity value and the slow turnover in land illustrates that only 10 per cent of the land has been purchased within any previous five-year period (2 per cent p.a.) Thus 90 per cent of farmland is sitting at an under-priced valuation, or interest/mortgage charge to its owner. Since 40 per cent of the farmland is tenanted, it must be assumed that this land has been in the same ownership for a long period. It would be modest to place a 'guesstimate' of a hundred years on this, when there are many large estates that have not changed hands for over five hundred years. The Church, for instance, has held certain farms continuously for over a thousand years.

If the value is the price another man will pay, then from 1950 onwards the first question a valuer would ask has been 'Who are the neighbours?', thus spotlighting the fact that the annexation and absorption of holdings has been a constant factor as farmers have amalgamated neighbouring farms in the process of rationalizing and restructuring the basis of British agriculture. This has been an important factor in determining and sustaining land prices, when farmers have been able to justify erstwhile exorbitant prices by 'equalizing' their overall capital commitment with a home farm (normally much larger) which had been purchased at a very much lower figure some years earlier. Thus land values have received this added bonus during the past two decades, with the result that general levels have appeared over-priced in relation to the profitability to be derived from farming the land.

The main criterion used by the Ministry of Agriculture in its categorization of farmland sales is the designation by size groupings. This has shown wide discrepancies in varying size brackets. The effects of the Agricultural Holdings Act 1948[1] have normally been a 20–40 per cent drop from vacant-possession price. Other classification by the Ministry of Agriculture subdivides land only, against complete farms.

In the half-year ending 31 March 1971 there was a variation of 30 per cent between vacant-possession land and that which was tenanted. The cash-differentiation amounted to £155 per hectare (VP £505; T. £350). By September 1974 the changed price levels made a variation of slightly under 17 per cent or £272 per hectare (VP £1,606; T. £1,334). During the Land Boom the gap was wider, at £339 per hectare, although even these average figures disguise the situation in the bracket of farm size 60–120 hectares, where there was a variation of £260, or a 40 per cent downgrading in the price of tenanted farms.

As vacant-possession prices have fluctuated in the peaks and troughs of national prosperity, bank-interest levels and taxation problems, the tenanted farms have shown a steadier graph, demonstrating a more solid and inflexible return engendered by rent controls. Many rents have been stabilized, and only started to rise on a very steady plane. While farmland prices have shown drops at three periods since 1945, rents have never reduced, and the investment equivalent has given a better equation to the capital involved.

Farm price figures: three methods

In a nation, and in an industry, dedicated to collecting and absorbing statistical information (some of which may be of doubtful relevance), it is amazing how few accurate, up-to-date figures have been available to illustrate current or changing land values. If so little land is actually sold, then any potential buyer will create his own value, to be determined by his available financial resources, the farming potential, or even his passionate and emotional desire to buy that specific farm. But for purposes of assessing farmland values for Capital Gains Tax (the appreciation between the April 1965 price and the actual selling price at a latter date), Death Duties, Estate Duty and now Capital Transfer Tax accurate and meaningful figures are vital to both the Treasury-nominated Probate Valuers and to the heirs with the tax bill to pay.

[1] See chapter on Land Laws, at p. 111.

The traditional 'change-over' date for farms was at Michaelmas Day (29 September or 11 October in some counties), with a minority at Lady Day (25 March). Thus the majority of farm sales took place in the heady summer months, with vacant possession in the early autumn. This pattern has changed to a more flexible timetable, and the Ministry Returns now show only a marginal majority in the six-monthly period ending in September. Land sales, therefore, are now less dependent upon the traditional pattern which was geared to the cropping cycle. Sophisticated valuation methods can assess inputs and field performance to allow a change-over at any time of the year, although in reality growing crops have no monetary value until harvested.

The problems attendant upon gathering sale statistics are because many sales are confidential, and by 'private treaty'. Public auctions cannot hide the facts, but private sales have to be disclosed to the Inland Revenue for purposes of levying Stamp Duty, which is on a graduated scale allied to the sum involved. Further complications are added inasmuch as the date of completion of the transaction (and therefore of notification to the Inland Revenue), may be many months after the initial agreement by purchaser and vendor.

There are four well-publicized sources of collection for the assessment of the ever-changing farmland market in the UK. They are:

Oxford University	Six-monthly figures published two months later
Ministry of Agriculture	Quarterly figures published ten weeks later
Country Landowners Association	Quarterly figures published six weeks later
Farmland Market	Figures published twice a year

The oldest of these publications is that of the University of Oxford's Institute of Agricultural Economics, which under the direction of Allen Maunder has collated and analysed the already published individual sales recorded in the *Estates Gazette*. This is authoritative, but considerably restricted to only those sales which auctioneers wish to submit as evidence of their own salesmanship. When the Ministry shed its cloak of reticence in 1970 it revealed, in comparative terms, that the Oxford figures were 30 per cent above the true average levels, but for any scholarly examination of the trends in farmland prices prior to 1970 the Oxford figures form a useful, if slightly suspect, attempt at an analytical survey.

Although the Ministry, like the Inland Revenue, was aware of the figures, it issued only four 'Technical Reports', compiled by its Lands Arm prior to 1970. In September 1971 it first commenced regular publication of farmland sales for England and Wales, Scotland and Northern Ireland. The first issue recorded information covering the period October 1970 to March 1971, making some of the transactions eleven months old before they became available. Realizing that the CLA was beating it to the deadline, in September 1974 the Ministry embarked upon the publication of a quarterly analysis, getting its figures out within ten weeks of the closing date.

Colin Clarke[2] wrote in 1973:

> The Inland Revenue are now publishing information on average prices of farms sold with vacant possession—How the Government resisted previous demands for the publication of such useful and harmless information for 60 years, or more, is one of the marvels of bureaucracy.

Collated and collected, but still not comprehensive, is the net result of these 'useful and harmless' figures. They still exclude seven categories of farmland transactions:

1 Where there are less than five transactions in a particular category, these are excluded to preserve the confidentiality and confuse the identity of individual sales.
2 Excluded is all sales of agricultural land under ten acres (four hectares).
3 Excludes sales of farmland sold for non-agricultural purposes; i.e. land for development and/or mineral workings.
4 Excludes all gifts and inheritances.
5 Excludes compulsory purchases by Local Authorities, Government Department or other Statutory Bodies.
6 Excludes commercial woodland sold as a complete entity. Included is farmland sold for afforestation.
7 Excludes legal fees and stamp duty.

The CLA's involvement in a regular collection and publication of land values commenced in November 1972. Why this landowners' trade union had not done this earlier remains a mystery. The origin of the 1972 commencement was the embarrassment that had been caused by the Land Boom during that heady summer, with its headline-hitting farmland sales at well over £2,470 per hectare. It was a rearguard attempt to disprove the headlines, and to convince those that needed convincing that these particular sales were isolated examples, but that the true value of agricultural land was well below such astronomical figures. The interests of the CLA's members could best be served by talking the price of land down, not up. This aspect of farmers' reaction is dealt with in the later sub-section on the 1972 Land Boom.

The method of collection of these statistics was from voluntary and unquoted sources. These were in fact certain leading companies of chartered surveyors and auctioneers. It was of necessity a token sample. CLA president Charles Graham said of the first issue that it covered only 25 per cent of the total sales in the quarterly period. This Survey was unique inasmuch as it recorded for the first time the percentage of farmland that was being bought by the much-despised 'Institutions'. Throughout the time since it was instituted, the CLA Survey has

---

[2] *The Value of Agricultural Land* (Pergamon Press, 1975). Colin Clarke was Director of the Agricultural Economics Institute at Oxford for sixteen years, 1953–69, when he moved to Monash University, Melbourne. He was unsuccessful Labour Parliamentary candidate three times: North Dorset, 1929; Wavertree (Liverpool) 1931; and South Norfolk, 1935.

gained in the width of its sample by a greater participation from more informants, and has added to the prestige of the CLA. It covers quarterly periods, and is available in time to be relevant, usually within six weeks from the closing date of the period.

Towards 1972

During the pre-War period of national depression many farms became unoccupied, farming was at a subsistence level and the value of land was below that obtaining during the 1860s 'Golden Era'. Poor land could be bought with full unfettered freehold title at prices down to £12 per hectare in the pre-1939 period, and good farms in arable counties at £62 per hectare. As in the opening up of the virgin prairies of Canada, land in the UK was almost given away, to anyone who would accept the challenge of farming it.

The battle for food during the War years put an urgent emphasis upon farming, and injected healthy profit levels. The aftermath saw the 1947 Agriculture Act, which put a bottom in the market, with the result that thirty years of stable prosperity have ensued. Inflation was not a major factor until the 1970s, and the farmers' borrowing rates for capital were related to the old bank rate (now base rate), which was 2 per cent in 1950, 5 per cent in 1960 and $7\frac{1}{2}$ per cent in 1970. A steady and unspectacular rise, with a few mild flutters along the path. But more dramatic events were around the corner.

The results of national and international moderation were reflected in a steady, if inexorable, rise in land values. Vacant-possession farms in the range 2-120 hectares were £235 per hectare in 1950, £326 in 1960 and £674 in 1970, although they had soared to £745 in 1969.

There have been three periods of downward trends in farmland values since 1945. They went from £247 per hectare in 1955 to £231 per hectare two years later, but bounced back to £258 per hectare in 1958 (FT Ordinary Share Index went down from 149 in 1955 to 138 in the following year, but recovered to 145 in 1957). Land prices dropped again in 1970 at the end of six years of Labour administration and three years of unfavourable seasons. The FT Index also dropped from 406 in 1969 to 359 in 1970, as general confidence levels evaporated. The relationship between the Stock Exchange and farmland is not always clear, and Bidwell & Sons, Chartered Surveyors and Land Agents of Cambridge and London, in their *Annual Review* at the end of 1964 said, 'We have found in the past that lack of confidence on the Stock Exchange invariably leads to increased activity in the property market, as the value of land as a commodity is more and more appreciated.' The 1970 drop manifested itself in all farm sizes except the 20–40 hectare group, which invariably represents a gentleman's residence more than any real working farm, the exception being when these were swallowed up by a rich neighbouring farmer. The *Estates Gazette* recorded a drop of £114 per hectare from £746, and the *Farmer and Stockbreeder* a drop of £81.50 from

£741. Mathematical variations apart, it was self-evident that something was wrong with the backbone of England.

Said Maunder, of Oxford, 'Everybody has been expecting a fall in prices for some time. The reason it has not occurred before may be that the effects of Capital Gains Tax have only recently been appreciated. Land is no longer such an attractive investment.'

In the *Daily Mail*, farming editor John Winter wrote:

> Land prices are one of the barometers of the economic health of farming, and the sharp drop is a clear sign that the industry has been squeezed beyond the point where it can offset rising costs by increased efficiency.

The first nine months of 1970 had recorded auction prices 15 per cent below the previous year, and while the CLA disdained to comment upon the subject at all, the NFU latched on to it as another example of the poverty of the farming industry.

> What more is needed to confirm something we all know, that farm income has been at a most unsatisfactory level for several years?

The third period of hiccoughs in the upward trend occurred in 1974, again with a Labour administration, again after a bad season, but forced more understandably by the general unsatisfactory economic state of the nation, rampant inflation, a diving Sharing Index, unheard-of high interest rates, the withdrawal of tax benefits on land, the imposition of new taxes, the cut-back in housing land requirements, the taxing away of those benefits, the rapid retreat of the institutional farmland buyers, the more violent price cycles emanating under the EEC Common Agricultural Policy, and quite simply because it had gone up too much too quickly during the Land Boom.

The highest-recorded figure for farms with vacant possession to be found in the CLA Reports was £2,127 per hectare for the quarter ending July 1973. The equivalent period one year later found a figure of £1,657, a drop of nearly 25 per cent.

The bubble had burst.

Having studied the rare periods of falling values, it is worth looking at the more general trend of rising land prices. It is noticeable that after each depression the upward swing has been reactivated, and one of the reasons given for the 1972 Boom was that as prices had remained static for almost five years, it was an automatic if dramatic readjustment process. In explaining this theory Dennis Britton[3] stated that land values had lagged behind the increase in farm income for nearly twenty years.

[3] Professor Denis K. Britton of Wye College, author of the HGCA sponsored book, *Cereals in the UK*, speaking at a Conference on 'Investment in Rural Land' sponsored by city insurance and investment company Matthews Wrightson, parent company of Fountain Farming, Ltd. Date: 23 November, 1972, when the Boom was in full swing.

Before the war, there was a relationship of 15 to one between land values—vacant possession land values—per acre, and the annual net income from farming per acre. The price was roughly £30 an acre, and the annual net income for a farmer farming his land was about £2 an acre.

The ratio was 15 to one before the war. During the 1950s it fell back to about 7 to one, but by 1964 was back on a pre-war relationship of 15 to one. It held at about that ratio until this year, (1972) when it has jumped to about 25 to 30 to one, the figures being about £600 an acre, and something between £20 and £24 an acre net income from farming.

So the factor of farming profitability was being used as a yardstick to measure and explain the changes in farm values. It still takes a strong imagination to understand the relation of the two factors.

Land has rarely, if ever, been an exact calculation that could link profitability to capital costs and involvement. The value of the house, free shooting, tax perks and the inexplicable and incalculable cash value that is allied to land-ownership, have always added to freehold land values. These values have roughly doubled every ten years since 1945, when £123.50 a hectare was a good price. Three decades should have shown a figure of £988 per hectare; in fact, this figure was reached by 1972, three years before the end of the third decade, but the approximation remains broadly correct. Expressed in another way, land has seen a steady 9 per cent per annum increase over the last twenty years at least.

Since so little land is sold annually, it has small effect upon farmers' ability to make use of the interest on the capital from annual farming profits, and bears no relationship to the efforts of the NFU to press for higher prices. Land values represent an area of only academic interest to farmers, except where the question of acquiring neighbouring farmsteads has arisen. The other field of interest is in the taxation liability that a high land price engenders.

When farmers saw the first land sold at £247 per hectare they sadly shook their heads at the entrepreneurial folly of the newcomer. The same applied as other numerical milestones were reached, and yet side by side with the rise of farmland was the inexorable rise in house-building land. A headline in 1970 revealed that land for private house-building had doubled in the previous seven years. Since the land supply in Britain is inelastic, the spiralling price of building land would eventually have dramatic effects upon farms, although there are continual worries that the new levels out-price genuine farmers, or even genuine farming methods.

In October 1972 the *Farmers Weekly* sought to discover if land at £988 a hectare (£400 an acre) made any economic sense. After carefully elucidating four possible farming systems, one of which showed an annual profit of less than £1,000, they came to the conclusion that, 'However you do the sums there does not seem to be much hope of making a start on 200 acres unless you have at least £40,000, and it would be better to have £60,000.' Earlier that year, in January 1972, the President of the Midland Agricultural Valuers Association, J. B. Mumford, said that the best land in Britain *could* rise to £1,235 per hectare when we joined the EEC. Horrified and incredulous hands were raised, but he concluded that he did not see a meteoric rise.

Before that year was over the average price of £827 per hectare had doubled, and a hitherto unknown estate in Hampshire had become a farmhousehold name, being sold at a figure 400 per cent higher than twelve months previously.

The land boom

'The past decade has seen fashion in investment dodge from mining shares, to furniture, to oil companies, to silver, to office property, to pictures. Now it happens to be land.'
Alistair MacGregor
'Farmers Weekly', 6 October 1972.

'The desire to own a bit of England seems to be a prime factor for some of today's inflation-minded buyers, because the present high prices make no farming sense—except that everybody is doing it.'
John Cherrington
'The Financial Times', 11 October 1972.

As 1972 dawned Heath was safely ensconced in Downing Street, Barber was at the Treasury, reflating a sagging British economy by wild and expansionist measures in a desperate gamble.

Two jolly farmers, Prior and Stodart, made up the Tories' team at the Ministry of Agriculture. It hadn't been an easy ride for Prior during his first eighteen months as a Cabinet Minister, but he had instituted many changes on the agropolitical scene; the negotiations with the EEC had been completed, and the date of accession (January 1973) had been agreed. Interest rates had fallen sharply from 8 per cent in 1970 to 4½ per cent, which was the cheapest money for ten years. Industry was investing hard, and even if the crash of Rolls-Royce (1971) had put a dent in the Tories' 'no help for lame ducks' policy, the economy was bursting to expand. Prior's slogan had been 'Get your return from the market,' as he instituted a new policy persuading farmers to turn their backs on twenty-five years of subsidies in order to line up the UK farm policy with Europe's Common Agricultural Policy.

The Barber reflationary policies had created an aura of confidence, even if production from British industry did not match the optimism. On the surface, however, things looked good in January 1972. It was to be two years before the three-day working week became a feature of life, as the confrontation with the striking miners finally precipitated the premature general election which toppled Heath from power, and eventually from the leadership of the Tory Party. Although the miners' confrontation dictated the timing of the 1974 General Election, a contributory factor in the overthrow of the Tories was the antics of the land speculators, who had made vast fortunes overnight from development activities. It is this land escalation that concerns us here, and its effects upon the value of farms.

There was to be an unprecedented farmland boom, as dramatic as it was unforeseen. This last point was emphasized by leading land surveyor Peter Trumper, speaking at a Conference in 1973, when he said:

> As every sailor knows, there are always signs before a storm . . . it is interesting, that the 1972 Boom in land prices came as a surprise to almost, if not absolutely, everybody. Certainly I do not think I have met, or heard of, anyone who foresaw it, even among the brilliant takeover tycoons.

Land prices in the previous year had jumped by 20 per cent within the largest section of farm sizes (20–120 hectares). The average price per hectare for 1971 was £684, a rise of £111 from 1970, but it only retrieved the lost ground and brought prices back to 1969 levels. There were, however, signs in late 1971 that the rate of increase was speeding up.

Other factors were at work. During 1971 the price of country cottages almost doubled, as an affluent working population fled from their surburban environment to the countryside. The oil crisis had not yet erupted, and neither petrol nor other costs had caught up with income. Inflation was running at 7 per cent, which although considered high enough, was minuscule in comparison with the rate two years later. During 1971 the value of land with planning permission, especially in the south-east, doubled. Farmland sales were dropping rapidly, and in 1970–72 the average that changed hands was only 58 per cent of that sold fifteen years earlier. It amounted to a decrease of 6½ per cent per annum compound.

It is worth while pausing to consider why a farm comes on the market, with 70 per cent of farmers today the sons of farmers, and presumably farming their father's land, whether it be owned or tenanted. A childless or sonless farmer might sell his farm on retirement, but not before, and farming bankruptcies are rare. Few farmers ever give up their farms and/or change their occupation during their working lives. It follows, then, that the majority of farms sold on the market are forced there by taxation or the death of the owners; and this applies more to the larger land-owners with low rent-rolls, and no pictures left to cash. High land prices can precipitate retirement, and low ones can encourage an elderly farmer (without heirs) to hang on for another year, but essentially farmers are not in the game for quick capital gains, and farms are never sold unless there are dire and urgent pressures to force them on to the market.

There is, then, little scope for fluctuation in the amount of land coming on to the market annually, and the steady reduction in the annual area sold could be attributed to the higher level of prosperity, which may have given some opportunity to accrue the necessary cash to meet the final taxation bills. The cash that was coming into farmers' pockets from the windfall of development money from the new housing and industrial boom meant that farmers were selling parcels of land and pocketing the cash. Finally, the last factor contributing towards the greater opportunity for landowners must have been their ability to avoid the taxation liability (at that time called Estate Duty), which legally incorporated a 45 per cent rebate on all agricultural land.

Unrealized also was the fact that although Capital Gains Tax had been introduced in 1965, it included a hitherto innocuous clause which allowed farmers relief from tax liability if within twelve months the money was reinvested into the same type of business asset as the one with which they had parted. This was labelled the 'roll-over' provision, and was the ploy that would play a great part in the scramble to reinvest development cash in new land: the escalating funds that were flowing into farmers' pockets were meeting a lower level of available land: a classic situation, that heralded some dramatic upswing in prices. At that time farmers were receiving up to £49,000 per hectare for new housing land, and although much of this was in small parcels for village development, there were enough large-scale farmland sales on the periphery of towns and cities to create many millionaires among erstwhile hard-pressed farmers.

What, then, were the signs? In late 1971 the Hampton Court Estate in Herefordshire was sold. It consisted of 800 hectares, half of which was let to tenants. It had an unmodernized mansion house, and the tenanted land placed a considerable restriction upon the investment return. It was not the most attractive of properties; the house was a liability, and the area not the most popular. Nevertheless, the prospective buyers flooded in, even by private helicopter, and some well-known millionaires were among them. Within four weeks a private treaty sale had been agreed at a price of £790 per hectare. Expert valuers had put the price at no more than £716, and valuers when selling are optimists anyway!

As the spring of 1972 developed it was becoming apparent that land was hardening. Very soon it began to rise violently to hitherto astronomical heights. In May Hundridge Manor Estate of 640 hectares in Buckinghamshire made £1,976 per hectare, a total figure of over £1·2 million, and almost £800,000 more than it would have fetched just six months earlier.

Newsells Park Estate, a fine 974-hectare property at Barkway, near Royston, Hertfordshire, and only a short ride from Piccadilly Circus, came up for auction on 8 June 1972. It had been owned by Captain Sir Humphrey de Trafford, the Jockey Club Chief Steward, and a relative of the Queen. At auction it fetched £2,425,000, a price of almost £2,470 per hectare, but a few weeks later the normal 10 per cent deposit had not been paid, and the legal contracts had not been exchanged. It was all very well watching these high prices, and many outsiders wondered where such vast sums of money were coming from. Rumour and worried looks were adding to the speculation over land prices, and in particular to this Hertfordshire estate.

Newsells Park had been bought at the auction sale by a 31-year old solicitor, acting on behalf of a distant relative, a Mr Simon Wilkinson-Fairfax. The young solicitor's name was Richard Scholes, himself a whiz-kid tycoon, who lived in a mansion on Holme Island in Morecambe Bay. He was a bachelor with two Rolls-Royces, and had risen from a working-class home. It was not known at the time that he only had £82 in his business account, when he had bid £2.4 million.

Scholes vacillated over the payment of the deposit, and various affidavits were made by Sir Humphrey's nephew, Mr Dermot de Trafford, in a High Court action. Eventually the sale was declared null and void, and on 8 May 1975, just one month short of three years after his 'fake' bid, Scholes was sentenced to four years' imprisonment at St Albans Crown Court. His ambitions to become a millionaire squire lay in ruins, but it all symbolized the fever that was gripping many real millionaires and other hard-headed business-men, who a year before would not have bought land at £741 per hectare.

In June also the *Farmers Weekly* had searched around for some scapegoats, or even for logical reasons for rising land prices. It examined the proposed entry into the Common Market, death duty concessions, and the role of the financial institutions as farmland buyers. In the end it blamed farmers themselves.

> It is nice to blame outside influences for our troubles, but it seems that the high price of farms is caused mainly by farmers bidding against each other—and that they are now prepared to bid £400 an acre for a good 100 acre dairy farm with a pleasant house.

Two items are noticeable from that quotation; firstly that the rise was already being labelled as a 'trouble', and that the general consensus of opinion was that this price, £1,235 per hectare, was uneconomic, if not idiotic. The *Farmers Weekly* concluded its articles:

> Where we go from here is anybody's guess, but with present values in Britain above those for similar properties in France, it is LIKELY THAT FOR THE TIME BEING PRICES WILL STABILIZE.

It could not have been more wrong in the final conjecture, but it was the popular view within the farming community, and was the cause of much rancour in the bitter aftermath.

Meanwhile property and development values were still soaring; four-fifths of a hectare eleven kilometres from Cardiff made £65,000, and the same price was paid for a similar area at Holt in Norfolk. Three hectares at Crowborough in Sussex made £½ million, and in Cheshire building land was now making over £74,000 per hectare. Country cottages, country houses, urban houses on new estates, office blocks in city centres, were all doubling up overnight. Modern houses built and sold in 1970 for £4,000 were now fetching £10,000 and more. The message of a farmland boom was certainly getting home to the farming community, and the pundits were out in force, avidly seeking reasons for this inexplicable event.

The *Farmers Weekly* again[4] weighed in that the soil was looking safer than the City, and the Editor wrote cynically:

> I wonder if we are going to see idle acres in the countryside appreciating for their owners like the empty office blocks in London—too dear to farm, and too precious to part with.

The *British Farmer and Stockbreeder* set out to prove that it was all the fault of

[4] 14 July 1972.

the Frenchmen who were trying to buy up our farms. Peter Clery[5] said that the increase was taking place partly as a result of the realization by investors that urban property had been too high for comfort. John Cherrington in the same issue said that the rich investors had just realized that agricultural land had shown a fifteen-year consistent capital growth, only to be compared with building land, and he deduced that land was a better investment than gold.

> Rich investors as a class are not particularly clever men. They usually follow trends, and the trend is towards something safe with a good record and no labour troubles. Land fills the bill rather better than gold because it carries the added bonus of Estate Duty Relief.

Although by July the pattern for the year had already been set, there were some of the most dramatic events still in the future. In August, South Farm, at Withcall in Lincolnshire, a farm with a tenant protected for life, and subject only to triennial rent reviews (which could be sent to arbitration in a case of disagreement), made £1,730 per hectare. It was the highest-ever tenanted farm sale, and the purchaser finished up with a net return of less than 1 per cent. The same month Sandhurst Farms, 470 hectares near Gloucester, made £2,048 per hectare with vacant possession, and 350 people attended the auction; many, no doubt, caught up with the fever of a Land Boom. Freehold prices were high, and the return either from rent, or from direct participation in the farming, could never hope to show anything like a reasonable return. The investors were gambling upon the capital appreciation inherent in previous land-price trends; and they had got caught up in a fever.

Brown Candover

'We chose to wind down to Brown Candover ... the country where the soil is stiff loam upon chalk is never bad for corn. Not rich, never poor.'
William Cobbett, 1822.

The Land Agents firm Strutt & Parker received instructions in 1972 to sell the 944-hectare Brown Candover Estate, near Alresford, in Hampshire, four kilometres south of Basingstoke and hard by the new M3 Motorway. As a name it was unknown; in fact until 1932 it had been part of the more famous Grange Estate of 3,290 hectares, which was dismembered at that time. Its greatest claim to fame lay more in its sport than in farming. In 1929–31 the average bag of partridges was 4,282 birds, and none were reared artificially. The annual pheasant bag averaged over 5,000. 1932 was a year of depression, and the Grange Estate was fragmented to facilitate its sale. Major C. J. P. Ball, a native of the Isle of Wight, who wanted a home in Hampshire, bought 960 hectares known as the Brown Candover Estate. For over thirty years, and later under Trustees, a new farming policy evolved to match the changing times.

[5] Farming Representative, National Westminster Bank, writing in the *British Farmer and Stockbreeder*, 8 July 1972.

Strutt & Parker, then, were able to offer an intact estate virtually within its own ring fence, with vacant possession of the whole, a seventeenth-century manor-house, a period farmhouse, 52 hectares of sporting woodlands and 30 cottages. It was an attractive property by any standards, and large enough to provide a complete landed estate in the best English tradition. Good shooting, a fair principal house, and what would have been more important in bygone days, close to the Court at St James—represented today by an adjacent motorway and near-by Heathrow Airport.

The auction was fixed for Thursday, 5 October 1972, with the usual proviso 'Unless previously sold'. There was little hope of a private buyer gaining acceptance of any bid, however wild, in the current euphoria of escalating prices. Valuers were weekly revaluing their own assessments. The Longwood Estate, 1,600 hectares of similar land type, and also in Hampshire, had been sold recently for £1,482 per hectare to property tycoon Ronald Lyon, and parts of Longwood were tenanted.

The Grosvenor Hotel at Stockbridge was the venue for the Brown Candover Sale, and in a holiday atmosphere George Judd, a senior partner of Strutt & Parker, mounted the rostrum to extol the virtues of the property for auction that day. It included the 944 hectares, and the house and cottages (the pedigree Friesian herd, a 250-sow unit and a flock of 750 ewes were taken over subsequently by valuation). Judd's tall, lean figure and his cultured voice dominated the room as he called for an opening bid. 'Shall we start at two million pounds, ladies and gentlemen?' he asked mildly. The hundred-strong onlookers were only there out of curiosity, a group of serious, dark-suited men sat near the front, and Judd's bland expression and well-pronounced vowels displayed an unemotional attitude.

Quickly the bidding went up at £100,000 per nod; getting close to £3 million the pace slackened, and one bidder, tycoon Lyon, dropped out. After a slight hesitancy, the figure cleared the £3 million hurdle, and a few minutes later Judd's hammer came down on the rostrum.

There it was. Brown Candover had been sold for £3·2 million. 'It's bloody ridiculous,' was one overheard comment as the successful buyer, Joseph Reiss, unobtrusively made his way to the rostrum. Reiss, who described himself as an exporter, would not disclose if he had bought Brown Candover for himself or as an agent for another person. The deposit cheque, itself a sum of £320,000, was quickly written, and Reiss slipped into his red Aston Martin and sped away with the single statement 'I'm terribly sorry—no comment.'

The realized figure was quickly analysed, and calculated at an overall £3,389 per hectare; by excluding the woodland it came out at £3,705 for the farmland. The story was, however, not yet over. Within a month it was announced that Brown Candover had been sold again; this time the unsuccessful bidder, Ronald Lyon, had negotiated a private price of £3,458 per hectare, leaving the original purchaser a cool £108,000 profit. The whole episode added further fuel to the inflationary land spiral by the speed and manner of the second deal.

Lyon was the son of an Essex poultry-packer, and imbued with a driving ambition, he had started his money-making ventures while still at school. At the age of fifteen he was making and installing loudspeaker equipment for local dances and vicarage fetes around the Essex villages. Unable to drive himself because of his age, he nevertheless purchased an old Ford 8 for £16 and hired a local lad of nineteen as his chauffeur to drive him around until he could obtain his own licence.

When he was sixteen he switched to making garden sheds, then to portable buildings, and then to steel buildings. There were plenty of old Nissen huts redundant after the War had passed by, and he rapidly built up his fortune from these and other Army surplus. Progressing, by 1952 he was rubbing shoulders with developers, and realized that the big money lay, not in the buildings, but in developing the land. He soon made his first million. Lyon attracted publicity as an entrepreneurial property-developer, and by the extravaganza of himself and his wife. In 1967, when the breathalyser tests were introduced, he held his annual Christmas cocktail party, and hired a fleet of fifty Daimlers—which cost him £400—to get his guests home afterwards. A year later he paid £7,500 with 47 other tycoons to dine at No. 10 Downing Street to raise funds for the United Nations Association. A broken marriage and numerous girl-friends had not stopped his astronomical rise in the property world, both in the UK and abroad, and in 1972 he followed the pattern of many rich men before him, making his millions finance the respectability which can come from farming and land-owning.

Lyon was also influenced, as others were, by the past track-record of land as an investment, and it was still showing up very favourably indeed. Perhaps he treated his farms as too much of a business, using the crude take over techniques of the brash international business world, with no ethics except the jungle rules of strength for survival. His advent into farming was spectacular.

He had bought, in addition to Brown Candover and the Longwood Estate, the 1,700-hectare English Farms Ltd in Wiltshire, and had invested over £7 million in 4,400 hectares within twelve months, and all at top market prices. His motives, he stated, were to acquire a hedge against inflation, although it was to be his undoing. He also said that he wanted to farm the land himself. He was quickly seized upon by the Sunday BBC TV farming programme as a subject, where he was depicted, against a background of pigsties, wearing rubber boots like a 'typical' farmer (even if the collar and tie put him in the 'Gentleman Farmer' class). He was the archetype of the new breed of City farmers; and was hated by the real ones.

When the spotlight departed Lyon settled down to his business of property development, and enjoyed his lordship over his extensive land. The writing was on the wall already, and even for a tycoon of his acumen, the sum of £7 million locked up in a low-yielding capacity was a heavy burden. The later decline in land values wiped away the anticipated capital appreciation. Lyon's resources were being strained, and the national situation had violently changed from 1972, when the Lyon Group found itself in trouble in May 1974. (Subsequent changes in tax regulations have rendered it unlikely that anyone could operate in precisely the way Lyon did.)

Wilson was back in Downing Street, inflation had jumped from 7 per cent to nearly 20 per cent, and more importantly for businesses working on overdrafts or borrowed money, interest rates had shot up to 13 per cent, with 15 per cent being charged by many sources. Additionally, there was a Government squeeze on the unpopular property speculators; businesses were crashing almost daily. Ronald Lyon did not escape, and in May 1974 amid considerable publicity the Lyon Property Group toppled; his tremendous efforts to hold it together failed, and with it went his farms. The purchase of this farmland contributed heavily to his total failure, and took a large part of the blame. With typical understatement, John Raynor of Strutt & Parker was quoted as saying, 'Mr Lyon has found he has too much money in rural property. It appears to have upset his cash flow.'

Certainly, with over 150 uncompleted factory and property sites, a stagnating economy with a reluctant purchasing public, Lyon was in deep trouble, but his final TV interview showed him a man with tremendous humanity for his dispossessed workers. The general impression he left was that of a man who had tried hard, but had gone too far too quickly. He may well bounce back again somewhere else one day, but it looks as if his foray into farming is over.

The farms Lyon had bought were again offered for sale at a reputed £1 million less. They were sold to the Post Office Superannuation Fund at an undisclosed figure, which may have been considerably less than the quoted price. But then the 1972 Land Boom was over.

The farmers fight back

After farmers had complained for years that the only salvation of British agriculture would be the injection of a massive capital sum of 'outside money', the increased value of farmland during the twelve months of 1972 probably nearly doubled the capital worth of the industry. Far from being joyful, the farmers' reaction was violently reactionary. Firstly, they saw their potential death duty problems magnified, they resented the way in which the 'outside money' had arrived, and they set out to lambaste the very people who were injecting vast sums of money into farmland for the first time.   As has been seen, one result was the CLA-instigated quarterly Land Price Surveys, which were designed to dispel any illusions that land prices—on average, anyway—were as high as the headline-hitting auction sales portrayed. Outsiders were talking the market up, while paradoxically the owners of the new wealth were desperately talking the price down. It is difficult to imagine a more poignant situation than this, where greater wealth—on paper, anyway—was being spurned by its recipients.

There were some features of the Boom that farmers disliked. Advertisements in newspapers had a brash North American ring about them. 'Land, the down-to-earth investment with the sky-high potential', from Towry Law & Co. Ltd; or, 'Buy agricultural land now. It's getting scarcer and more valuable every day', from Antony Gibbs (Personal Financial Planners) Ltd, were alien to them.

If farmers were going to fight back against the intrusion of City money into the countryside they had first to prove that it was indeed the City institutions that were to blame. They needed an easy scapegoat, but nobody was quite sure, and there were different motives for wanting to talk down the price of land. Firstly, you had to prove why it had gone up. The CLA viewpoint was expressed by its President, Charles Graham, at the AGM in October. He put the blame unequivocally upon weakness of the pound, lack of confidence of industry and the falling share market, while admitting that the 'roll-over' relief was contributory. Graham advocated that the twelve months allowed for reinvestment of the profits of development sales should be extended to three years. This would take the pressure off the mad scramble to reinvest the vast funds that were flowing into farmers' pockets from the escalation of industrial and domestic land development values. The tax, if not reinvested within the prescribed period, was 30 per cent.

The NFU was mainly concerned that high land prices would push up rents to tenants.

There was not, however, complete unanimity that the new levels were bad. Some farmers with potential developable land saw the enhanced values as a passport to riches; others nearing retirement saw a more rosy future, and the two-bedroomed bungalow by the sea became a veritable mansion. Others used the newly found wealth as collateral to convince bank managers to increase their overdrafts. Farmers might not always be cashing in on the new values, but as security they could be used as a springboard for developing the farming profitability from new capital injections.

In a letter to *The Times*[6] Mark Strutt and George Judd (who had sold the Brown Candover Estate earlier that month) concluded:

> To the CLA the accretion of new landowners, with the capital at their disposal to carry out much needed improvements to fixed equipment, and the land itself, can be nothing but a blessing.

Earlier in the same letter the two senior partners of Strutt & Parker had come to the conclusion that with land at its present levels there were few people who could afford to be both owners and farmers, and they forecast a return to the old landlord and tenant system.

The Party Political Conferences that October did mention the subject of land prices, but characteristically achieved nothing more. For the Tories, Secretary of State for the Environment Peter Walker talked about the problem as it affected house-building. The Agriculture Minister, Prior, answered a debate on horticulture and ignored land prices completely. For Labour, Joan Maynard

[6] 30 October 1972.

called for the nationalization of all land—including farms. Everybody yawned.

The *Sunday Times*[7] said that land was always scarce, and always dear, but added, 'Does it matter?' Answering its own question, it proceeded that in farmland it did matter, because the effects would be felt on farming methods and prices. What it omitted to say was that this might put up the price of food to the majority of its readers. Everyone had a comment, but while the farmers castigated the City institutions, the *Daily Telegraph* put forward a clear thesis that even if the farmers had not caused the Boom, they were responsible for sustaining it. They stated that adjoining owners purchased 37 per cent of farms, and tenants another 45 per cent, leaving only 18 per cent for 'first-time buyers'. The figures came from the AMC, and while they were traditionally correct, 1972 was making strange bedfellows. Nevertheless, the *Telegraph* illustrated in considerable depth a long list of expensive farms that had been purchased by private individuals. How many were 'first-time buyers' was not known, but at least they were moving the heat away from the mandarins of Throgmorton and Threadneedle Streets.

Robert Bernays of First Investors & Savers, a Vavasseur offshoot, pointed out that the outside buyers had paid an average of £1,976 during 1972, whereas the more expensive sales at over £2,470 per hectare had been to private individuals. It seemed that landowners with development cash were paying 50 per cent more to buy farms, in an effort to save a 30 per cent tax. Perhaps there is great satisfaction is not paying tax.

Bald, bespectacled editor of the NFU official organ, the *British Farmer & Stockbreeder*, Monty Keen, pointed out that rents (still averaging £15 per hectare) must not be matched to freehold land prices, and told his boss, NFU President Plumb, that he need have no fears of rent increases while land prices continued to rise, although he admitted that if the increase resumed a jog-trot, then rent-increase fears might be justified. At the same time Keen slammed his leading contributor, Cherrington, for his naivety in expecting that a time-qualifying clause on the 45 per cent abatement would provide a remedy for high prices. In a desperate attempt to place the blame somewhere, and to understand the impact of this new phenomenon, the plaintive cry 'Do something' was heard at the November NFU Council Meeting. They did. They set up a Committee. It finalized its report eighteen months later, in May 1974, by which time the heat had subsided and the whole situation had changed.

The NFU 'Panel on Land Prices' was chaired by bald, broad and blunt Tom Boden, Staffordshire farmer and Justice of the Peace. His pugnacious Midland accent had already brought him to the Chairmanship of the Taxation Committee, but the new Panel was an ad hoc working party without the status of a full Committee. It wrote to the Chancellor of the Exchequer within a month, advocating restricting the agricultural tax-abatements to bona-fide farmers and agricultural landowners (an impossible definition). It advocated that Estate

[7] 5 October 1972.

Duty should be related to a qualifying period of ownership. It suggested that roll-over should apply to compulsory purchase, but not to land which was sold above its agricultural valuation, and blithely asked for the roll-over time limit to be extended to five years (CLA three years). A few more minor suggestions for manipulating the price of land were advanced in this unsatisfactory package. Predictably, Chancellor Barber ignored it all, and even the *B.F. and S.B.* was prompted to record: 'Nothing along these lines is likely to be politically acceptable or workable in practice.'[8] Meanwhile land prices were still merrily holding their own. In December the Silchester Estate, situated near the Hampshire home of the Duke of Wellington at Stratfield Saye, was sold by auction. It fetched £3,211 a hectare for indifferent land with vacant possession, £2,297 per hectare for farmland subject to tenancy, and £1,235 for woodland. A general comment concluded that the realized price was nearly 500 per cent more than it would have been twelve months earlier.

The year in retrospect

1972 had seen a remarkable boom in land prices; it was a historic year, which exploded upon an unsuspecting farming and business community, and it forced a new appraisal of the financial structure of farming. The reasons were complex and manifold: a sagging economy, falling share prices, the optimism of the Common Market, and a general fever which always grips uncontrollable booms. The farmers' wrath at the events was almost (but not quite) unanimous in opposition to such radical changes. Although the outside City investors could have analysed the performance of farmland values at any time in the previous decade, noting its gilt-edged security and above-average return on capital, they remained somnolent, until they all scrambled to climb on the band-wagon at the same time. 1972 certainly brought both the NFU and CLA into a much closer appreciation of land prices, and the whole period resulted in farmers becoming obvious targets for taxation.

Even if this greater vulnerability would present problems in handing over farms and estates to the next generation, nevertheless the Land Boom created more millionaires in farming than in any other sector of society.

The bubble bursts

'Life is mostly froth and bubble.
Two things stand like stone,
Kindness in another's trouble,
Courage in your own.'
> Adam Gordon

By January 1973 Prior had departed for higher things, and Godber had taken his place on the previous Guy Fawkes Day. Barber was still at the Treasury, and

---

[8] 23 May 1973.

Heath still the boss. The FT Index had gone over the 500 mark, and property and land values had spiralled by any percentage you care to mention. The rises had come during the second half of the previous year, and no one seemed to question whether the top had been reached, or how long such levels would be sustained. Current levels were firmly fixed in people's minds, and there was a euphoria of anticipation that yet further rises would transpire tomorrow. No cautionary voices were raised. The Boom was on, and it was here to stay.

Despite Heath's fervent advocacy of EEC membership, there were few bonfires lit in celebration when we joined. Most people viewed it as the lesser of two evils, and the UK slipped into Europe furtively by the back door on an inauspicious January morning, more than a decade later than it should have done, and in many people's view, wrongly.

This was not, however, the viewpoint of farmers, who, despite their original opposition to Macmillan's abortive application, were now welcoming the event with greater joy than were most sections of industry. The anticipated higher prices for most farm products were not scheduled to be operative until the end of the five-year transitional period. Nevertheless, by easy steps there was a future unfolding that seemed better than the more recent past. After all, when British farmers were getting £30 for their wheat, the French were getting £40 plus. New prosperity was heralded, and confidence in farming circles had never been higher. Wrote Peter Hopper,[9] 'If one word can sum up the present mood of agriculture, still Britain's premier industry, it is expansion.' He was right. The green light for expansion was flashing; farmland prices were also trying to catch up with their European counterparts.

Just what were those magical European land prices? And what had happened while Britain was engaged in its own Land Boom?

In the USA, despite its vast land area, the price had appreciated by 7 per cent per annum from 1955 to 1972, despite the fact that the American consumer price index only rose by an average of 2·7 per cent in the same period. Land, however, rose by 13 per cent in the twelve-month period to March 1973, while net farm income that year increased by no less than 32 per cent. Land prices, however, remained much closer to farm productivity and profitability.

On the mainland of Europe the true land values are as confusing as the laws governing land are complex. Britain is the only country in Europe with an open land market, and one of the few in the world where there are no restrictions upon anyone buying a farm. In every other country these restrictions apply to a greater or lesser degree, and are contrived in an effort to keep the farms for the farmers, France for the Frenchmen, and Denmark for the Danes. Although nations such as Spain and Portugal welcome the infusion of new capital and new landowners, many countries are coy and careful about who buys what. Australia, for example, will allow outsiders to buy land, but may restrict the release of that capital from the country at any later date, thus providing a limiting factor when

[9] Agricultural Editor of the *East Anglian Daily Times*, 27 February 1973.

viewed as a potential area of investment by non-Australians. In Britain, despite the antagonism towards outside buyers who were blamed for the Land Boom, the farmers still maintained seriously that any form of closed market would be detrimental. A few suggested that it would bring down the price of land, but the majority defended the status quo.

In general terms, European land prices were much higher than the UK, but then most European farm prices had been ahead of British levels for at least two decades. Costs of production too were higher.

Estimation of farmland values
£s per hectare

Country	1970 values
United Kingdom	479
France	543
Italy	617
Luxembourg	901
Holland	1,029
Germany	1,210
Belgium	2,408

The table of European prices must be treated as less reliable than the UK figures because of the lack of compulsory and comprehensive statistics, excepting possibly in Holland and Belgium. In France the returns are voluntary, and in Germany (traditionally higher-priced than Britain), they only apply to some of the best northern areas. The vast difference between Holland and Belgium is explained by the fact that until 1963 prices had been strictly controlled in Holland. Belgium—the odd one out in Europe, and subjected to a boom period similar to the UK—had started planning and zoning controls in the 1960s, whereas the UK muddle basically stemmed from 1947.

In France there is a prescriptive right by the State to purchase available land for the creation of new holdings, or amalgamation schemes. Additional restrictions on who may buy farms are made by the State-controlled SAFER (Rural Restructuring Agency). Private buyers may only compete when the official agency has satisfied itself that it has no interest in the property for sale. Non-Frenchmen are also discouraged from buying French farms, and when we were about to enter Europe the *Farmers Weekly* was prevented from buying a French farm to set beside its six British ones as examples it could cite when reporting the state of farming. There are also curbs in France upon the amount of land that can be annexed by one individual farmer wishing to expand his property. No such curbs occur in the UK. The Belgian oddity reached a peak of almost £3,000 per hectare around 1971, but two years later this figure had been halved.

UK prices exceeded even the Belgian levels, and the excuse that British land prices must rise to EEC levels was facile in the extreme. Within the original Six there were (and still are) so many national variants to the rules that equality is not only non-existent, but most nations seem determined to preserve regulations that will ensure inequality.

The Danish example

Inspired, as was the UK, by the prosperity that would endure from joining the EEC, the price of land in Denmark had gone up by 60 per cent in the pre-joining period to a figure of around £1,000 per hectare. This followed a fifteen-year static period when low farming prices had produced low farming profits, despite the British farmer's perpetual complaint that Danish bacon imports were ruining his own markets.

The Danish land owning-system has an important variation from that of the British. The Danes have 'land bonds', stemming from the aftermath of the 1914–18 War, when this form of official subsidized cash handout was instituted to finance land. It works like a mortgage, with the important difference that the cash loan remains with the property, and not the farmer, thus considerably reducing the cash required to buy a farm. Danish farmers—mostly smaller-scale than their British counterparts—are indebted to various sources to the tune of 50 per cent of the total capital worth of their industry: British farmers owe under 10 per cent.

In June 1973, worried about the antics of land speculators, and in an effort to stem the movement of big business into the Danish farming industry (which is important to the Danish economy by exporting two-thirds of its total produce), the Danish Government set about devising some restrictive land laws. It was vital to their economy in a much more dramatic way than would be a similar situation in the UK, and Danish farmers who had never had the protection of guaranteed prices suddenly found themselves the golden boys: the high level of European prices affected them much quicker than happened in Britain.

Whereas Britain vacillated over the problem of high land-prices, the Danes swiftly introduced drastic measures to curb their speculators. The object of these stringent new laws was simple. It emanated from the pressure of the powerful Smallholders Union, which persuaded the Government to institute land constraints and protect themselves. As one Copenhagen official said: 'Controlled evolution—not revolution.'

The new laws were:

1 The buyer of a farm must make more than 50 per cent of his living from farming.
2 He must live at the farm, unless he lives on another farm he is already farming.
3 The buyer, his wife or children under twenty, must only own one other farm in Denmark or any other country.
4 He must be over twenty years old.
5 There must not be any farm over 200 hectares.

In 1977 they tightened the rules still further by barring anyone from farming without formal farm training. They reduced the maximum farm size from 200 hectares to 150 hectares and tightened the Income from Farming rule.

Certainly such stringent laws quickly stopped town-based businessmen from investing in farmland or having interest in a farming business. It would never have been passed by a British House of Commons, either Tory or Socialist-controlled.

The de Paula plan

In Britain during early 1973 the debate continued, and in the opening days of the year Ian Reid,[10] the smooth-haired, silver-tongued Wye lecturer who became Director of the first European Studies Centre, put forward a staggering figure of £1,000 million, or $2\frac{1}{2}$ per cent of the GNP, as the amount of money that was floating around urgently seeking reinvestment in farmland, half of which, he said, was in the pockets of owner/occupier farmers. Anthony Rosen, who played a controversial part in the aftermath debate,[11] was clapped whole-heartedly when he suggested emphatically that 'roll-over' was the culprit. (He perhaps had a vested interest in directing publicity away from the institutional buyers since his own company, Fountain Farming Ltd, a subsidiary of Matthews Wrightson (Land) Ltd, had bought nearly 4,500 hectares itself in the previous year.) The emphatic applause that greeted Rosen's outburst was symptomatic of the feeling among farmers that someone was to blame, but it seemed incredible that they were actually advocating the withdrawal of a 'perk'. Roll-over applied to any type of business asset, and was not designed specifically with farmers in mind. Farmers were also advocating the abolition of the 45 per cent agricultural abatement in Estate Duty because it was attractive to outside death-bed purchasers as a piece of chicanery. They were prepared to forgo undoubted benefits in a wild effort to take the steam out of land prices. At Oxford that year one speaker went as far as to suggest that the answer was to nationalize the land; even he was listened to with quiet politeness. In this climate Clive de Paula, the new dynamic head of the Agricultural Mortgage Corporation, unveiled a plan to allow his Corporation to partake in the equity of the farm. A maximum stake of 49 per cent was proposed, and by this method he suggested farmers could relieve their tax burdens and still retain control and occupation of the farm. The Government-owned AMC by owning a percentage of the total equity would be in a position to grant higher sums and recoup low interest rates from the eventual capital appreciation. The plan was revealed at a farming conference organized by a firm of corn merchants, in a hotel near Ipswich, and despite the fact that it amounted to a back-door method of increasing State ownership of farmland, it was not howled out of court by farmers. The *Farmers Weekly* said, 'The proposal merits consideration,' and added plaintively, 'Can we still afford to own the land we farm?'

[10] At the Oxford Farming Conference, 8 January 1973.
[11] See Fountain Farming. p. 241.

For several months the de Paula Plan was kicked around, until it found its way into a Whitehall pigeonhole, where it remains.

As a source of new capital for a tax-milked farmer, it had merits, but the inherent dangers of State participation in erstwhile privately owned and commercial farmland were obviously recognized by Tory Godber. Surprisingly, the plan was not resurrected by Peart later, nor did the NUAWW clamour for its rebirth. How fortunate for British agriculture that Wedgwood Benn has never been its Minister!

The Opposition Leader, Wilson, jumped on the anti-speculators bandwaggon in an uncharacteristic role of protecting the capitalist farmers. He spoke at a Welsh Labour Rally at Newtown, Montgomery, on 1 July 1973, on the eve of the Royal Show. He said, 'It is not our policy to take over owner-occupied farmland, but the would-be owner is entitled to protection against land speculators.'

Wilson then hinted at possible future discriminatory taxes against the non owner/occupier, and against land development profits. The net result of his intervention was to create more apprehension about taxation of development money, and the influx into farmland was if anything increased.

Throughout that summer the heady levels of 1972 were maintained, minor farms of little consequence and bad buildings sold for over £2,500 per hectare without any problems, excepting those that might accrue to the new owner. The sales list in one issue of the *Farmers Weekly* alone recorded over £5,000 per hectare for a 27-hectare 'farm' near Exeter (it was more like a gentleman's residence with its own park than a farm). Farms in Wiltshire, Herefordshire and Somerset sold at four figures, but one large estate made only £1,124 per hectare. It was a wide range from the highest to lowest of £3,900 per hectare.

There were obviously still bargains to be shopped around for, and the Wellvale Estate of 889 hectares at Alford in Lincolnshire was sold for £1 million, or £1,120 per hectare, to Tiller Farms Ltd, part of the Slater Walker Group. Why should some land be worth so much less than other? Wellvale was all tenanted land, and produced a rent roll of £15,420 per annum (a 1·5 per cent return on the £1 million investment), but it was not a single compact estate like Brown Candover. It was two entirely divorced blocks of land on opposite sides of the retained central portion of the estate. As such, it did not present an attractive proposition. Nevertheless, in June 1973 Slater Walker got a bargain.

Table of 1973 quarterly price levels

January–March	1973	£1,793	February–April	1973	£1,487
April–June	1973	£1,862	May–July	1973	£1,551
July–Sept.	1973	£1,912	August–Oct.	1973	£1,744
October–Dec.	1973	£1,638	November–Jan.	1974	£1,366
Source: Average sales in *Farmers Weekly*			Source: CLA Land Price Survey		

Prices were stabilizing during that summer, and modest increases of 10 per cent were in line with the current rate of inflation. The wide boys who had come in looking for capital appreciation saw their investment holding its own, but not appreciating on the scale of the past. By the autumn the Boom had ended, and prices were slipping heavily. There was a build-up of national insolvency and political troubles from various strikes which led to the three-day week in early 1974, and the two General Elections of that year.

The message from both sources was the same, and, looking at vacant-possession land, the CLA Survey revealed a peak of £2,127 (quarter ending July 1973), which dropped by £200 a hectare to £1,427 six months later. The seasonal variation accounted for some of this, and figures in mid-1974 were in fact higher, but the message was getting home. Land prices were actually dropping.

During 1974 the status quo remained, with a tendency towards a gentle slide— nothing dramatic—and in 1975 the same pattern emerged. There had been changes in the affairs of the nation, and there had been changes in farming prosperity. We were never again going to see prices back at their pre-boom levels, but a greater degree of sanity was emerging.

The reasons for the Boom were:

1 The anticipated prosperity in joining Europe.
2 The vast flow of development money into farmers' pockets.
3 The roll-over relief and its ensuing scramble for reinvestment.
4 The prospects of appreciation.
5 The scarcity of land for sale.

By 1975 all these factors had disappeared. European prices were being eroded by inflationary costs, and the prosperity was tempered by two inclement seasons. The development money had dried up, as house and office building had stagnated. Barber in December 1973 had effectively abolished roll-over by lumping any development sums accrued on to net income in the year of accumulation. This meant that much more would be taxed. Once these other factors had fallen into place, the prospects of capital appreciation naturally disappeared, and lastly the scarcity of land for sale was a factor that could be manipulated as landowners with a vague idea of selling were encouraged by attractive price-levels.

After the usual breathing space the market edged upwards again in 1976, the pension fund managers recovered their nerve and came back again in 1977— but by this time a Socialist government had appointed a strange-looking committee to take a hard look at the whole business of landowning.

Conclusion

The overriding consideration in this chapter on the land market must still be that most farmers do not consider it part of their business worries. Traditional landowners have never charged rents that bore any relation to the open-market value of their estates, and tenant farmers were always protected from eviction by the law. If the farmland value is of consequence to the newcomer attempting to enter the industry, then farming is a closed shop. The outright purchase price of a farm becomes an impossible liability, and prevents the young man from entertaining the idea, but this is nothing new. When land was £250 a hectare entering farming was not for the faint-hearted. The long-term results have obviously justified those entrepreneurs of twenty years ago, and yet every generation will produce a new William Morris or Henry Ford. The only question must be: is farming attractive enough for these young tycoons?

What the escalation in farmland values has done to the farming community has been to create a much greater awareness that they are now vulnerable to the tax-collector. Many more articles on tax problems are read today by many more farmers. The problems of succession (which were always considerable with the aristocrats) have now become a reality for the yeoman, and the present tax structure, coupled with land values, must raise serious doubts whether the present generation of owner/occupiers might not see the ending of a traditional pattern of English landowning.

Indicators of land price in England and Wales

Sales reported in the period	Average price of land sold (£ per hectare)	Average land value (£ per hectare)	Land sales price index (mid 1970 = 100)
Oct. 65–Mar. 66	420	420	88·3
Nov. 66–Apr. 67	427	415	89·8
Nov.–Apr. 68	447	442	94·6
Nov. 68–Apr. 69	499	472	103·4
Oct. 69–Mar. 70	497	430	101·1
Oct. 70–Mar. 71	482	432	104:1
Oct. 71–Mar. 72	514	452	110·4
Oct. 72–Mar. 73	939	830	200·0
Oct. 73–Mar. 74	1,512	1,275	308·3
Oct. 74–Mar. 75	1,299	1,196	252·3
Oct. 75–Mar. 76	1,076	917	225·8
Oct. 76–Mar. 77	1,667	—	335·4

Source: Ministry of Agriculture statistics

What is even more revealing is the sharp decline in the amount of land sold, and number of transactions this involved. It demonstrates that there is a continuing slide that has reduced the number of sales by half between 1960 and 1974, with a corresponding drop in the area, demonstrating that the average farmland sale is still only about 35 hectares.

Year ending	Number of Transactions	Hectarage sold
30 Sept 1960	9,900	330,645
30 Sept 1965	8,401	284,740
30 Sept 1970	5,762	179,742
30 Sept 1974	4,531	160,734
30 Sept 1977	3,219	101,921

9 The Landowners

'Property has its duties, as well as its rights.'
Thomas Drummond

The most extraordinary aspect of any study of land-ownership in Britain is that nobody knows who owns what, how much or where. There is no central register of the ownership of houses, property or land. Motor-cars, yes. The Swansea HQ of the Vehicle Licensing Department knows the ownership of every car, bus or lorry on the road, and ships the world over have their names and registered owners recorded at Lloyds. Since both cars and boats are subjects for insurance, and land is not, perhaps herein lies the distinction.

Journalist and landowner Quintin Crewe set out to establish who owned the land of Britain. He wrote:

> We tried the Central Statistical Office, who referred us to the Department of the Environment, who suggested the Planning and Land Use Department. They advised us to consult the Ministry of Agriculture, who referred us to the Central Statistical Office.

The Ministry of Agriculture knows who the farmers are; for purposes of grants for capital improvements the applicant answers the question 'Owner; Owner-occupier; Tenant?' But this information is not collated. Local councils are aware of the ownership of any land at the time of a planning application, and the Inland Revenue knows what we own the moment we die.

Knowledge of ownership is a matter of hearsay, and local gossip, rather than any statutory and central register of land-ownership. A lovely anchronism of England. Long may it remain

Domesday onward

There have been three surveys of land-ownership in the last thousand years. William the Conqueror conducted his Domesday Survey, which provides a valuable and fascinating glossary for students of farm history (it sometimes adds a touch of antiquity at any auction sale to add the words 'mentioned in the Domesday Book'!). It is a written document, county by county, and has been mostly transcribed into modern, but not contemporary, English.

The second survey was contained in the series of tithe maps drawn up during the 1840s. Prior to that period the collection of tithes had been haphazard, and subject to disputes between parson and laity. There were endless arguments over the methods of payment, but such was the respect for the Church that both Whigs and Tories collaborated to pass the Tithe Act 1836. It linked tithe payments to corn prices and gave powers to commute payments by a lump sum, while both Sir Robert Peel in 1835 and Lord John Russell in 1836 agreed that payments should be transferred from occupier to owner. An early attempt at knocking the rich!

This last point necessitated a survey to identify the landowners, and the tithe maps and registers are the result. For farm historians the tithe maps illustrate field boundaries and shapes (before the bulldozers arrived) and ownership of infinitesimal pieces of land with a pedantic exactitude. But they have no relevance to present-day land-owning information.

In late Victorian times there was an anti-landlord movement. In an attempt to demonstrate that land-ownership was indeed more widespread than popularly believed, the Earl of Derby, with 27,560 hectares of his own, pressed Parliament to instigate a new Domesday Survey. Parliament agreed, and the result of this 1872 Act listed a million landowners. It revealed, to Derby's embarrassment, that four-fifths of the land was owned by 7,000 people. Twenty peers owned more than 40,000 hectares each, and 90 per cent of the peerage (then 500 strong) owned sizeable estates.

The 1872 Survey was grossly inaccurate, as landowners filled in their own forms, but it does give a basis for studying the changing status of the peerage, and the changing nature of the ownership of England. The Duke of Sutherland came out as the largest landowner with 543,418 hectares, and there were 15 landowners with incomes from land in excess of £100,000 per annum. In all, 10 per cent of Britain was owned by only 35 people. While it rebounded upon Derby, this survey of the great landowners showed how the large estates and small kingdoms had lasted until Victorian times. The story during the last century is one of decline, but even today there are substantial estates still remaining, while one can only admire the tenacity of some aristocratic families, who have actually increased their estates since that time.

That there has been a vast movement in land-ownership is self-evident; what is less clear is the extent of that movement, although in monetary terms many individuals are more wealthy than their predecessors who had more extensive ancestral land. The enhanced land values today have kept the status quo in cash terms, but with diminished territory has gone diminished power. Quintin Crewe has suggested that between one-third and three-quarters of the land has changed hands in the last hundred years. George Howard[1] has said, 'I would hazard a guess that no more than 25 per cent of the land in England is now in the hands of those families who owned it at the beginning of the century.' This illustrates a suggested change-over of 75 per cent. Possibly a high figure, but the real significance of these cock-shies is that they are all wild guesstimates with

[1] *The Destruction of the Country House*, page 168.

little solid facts to substantiate them. Certainly, looking at the ratio of tenant farmers, we might get some further clues.

England and Wales

	Area rented	Total area
1887	9·28 m hectares	11·12 m hectares
1966	5·8 m hectares	11·4 m hectares

A movement in the designation of the farmland tally of about 3·6 million hectares, or approximately 30 per cent of the total agricultural area, and a movement from 90 per cent tenanted in 1900 to 40 per cent tenanted today would suggest that 50 per cent has changed hands. This takes no note of the fact that many traditional landowners have taken to farming for themselves every property that has become vacant, thus confusing the land-ownership change-over, excepting that it must be less than the change-over from tenanted to owner-occupied land. Since farmland sales run between 1 per cent and 2 per cent of the farmland annually, even these statistics confuse the facts that many sales throughout the last hundred years could well be the same farm. Certainly the big movement into genuine owner/occupiers has gathered momentum since 1945. These new owners may present a vulnerable sector which could succumb to the tax man, with little but their land and with no Van Dycks, Rubens or Holbeins to cash in as the generation changes produce tax liabilities. Conversely, the fragmentation may well present a greater opportunity for private ownership to continue. This is explored at the end of this chapter.

Looking today at the pattern and numerical strength of the landowners of Britain, it would seem that if 60 per cent of the 230,000 farmers are owners this ownership vests within the small number of 138,000 the vast majority of the ownership of Britain. In fact, the numbers are much smaller. The CLA boasts a strength of 45,000 members, who certainly own the greater part of the rural land. We have little information upon private landowners other than their own public statements; for instance, ex-Commando leader Lord Lovat includes in his entry in *Who's Who*: 'Owns about 190,000 acres.'

Although ever more of Britain is owned by public institutions, and by the myriad of Governmental Departments, the farming land of England and Wales had also been reduced by 400,000 hectares in the twenty years 1956–76, which has been of considerable financial benefit to the previous owners. Despite these subtle land changes, the turbulence in society and penal taxation, the fact remains that half a century after the Great War a vast proportion of the total land of Britain remains shakily in private hands.

In one of the rare pieces of research into land-ownership, Gibbs & Harrison[2]

[2] *Land Ownership by Public and Semi-Public Bodies in Great Britain*, Richard Gibbs and Alan Harrison (Reading University, 1974).

discovered that the public and semi-public bodies had increased their land-ownership since pre-War days by 300,000 hectares, and that the total area of land owned by public and semi-public bodies was around 15 per cent of Great Britain. This leaves 85 per cent privately owned. With regard to farmland, it recorded that only 8 per cent was publicly owned, 92 per cent private.

The monarchical estates

'I entirely agree that we are old-fashioned; it is an old-fashioned institution.'

HRH Prince Philip, 1964.

| | **Great Britain** | |
	Total	Farmland
Crown Estate	119,644	94,480
Duchy of Cornwall	52,600	52,580
Duchy of Lancaster	21,120	15,240

The Crown Estate today is in no sense of the word an 'Estate', and a better description might be the Crown Lands, for in essence they are the land which had not been given away by various monarchs to their courtiers. The Crown Lands Act 1702, at the time of Queen Anne's accession to the throne, was the first of many Acts of Parliament restraining the Sovereign from alienating any part of the properties. It followed the decimation of the various lands by William III, who had given away large areas to his supporters. The Duke of Portland received five-sixths of the county of Denbigh, and William so reduced the value of the holding that the revenue was down to £6,000 (1973–4 rents £7·1 million).

The Civil List Act had been passed in 1697, which granted £700,000 for the expenses of the civil Government, including the monarch. Eventually, at George III's accession in 1760, a bargain was struck. The monarch was relieved of the expenses of running the Government, which included Ministers, Judges and other public servants (MPs were not paid until this century) and in return he surrendered the Crown Lands, which were at the time in a near-bankrupt state. Thus for over 200 years, the Crown Estate has been the property of the State, but the monarch did retain the duchies of Cornwall and Lancaster.

The Crown Estate is run by the Crown Commissioners, eight in all. Their Annual Report is printed and published by HMSO.

They hand over the surplus funds to the Treasury, and it has been used as an argument that Britain makes a profit out of its monarch. The Civil List was fixed at £1·4 million on 1 January 1975, and the Crown Estate showed a healthy surplus of £4·7 million (1973, £4·4 million; 1972, £3·9 million).

The headquarters are at Carlton House Terrace, S.W.1., and the Commission costs £½ million a year to administer.

The Commissioners have entrusted to them 23,000 hectares that is partly urban and partly forestry, in addition to their farmland, but by far their most valuable assets are the areas in Central London from which they derive rents of over £4 million annually.

Although not bound by the normal law regarding rents, the Commissioners did bend to the Counter-Inflation Act 1973, and remitted some £136,000 in rent. The mind boggles at the resulting outcry if they hadn't. They are, however, subject to the frustrations of planning ineptitude and vacillation. The 1974 Report sadly recorded: 'Our loss of rent on eight schemes currently affected by planning delays is now running at the rate of over £1 million a year.' Additional lucrative inheritances bestowed upon the Crown Commissioners are the foreshore and seabed rights (again dispelling the misconception that the Queen owns the beaches). Sea-dredged aggregates, amounting to 11 per cent of the total national production of sand and gravel, add to the Crown Estate's coffers, and more recently the advent of North Sea oil has resulted in money for the seabed and foreshore requirements of the oil pioneers.

The control of Windsor parks is an item with which the Crown Commissioners would happily dispense. It costs them nearly £½ million per year. The Estate is not static. In 1973 the Commissioners bought 163 hectares at a price of £1,000 per hectare, including 84 hectares of Romney Marsh, but when land prices boomed they found an excuse to sell 1,619 hectares for £2·4 million (£1,480 per hectare). They sold the Wotten Estate (732 hectares) in Oxfordshire, Graveney Estate (450 hectares) in Kent, and 360 hectares of the Holmewood Estate in Cambridgeshire, but they did buy another 348 hectares at Romney and at Everby in Lincolnshire.

THE CROWN ESTATE
AGRICULTURAL

County and Estate	Hectares	Acquisition
ENGLAND		
Bedfordshire		
Chicksands	114	Purchased in 1936. Bulk of Estate sold to farm tenants between 1959 and 1962. Remainder is woodland leased to Forestry Commission.
Berkshire		
Windsor	752	Ancient possession considerably increased by purchases. Includes agricultural property at Ascot, Datchet and Bagshot.
Buckinghamshire		
Wotton	742	Purchased in 1930.
Cambridgeshire		
Holmewood	2,118	Purchased in 1947.
Cheshire		
Delamere	73	Ancient possession, originally part of Delamere Forest.
Cumbria		
Aldingham	400	Ancient possession (part of Manor of Muchland) supplemented by purchases in the nineteenth century.

County and Estate	Hectares	Acquisition
Manor of Muchland and Torver	1,038	Forfeited to the Crown in the sixteenth century. Hill and waste lands subject to rights of common.
Dorset		
Bryanston	1,589	Purchased in 1950.
Essex		
Stapleford Abbots	1,123	Partly ancient possession, partly allotted under enclosure awards and partly purchased. Some of the estate is in Greater London.
Gloucestershire		
Clearwell	573	Purchased between 1907 and 1912.
Hagloe	294	Purchased between 1853 and 1902.
Hertfordshire		
Gorhambury	1,917	Purchased in 1931.
Putteridge	1,412	Purchased in 1932. Part of the estate is in Bedfordshire.
Wallington	339	Escheated to the Crown in 1956 and 1962.
Humberside		
Derwent	1,250	Some ancient possession but mainly purchased in 1947/48.
Gardham	439	Purchased in 1950.
Hallatreeholme	70	Reverted to the Crown on dissolution of the Savoy Hospital in 1702. Leased for 700 years from 1565.
Sunk Island	4,942	Largely reclaimed from the Humber Estuary during the seventeenth, eighteenth and nineteenth centuries and partly purchased in 1913 and 1947.
Swine	1,940	A small part is ancient possession, the bulk being purchased in 1859, 1871 and 1962.
Kent		
Bedgebury	935	Purchased in 1919.
Neats Court (Isle of Sheppey)	315	A small part is ancient possession, the remainder being purchased between 1850 and 1900.
Romney Marsh	2,955	Purchased from 1958 onward. Part of the Estate is in Sussex.
Leicestershire		
Gopsall	3,240	Purchased in 1932.

County and Estate	Hectares	Acquisition
Lincolnshire		
Benington	190	Part purchased in 1970. Remainder reclaimed from the Wash in 1971.
Billingborough	4,860	A small part is ancient possession, the bulk being purchased in 1855 and since.
Croft	77	Ancient possession.
Ewerby	1,868	Purchased in 1948.
Whaplode	2,370	Partly ancient possession, partly allotted under Enclosure awards, and partly purchased.
Wingland	3,500	Greater part reclaimed from the Wash mainly in the last hundred years. Latest reclamations in 1972.
Norfolk		
Croxton	3,340	Purchased in 1930. Major part of estate is leased to Forestry Commission.
Kings Lynn	784	Part purchased in 1964. Part reclaimed from the Wash in 1965 and 1966.
North Yorkshire		
Boroughbridge	1,290	Partly ancient possession and partly purchased between 1860 and 1876.
Nottinghamshire		
Bingham	3,340	Purchased in 1926 and 1938.
Oxfordshire		
Wychwood	744	Ancient possession—originally part of Wychwood Forest, disafforested after 1850.
Somerset		
Dunster	3,750	Purchased in 1950.
Taunton	4,650	Purchased in 1944 and 1952.
Staffordshire and Shropshire		
Patshull	1,576	Purchased in 1969.
Surrey		
Oxshott	670	Purchased mainly in nineteenth century.
Sussex		
Poynings	1,540	Escheated to Crown at the end of the eighteenth century.
Warwickshire		
Coughton	1,590	Purchased in 1934.
Wiltshire		
Devizes	3,854	Purchased in 1858 and 1862–4.
Savernake	4,162	Purchased in 1950.

County and Estate	Hectares	Acquisition
SCOTLAND		
Central Region		
District of Stirling		
Arngomery	100	Purchased in 1962 under the terms of the will of the late owner.
Fintry	1,350	Purchased in 1930. Two sheep farms and some fishings.
Stirling	180	Ancient possession added to in 1972.
Dumfries & Galloway Region District of Annandale & Eskdale		
Applegirth	7,103	Purchased from 1963 onward.
Grampian Region		
District of Moray		
Fochabers	5,654	Purchased in 1937.
Glenlivet	19,386	Purchased in 1937. Includes considerable areas of hill and moorland.
Highland Region		
District of Caithness		
Lythmore	424	Ancient possession.
Scotscalder	243	Purchased in 1909. Bulk of Estate sold.
Lothian Region		
District of Midlothian		
Whitehill	1,413	Purchased from 1969 onward.
City of Edinburgh		
Edinburgh	5	Ancient possession. Amenity land comprising part of Princes Street Gardens and including the Castlebanks.
URBAN		
WALES		
Gwent		
Tintern	100	Purchased in 1901.
Berkshire		
Bracknell		Crown Estate Office. Purchased 1969.
Devon		
Drake's Island		
Plymouth	2·4	Old Land Revenue property. Relinquished by the War Department in 1961, let to the National Trust and used by the National Association of Boys' Clubs as an Adventure Training Centre.

County and Estate	Hectares	Acquisition
Dorset Portland	244	Ancient possession formerly part of Manor of Portland. Comprises common lands and miscellaneous properties including two stone quarries.
Essex Tilbury		Ferry rights only.
Hampshire Portsmouth and Gosport		Ancient possession.
Isle of Wight Osborne	11	Residential and industrial.
Kent Dover		Ancient possession, residential.
LONDON City of London		Ancient possession, residential. by purchases in latter part of nineteenth century and since. Mainly blocks of offices in Holborn Viaduct, Ludgate Hill and Leadenhall Street.
New Oxford Street and Soho		Ancient possession, supplemented by purchases. Mainly office buildings and shops in New Oxford Street. Oxford Street. High Holborn, Brewer Street and Wardour Street.
Regent Street		Largely purchased in early nineteenth century for formation of New (Regent) Street. Further recent purchases in Carnaby Street area. Mainly shops and offices. Includes St George's Hotel (formerly the Queens Hall site), Piccadilly and Regent Palace Hotel.
Regent's Park		Originally part of the Manor of Tyburn acquired in 1544. Comprises about 800 buildings surrounding Regent's Park, together with a number of Regency villas, the Royal College of Physicians, the Royal College of Gynaecologists & Obstetricians, Bedford College within the park and a housing estate at Cumberland Market.

County and Estate	Hectares	Acquisition

LONDON (contd.)

Kensington | | Partly acquired in late seventeenth century, supplemented by purchases in late nineteenth century and since. Residential property and embassies in Kensington Palace Gardens, Palace Green and Kensington, with shops in Kensington High Street. Includes Kensington Barracks.

Millbank | | Purchased in 1799. Housing estate, wharves and business premises, including the site of the Vickers tower building.

Victoria Park | | Purchased between 1842 and 1845. Housing estate.

Lower Regent Street and Haymarket | | Mainly acquired in sixteenth century, supplemented by purchases. Shops and offices in Piccadilly, Lower Regent Street, Haymarket, Jermyn Street, Waterloo Place, Pall Mall, Suffolk Street and Whitcomb Street. Includes the Theatre Royal, Haymarket and New Zealand House.

St James's | | Mainly acquired in sixteenth century. Clubs, offices, shops and flats in Piccadilly, St James's Street, King Street, Ryder Street, Bury Street and St James's Palace. Includes Stornoway, Warwick and Lancaster Houses and the Economist Building.

South of Pall Mall | | Ancient possession supplemented by purchases between 1961 and 1964. Clubs, offices and some residential property in Carlton House Terrace, Warwick House Street, Cockspur Street, Spring Gardens and Pall Mall.

Trafalgar Square and Strand | | Partly ancient possession and partly purchased. Offices and shops in Trafalgar Square, Strand, Orange Street, Cranbourne Street and St Martin's Lane. Includes Canada House, South Africa House and the Strand Palace Hotel.

County and Estate	Hectares	Acquisition
Whitehall and Victoria		Partly ancient possession and partly purchased. Mainly offices and shops in Whitehall, Great Scotland Yard, Northumberland Avenue, Buckingham Palace Road, Buckingham Gate, Queen Anne's Gate and Victoria Street. Includes Whitehall Court and part of Wellington Barracks.

LONDON (GREATER LONDON)

County and Estate	Hectares	Acquisition
Blackheath		Ancient possession, residential.
Brentford		Purchased in 1960, Business premises.
Eltham	283	Ancient possession. Residential estate with some commercial properties. Includes Royal Blackheath and Eltham Warren Golf Clubs.
Hainault		Residential.
Hampton	23	Ancient possession. Mainly residential.
Hornchurch		Purchased in 1962. Business premises.
Richmond	163	Ancient possession. Residential with some light industrial premises. Includes the Old Deer Park and the Royal Mid-Surrey Golf Club.
Sudbrook	43	Purchased in 1841. Residential. Includes Richmond Golf Club.

SURREY

County and Estate	Hectares	Acquisition
Oxshott	18	Purchased mainly in nineteenth century. Mainly residential.

EAST SUSSEX

County and Estate	Hectares	Acquisition
Hastings		Formerly foreshore reclaimed from the sea. Shops and residential.

SOUTH YORKSHIRE

County and Estate	Hectares	Acquisition
Doncaster		Purchased in 1954. Shops.

WINDSOR

Berkshire

County and Estate	Hectares	Acquisition
Ascot	255	Partly ancient possession, partly allotted under Enclosure awards. Residential, and includes the Race-course.

County and Estate	Hectares	Acquisition
Windsor		Partly ancient possession, partly allotted under Enclosure awards and partly acquired by purchase. The estate may be divided as follows:
(a) Parks and Woods	4,882	The Great Park and Home Park (Public) extend to nearly 2,000 hectares.
(b) Lands adjoining	85	Residential.
(c) Town	22	Chiefly residential.
Berkshire and Surrey Swinley	272	Acquired mainly by purchase and exchange but part allotted under Enclosure awards. 2 golf courses with a few residential and some industrial lettings.
Buckinghamshire Datchet	31	Purchased at various times. Residential, a golf course and miscellaneous lettings.
Bagshot	36	Partly ancient possession, partly allotted to Crown under Enclosure awards and partly acquired by purchase and exchange. Includes Bagshot Park.

Source: *Annual Report of The Commissioners*, 31 March, 1976.

The Duchies

'To ask for information about the Duchy of Lancaster, and still more about the Duchy of Cornwall, is like trying to get information from the KGB.'
William Hamilton, MP, 13 May 1975

These two estates, comprising in total 72,480 hectares, of which 66,660 hectares are farmland, are more generally considered the property of the monarch, but not in a personal sense. The revenues from the Duchy of Cornwall are vested by custom in the Heir to the Throne, who commonly bears the secondary title Duke of Cornwall. Parliament has no jurisdiction over these estates, but their accounts are annually submitted to Parliament. The Inland Revenue does not collect Income Tax, Capital Gains Tax or Capital Transfer Tax. While the Queen pays rates on Sandringham and Balmoral, the Duchies, and the Crown Estate, do not. But neither does the Army.

The Estate of Cornwall is nearly three times the size of Lancaster, and the origins are not dissimilar. They vary in their location, and in their powers, Lancaster was certainly in the past more feudal. The Duchy of Cornwall is run from 10 Buckingham Gate by a Council. Prince Charles, although entitled to the revenues of the Duchy of Cornwall, does not in fact take them. In the first eighteen years of the Queen's reign the Duchy contributed £8·5 million to the Chancellor of the Exchequer, while during this whole period only £½ million was drawn. While both Estates submit their Annual Reports, these are not generally circulated to MPs, much to the chagrin of arch Royalty baiter Willy Hamilton.

There are links with Government, inasmuch as the Prime Minister was Chancellor of the Duchy of Lancaster for many years. Both Churchill and Attlee occupied this sinecure. More recently it has been vested in the Chancellor of the Exchequer, and occasionally used as the excuse and title for a 'Minister without Portfolio' who could be a member of the Cabinet, accept roving commissions, and look after party interests without the responsibilities of a full Department. Lancaster had also important judicial authority over its area, such as the administration of the Lancashire Chancery Court (this ceased in 1971); appointment of magistrates (normally appointed by the Lord Chancellor) and appointments to forty Church of England livings. One previous Chancellor insisted upon hearing sermons from prospective applicants. Both estates collect the money from inhabitants who die intestate and without relations. These are not inconsequential sums, which in other parts of the country accrue to the Treasury.

Duchy of Cornwall

This Estate goes back to 1337, when the eldest son of Edward III was created Duke of Cornwall. The present estate of 51,600 hectares is mainly situated in the West Country, originating in Cornwall and Devon, but now extended into Somerset, Dorset, Wiltshire and Gloucestershire. It also includes the Isles of Scilly and the Oval Cricket Ground at Kennington in South London. Indeed, its 20-hectare London Estate brings in as much income as does the agricultural farms.

Duchy of Lancaster

Unlike the Peerage, most of whom have no connection with the county or town of their own title, both duchies are closely identified with their name. Lancaster goes back to 1265, when Henry III granted it to his second son, Edmund. It had been land belonging to Simon de Montfort and Earl Ferrers, and forfeited after their defeat by the King in 1265–6. It changed hands during the Wars of the Roses, expanded with the Dissolution of the Monasteries, and was reduced again by William III in rewarding his supporters, as he had done from the Crown Estate. In 1760, when George III exchanged the Crown Estate for the Civil List, the Duchy was excluded from the deal. It had been chartered independently from the time of Henry VIII.

The Estate itself is concentrated in Yorkshire, Lancashire and Staffordshire. There is a vast moorland area of over 8,000 hectares in Yorkshire alone, but it also contains many urban and industrial properties. There are residential leaseholds in the Strand and the City of London, properties in Aldershot, Bedford, Bristol, Kettering, Leeds, Leicester, Lewes and Northampton, including a fish and chip shop in Pickering, York. The Duchy has properties spread over twelve counties.

The aristocrats

'The most noticeable thing about those noblemen who still own land is that they nearly always do so abundantly.'

'The Aristocrats' (Perrott), 1968

'My Lord Tomnoddy is thirty-four.
The Earl can last but a few years more.
My Lord in the Peers will take his place,
Her Majesty's Councils his words will grace.
Office he'll hold and patronage sway.
Fortunes and lives he will vote away.
And what are his qualifications?–ONE,
He's the Earl of Fitzdotterel's eldest son.'

R. B. Brough

The largest private estates are on the poorest land, principally in Scotland, where mountains, moors and heather lend themselves to vast territorial regions, with strong traditions of Chieftains and tartan. Not here the clutter of urbanization with flowering cherries and psychedelic Cortinas. The territorial magnates with their mini kingdoms still own tracts of countryside, rather than estates in the accepted lowland sense.

There are today only seven owners with more than 40,000 hectares, or 400 square kilometres each. They are:

Mr Aylwin Farquharson	142,000 hectares
Duke of Buccleuch	89,000 hectares
Lord Seafield	86,200 hectares
Lord Lovat	77,000 hectares
Countess of Sutherland	61,000 hectares
Duke of Westminster	56,000 hectares
Duke of Atholl	49,000 hectares

Crewe & Perrott do not list the Duke of Sutherland, but Roth[3] gives him 101,000 hectares. Roth is often unreliable.

Since all land was originally in the gift of the monarch, and the Queen is titular head of the aristocracy, it is surprising that neither she, nor her father before her, figure in the top bracket of territorial landowners. Her own mere 19,000 hectares (eight Dukes own more) consists of Balmoral and Sandringham. Balmoral, 13,800 hectares on Deeside, was purchased by Prince Albert in the 1840s for £31,000, and Sandringham, 5,300 hectares of sandy Norfolk soil growing magnificent rhododendrons in its windswept woods, was bought by the Prince of Wales (later Edward VII) as a home for himself on his wedding in 1863. These two estates form the only land owned by the Queen today.

The 26 Dukes (excluding the Royals) have, it is estimated,[4] just over 450,000 hectares today, but had nearly 1,800,000 hectares in 1873. Perrott[5] set out to tabulate the dimination of the aristocratic acres, and found one Scottish peer, the Earl of Breadalbane, who had lost the whole of his 177,000 hectares between 1873 and the present time. Emerson in 1856 had described how the Marquess of Breadalbane (the marquessate is now extinct) could ride 100 miles in a straight line, and all on his own property, while the Duke of Sutherland with his 530,000 hectares owned the whole of Sutherland from sea to sea. The Sutherland estates diminished by 90 per cent, but they still retain 55,200 hectares. Although separated from the Dukedom, they are held by the Countess of Sutherland, a title dating back to 1235, the 24th in line, and chief of the clan. She is a granddaughter of the fourth Duke, a title created only in 1833, and a niece of the fifth. She succeeded to her uncle's titles in 1963.

The other *grande dame* of the Scottish aristocracy, and at one time the largest landowner in the UK, was the Countess of Seafield, who died in 1969 (a mere twelfth in line), but who held her title for fifty-four years from 1915 onward, thus escaping death duties. The Seafield Estate centres in Banffshire. An enigma exists concerning the Sutherland estates. By a quirk of succession, the Earldom of Sutherland (also an appanage of the Dukedom), was inherited by the fifth Duke's niece, while the more modern Dukedom passed to a distant cousin. This situation can fragment ancient family estates, although in many instances the title, if going to a distant relative, often goes without the lands which succeed through the female line.

Roth credits the Countess with '150,000 acres, comprises 9 farms of altogether 2,200 acres, 40,000 acres made up of two deer forests, 4,100 acres of woodland, and the remainder farmed by 357 crofters, grouse shooting, small saw mill, caravan site, a mineral survey, a creosote plant and several angling clubs.' The Duke of Sutherland has a reputed 100,000 hectares, and included are his 5,300-hectare Berwickshire Estate, and Sketchworth Park near Newmarket.

[3] *Lord on the Board* by Andrew Roth. (Parliamentary Profiles.)
[4] Quintin Crewe, *Sunday Times*, 17 August 1975.
[5] *The Aristocrats*, 1968.

Although there has been a contraction in the larger aristocratic estates in the last hundred years, a few have increased. They are:

Duke of Beaufort (Gloucestershire)	up by 400 hectares to 21,000 hectares.
Earl of Lonsdale (Cumbria)	up by 1,200 hectares to 28,750 hectares.
Lord Feversham (Yorkshire)	up by 2,830 hectares to 19,000 hectares.

The Duke of Westminster (Grosvenor family), while losing over 800 hectares of his Cheshire and Shropshire estate and a few golden hectares in Central London (where he still had 120 in 1967) has increased his Scottish estate from nil in 1873 to 24,000 hectares today. Among the newer recruits to the Peerage, Viscount Cowdray (finance and newspapers) has 7,100 Sussex hectares and a polo ground; Lord Iliffe (newspapers) has 4,000 rolling Berkshire hectares; the Earl of Iveagh (Guinness) 9,700 Norfolk hectares and Viscount Leverhulme (soap) 40,000 in Cheshire.

The retention of the family land has often been a matter of succeeding at an early age. For instance, the tenth Duke of Beaufort succeeded at the age of twenty-four in 1924; thus for over fifty years the Beauforts have not faced any death-duty problems. The Duke of Norfolk held his title and estates for fifty-eight years, until 1975, but those aristocratic acres that have become dissipated have largely been the result of untimely deaths in quick succession.

The larger landowners in England do not always own a cohesive block of land which in any sense compares with the mini-kingdoms, the prerogative of the Scottish peerage. The late Duke of Norfolk, for example, had 6,000 hectares, and his castle at Arundel in Sussex, but at Castle Stud (where his racehorses were trained) there was another 2,600 hectares, of which 1,000 were woodlands. He was also described as Sheffield's biggest private landlord, with about 2,000 hectares, and had the 1,600-hectare Everingham Hall Estate near York.

Bernard, Duke of Norfolk, had succeeded to his dukedom and estates at the age of nine. On his death the Dukedom went to Lord Beaumont, his distant cousin, but the Barony of Herries, dating from 1490 and succeeding through the distaff line, went to his oldest daughter, Lady Anne Fitzalan-Howard, as did the Everingham estate. Since Norfolk's father had married the Baroness Herries, he inherited his mother's title, but it was one of many: sixteenth Duke of Norfolk; Earl of Arundel; Baron Maltravers; Earl of Surrey; Baron Herries; Baron FitzAlan; and Earl of Norfolk. The new (seventeenth) Duke, Lord Beaumont, was previously Lord Howard of Glossop, before succeeding to the Dukedom and the hereditary post of Earl Marshal of England. He did not inherit the Herries Barony, but added two more to the future line of the Norfolks. Likewise, the family lands have grown.

Beaumont lost the Everingham Estate to Lady Anne, but added to the ducal territory his own Carlton Towers Estate in the West Riding, and in 1975, within months of succeeding, he paid £250,000 for 2,600 hectares, part of one of the finest grouse moors in England, at Arkengarthdale in the North Riding. It had been part of the estate of air pioneer Sir Tommy Sopwith, and the new Duke bought it for his son, complaining that it would have been too expensive to buy the whole place. A Swedish company bought the eastern section.

The seventh Lord Hotham (died 1967) increased his 4,900 hectares to 7,700 during his lifetime. Certainly, during a period when many estates have been broken up there have been exceptions who have proved that it was possible to retain the family land, or even to increase it. Not all the members of the House of Lords are landed. There were 931 hereditary peerages in existence before Life Peerages were instituted, the last hereditary peerages being granted in 1964. But only 350 were landowners on any traditional scale.

The ducal estates tended to be the largest, and the general scale to diminish from north to south in Britain. Of the 26 surviving dukes in the UK (who own collectively just over 400,000 hectares) some are landless. Leinster and St Albans have no land. Two more, Montrose, who has 1,200 hectares in Rhodesia, and has been a member of Ian Smith's cabinet, and Manchester, with 4,900 hectares in Kenya, have little connection with the UK. Abercorn has some 800 hectares in County Tyrone.

The fortunes of the Duke of Newcastle illustrate the strong tradition of family land-owning. In the eighteenth century the Pelhams had vast estates in twelve counties; their annual rent roll was £30,000 (something like £1 million today). The estate diminished, and in the Derby Census in 1873 they had 12,200 hectares left. Until the 1930s much of this remained, including 2,000 hectares of Sherwood Forest. The need for two sets of death duties within twelve years during the depressed farming times decimated the estate. In 1941 the present Duke's father died, and the thrice married Duke was a Squadron Leader in the RAF. He left England in 1947 to farm in Rhodesia. There was nothing left of the old English estate, but his success at farming in Africa allowed him to return, and he has rebuilt the Newcastle holdings to their present size of 3,600 hectares, though in Somerset, far from Sherwood Forest. Such stories are rare, but they illustrate the tenacity of the aristocracy.

Others have laid the foundations for the future by embarking upon the 'Stately Homes' business; notably John Russell, thirteenth Duke of Bedford, who found himself with £4½ million death duties when he returned from South Africa to claim his ducal inheritance in 1953. Twenty years later, the job completed and the estates on a sound footing, he handed over to his son, the Marquess of Tavistock, and left England again. While it is easy to lament the break-up of the great estates, the retention of considerable areas by comparatively few families is a remarkable example of durability. The dukes alone own 3 per cent of the farmland.

Although a few have been prudent enough to save substantial portions, some have lost all their land. The Socialist Earl of Huntingdon, an eminent mural painter and married to authoress Margaret Lane, has none of the 5,500 hectares his forebears possessed. The Tory Earl Ferrers, six foot six, grey-haired, a former

PPS at the Ministry of Agriculture, and now a small farmer of 150 hectares in Suffolk, saw the hammer come down on his family estate at Stauntonferrers in Leicestershire. The Ferrers date back to the Conquest, but the old mansion is now a convalescent home, and the 3,500 hectares had dwindled to only 690 when Lord Ferrers' father was finally forced to sell up. He in fact died the day before the sale.

Below the top tier of landowners come a number of usefully sized estates. In Gloucestershire, apart from the Badminton estate of the Beauforts, is the 6,500-hectare Cirencester Park of Henry, eighth Earl Bathurst (1772). He succeeded to the estate when he was sixteen, and also became heir to his aunt, Lady Apsley. The estate today embraces three complete villages, and much of the land has remained in the family since 1648.

If one leaves out of account Scotland and Wales, the landed estates in England also are to be found in the 'gaps in the map'. Essentially they get smaller the farther south, with the exception of the Celtic fringe, and many aristocrats with large territorial tracts saw fit to have a smaller place nearer to the Court of St James. In the Midlands there are still a few estates over 8,000 hectares, although there is one farming enterprise which owns more land. It is the Co-Op, with 14,000 hectares mainly in Cheshire, where it concentrates on dairying. Strutt & Parker (Farms) Ltd farms 8,500 hectares in Essex and Suffolk; it owns 5,300 of its own, and another 3,200 of the Terling estate of Lord Raleigh. Another farmer, Frank Arden, farms 8,500 hectares, but much of this is rented land. Earl Fitzwilliam, with 10,000 hectares near Peterborough; the Marquess of Exeter; former Olympic hurdler Lord Burghley, descendant of Elizabeth I's Chancellor, with his 8,800 hectares at Stamford (also in Lincolnshire and landlord of the *Farmers' Weekly*) Easton Lodge Farm stand out as major landowners. The Duke of Grafton, who is a descendant of Charles II, has 4,400 hectares in Norfolk, but none at his old traditional home at Grafton in Northamptonshire. Below this line the larger estates are rare, although the Earl of Pembroke has 6,400 hectares down in Wiltshire.

The new yeomen of England

The CLA, in an attempt to popularize its image, declares that half its 45,000 members own less than 40 hectares each, and 90 per cent of its members are owner/occupiers. The CLA does not embrace Scotland, but making allowances for the English and Welsh farmland area returned by the Ministry of Agriculture of 11·4 million hectares, it would seem that 10 per cent of the CLA membership are estate-owners in the traditional sense. There are only about 350 landed aristocrats, and possibly double that number of untitled landed gentry who combine to control the larger estates. We have seen that 21 dukes own 400,000 hectares, and four out of the top seven are not dukes, so that it is possible that no more than 20 owners hold the next 400,000 hectares. The pattern of private land-ownership reveals that a remarkably large part of Britain is owned by a remarkably small number of people.

As political dogma it may be anathema, but for a healthy, stable, progressive farming industry it is highly desirable that there are landlords, so that young farmers do not necessarily have to buy land in order to farm it. Neither must we forget the lead in farming technology that started with the Woburn Sheep and Cattle Fairs. These were probably the forerunner of today's agricultural shows, and were the initiative of Coke of Holkham (Earl of Leicester) and 'Turnip' Townshend (Viscount Townshend his descendant, the present Marquess of Townshend, is Chairman of Anglia TV). Nearer our own times, the late Norfolk landowner Lord Iveagh, of Guinness fame, pioneered, with his neighbour the late Duke of Grafton, the farming of that light and sandy Norfolk soil. These men had large enough estates to be able to afford to make mistakes. They also had time to think, and their thinking has been of inestimable benefit to farming.

As long as the Clores of this world (and Sir Charles has his 3,000-hectare Stype Estate at Hungerford in Berkshire) continue to invest in an English country estate, then there may yet be a future for tenant farmers under a private landlord. It may not please the Socialists, but the continuity of the traditional structure of the countryside is vital if farming is to continue.

The decline of the landed estate has meant the advent of more farmers owning their own land. As the rise in direct owner/occupation has gone from 10 per cent in 1900 to 60 per cent today, and allowing that 10 per cent of that change-over had been landlords taking their own land into direct owner-occupation, then 40 per cent of the farmland is now in the ownership of the new yeomen. This may conflict with Howard's assumption that no more than 25 per cent of the land is held today by those families who held it at the turn of the century, but there have been more changes in the last three decades than in the 50 years prior to that. The Agricultural Mortgage Corporation may help to clarify this situation. Since inception in 1928, it boasts that it has provided the finance to purchase 1·7 million hectares, or 16 per cent of the farmland of England and Wales. Just under half the total land that may have changed hands. This £268 million advance from the AMC now stands at £79 million less, the amount having been repaid by borrowers, and in 1972, 800,000 hectares had been repaid of the original, and a total of 1·7 million hectares since 1928. It represents an average loan of only £99 per hectare anyway. Today the AMC has 11,000 farmer customers, with 920,000 hectares on mortgage.

Although many Scottish estates have been sold, many remain, and the Great Glen Estate of Lord Lovat, with his 76,000 hectares, is an example. The generally lower land values of much of this mountain and moor have resulted in a lower taxation problem. After the AMC loans it is clear that the remainder of the change-over has been financed by the Joint Stock Banks, with an indebtedness by farmers of £1,000 million (AMC £179 million). Ostensibly the money has been advanced for current trading liquidity, and the sum represents little more than three months turnover of the industry; but the title deeds of more British farmland rests in bank strongrooms than in solicitors' black boxes.

The new yeomen have few more financial burdens than the traditional ones, and since they have the benefits of farming profits, as well as the capital appreciation, this may well represent a better chance to combat the rising tide of taxation and perpetuate private land-ownership of the farmland in the future. Nearly 2,000 élite are members of the '400-hectare Club' as owner/occupiers, and 10,000 more have between 120 and 400 hectares (a total of 2 million hectares). The mopping up of the very small, uneconomic farmsteads is a continuing operation in the UK, though it gains momentum when land prices show a greater affinity to farming profits. The fragmentation of British soil may yet be the salvation of British rural life and farming.

10 Public Landowners

The Ministry of Agriculture

'At present the Minister is in possession of some 230,000 acres of agricultural land.'

Government Report, April 1956

'The acreage under the management of my Department is now about 25,200 acres.'

Rt Hon. James Prior, MP, 19 April 1972

Ministry-held land

	Hectarage
Experimental husbandry farms	6,030
The farm settlements (Lincs)	2,444
Land Settlement Association	1,770
The Laxton Estate (Nottinghamshire)	740
Intended forest land[1]	3,720
Remainder[1]	3,040
	17,744

The Ministry of Agriculture are the owners of the 17,000 or so hectares shown above. Some has been in their ownership for a long time, but the figure now remaining must be as slim as it can reasonably be expected to remain. There has been a continuing policy of relinquishing farmland, and the considerable quantity acquired by requisition during the War has now largely been returned.

The wartime farmland of the Ministry was an example of the National Government taking control of farms that were under-producing for the national well-being. They were farmed by the 'War Ag' Committees, but in many instances the ownership was not changed. The profit or loss of the farming operations was gained or lost by the landowner. Other land was acquired by direct purchase, and by 1956, when the dust had settled and the independent Ministry of Food had once again become amalgamated with agriculture to form the Ministry of Agriculture, Food and Fisheries, there was 92,000 hectares in possession. The Agricultural Land Commission had been set up under the 1947

[1] *Hansard,* 4 April 1972.

Agriculture Act to manage these lands, but a policy of reducing the area was already under way. It was in tune with the times as post-war Britain began the road to recovery that was to lead to the affluent society.

In the early 1950s a new Tory Government embarked upon a policy of shedding the land that the wartime emergency had forced upon Government Departments. Sir Thomas Dugdale, as Minister of Agriculture, was forced to resign after the Critchel Down scandal, when demilitarized land was perfunctorily sold, without recourse to the owners from whom it had been compulsorily acquired during the wartime emergency.

The sales policy had earmarked over 680 hectares for sale; 400 hectares had actually been offered, but only 92 hectares sold. Nevertheless, at that stage they were envisaging a reduction of up to 40,000 hectares in the Agricultural Land Commission holdings. Much of this was not primarily first-class farming land. The Arton Wilson Report in 1956 stated unequivocally:

> A good deal of it will be of poor quality, and will often present special difficulties owing to its scattered nature or lack of adequate buildings and fixed equipment. Under present policy, it is not likely there will be any significant addition to this acreage.

Fifteen years later, there were only 15,240 hectares left, excluding the Experimental Husbandry Farms. A vast amount had gone from out of the Ministry's hands; some had gone to the Forestry Commission, and some had been sold back to private ownership, but there remained some anomalies. There was still another 4,400 hectares originally purchased for forestry. This was immediately transferred to the Forestry Commission in the Prior Re-Appraisal of the Ministry's land in 1972. The 272-hectare Bosbury smallholdings estate in Herefordshire was transferred to the County Council. The real transference from Government Departments to private ownership was 480 hectares, which realized the sum of £345,000. Thus the *Hansard* quotation of 25,200 acres constitutes the results in a reduction in existing anomalies.

Among the land that has at times in the past come under the wing of the Ministry has been amounts of land taken by the Treasury in lieu of death-duty payments. This has been only isolated examples, as the Inland Revenue is not accustomed to the barter system. Even the National Trust will not accept land or property unless it is suitably endowed. Although oil paintings have been accepted, the only example in respect of land was the Glanllyn Estate at Bala in Merionethshire, which was accepted by the Treasury in lieu of death duties in 1949. It was the first case arising under the Finance Act 1946, presented by Labour's post-war Chancellor, Sir Stafford Cripps. The Estate was transferred to the Ministry of Agriculture, and consisted of 14,800 hectares, including Bala Lake, and the village of Llanwchllyn. There were 150 holdings, and the lowest was 150 metres above sea-level. During the Ministry's ownership 1,000 hectares was transferred to the Forestry Commission, and then in 1961 it was decided to sell the estate. By this time the 150 holdings had been reduced to 95 by amalgamations, and in 1963 a consortium of tenants completed the purchase.

Bala Lake was sold to the County Council for recreation and amenity purposes, and the Welsh League of Youth bought the mansion-house.

It may seem anomalous that within the general complex of agricultural research, development and education the Agricultural Research Council own the research farms, the county councils the farm colleges, and the Ministry are left with the experimental husbandry farms. The National Smallholdings Estate has been paid for by the ratepayers through the county councils, but the estates of the Land Settlement Association and the estate of the Farm Settlements in Lincolnshire are under the management of the Ministry. The origins have dictated the present position. The LSA owes its success to co-ordinating the sale of produce from its tenants, who are today the successors of those men who fled from the unemployment of industry in the depression before the last War, while the farm settlements were created for establishing ex-Servicemen on the land after the 1914–18 war.

The day has gone when public-spirited citizens leave the Government gifts in their will, but in more gracious, and spacious, days it happened. There are two instances of the Ministry of Agriculture being the happy recipient of such bequests. It was left 48 hectares in the middle of Wrexham for the purpose of settling ex-Servicemen after the First World War. About sixteen smallholdings were created. The estate was administered by Trustees, but was eventually sold to the Wrexham Corporation as a public park, and the proceeds given to the King's Fund. This fund was established by King George V in 1918, and extended by King George VI for the 1939 War. It has since been extended to include those disabled or bereaved by service in operational areas such as Korea and Malaya.

Another contributor to the King's Fund was the Paglesham Estate in Essex. It was the gift in 1943 of A. D. Martin to the Ministry of Agriculture and Fisheries. It consisted of 382 hectares adjacent to the rich grazings of the Essex marshes, and close to the ill-fated Maplin site. Mr Martin did not make any restrictions concerning the use or disposal of his estate, but it was wartime, and it was known that he had the welfare of ex-Servicemen in mind. Twenty years later 294 hectares were sold by public auction for the sum of £129,300. The remainder, mainly saltings, are still used for fishery research, but Paglesham became known as a vegetable research centre, and 60 hectares were later transferred to the Agricultural Research Council.

Another bequest to the Ministry was that of Arthur Rickwood, of 60 hectares of bare fenland for the purposes of agricultural experiments. It is still well known today as the Arthur Rickwood Experimental Husbandry Farm in the Isle of Ely. Subsequently 13 hectares have been added to the original gift, and new buildings, cottages and an office block have been added. It has cost £70,000 to make these additions, but today this EHF earns a high reputation in its experimental work on cereals, potatoes, carrots, celery and onions in fen soils.

The chain of Ministry EHFs today is the result of the thinking that emanated from the revolution that took place in farming during the period 1939–45. Even when farming was stagnating under the depressive financial constraints prior to

1939, technical innovations were still being evolved, though few were translated into practical applications on the farm. There were many discussions on the proper process of advising farmers about these new techniques, and encouraging their adoption. The impetus of wartime had to be continued into the aftermath of war, and thus when the National Agricultural Advisory Service (NAAS) was created in 1946 such considerations were paramount. From this came the establishment of a chain of farms throughout England and Wales (why not Scotland or Ireland?).

These experimental farms were to be open demonstration areas where the farmers could see up-to-date methods being practised. They were spaced to cover every climatic condition experienced in these islands, to include the complete range of soil types, and specialized farming enterprises. The original proposals in 1946 were for eighteen husbandry farms, and six horticultural stations; in the event, only twelve husbandry farms were founded, although eight horticultural stations were established. The Arthur Rickwood EHF in the Isle of Ely made the number up to thirteen, where it remains today. These Ministry farms have gained in stature by the practical approach and sound advice which has flowed from them for over thirty years.

The Manor of Laxton

When a Minister of Agriculture accepts the seals of office from the Queen on his appointment he assumes the title 'Lord of the Manor of Laxton'. Laxton is a village in north Nottinghamshire, just west of the A1 and north of Newark, where the land is flat and fertile. Farther west lie the remnants of Sherwood Forest, and beyond rises the rugged attractiveness of the Pennines. Beyond lies the Peak District, which provides only a peasant-like survival for farming and farmers. Almost ironically, the reason why the Ministry purchased the Laxton Estate in 1952 was to preserve the traditional peasant farming embodied in its medieval open-field strip-farming system.

This estate of 740 hectares has 21 farms, varying in size from 16½ to 58 hectares, a smallholding of 4 hectares, 8 houses and cottages, 3 old alms-houses, and a pub, the Dovecoat Inn; as late as the seventeenth century the open fields at Laxton comprised over 520 hectares, which were then being farmed in over 2,000 strips. By 1952, at the time of its purchase by the Ministry, the area of open fields had been reduced to 193 hectares farmed in 167 strips. West Field, with 58 hectares of arable land, contained 51 strips; the 56½-hectare South Field was, and is, farmed in 47 strips; and Mill Field, the largest of the three with 78 hectares, contains 69 strips.

Without the intervention of the Ministry this working museum of medieval farming (which is the only known example of the open-field system remaining in Britain), would have disappeared completely, but it has been a costly operation. Since 1952 over £100,000 has been spent on capital works, and another £50,000

In the heart of the City of London stands Fountain House, headquarters of one of the new breed of large-scale farmers *Photo Anthony Rosen*

A modern cow complex at East Atton, operated by Fountain Farming *Photo Anthony Rosen*

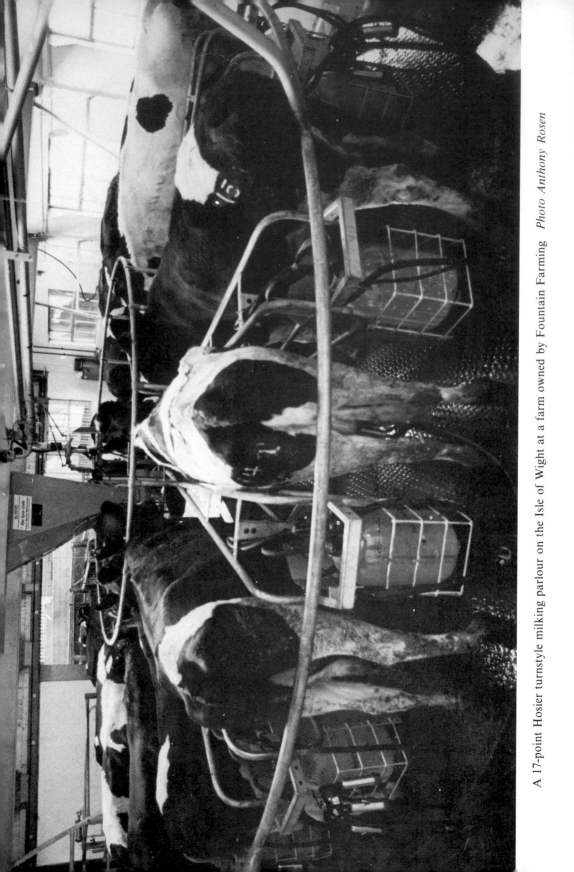

A 17-point Hosier turnstyle milking parlour on the Isle of Wight at a farm owned by Fountain Farming   *Photo Anthony Rosen*

Britain's largest farmer is the Co-Operative Wholesale Society. Here they are harvesting grain on the Weston Hall Estate, near Crewe, Cheshire
Photo Co-Operative Wholesale Society

A prize-winning set of new farm buildings at Stamp Hill Farm, Kirkby Thore, Penrith
Photo Country Landowners Association

Rovie Estate, Rogart, Sutherland. In this topography farming achieves a different image. *Photo Savills*

on maintenance and repairs. Three farmhouses have been built, thirteen others re-roofed; modernization programmes to the fixed equipment have been carried out. Dutch barns, cattle yards and general purpose buildings have been erected, but the rent roll (which stood at £2,000 per annum in 1952, and was little over £2.50 per hectare) had risen to over £10,000 by 1974. The original twenty-one farms have been reduced to sixteen, but the open-strip system with its medieval ancestry remains. The Minister might also remember that the Dovecoat Inn is part of his jurisdiction. Probably the only Cabinet Minister to own a pub!

The Farm Settlements

Location	Total Hectares	Area Tenanted	Full-time	Part-time	Total
Sutton Bridge, Lincs.	2,200	2,067	118	33	151
Holbeach, Lincs.	397	393	36	42	78
Total:	2,597	2,460	154	75	229

The basic differences between the LSA, the FS and the National Small-holdings Estate is that the latter was instituted in 1908, with the objective of providing small farms to meet the demand. There were no particular social problems at the time, except that the Liberal Government was in a reforming mood. Many other innovations stemmed from that busy period. The smallholdings were to be a rung on the ladder into farming, to be used as a stepping-stone, and this remained so until the Wise Report in 1966. The farm settlements were established, however, as a reward to the returning soldiers from the 1914–18 War, the war which was to end all wars, and be followed by everlasting peace. It was to provide for these soldiers a small measure of the land they had fought to protect in Flanders mud and on the Somme.

The Land Settlement Association, on the other hand, was the result, a decade later, of the disillusionment of the depression years. By establishing small farms the Government sought to placate urban discontent.

Today the farm settlements are confined to two small estates in Lincolnshire, which are almost a museum for a bygone attempt at agrarian resettlement. During the 1914–18 War little action was taken to expand the smallholdings estate which had been created in 1908, and was being unenthusiastically and slowly adopted by the county councils. Discussions on the role of smallholdings took place during the War against a background of food shortages, and the submarine menace to merchant vessels. It was a commonly held assumption that smallholdings would lead to increased productivity, but there were arguments against this, and in general the thinking was prompted by social reasons.

In 1915 a Committee was appointed by the President of the Board of Agriculture. Sir Harry Verney Bt MP, Parliamentary Secretary to the

President, Lord Lucas and Dingwall, was appointed to chair this Committee. They took the view that a vigorous land-settlement policy for ex-soldiers and sailors, and for townsmen as well as countrymen, should be embarked upon. The recommendations of the Verney Committee assisted in the Small Holdings Colonies Act 1916, which gave the power to establish farm colonies on which a few hundred ex-Servicemen were settled, even before Germany was beaten and the War concluded. By 1918 the Holbeach Colony, one of only two remaining today, had been established, as well as a profit-sharing farm at Patrington in Yorkshire. As the Armistice was signed the Government took powers to raise the limit of Small Holdings Colonies to 24,000 hectares, and three years later, in March 1921, had acquired only fifteen properties totalling 10,400 hectares.

The expansion never went beyond this point. The aftermath was not proving as rosy as had been painted. There were difficulties in the high costs of establishment, and the inexperience of newcomers was an unavoidable but unfortunate fact. By 1920 only one of the six farms showed a profit. For the 380 civilians and ex-military there was an average loss of about £70 per man. In 1921 the Ministry disposed of 6,800 of the 10,400 hectares that had been acquired, and the scheme was abandoned. The remainder were converted into smallholdings estates, and by 1938, just twenty years after its inception, the Ministry had 4,049 hectares as smallholding colonies on six estates.

Some 49,000 ex-Servicemen from the 1914–18 War had applied for holdings at the time of its origin, and although today the colonies are a bygone relic the expansion of the National Smallholdings Estate has largely filled the gap. Perhaps today this romantic urge for a small farm in the country has been replaced by the urge for a small country cottage, from whence the occupier can commute to the nearest city centre; but in the aftermath of the First World War the feelings towards farming and the joys of country life were much more romanticized and emotional.

Land Settlement Association

There are ten estates of the LSA, over half of which are grouped in Bedfordshire, Cambridge, Essex and Suffolk. One is geographically remote, at Newent in Gloucestershire, near the Bristol Channel, but the more northerly ones have been clipped off the national LSA Estate.

These estates, or groups of small farms, are on average about 160 hectares each. The average size of each holding is less than 4 hectares and they are essentially designed as intensive horticultural holdings.

Today the LSA has become known as the producer of high-class horticultural products such as tomatoes, lettuce, celery, cucumbers, rhubarb, some other soft fruits, flowers and plants, with an emphasis upon chrysanthemums. Pigs and poultry also came within the scope of these dedicated horticulturalists, but livestock output occupies less than 14 per cent of the average annual sales.

As a general principle crop-production and the exclusion of livestock has been the LSA's dominant policy for many years. With this in mind, the decade from 1965 to 1975 saw the size of the Estate almost halved. On 31 March 1968 the four northern estates at Crofton, Broadwath and Dalston in Cumberland, and at Stannington in Northumberland, were axed. The LSA Estate at Elmesthorpe in Leicestershire, Harroby, Lincolnshire and Oxcroft in Derbyshire have also disappeared since that time. The Wise Committee (June 1967) recommended that the horticultural concentration could be further improved by axing four more estates: Fulney (Lincolnshire), Snaith (Yorkshire), Abington (Cambridge-shire) and Andover (Hampshire). In the event, however, only Andover left the LSA Estate (1974), and now ten remain.

The Andover Estate comprised a total of 196 hectares, divided into 35 holdings, although only 31 tenants and 140 hectares were involved in the scheme. It was the livestock emphasis at Andover which prompted its exclusion by the Minister of Agriculture; at that time on this estate the tenants were acquiring 78 per cent of their livelihood from livestock sales, compared with the LSA average of 14 per cent.

The strength of the LSA is in its example of co-ordinated marketing, its collective farm image and the discipline which its tenant farmers have evolved. It is also the only example in the UK of any form of State-controlled collective farming, even though it is voluntary. Its accrued marketing expertise, with its distinctive trade mark, has been its salvation. The marketing service has enabled many smallholders to remain solvent when the emphasis upon mass production and standardized marketing labels has been the trend of our times.

The produce from the LSA farms is centrally graded at a packing shed on each estate. The Pack House Managers are co-ordinated by the Central Marketing Manager in London, who negotiates contracts on the national level; as such the LSA tenants are insulated from market fluctuations by contracting 25 per cent of their produce direct to retailers. This also ensures that they are not cutting each other's throats. The equalization of sales and a pool price means expert grading, and the eventual profits are paid back to the tenants. The discipline extends to forbidding growers to market any of their produce privately, although they do sell eggs at the gate; there is also a planning of the planting intentions between tenants, and between estates, to build up a national picture of production trends in the highly volatile horticultural market. The success is illustrated by the position of LSA growers in the league table of specialized production. They have acquired 75 per cent of the spring lettuce market, about 10 per cent of UK tomato-production, and are almost the only producers of early and late self-blanching celery.

The Newent revolt

The story of the LSA has not, however, been, all smooth sailing. In 1971 the tenants of the LSA Newent Estate in Gloucestershire came into open conflict with the Association's management. They complained that the dictatorial methods of the central management and the 'pooling' system of payments was acting against the Newent growers, who claimed to be above average. They also complained of the lack of autonomy in the administration of their affairs, and stated that the four representatives of growers on the ten-man National Committee were appointed by the Minister of Agriculture, but on the recommendation of the Management.

The 49 tenants in 1971 refused co-operation for the central scheme. On the 80-hectare estate, with an average of only 1½ hectares each, these small farmers had invested up to £30,000 of their own money on intensive glasshouses and equipment to grow high-priced salad crops, soft fruit and green beans. They had also erected a large modern packing-house for the central grading of their production. What they were complaining about was out-of-date philosophy on the part of the LSA.

In a letter[2] W. A. Offord, Secretary of the Newent LSA Growers Association, concluded:

> When will the Minister wake up to the fact that the days of re-settlement of miners and agricultural peasants are over in most cases? It is time the LSA became truly democratic in practice.

This cry from the heart showed that the original concept of the LSA had long since been forgotten, and the review of the Ministry-held land seemed to furnish little excuse for retaining this successful commercial venture within the Ministry orbit. Nevertheless, it remains as a quasi-Governmental anomaly, operating entirely independently, but with its management team appointed by the Minister, with an Annual Report to the Minister, and with the land owned by the Government.

The LSA is managed by an Executive Committee of which Josclyn Gibb, Merchant Banker, was its Chairman until 1977. Former NUAAW General Secretary Lord Collison is now the Chairman. Its centralized administrative Headquarters is situated in unsalubrious Cromwell Road, London. Since 1953 the estate has been required to pay its own way, and although it has made losses in only two years since that time (loss in 1962–3 £17,284; and in 1965–6 loss £10,299). Overall it has fulfilled its profit-making requirements. In 1972, 49 per cent of the tenants made over £3,000 profit. Only 9 per cent made under £1,200.

Location of remaining L.S.A. estates

Abbington, Cambs.	Newbourn, Suffolk.
Fen Drayton, Cambs.	Fulney, Lincs.
Chawston, Beds.	Sidlesham, Sussex.
Potton, Beds.	Newent, Glos.
Foxash, Essex.	Snaith, Yorks.

[2] Farmers Weekly 11 June 1971.

The original concept of stultifying industrial unrest and providing work for ex-miners has been forgotten. There are now less than half the original number of holdings in existence, but it represents an interesting example of a unique operation. Its tenants have successful lives, and it does not cost the British taxpayer a single penny.

The experimental husbandry farms

Even when farming was stagnating under the depressive financial constraints prior to 1939, there were still technical innovations, the main problem being to persuade hard-pressed farmers to put these into practice, and there was much discussion on the proper process of advising farmers about these new techniques. Although the wartime impetus promulgated new ideas like a spreading bush fire, there was a determination to continue this advisory role, and the dissemination of knowledge in the peaceful aftermath. Thus when the National Agricultural Advisory Service (NAAS) was created in 1946 this consideration was uppermost. It was one thing advising farmers and another to educate the advisers, and the thinking centred around the establishment of a chain of farms throughout England and Wales, which could act as experimental farms where farmers could see the new ideas in action.

These farms between them were to cover every climatic condition experienced in these islands, as well as a range of soil-types and specialized farming enterprises. The original proposals in 1946 were for 18 husbandry farms and 6 horticultural stations, but in the event only 12 husbandry farms were founded, although 8 horticultural stations were established. The Arthur Rickwood EHF in the Isle of Ely makes the number of EHFs up to 13. It was the bequest in 1964 of 60 hectares of bare fen-land donated to the Ministry for experimental purposes that enabled the establishment of another experimental farm. Today an additional 13 hectares have been purchased, and the additional land has been equipped with buildings. In total it has cost the Ministry £70,000 to provide buildings for storage of crops and implements, two cottages and an office block. There is no livestock on this farm.

The National Smallholdings Estate

There should be no general expansion of the present National Smallholdings Estate.

Wise Committee Report, 1966.

Westmorland is the smallest, with only one smallholding of 17 hectares. The GLC and some Country Boroughs and Cities are also Smallholdings Authorities, and even Birmingham has 51 tenants on 1,475 hectares.

The only example of community landlordism in England and Wales is the

County Smallholdings Estates; The Top Ten

	Tenants	Hectarage
Cambridgeshire and Isle of Ely	1,239	13,486
Norfolk	782	12,190
Somerset	371	6,991
Huntingdon and Peterborough	363	5,428
Yorks (West Riding)	240	5,347
Wiltshire	208	5,288
Lincoln (Holland)	740	5,258
Cheshire	298	5,142
Devonshire	236	5,067
Gloucestershire	272	4,833

National Smallholdings Estate, which covers just over 160,000 hectares, supports nearly 11,000 tenant farmers and is owned and managed by Departments of the County Councils. This is not the only involvement of these bodies in farm-landlord management; they also act as custodians of the Green Belt farms surrounding the larger cities, though they have acute vandalism problems in many areas.

The National Rent Roll of the Smallholdings Estate is over £3 million, but administrative expenses average 40 per cent, with four counties actually absorbing over 50 per cent in expenses in 1972[3]. This is a percentage that would be unacceptable to any private landlord; but perhaps this is the price of democracy. The profits of these estates accrue to the councils as an alleviation of the rate burden, but the return on the investment is minuscule. At a figure of £2,470 per hectare, it represents a return of about ½ per cent. Much of the present-day National Estate was purchased before 1926, when at 175,200 hectares it was larger than its present size. At that date it had cost £20 million, giving the councils a net return on their original outlay nearer 10 per cent. However, the ownership of these large land areas has given them the opportunity for making large sums of money from development on their land. They have sold and continue to sell around 1,000 hectares annually. Despite the bad rate of return which this land represents, with the social needs for which it was created no longer relevant, it represents an increasing asset.

Since 1945 the number of holdings has halved, the average size has doubled, and the total UK area has gone down by more than 8,000 hectares. The structure has been modernized, and there are plans for the complete reorganization of these farms pigeon-holed away in County Halls. These reorganization plans, which were drawn up as a result of the 1970 Agriculture Act, will gradually be put into operation as tenants die or holdings become vacant. It will raise the average size of smallholdings to an approximate figure of

[3] Yorks East Riding 53 per cent; Worcestershire 53 per cent; Oxford 52 per cent; Durham 65 per cent.

32 hectares. Today in England the average size is 15 hectares, but 17 in Wales. This has risen by about ½ hectare per year over the last two decades. It was only 5 hectares in 1914, and only 9 hectares in 1949.

The present-day average of 15 hectares per holding is achieved within a range of only 6 hectares in Worcestershire to 38 hectares in arable East Suffolk. The National Estate expanded steadily up to 1915, and it was a plank of official policy that the creation of smaller farms would be more productive. This emphasis continued, and between 1918 and 1925 the proportion of small farms rose dramatically. By 1964 Local Authorities Smallholdings formed 4·7 per cent of the number of farms in England and Wales, but because of their size, covered only 1·7 per cent of the farmland area. The original 'social' objectives of the smallholdings policy may look like perpetuating peasant farming, but the Local Authorities farms in fact represent only one in ten of the farms under 40 hectares.

Smallholdings were created by buying estates or large farms and sub-dividing them, splitting the farmhouse into two, building new farmsteads in outlying parts of a large farm, creating sets of farm buildings and generally fragmenting the agricultural structure. Unlike the LSA, there are no centralized marketing facilities, and no more co-operation between smallholdings tenants than any other types of farmers. Few counties ever hold an annual dinner for their tenantry, and the land within each county being utilized for the statutory provision of smallholding is usually spread throughout its whole area. It forms a disjointed 'estate', occasionally distinguishable by the common architectural design of the farmhouses and cottages.

The present-day National Smallholdings Estate owes its origins to the 1908 Smallholdings and Allotments Act; prior to this there had been agitation and controversy dating from around 1860, when such Victorian political figures as Joseph Chamberlain, John Stuart Mill, John Bright and Jesse Collings had advocated a policy of State-sponsored smallholdings as an antidote for the revolution in agriculture which was destroying the yeomen farmers. By 1908 there was a saga of Acts of Parliament dealing with these matters. Perhaps significantly, the farm-worker had been given the vote in 1884.

The dilemma of the Victorians was resolved into action in the twentieth century when the county estates were built up following the 1908 Act, but the individual enthusiasm of county councillors accounts for the wide disparity in the County League Table today. Another problem which existed up to the Wise Report in 1966, and which has still not been solved, is the general objective of the smallholdings policy. Although rationalization in the size of holdings is a continuing policy, the general need is undetermined, and the policy a static one.

The Wise Report

Just before Harold Macmillan terminated his six gruelling years as Prime Minister with a sudden illness, the Minister of Agriculture, Christopher Soames, set up a Committee to review the workings of the National Smallholdings Estate.

It was under the chairmanship of Michael Wise, a Professor of Geography at the London School of Economics. It conducted its review at a cost of £3,670, of which £1,500 was for printing its own report. It reported in March 1966, by which time Sir Alec Douglas-Home had passed through the Premiership, and his Earldom, lost the 1964 Election, and ex-schoolmaster Fred Peart had been at the Ministry of Agriculture nearly two years. Although the Report was accepted, it was 1970 before any real legislative process was incorporated into the Agriculture Act of that year.

The original concept, embodied in the 1892 Act, was for the tenants eventually to purchase their holdings; indeed, the terms of the tenancy stated this, though the purchase payments were to be spread over a fifty-year period. Before and after the 1914–18 War, the thinking had developed into a 'ladder', as it was envisaged that tenants would use a local-authority smallholding as the first rung, moving on to a larger farm. Plainly, by the time the Wise Committee was set up, this concept was not working. Tenants stayed put, thus closing the door to new entrants, but since another provision of the 1908 Act and the 1926 Settlement had been the furnishing of smallholdings according to the need, this was obviously impossible unless the councils were continually, and rapidly, buying more and more farms for smallholding purposes.

The Wise Committee saw this problem, and recommended that the time for change had arrived:

> The policy should not rest on so-called 'social' considerations, in which we include the provision of career opportunities for agricultural workers in general. Smallholdings should be thought of as a 'gateway' to farming, through which only the best young men may enter, rather than as part of the 'farming ladder'.

It further stressed that new entrants should have technical knowledge and practical experience, but the objective would be to encourage and facilitate the entrance of keen, qualified young men into a farming 'gateway'. Existing farmworkers were not excluded, but in essence this was a changed policy that recognized the current situation, even though it differed from the original concept. The committee also recommended that the 15,000 smallholdings should be drastically reduced to only one-third of that number, and that there should be a target size of about 32 hectares. At that time only 645 were more than 32 hectares in extent.

After Wise in 1966 the National Smallholdings Estate settled down to follow its new guidelines, but in the early 1970s two new factors arose. Firstly, the price of land shot up violently after 1972–73; and secondly, after the reorganization of local government and the spiralling rate demands, there was pressure on councillors to find new ways of aiding hard-pressed ratepayers. Councils had a valuable asset in its farmland and looked closely at its vast estates.

The dilemma had political overtones, with the Conservatives, traditionally supporting small business-men and in favour of selling council houses to their tenants, ranged in 1977 on the side of selling off the smallholdings estates. This policy was bitterly opposed by the Government and by the NFU, who came down unequivocally in opposition to the sale of county council smallholdings. Since these small farms could be sold only to their tenants, and since the tenants could not afford to buy them, the Tories' stance would appear to have been more socially conscious if they had retained a subsidized section of the community. It was a decision that caused splits and rifts in the Conservative Party.

The original move came from a Cambridgeshire councillor and farmer, Geoffrey Woollard, who put forward a plan to dispose of the Cambridgeshire estate—one of the largest in the country, at 19,000 hectares. His arguments were economic, and he assessed the net return to Cambridgeshire as three-quarters of 1 per cent, on an asset worth £40 million. Derbyshire, Shropshire and Norfolk jumped on the band-wagon, and the Norfolk county council adopted a flexible policy of selling 10 per cent of its estate. Opposition from the Government, and within the Tory ranks at Norwich, curbed this euphoria, and young farmers saw their last chance of getting into farming fast disappearing. In the end very few farms were actually sold.

The concept of creating a national smallholdings estate was an anachronism. As for a farming ladder, even the Wise Committee had recognized that this had not worked out in practice. The smallholdings estate continues to exist but will probably neither grow nor diminish. More important than its strictly agricultural purpose is its social influence; it provides a bedrock for smaller farmers, enabling many of them to gain a reasonable living. It also acts as a buffer to prevent the whole of Britain becoming carved up into vast farming empires

Scotland

The so-called smallholdings estates in Scotland are nearly as large as the whole area in England and Wales, so the word smallholding becomes open to interpretation. The estates were created in Scotland under various Acts of Parliament, dating from the Small Landholders (Scotland) Act 1886, and various succeeding Acts, designed to alleviate the social problems of the industrial unemployed, and for the resettlement of ex-Servicemen. As in England and Wales, the remaining estates survive from a bygone social—not agricultural —policy.

The move to dissolve these holdings made more progress in Scotland. There have been amalgamations to create fewer, more viable holdings. A tally of over 2,000 in 1961 has slumped to 1,200 in 1975. As holdings become vacant they are immediately amalgamated with their neighbours, although a few are sold off.

Scottish Smallholdings Estate

	Hectares	Holdings	Average size
Lowland	16,912	1,263	13 hectares
Highlands	151,380	69	219 hectares
Total	168,292	1,332	

Additionally, the Department of Agriculture for Scotland is responsible for other land devoted to forestry, as opposed to the local-authority administration of smallholdings in England and Wales.

The public landowners

'Government is a contrivance of human wisdom to provide for human wants. Men have a right that those wants should be provided for by this wisdom.'
Edmund Burke

With the sophisticated demands of an ever increasingly affluent society, the demands upon land use for non-farming purposes must grow. Not only does a more educated and organized society demand expansion in the services provided by the State, but the State seeks increasingly to upgrade the standards. Road widths of a standard 24 feet (7·315 metres) carriageway for two-way traffic, additional school playing-fields, and spacious estate layouts are continually straining land resources.

It is not the intention of the Government, or local authorities, to engage upon the business of farming, or particularly to become agricultural landlords, with the exception of the National Smallholdings Estate vested in the county councils; but nevertheless three quasi-Governmental bodies do hold substantial farmland areas as landlords. They are:

Name	Tenanted Farmland	Total Land
Water Authorities	111,248	161,212
National Coal Board	54,370	103,561
Ministry of Defence	49,145	224,252

Source: Harrison/Tranter/Gibbs. 1977.

The Water Undertakings hold their farmland, which basically abuts to reservoirs or catchment areas, as a source of control over pollution into their water, and there are often restrictions upon the farming of the land in relation to the application of fertilizers or any concentrated livestock which could produce an effluent overflow. The NCB maintains that it is not its intention to be a landowner, and has been disposing of 1,000 hectares per annum, although it is continually purchasing more for open-cast operations, and holds 13,600 hectares in reserve for that purpose. Its disposals are invariably to county councils or other official bodies who will carry out reclamation work.

The last substantial owner of farmland is the Ministry of Defence, which has held much of it for many years, and keep tenacious grip on it, despite occasional agitation. It is indefensible that the Defence Ministry should be farming landlords. Many of its tenancies are on a 364-day arrangement to circumvent the Agricultural Holdings Act 1948, tenants are liable to dispossession at short notice, and in some instances can only graze land while firing is not taking place. (It must also be said that very little of their land is of high quality.)

The land held by the Ministry of Transport, Department of Health, British Rail, British Waterways Board, and the British Airports Authority amounts to more than 480,000 hectares. None is utilized for farming, being wholly absorbed by the purpose for which it was purchased, the main exception being that some lesser airports permit haymaking on their grass areas between runways.

Department	Hectarage[4]
British Rail	71,226
British Steel Corporation	23,958
Electricity Undertakings	21,064
British Waterways Board	7,285
British Transport Docks Board	4,209
British Airports Authority	3,541

This selection from the largest bodies illustrates the massive land holdings held in the interests of the activities for which the organizations exist.

The area of Britain owned by the county and district councils is unknown, even to themselves. The road network is divided between the DoE and the county councils. Schools are owned mainly by the county councils, and council houses by the district councils. All that *is* known is that the land owned by these bodies for such purposes rises inexorably. The land owned by the Government in one way or another is constantly increasing, although the Government is increasingly paying more for it. Rates and taxes are thus sometimes transferred into solid assets.

Publicly owned farms covering 22,574 hectares are held for the triple functions of research, experimentation and teaching: the general aim is the improvement and practice of farming, but these three objectives are disparate, and are today the concern of three different groups(sometimes with diametrically opposed results).

Directing Body	Hectares	Owned by
Research Farms	7,244	ARC and Department of Education and Science
Experimental Husbandry Farms	6,030	Ministry of Agriculture
Agricultural Colleges	9,300	County Councils
Total:	22,574	

In view of their main objective, neither the Research Farms nor the EHFs are run for commercial profitability, and farmers visiting these establishments do not expect to find a model of up-to-date farm management. The object is to study

[4]*Land Ownership by Public and Semi-Public Institutions in the UK.* Alan Harrison, R. B. Tranter and R. S. Gibbs, Centre for Agricultural Strategy, Reading (December 1977). They estimated that 11 per cent of the farm and forest area is owned by the non-private sector.

individual experiments in the research establishments and the practical application of them at the EHFs, some of which by necessity will never become widely applied on practical farms. The Agricultural Colleges' farms, however, while used for demonstration purposes by the students, are usually more viable, profit-making concerns, although they do collaborate in small way with some of the EHFs. The farming profits from the College farms are absorbed by the county councils as a rate-support.

The Government's lack of participation in direct farming, and lack of interest in it, shows in their acceptance of the fact that it is an individual, profit-making concern, unlike the Russian collective farms which are State-directed. One Soviet collective farm received no less than 799 telegrams or directives from higher authority prior to collecting in its harvest. The Government is not concerned with nationalized farming, yet it has continually reappraised its own land holdings. The Defence Lands Committee and the Prior reappraisal of the MoA land are examples of this.

If the Government is a reluctant landlord, the councils are not. The GLC, for example, has over 16,000 hectares in total, of which 3,600 hectares is viable farmland, let to tenants, but this is part of London's statutory Green Belt.

It might have been expected that the Ministry of Agriculture would be a substantial landowner in its own right, but even among the League Table of Government Departments it is well down on the list; although Britain's largest landowner, the Forestry Commission, does submit its Annual Report to the Minister of Agriculture and the Secretaries of State for Scotland and Wales. Its annual deficit is also included in the Government Appropriation Accounts under the agricultural expenditure grants and allowances. The 17,700 hectares held by the MoA is small beer even within the range of land held by other Government Departments. The Ministerial responsibility in Scotland is, however, more substantial, even though Scottish land is generally less productive. The Scottish Smallholding Estate and the land held by the Crofters Commission is only marginally smaller than the Smallholding Estate for England and Wales together. In Scotland also the Department of Agriculture hold the land let to Research Institutions, Experimental Stations and Agricultural Colleges.

The defence lands

'The British Army should be a projectile to be fired by the British Navy.'
Lord Grey

'Public interest demands both that the Armed Forces should be properly trained and equipped, and that they should take up as little land as possible for their purposes.'
White Paper on Report of Defence Lands Committee,
August 1974

Although classified as Defence land, the land held by the Services was acquired

Land held by the Armed Forces (in hectares)

England		Wales		Scotland		Gt. Britain	
Total	– Farming	Total	– Farming	Total	– Farming	Total	– Farming
187,798	47,940	20,296	479	19,656	1,176	227,750	49,596

Area held at various dates

Date	Hectarage	Source
1938–9	147,400	Reports of Select Committees on Estimates
1947	600,000	Reports of Select Committees on Estimates
1952	314,800	Reports of Select Committees on Estimates
1958	360,600	Reports of Select Committees on Estimates
1968	243,741 (110,760 farming)	Hansard Vol. 794 p. 142.
1973	302,800	Nugent Report
1977	224,252	Centre for Agricultural Strategy, Paper No. 3

for purposes of training, manoeuvres, barracks and airfields, rather than stretches of coastal cliffs to repel invaders and has increased as a result of two world wars. The quantity of land held has varied as shown above, but a hard core remains. Battle areas on Salisbury Plain, parts of Dartmoor, gunnery ranges at Lulworth and at Castle Martin in Pembroke, firing on the Pentland Hills near Edinburgh and tank training near Thetford Chase—all these are traditional battle training areas. Garrison towns normally have adjacent and extensive military lands for training purposes; at Colchester, for instance, there are 3,200 hectares stretching from the centre of the town to the battle ranges on the Essex marshes. Farther along the same coastline, Shoeburyness and Foulness Island are used for hush-hush military experiments.

The chart showing the fluctuations in the area of defence lands demonstrates that the massive wartime requisition was halved in five years, as land was handed back. Much was not in fact purchased, but compulsorily taken over for the 'duration', however long that might be. The problems of returning land after an airfield has been constructed upon it are immense, but after the Crichel Down fiasco the methods of returning land to its former owners were considerably rationalized. Many farmers who discovered themselves to be owners of great stretches of solid concrete gained a useful bonus by breaking this up and selling it for hard core. It is the thirty years of peace which provides a more interesting picture of the attitude of the High Command towards its land requirements. Longer-range missiles and greater security measures, plus the Northern Ireland involvement, have been sufficient reasons for the military to hold on to their training areas, or even to extend them.

The Nugent Committee

Under the vigorous reappraisal of everything in sight instituted by the Heath administration when it took office, the Defence Land Committee was set up in January 1971, to look at the land held by the Armed Forces. It reported in July 1973, by which time the Government had lost enthusiasm; it was pigeon-holed, and a year later under Wilson there was a White Paper to quell the passions that had been aroused.

The Tories had instigated the Report, as part of their philosophy of the individual, and Labour is by tradition pacifist and anti-military; so that it might have seemed that whatever Government was in power there would for different reasons be a move to reduce the land holdings of the Forces. If results are the criteria of success, then the field-marshals won. Very little land has ever been returned to private ownership, although the para-military do allow 500 cattle and 12,000 sheep to graze the Castlemartin Training Area when firing is discountinued during the winter months; and on the Thetford battle area the TV cameras have been allowed to film episodes of 'Dad's Army'.

Lord Nugent was appointed to chair the Defence Lands Committee, with such helpmates as John Cripps, Chairman of the Countryside Commission, who later registered his dissenting voice in a minority report. The terms of reference did not include looking at the farming possibilities of the land to be released; it said:

> To make recommendations to the Secretary of State for Defence as to what changes should be made in these holdings, and in improved access for the public, having regard to recreational, amenity, or other uses which might be made of the land.

The Committee pinpointed no less than 465 individual sites occupied by the armed forces. They examined 251,600 out of a total of 302,800 hectares and made five recommendations:

1   The release of some 12,400 hectares, involving the complete release of 40 sites and partial release of areas on a further 57 sites.
2   Improved public access should be granted at 57 sites.
3   In addition 15,600 hectares will be given up at Shoeburyness as a result of the Government's decision to site the Third London Airport at Maplin.
4   The Committee also endorsed the disposal of certain areas of Defence Land along the coast, involving some 25 kilometres of coastline and 680 hectares.
5   Improved arrangements should be made in respect of amenity and conservation, particularly in training areas.

Among the small print of this two-part voluminous verbiage was a recommendation that the RAC Gunnery School situated on Lulworth Ranges in Dorset should be re-sited at Castlemartin in Pembrokeshire at a cost of £14 million. The 960 hectares at Okehampton, Dartmoor, should cease to be a firing range, greater public access be granted, and firing should cease at Dreghorn, thus permitting uninhibited public access to the northern slopes of the Pentland Hills adjacent to Edinburgh.

It was the Castlemartin proposals that angered Welsh farmers. The 2,354-hectare site on the south Pembroke coast is mainly level grassland, and comes within the Pembrokeshire Coast National Park. Said Lord Nugent, 'The Ranges would be used throughout the year, and the sheep-grazing would have to end, but taking all the factors into account, environmental and otherwise, these changes would be justified.'

T. L. Herbert Miles, Secretary of the Pembrokeshire FUW Branch, retorted:

Where are the cardboard cavaliers of the Countryside Commission, the Council for the Protection of Rural Wales and Nature Conservation generally? Here in the ancient Kingdom of Dehenbarth is a land of extraordinary interest and value in history, legend and natural beauty. It is essential that real action is taken now to safeguard this Welsh jewel from vandalism under the guise of Defence Training.

The NFU in London called the whole exercise a 'sad disappointment', lamented that only 5 per cent of the 302,800 hectares was to be released, and this was to be used for recreation and development as well as agricultural purposes. It concluded:

In addition, it appears that amenity considerations have been the overriding factor in the choice of areas to be released.

One year later, with a new Government in power, the Welsh sheep-farmers had won the day. Castlemartin was saved, though at the expense of Lulworth. It remained a Gunnery Range on its previous scale. Said the White Paper:

In the case of Lulworth, there have been arguments both for and against the suggested move—though the Local Authorities and a large number of local residents are in favour of the Army staying. The Government has concluded that the RAC Gunnery School should remain at Lulworth.

T. L. Herbert Miles said that common sense had prevailed, and the NFU in London, who had decried the proposed release of 12,400 hectares as a 'sad disappointment', now welcomed the release of 9,000 hectares, and no longer derided the amenity and recreational angle.

We are particularly pleased to see that the Government feels that it may be able to hand back even more land as a result of the current review of Defence expenditure. Not only would this release further farmland, but, in certain areas, especially the south east, it could be used for development or recreation, and thus safeguard existing farmland from urban development.

We are pleased to note that the Government has decided not to move the Gunnery School from Lulworth to Castlemartin. Such a move—recommended in the Nugent Report—would have had disastrous implications for farmers in Pembrokeshire, and was also resisted by farmers and local inhabitants in Dorset, where the School is an integral part of the local economy, and extensive agricultural use is made of the Ranges.

It seemed that neither the Government, the farmers, nor the general public at large was very concerned that the armed forces were holding unnecessarily extensive land. Nugent had done his work, and it remains a dusty memorial in a dusty pigeon-hole.

The Forestry Commission

'A tree in Scotland, is as rare as a horse in Venice.'
Samuel Johnson 1773.

'The plans of the Forestry Commission have been more ambitious than its performance.'

'Farming in Britain Today'
(Donaldson & Barber, 1969)

'It is important that the Forestry Commission should not be regarded as a large State Institution.'

Lord Taylor of Gryfe

Land purchases of Forestry Commission

Year ending	purchased hectares	England	Scotland	Wales	Total cost per hectare
31.3.70	13,200	2,348	9,600	1,480	£47.52
31.3.71	21,200	800	19,200	1,200	£47.52
31.3.72	16,800	82	15,440	1,280	£51.33
31.3.73	6,520	96	4,960	1,480	£59.95
31.3.74	6,520	756	5,160	626	£125.97

Britain's largest landowner is the Forestry Commission, whose rolling hectares are so vast that it owns one hectare in every fifteen of the total area of Britain, including cities, towns and countryside. The total of over 1·2 million hectares includes 14,922 kilometres of forest road, the equivalent of three times across the Atlantic Ocean. It has 2,750 houses and employ over 8,000 people. The largest extent of the Commission's lands are in Scotland, with 60 per cent; England has 25 per cent, and Wales 15 per cent. The emphasis upon Scotland comes from the more suitable afforestation schemes, and the greater expanse of unutilized or low-output land coupled to a high rainfall, conducive to more rapid tree-growth.

The Commission's land has been purchased by private sale and public auction, but it does hold some on very long leases from private individuals. The fact that it paid only £10 per hectare for the 20,000 hectares purchased in 1960 emphasizes that the land is the poorest available. The table above sets out the more recent pattern of the Commission's land-buying programme. It shows that the acquisition of new land has fallen as the average price has risen; and shows also that the Forestry Commission's land-buying department are not for ever seeking to enlarge their estate. This remains the policy until someone changes it. In the natural course of events, one would expect that as forests become mature they can be replanted, even though the actual size of the Commission's lands may have reached maximum. A maximum would also be achieved when the Commission has bought up all the suitable forestry land that private owners are willing to sell.

Allowing for the many large areas of Scotland as yet unafforested, where the expense of afforestation would be astronomical even to a Scottish duke, it may be that there is scope yet for the continuance of their land-acquisitions.

During the period 1961–70, the Commission bought just over 120,000 hectares. Current acquisitions have fallen, but recently more hectares per annum have been planted than new land acquired. The emphasis upon land-buying will therefore continue, and we can expect another 400,000 hectares to be added to this vast landowner's property every thirty years. It has built up its present 1,200,000 hectares in some fifty-five years.

As a Government-constituted body, it is in a sense a British Forestry Board operating concurrently with private enterprise, as does British Road Services or the shipping section of British Rail. The Forestry Commission when it was inaugurated in 1919 was modelled on the Ecclesiastical and Charity Commissions, as the Government at that time had no patterns to follow. A latter-day example of this type of independent organization (but nevertheless under the wing of Government) is the BBC. In its original form, it was decided that it should include at least one Member of Parliament, and in fact three were appointed. A far cry from today, when it is taboo for an MP to be a member of any nationalized board or State industry.

Its composition today is Government-appointed, and its Chairman was Lord Taylor of Gryfe, a Scot who was President of the Scottish CWS 1965 70, Chairman of the Scottish Railway Board, who received his Life Peerage from Wilson in 1968. He was succeeded in 1977 by an ex-socialist MP and former Parliamentary Secretary to the Ministry of Agriculture when Peart was Minister. A Scot with a farm in Essex, John Mackie the Deputy Chairman, with full-time Director-General, John Dickson, another Scot, joined the Commission in 1938, and has worked his way through the ranks. The other Commissioners are a past President of the CLA, a trade union official and a Scottish landowner.

In addition to its role as a Government forestry authority, the Commission is used as a vehicle for the administration of all matters timber-wise, with the exception that in the matter of Tree Preservation Orders the Commission's officials act only in an advisory capacity. However, it was used for the disbursement of the Forestry Grants, and was instrumental in co-ordinating the efforts of the county councils to combat the epidemic of Dutch Elm Disease which burst upon Britain from 1971 onward. This largely failed, but the failure cannot be laid at the door of the Forestry Commission. It has been a shuttlecock between Ministries, being mainly under the wing of the Minister of Agriculture, the Secretary of State for Scotland and the Secretary of State for Wales, but in 1964 it was translated to the newly created Ministry of Land and Natural Resources (a fair enough designation), but it returned to its natural parents when that Ministry was dissolved in 1967.[5] Its title has remained unchanged since inception, if only because the cost of repainting its public sign boards would be

[5]See Land Commission, p. 118.

excessive; but it does present itself as an ideal target for a name-change if a future zealous and bright new Government wants to create an image of progressive reform. Meanwhile, as an example of British solidarity, it has become identified in the public mind as a friendly monster, which allows camping and picnicking within its confines. Few people now challenge its existence or its antecedents; or criticize its cost. In the past, however, it endured much criticism. In spite of an apparent lack of viability, it has planted millions of trees—conifers, it is true—in places where none grew before: Dr Johnson's remark, quoted at the head of this section, is far from true today. It puts the Bryant and May forests in the shade.

The Commission's viability is in fact a puzzle; after nearly sixty years of existence, a rolling programme of thinnings, and harvesting, should be counterbalancing planting costs. This has not occurred, partly because it has never made up its mind as to whether its role was strictly timber-production, or a social service to relieve unemployment in low-employment areas. Changing Government policies have not helped.

In 1931, during the depression, millions of young trees had to be destroyed to conform with revised budgets imposed by a distraught Treasury. The Forestry Commission had been created due to the recommendations of the 1917 Acland Committee, when the benefits of home production were of paramount importance, although the vast majority of its planting has been done since 1947.

The plantations will eventually produce useful economic results, but a heavy administrative structure and the new role as custodian of a vast national park to which the public should be admitted have added to the Commission's social obligations, at the cost of pure economic returns.

The objective of the Forestry Commission and its land-buying programme is obviously forestry, but it does own over 160,000 hectares of farmland, has just over 2,000 lettings, and receives rent of only just over £2·50 per hectare, proving the impoverished nature of its soil: ideal for afforestation, but pathetic in its agricultural potential. The farmland total has fallen by over 24,000 hectares since 1965, and since 1970 there has been a greater desire to dispose of surplus properties. The 1970–71 Annual Report stated unequivocally, 'If this land cannot serve the objectives of the Commission, it will be sold wherever it is practicable to do so.'

Over £7 million worth of property was disposed of in the four years to 1974. During the years have gone a hotel, a vehicle-repair depot, building plots and land for development, a former Forestry School at Pitlochry and a former Conservancy Office at Woking. Even a pier in Scotland has been sold. The Commission's leasehold interest in the Headquarters Office at 25 Savile Row, London, was sold to the DoE in 1973, and Northerwood House, the Commission's former Training Centre in the New Forest, which had been given to them in 1945 by the late Major Herbert Aris for use as an Educational Centre, was sold. By agreement with Major Aris's son and daughter the proceeds of the sale were used to set up the 'Aris Travelling Fellowship' under which two Forest

Officers are selected each year as leaders to conduct parties of undergraduates on organized visits to study forestry in various European countries.

Forest, farm or fun?

'It is over fifty years since a National Forestry Policy took shape in this country; and nearly thirty years since it was publicly reviewed as a whole.'
'Forestry Policy' (Government White Paper, 1972)

Farming and forestry are often opposed to each other. The land absorbed annually by new plantations is included in that area lost to agriculture, and in many instances there is antipathy by farmers towards tree-planting; perhaps the origins of this animosity stretch back to Saxon times, when the creation of open fields was only accomplished by felling the encroaching forests.

This is patently not true when shelter belts in the sandy Norfolk area are planted to prevent complete soil erosion, while in upland areas the warmth created by the shielding coniferous plantations has increased land fertility. In the softer southern counties the addition of woodlands may not help arable farming, but it does provide cover for the pheasants. Isolated hedgerow trees, however, are of little consequence to the arable farmer, and fellings have taken place as field sizes have been increased. For arable farming purposes, trees have more detrimental than beneficial effects. The aesthetic charm of the landscape does not, unfortunately, bring the farmer any financial rewards, and is often directly opposed to it. Nevertheless, in Britain today the forest area is expanding as each decade passes.

There is approximately 1,840,000 hectares of forest and woodland in Great Britain, covering about 8 per cent of the land surface, which produces 8 per cent of our national timber requirements. Such items as our daily newspapers alone absorb 600 hectares of woodland each day of the year. The area is 30 per cent greater than in 1913, and 20 per cent of this forest expansion has taken place since 1947. The Forestry Commission has planted 400,000 hectares of trees in the last two decades; when it was set up in 1919 its share of the total national forest was only 2 per cent, it was 18 per cent in 1947 and 38 per cent today. The trend towards planting softwoods has endured simply because these are more in demand.

Of the 1,200,000 hectares owned by the Forestry Commission, nearly 800,000 are planted in a giant 'National Forest', and there is an annual planting rate of 20,000 hectares. It also has five years' planting-land in reserve, the remainder being mountain-tops or unusable areas. Despite the Commission's frenzied efforts, and its annual cost to the taxpayer, it is private owners who plant the greater number of trees annually, and they hold 60 per cent of the area of 'managed' woodlands. There is an additional unknown area of rough woodlands in the countryside, and the MoA returns reveal 96,000 hectares of woodlands 'ancillary to farming' in England and Wales alone. This in fact amounts to an average of less than a hectare per farm.

Since the main objective of the Nugent Committee on Defence Lands (set up in January 1971) was to open up the hitherto closed areas of countryside owned by the MoD, the White Paper issued by Prior, Campbell and Thomas[6] was in the same vein aimed at questioning (perhaps for the first time), the national benefits of the State stake in forestry and the possibilities of opening up areas for amenity purposes. To be fair, it was an honest appraisal of forestry policy, without being an examination of the Forestry Commission.

As already noted, the Acland Committee had recommended the whole forestry project in 1917. A Report was presented to Parliament in 1943 entitled POST-WAR FOREST POLICY. This Report proposed a fifty-year programme to build up a forest estate, in both private and national ownership, covering 2 million hectares. In post-war Britain the Forestry Commission set about its new policy. Other cursory glances had been thrown at the operation of the Commission at various times; the Zuckerman[7] Committee who had broadly advocated the status quo refused to admit that forestry and farming were ever in conflict. If this is in any doubt, Donaldson and Barber[8] wrote:

> It is said that in Wales the hatred of the farmers for the Forestry Commission is so strong that they sometimes give expression to their feelings by turning their ewe flocks into the young plantations. Here the ewes straddle the small trees and employ a see-sawing motion to scratch their bellies, with results that are imaginable.

The Prior White Paper in 1972 was a real attempt to equate forestry to a cost/benefit analysis. Prior himself, as an East Anglian farmer, obviously saw forestry in business-like and unemotional terms. It was a propitious moment to examine, re-examine and reappraise all those factors which had not been looked at for some time.

The Commission operates and survives its annual loss by means of a Parliamentary grant-in-aid. In 1971–2 it cost £26 million to operate, collected £10 million from timber sales and made up the deficit of £16 million from the Treasury as a grant-in-aid. This is a direct payment written off in one year (which only Government Departments can do, unlike the nationalized industries whose accounts are for ever bogged down in massive interest charges on borrowed capital). Thus the Forestry Commission has no overheads for its 1,200,000 hectares and its trees, and only needs to account to Parliament for its annual operating costs.

How long the Forestry Commission will remain a Department of Government depends upon how long it remains an unviable proposition. A case in point is that of the Post Office, which was until October 1969 a Department of Government, even though it made a profit of £37 million in its last year of operation as such

[6] Minister of Agriculture, Secretary of State for Scotland, Secretary of State for Wales.
[7] Lord Zuckerman (Life Peer 1971), Chief Scientific Adviser to the Government 1964–71, Agricultural Research Council 1949–59, but Chairman National Resources Committee 1951–64, which looked at the operation of forestry.
[8] *Farming in Britain Today* (Penguin, 1972).

(telecommunications £61 million profit; postal services £24 million loss), and it had become the largest commercial concern within any Government Department. Railways, coal, electricity, gas, being nationalized industries, operate as separate entities although their Chairmen and members are appointed by the Government. It was John Stonehouse as the 133rd PMG who effectively reduced the Civil Service by 417,022 personnel at a stroke when the Post Office became a nationalized industry; the Post Office itself reduced its staff by 10,000 more within six months. The first head of the new Post Office was the second Viscount Hall, son of a former miner and Socialist MP, as well as First Lord of the Admiralty 1946–51. This political appointment lasted only one year. The other effect of transferring the Post Office was that to safeguard the pensions of the employees the Post Office Superannuation Fund was created, which has put a good deal of money into farmland as part of its investment policy.[9]

Removing the Post Office from the orbit of a Government Department has left the Forestry Commission as one of the largest areas of commercial activity within a Department. In commercial terms, it is difficult to assess, its 1,200,000 hectares producing a relatively modest annual deficit of under £20 million, with the prospects of one day breaking even; its total staff of civil servants of 8,300 is less than 1 per cent of the Civil Service, although since 1973 it has taken over from the Civil Service Department the responsibility for its own staff Superannuation Awards.

The emphasis of the Prior White Paper was upon the cost/benefit analysis of forestry: an impossible equation, although timber-production has a *long-term* commercial viability, but a target of 3 per cent return on capital was suggested; and the problems were further exacerbated by the Commission's role as a grant aiding department of Government. Additionally (and unlike the Post Office which was purely commercial), the Commission has a role to sustain the economy of areas threatened by depopulation. The White Paper also announced a target of reducing the annual plantings to 22,000 hectares annually, including restocking; previously in the year ending March 1971 a total of 28,195 hectares had been planted (entirely new 23,094 hectares; restocking 5,101 hectares).

The Commission defends the planting of conifers as being the most suitable for the poorer lands which it inevitably acquires and plants. Job prospects can be shown to be greater in the afforested areas when compared with the labour requirements of hill farming, although the cost to the Exchequer per job is far in excess of normal standards. If one divides the Commission's deficit by the number of industrial workers employed, the costs are £4,000 per man; although perhaps this is an unfair equation, since the cost of planting trees has not yet caught up with the revenue from those that reach maturity.

Moreover, this spin-off in the prevention of rural depopulation is affected by the increasing use of forest machinery. The Commission reduced its outdoor staff by 1,536, or 20 per cent in the four years from 1970 to 1974.

[9]See pages 207, 209.

Changes in Forestry Commission total staffing

Year to 31 March	Industrial	Non-Industrial
1970	7,487	2,617
1971	7,005	2,510
1972	6,641	2,415
1973	6,144	2,382
1974	5,951	2,347

Comments varied after the publication of the White Paper. The Timber Growers Organisation, which represented private forestry interests, questioned the wisdom of cutting back the planting programme, and said:

> We do not believe it can be sensible to continue to spend year after year on buying timber and timber products from abroad, a sum which annually is about equivalent to the total expenditure by Governments over the past fifty years on the development and expansion of our own timber resources.

Countryside Commission's Chairman, John Cripps, welcomed the Government's view that recreational facilities should be extended in forests and woodlands, and the NFU welcomed the suggestion about more selective use of sites. It further welcomed the thought that the Commission would no longer be such competitive bidders against farmers for buying land.

Sixteen months after the original White Paper, the Government announced its new forestry policy, but in the intervening period there had been an unprecedented and dramatic rise in world timber prices which threw out of balance the entire cost/benefit analysis. If anything could have come at a more fortuitous moment, it was this change in world timber prices, and the eventual policy announced showed that a reversal of thinking had taken place. Anthony Stodart, Prior's Number Two, announced that this massive reappraisal of forestry policy would result in a closer affinity between farm and forest, and the amenity aspects. He reiterated that stemming the tide of rural depopulation was still a factor, and in the event the only significant changes were in the manner in which the £2 million per year would be paid to private woodland owners in the from of grants. As a sop to the conflicting interests of farm and forest, the Commission are now required to consult the agricultural departments and local authorities on the amenity aspects of land proposed for planting. This is little change from the past, when the Commission always had to get permission for afforesting any areas they required.

The land the Forestry Commission requires to carry out its planting programme may in future be governed by the amount available; yet despite the criticisms many areas are now open for picnic and camping sites, and the national benefits of a viable home production of timber are obviously inestimable. The criticism that 'only' 8 per cent of British is afforested, compared with much larger areas in the Scandinavian countries, is facile, since tree-planting—either on the

Scottish and Welsh hills, in East Anglia's Thetford Chase, Hampshire's New Forest, or on private farms—will only take place where the alternative farming potential of the land is of lesser importance. The Saxons cleared the woods and created their settlements, and we are busy replanting the trees.

11 Old and New Landowners

The Church Estate

'An old and worm-eaten ship afloat on the deep, breaking up as in a shipwreck.'

Pope Gregory I (on describing the Church)

'An invitation to attend a tenants reception and supper provided a most pleasant introduction to the Church Commissioners for England, landlords of over 600 farms and 160,000 acres in 35 counties.'

'Farm and Country' (Geoffrey West, 1970)

Total Church Commissioners' tenanted farmlands: hectarage at 31 March

1948	114,080	1961	84,344
1953	91,680	1962	83,504
1954	86,800	1963	82,035
1955	89,172	1964	70,390
1956	90,800	1965	67,350
1957	92,000	1966	65,406
1958	91,200	1967	64,252
1959	91,600	1968	63,899
1960	85,408	1969	65,025

Year	Hectarage	Rent per hectare	Hectares bought during year	Hectares sold during year	Total value
1970	65,913	£20.28			£27·7 million
1971	66,483	£22.11	633	722	£28·4 million
1972	63,228	£23.14	462	4,161	£27·0 million
1973	62,999	£25.07	974	107	£41·9 million
1974	64,072	£27.64	1,319	140	£45·0 million
1975	64,356	£33.57	452	80	£46·8 nillion
1976	65,149	£40.53	923	64	£59·2 million
1977	65,578	£45.52	432	145	£67·8 million

The agricultural estate of the Church Commissioners today represents the last remaining bastion of the landowning bishops of yesteryear; farms only represent 7 per cent of their total investments, but yield 5 per cent of their income (a quite normal equation for land-owning). With the total asset value of the Commissioners in excess of £600 million, the 64,000 hectares valued (in March

1976) at £67·8 million—about 19 per cent of its property portfolio—is a modest stake. It is a far cry from the days when the power, influence, and cash of the Church was wrapped up in its landed estates.

The Church Commissioners were created in 1948 by the amalgamation of the Ecclesiastical Commissioners and Queen Anne's Bounty. The Ecclesiastical Commissioners were the democratic successors of the landed bishops, and were designed to effect a more equitable share of the ecumenical cake. They originated in 1836, with two strengthening Acts of Parliament in 1860 and 1868, by which time the wealth of the Bishops, Deans and Chapters had been transferred.

Queen Anne's Bounty dated back to 1704, when Queen Anne set out to improve the lot of the poorer clergy by the restoration to the Church of two special taxes to which the clergy had been subject from the twelfth century. 'First-fruits' involved payments by parsons of the whole of their first year's income, and 'tenths' one-tenth of each succeeding year's income. From that date until 1926, when their collection was abolished, the funds were paid into Queen Anne's Bounty for the primary purpose of the repair and improvement of parsonages. From 1927 to 1936 the money was used additionally for the collection and administration of benefice tithe rent charges. By 1948, when the system was merged in that of the Ecclesiastical Commissioners to create the Church Commissioners, Queen Anne's Bounty was paying out £2·25 million per annum to the clergy.

The size of the estates of the Church in earlier years is indefinable. It suffices to say that throughout history it was collectively the largest landowner in Britain, with land in every parish, while in the seventeenth century many parsons were weekday working farmers. In modern Britain the name Glebe Farm or Glebe Lands recurs frequently, and betrays the bygone days of the parson's farm

The Church Commissioners' jurisdiction extends only to England, and the figures for the Church of Scotland are not available, but it is known that in Scotland Church lands are very fragmented, with a church, a manse and a portion of glebe land in every parish. Other denominations, such as the Congregational Church, the Roman Catholics and the Methodists, are wealthy landowners in terms of their churches, parsonages and graveyards. But they do not own such vast tracts as does the Church of England.

Since the whole land area was united under the control of the Ecclesiastical Commissioners from 1868 onward, there has been a diversification of investment which has increased since the creation of the Church Commissioners in 1948; but even after the First World War the Commissioners followed a prudent if not mercenary outlook upon their investments.

> One effect of the 1914–18 War was the increase in the value of agricultural land. Consequently, the Commissioners decided to reduce their holding in such land, and instructed the Firm to sell 25,000 acres. The lands selected for sale were those considered to be 'outlying lands' and were offered by auctions. The larger parcels were at Castlemorton near Malvern and Acle in Norfolk.[1]

[1] W. J. G. Beach, *The History of Smiths* (Gore & Co., 1962).

In 1948 the Commissioners' total tenanted farmland amounted to 114,080 hectares, all of which was in England. In 1950 they inaugurated a sales programme in order to dispose of their poorer farms, and within three years they had sold 22,400 hectares, reducing the estate to around 91,600 hectares, a figure at which it stayed until the early 1960s, when the Commissioners decided to dispose of further land in order to provide finance for other projects. By 1965 their total holding had been reduced by over 24,000 hectares. In one year alone, 1963, they disposed of 12,000 hectares. The estate has remained marginally the same for the last ten years, with the fluctuations as shown in the chart above, but they did buy the Fylde Estate, 3,464 hectares, from Lord Derby in 1955 for £625,000, but sold 3,460 hectares again in 1971. Apart from these two main sales programmes, small estates have been bought and sold. They did at one time own an estate in Scotland, but this was subsequently sold.

No fragmented estate can hope to preserve the feudal unity of such a property as the Duke of Devonshire's Chatsworth Estate, but the Church Commissioners, with above 500 farmer tenants of over 20 hectares, have instituted a policy of visiting every farm personally by a Commissioner at least once every five years, and holding receptions for tenants and wives at suitable centres. They made a token gesture towards European Conservation Year by launching a scheme in October 1970 to encourage the preservation and planting of trees on their farms. Each tenant was invited to plant one specimen tree, free of charge; 697 trees of 32 species were planted. One tree for every 92 hectares!

The Church Commissioners have siphoned off their farmland holdings in a big way since 1948, and have transferred their capital into assets with higher-yielding potential. Farmland as an investment can never be high-yielding. By law, the Commissioners are forbidden to spend any of their capital, but since the objective is income for stipendary advancement, the policy has been sound. Nevertheless, the assets have swollen as well, and in their wide portfolio they have five main residential property estates in high-priced London. They are at Maida Vale, Kensington, Chelsea, Hampstead and Hyde Park. These cannot but be a valuable investment, with both good annual yields and long-term potential.

Although Stock Exchange Equities represent 40 per cent of the Commissioners' investments today, they do not invest in armaments, gambling, breweries, tobacco (not surprising), newspapers, publishing and broadcasting (surprising). They found themselves in some embarrassment in 1973, holding as they did £175,000 worth of Consolidated Gold Fields, a British company in association with Gold Fields of South Africa, producing 17 per cent of South African gold, when the latter company were accused of under-paying black workers. This is one of the hazards of such a vast and comprehensive investment portfolio. The future pattern of the Church Commissioners' agricultural estate seems to be static, unless they decide once again upon a selling spree.

Who are the Church Commissioners? Today they consist of a body of 100 people, 97 men and 3 women, presided over by the Archbishop of Canterbury, and including York. There are 41 Bishops, 25 appointed by the General Synod, 2 appointed by the Queen and 4 nominated by her (there must be a difference), one each from Oxford and Cambridge Universities, plus the Lord Mayors of London and York, and a selection of the top Governmental politicians such as the Chancellor of the Exchequer, the Lord Chancellor and the Speaker of the House of Commons.

The colleges

'For Cambridge people rarely smile,
Being urban, squat and packed with guile.'
                                    Rupert Brooke

'I was a modest, good-humoured boy. It is Oxford that has made me insufferable.'

                                    Sir Max Beerbohm

Land owned (in hectares)

Name	Farming	Total
Agricultural Colleges		
(County Councils)	9,300	10,236
Other Universities	10,060	14,640
Oxbridge (Colleges)	66,184	68,160
	85,544	93,036

Land, as part of the endowments of the ancient colleges of Oxford and Cambridge, was a source of investment. Today the total lands held by the Oxbridge Universities stands at 68,160 hectares, a comparable figure to the Church's 65,000-hectare estate, but unlike the land of the Church Commissioners, that of the Universities is separately owned, controlled and managed by the individual colleges.

The major land-owning colleges tend to be those of more ancient foundation. Oxford University dates from 1249 and Cambridge from 1284 (St Andrews followed next in 1411). Today Cambridge has a few hundred more undergraduates, but much less land. Like the Church, the colleges have adopted a policy of getting out of farms in favour of a more lucrative form of investment. Their land holdings are purely a source of income, and not investment.

It is of interest that in the UK today the more ancient land-owning bodies have gone out of land as quickly as the more modern bodies have come in. The investment policies of the Pension and Insurance Funds have been to include a selection of agricultural properties in their portfolios; although this is a small percentage of the total amount (5–10 per cent), they have nevertheless accumulated substantial amounts of land.[2]

[2]See p. 206.

The mood of the colleges is best summed up by the accountant of University College, Oxford, who wrote,[3] 'The sentimentality of retaining our ancient estates has gone. The holding of agricultural property is assessed in relation to our other forms of investment.'

The exact total of land held is an ever-changing figure, but it would seem, in approximate terms, that if 68,160 hectares can be credited to Oxbridge, and Oxford on its own admission (see below) has nearly 52,000 hectares, then Cambridge is very much the poorer relation in this context.

Approaches to the twenty land-owning colleges (out of a total of thirty-nine) at Oxford brought replies from nineteen (Jesus refused to disclose their holdings). A similar survey of Cambridge colleges was rebuffed. After voluminous correspondence, it transpired that they were not prepared to allow their land-holdings to be disclosed. Seven colleges replied before an embargo was enforced by the Cambridge University Bursars Committee. Only two of the seven had any farmland, and the substantial estate owned by Trinity (6,400 hectares) was revealed in the *Sunday Times*.[4] The colleges have the privilege of tax alleviation as a registered charity, without the obligations to file accounts with the Charity Commissioners.[5]

Most of the major public schools own endowment and investment farmland outside their own playing-fields, and Winchester, for instance, sold the 468-hectare Manor Farm, Woodmancott, Hampshire, in 1974 (adjacent to the Brown Candover Estate).

Cambridge colleges land survey

College	Hectarage	When Purchased	Location
Trinity	6,400		
Pembroke	1,200	14th–20th centuries	East Anglia
Queens'	124	25 hectares 1909 104 hectares 1952	Cambridgeshire Lincolnshire
Downing	nil		(Only adjacent properties to the college)
Newman Selwyn New Hall	nil replies		

Remainder embargoed by Bursars Committee.

[3] In a letter to the author.
[4] 5 January 1975.
[5] Harrison/Tranter/Gibbs also had a poor response to their questionnaire, but came up with a total of 48,303 hectares for Oxford, and 23,196 hectares for Cambridge, proving the point that Oxford has about two-thirds of the total farmland owned by the Oxbridge duo.

Oxford Colleges land survey

College	Hectarage	when purchased	Location	Policy
Christchurch	8,000	300 yrs–1970	11 counties Northumberland to Kent	Diminishing since 1945
All Souls	6,571	14th C. onward	Several counties between Lincs and Kent	Diminished 1945 expanded 1960
Merton	6,400	1264 onward	8 counties	Expanded 1945 then static
Magdalene	5,600	500 yrs to present day	10 counties	To reduce to 4,000 hectares
Corpus Christi	4,000	1517–1973	9 counties	Diminished very slightly since 1960
New	4,000	1350 onwards	80 km from Oxford	consolidation rather than expansion
Queens	2,600	17th C. onwards	Cumberland to I.o.W.	Overall no substantial change
Brasenose	2,200	Pt Middle Ages pt. since 1900	Herefordshire Essex. Hants. Oxon. Wilts	Diminished until 1960. Now static
St. Johns	2,096	300–400 years ago	Oxon, Berks Warwick	Sold 1,728 hectares between 1960–70
Lincoln	1,265	Since 1960	Essex, Wilts Oxon	Farmland remains a sound long-term investment
Exeter	1,200	1600 onwards	Five counties	To continue holding land as capital security
Trinity	1,200	800 hectares–1555; 400 hectares after 1930	Oxon. and Northampton	400 hectares sold since 1945 40 since 1960
University College	1,200	600 hectares in 1970 600 hectares in 1945	Linton on Ouse Yorks.	Buying and selling static hectarage
Wadham	1,192	1611–1973	Exxex, Lincs Oxon, Shrops. I.o.W.	
Keble	400	1947	Norton Northants.	static
Worcester	80	1949	Marlow	Sold 200 hectares since 1970 ('will not be purchasing farms as investment any more')
Balliol		No longer owns any farmland		
Oriel		Disposed of rural estates, now only urban property		
University Chest Estates Office	6,392	1612–1948		
Total Hectares	54,396			

New owners

'Good progress has been made in the assembly of an Agricultural Portfolio of high quality.'

6th Report Abbey Property Bond Fund, October 1973.

'What a healthy and wholly admirable development this must surely be!'

Derek Barber,
'British Farmer and Stockbreeder', November 1972.

'We're not a bunch of city tycoons.'

Mark Strutt

'Lord Nelson courted Lady Hamilton there. There was trout fishing, a pheasant shoot and a herd of nearly 500 Friesians. You couldn't find a more English valley than Cricket St Thomas – until last week when the Arabs bought it.'

Ann Kent,
'Daily Mail', 7 October 1974.

	Hectares	First purchased
Eagle Star Group	28,400	1948
Post Office Staff Superannuation Fund	10,177	1971
Norwich Union	9,600	pre 1900
Morgan-Grenfell	9,200	—
Slater-Walker Ltd	9,479	1973
Property Growth Assurance Co. Ltd	8,400	1970
The Prudential Assurance Co. Ltd	7,047	1970
Abbey Property Bond Fund	4,699	1972
Equity & Law Life Assurance Society Ltd	2,000	—
Agricultural Land Share Investments Ltd	1,151	Feb. 1972
Barclays Bank Trust Co. Ltd	24,000	1920s
Airways Pension Fund	600	1976
Gallaher's Pension Fund	1,760	1976
Refuge Assurance	1,000	1976
Kleinwort, Benson Lonsdale	8,000	1976
Hill Samuel	N/A	1976
Total:	125,513	

As the Crown, Church and Colleges have diminished their estates, the pension funds and insurance companies have taken their place. In one instance the Post Office bought a farm from the Crown. Although the pace gathered momentum in 1972, when collectively the financial institutions increased their land by 40 per cent, they withdrew from the fight during 1974, but insidiously crept back again in 1975. The Prudential, whose land had cost them an average of £1,900, were back again buying good Hampshire soil at £1,371 per hectare.[6] Some institutions had

[6] The Prudential had £7·5 million (1974) invested in farms, but it was only 1 per cent of its total funds.

been landowners for many years. The Norwich Union, originating in the more fertile East Anglian countryside, became owners of farms before the turn of the century. Barclays started in the 1920s, and Eagle Star, who are probably the largest institutional farm-owner, in 1948.

The exact totals are difficult to assess; some, like the Abbey, give full details in their Annual Reports, and have indeed advertised the quality and quantity of their farming estate in the Sunday 'heavies', but others have been very shy in forwarding figures. Gibbs & Harrison put the total at 48,000 hectares in 1971, whilst the table above (which may be incomplete), shows the marked change by 1976, with over 120,000 hectares in direct freehold ownership. There is a further vast amount of land which has been partly financed, but of which the farmer holds the equity, normally through a life policy.

Many of the larger financial insurance companies do not invest in farmland. They are:

> Halifax Building Society
> Legal & General Assurance Society, Ltd
> Sun Life Assurance Society, Ltd
> Co-Operative Insurance Society, Ltd
> Royal London Mutual Insurance Society, Ltd
> I.C.I. Pension Fund
> Commercial Union Properties, Ltd

The 8,600-hectare Tulcan Estate of Slater-Walker in Moray was hardly healthy farmland, but the firm became involved in the development of this estate for amenity and recreational purposes. The other land owned by Slater-Walker was the Welvale Estate in Lincolnshire, 879 hectares bought for £1 million by their subsidiary, Tiller Farms Ltd.

The Post Office

The Post Office Staff Superannuation Fund came in late, but may yet prove to have been all the more prudent for that. Its modest start in 1971, with a 500-hectare farm in Norfolk acquired on a lease-back basis by invitation of the owner, was in advance of the higher price-levels to come, and it bought nothing more until 1973. It was two years after that before it concluded a deal with the Official Receiver for the 5,200 hectares of the bankrupt Lyon Group.

Its total fund of £500 million, with properties in the UK, Canada and France, administered on behalf of 400,000 members, means that the agricultural portfolio is still a very small percentage of the total investment.

Lease-back is a basis where an existing owner, plagued with a shortage of cash, sells his land to release capital, with the proviso that he then becomes the tenant. Since he cannot be dispossessed, the capital sale figure will be about two-fifths of full vacant-possession price. This method released capital for a farmer wishing to expand his farming activities—possibly into an additional farm—and it sometimes signifies that a farmer has got himself into a muddle. By a lease-back sale the farmer loses any capital appreciation in the property, which passes to the new owner. It has not been a system widely adopted, but has in some instances enabled farmers greatly to increase the scale of their farming business.

The Prudential

With a figure rising towards 8,000 hectares since 1970, the Prudential have concentrated their land-holdings on the better land of Shropshire, Herefordshire, Oxfordshire, Hertfordshire, Norfolk, Lincolnshire, Dorset and Hampshire. Although they had a small amount originating in the 1930s, they showed little interest for forty years. They say themselves, 'Whilst the company do buy on the market, a surprisingly large proportion of the investments considered arise from initial approaches from the present owners or tenants.'

The Prudential manages its estates with a large qualified Estate Department, which covers all types of real estate.

The Abbey

The Abbey Property Bond Fund has units down to £100 each, and investors in this £242 million fund share stakes in offices, shops, factories, warehouses and farms, both in the UK and in Europe. The Annual Report highlights the farms and estates, using coloured photographs. Like the other institutional buyers, it concentrates on the better land, most of which is in the Eastern Counties.

The Abbey has made no secret of its interest in farmland, and in 1974 it represented just over £7 million, or approximately 4 per cent of their total fund value (as against the Prudential, with only 1 per cent). It stated that concentration had been on the areas of England where the prevailing soil quality was first-rate, and the management ability excellent, adding:

> As far as our future policy is concerned, we are interested in the larger blocks of land where the land quality and the farming ability is first rate. We would be interested in existing let situations, sale and lease-back or vacant possession units. Many of our purchases have in fact been from farmers who have wanted to carry out sale and lease-back operations incorporating a full repairing and insuring lease.

The institutions became a natural scapegoat for the Land Boom in 1972. Reports of a massive takeover of farmland were wildly exaggerated, and although the vast funds at the disposal of bowler-hatted City investment managers caused considerable uproar, the facts revealed that these were not leading the field in land prices. The farmers feared that City moguls would not understand the vicissitudes of farming practice, and would become relentless absentee landlords. They were blamed for causing the price rises, and yet the evidence seems to point towards voluntary sales by hard-pressed farmers on a lease-back basis, or to prospective farmers cashing in on the institutional interest by making approaches to purchase farms, that they might then continue to operate, and leaving the ownership to the institutions.

The institutions were certainly not responsible for the Land Boom, but they did help to sustain it, and made their largest land acquisitions during the periods of highest prices. As farms become larger, by amalgamation, and inflation continues, it must be increasingly more difficult to find personal buyers with the ability to write out a six-figure cheque. The declining interest of the more ancient institutions has been counterbalanced by this new expanding interest. The day may yet dawn when a trade union could find itself in the role of a landed owner of an erstwhile ducal grouse-moor.

Percentage purchased by institutional buyers (CLA land price surveys)

Three months ending	Percentage	Three months ending	Percentage
31.10.72	11	31. 7.75	33
31.11.73		31.10.75	15
30. 4.73		31. 1.76	12
31. 7.73	35	30. 4.76	30
31.10.73	15	31. 7.76	10
31. 1.74	13	31.10.76	12
30. 4.74	4	31. 1.77	44
31. 7.74	1	30. 4.77	8
31.10.74	5	31. 7.77	24
31. 1.75	9	31.10.77	39
30. 4.75	9	31. 1.78	40

Year ending: 31 January 1976 19 per cent
Year ending: 31 January 1977 24 per cent
Year ending: 31 January 1978 28 per cent

Post Office Staff Superannuation Fund

Date	Location	Hectarage
1971	Norfolk. Lease-back	500
1973	Yorkshire. Tenanted	904
1973	Hertfordshire. Lease-back	984
1974	Four tenanted farms (unlocated)[7]	920
1973	Wooten Estate, Aylesbury, Bucks. Tenanted ex-Crown Estate[8]	800
1973/4	Haverholme Estate, Sleaford, Lincs.	850
	Baliffs Court, Littlehampton, Sussex (ex Marquis of Normanby)[9]	
1974	**Ex property tycoon, Ronald Lyon, (in Receivership)**	
	English Farms, Ltd, Wilts.	1,720
	Brown Candover, Hants.	932
	Longwood Estate, Hants.	1,834
	Manor Farm, North Oakley, Hants.	460
	Upham Farm, Marlborough, Wilts.	264
		5,210

Total: 10,177

[7] POSSF Property Manager.
[8] *Farmers Weekly*, 21 September 1973.
[9] *Country Life*, 4 April 1974.

Abbey Property Bond Fund (1974 Report)

Date	Location	Hectarage
1973	Plantation House Estate, Littleport, Cambs.	828
1973	Hiam Farms Estate, Cambs. and Ely.	636
1973	Grainthorpe Estate, Lincolnshire.	551
1973	Grange de Lings Farm, Lincolnshire.	292
1973	Manor Farm, Grateley, Hampshire.	244
1973	Burnt House Farm, March, Cambs.	193
1974	Lotherton Estate, Leeds— Abberford, Yorks. 8 farms.	1,269
1974	Hill House Farm. Sprites Hall Farm, Needham Market, Suffolk.	294
1974	Brewers Hill Farm, Isle of Sheppey, Kent.	392
	Total:	4,699

From airways to cigarettes

The Airways Pension Fund bought the Ashby St Ledgers Estate from Lord Wimborne in April 1976 for £2 million, 600 hectares complete with their stately home and farms. But the objective by 1976 was for direct farming, thus not only accruing the capital appreciation of the property, but seeing a more sizable return during the interim years. Gallaher Ltd spent £5 million in just eight days in August 1977, buying 1,188 hectares in Lincolnshire; they had forayed into farmland the previous autumn, and had seen their investment grow sufficiently fast to decide that buying land must be a good thing. Gallahers formed a farming company S. N. Farmers Ltd, and went into partnership with the well-established Velcourt Ltd, whose aim is to take over the direct farming operations for landowners without the inclination or the capital to involve themselves directly. It has built up an 'Empire' of 7,500 hectares in the UK and another 12,500 in Western Australia.

Merchant bankers Hill Samuel came in with Hillcourt Farms, bought eleven farms, three with vacant possession, and started farming. The Refuge Assurance Company created 'Refuge Farms Limited' in October 1976, and a year later had just over 1,000 hectares, partly tenanted, and part direct farmed. Bankers Kleinwort Benson, Lonsdale Ltd started in the same month in 1976, and Kleinwort, unsure what all this farming business was about, formed a tie-up with a farming company called Hallsworth which had just been formed by a Norfolk agro-businessman Dick Bilborough, whose background had been importing farm machinery. They had acquired nearly 8,000 hectares within 18 months.

It was the implacable hostility of the farming community towards this direct involvement in farming by the new landowners that led to a flippant remark at the Bath and West Show in 1977 by Silkin which in turn led to the setting up of the Northfield committee later that year.

Trusts and Bonds

'The second class of land owner . . . with the additional bonus of receiving the feudal homage – which still persists north of Potters Bar and west of Uxbridge – is comfortably reflecting on the wisdom of his judgement.'

Laurence Gould,
'Daily Telegraph', 1973.

There are seven principal operators in the field of land trusts and bonds. They are:

	Units £
Barclays Bank Trust Co. Ltd (Barclays Bank Ltd)	
Property Growth Agricultural Bonds. (Shenley Investments Ltd., Principal Shareholders Friends Provident Life Office. Lazard Brothers & Co., Ltd)	250
Agricultural Land Share Investments. (National-Westminster)	10,000
First Investors and Savers Ltd (Vavasseur Group. Financial difficulties, 1975. Rescued by Prudential).	
Matthews Wrightson Land Ltd (Matthews Wrightson Holdings)	25,000
Farmland Trust Company. (Save and Prosper and Merchant Bankers Singer and Friedlander)	20,000
Robert Silk Agricultural Bonds.	100

One motive for buying farmland is as a means of salting away funds contributed by employees towards their ultimate pension. This is not only inherently long-term, but will never need to be capitalized, as in later years pensions can be paid from current income of a new generation. But there has been another movement to attract interest in land, through the advent of Property Unit Trusts.

The schemes vary from the £100 units of Robert Silk to the £25,000 units of Matthews Wrightson, but the £17,000 units of First Investors do offer participation in the farming profits as well as land-owning. In the case of Matthews Wrightson, who set up their own subsidiary (Fountain Farming) to farm the land, the baby has outgrown its parent, and is now farming more land than they were able to attract investors to buy. Property Growth is probably the most successful. Apart from Barclays (which comes into a category of its own) these companies have all been created since 1970, and have been designed to allow the small investor a stake in land-owning.

Their success rate is questionable; the great British investing public has shown little inclination to get involved in anything as imponderable as land—and even less in farming it. Nevertheless, the bonds herald a new class of landowner. There has been no ballyhoo such as attended investment by the insurance and pension companies, yet the Bonds are quietly catching on. Admittedly, they have never caught the imagination of the taxi-drivers in Birmingham or Leeds—unlike their counterparts in New York, who speculated wildly with Grain Futures during the Great Russian Grain Raid in 1972.

Barclaytrust

Barclays Bank Trust Company Ltd is a wholly owned subsidiary of Barclays Bank Ltd, and is involved in the ownership of land in two categories. Barclays additionally, in 1968, launched the Grasshopper Property Unit Trust, but the first acquisition of land as an investment from their property unit trusts was in 1972–3.

Within the 24,000 hectares held by Barclays, the Trust Company owns a substantial number of farms of all sizes, most of which are held as investments in private trust portfolios of which the Company is a Trustee. Some land is also held which is farmed by the Trust Company as executors for deceased farmer/land-owners. Its second role of landowner arises from its management of property unit trusts and pension funds. Land is held in the same way as an office block or a holding of shares might complete a widely spread but prudent portfolio.

The Trust Company has built up its 24,000 hectares since the 1920s. This figure does not include farms of less than 24 hectares in extent, and the Company emphasizes that many are held for short periods. Barclays ownership extends to all but eleven counties in England and Wales (old-style counties, that is, before local-government reorganization). Its farms and estates vary considerably in size, here being unlike the pension funds, which seem to dislike anything less than 200 hectares. It has 3,720 in Northumberland, 2,560 in Cornwall, and 2,200 in Norfolk. It also has a small area of land in Scotland, and employs professional Land and Estate Agents to manage its property, using such national firms as Strutt & Parker, Savills, and Bidwells, but it will employ small local agents where local knowledge and expertise is required; unlike other land investors, who tend to concentrate their land agency arrangements with one particular firm.

Property Growth Agricultural Fund

> '*I compare the Institutions to the Dukes.*'
> Guy Lyster (Strutt & Parker).

Property Growth had the advantage of getting off the ground in 1970 before the big land rises, and thus when farms were fetching £2,470 plus per hectare, it was able to announce that its average purchase price was only £1,334 per hectare, but since all its land was bought on a lease-back basis from existing owner/occupiers, perhaps the figure was not so outstanding.

It was launched in 1970, but never quite got off the ground until the Boom was in full swing. The essence of its attraction to investors did not become apparent until land became popular. By its first year it had attracted £100,000, and owned one farm. By September 1972 it had attracted £1 million, and was negotiating for six farms. Soon the money came rolling in at the rate of £1 million per month, and a year later it had accepted £10·5 million (it became £14·9 million a year later), and by the end of 1973 had accumulated 3,880 hectares. Twelve months later this figure they had almost doubled, to 7,290 hectares, with 52 farms, and there was nearly £5 million in hand, waiting for the propitious moment. The dip in land prices followed, and P. G. found the euphoria that has accompanied its initial foray into farming suddenly vanished. It hurriedly sold off 2,000 hectares or more, consolidated what it had, licked its wounds, and waited. By 1977 it had £12·9 million invested in farms (which were now appreciating again), held in 40 farms, of which 80 per cent were in arable areas. However, by this time a new movement was in evidence, the advent of direct farming participation by the institutional landowners. This was strongly resisted by the farmers, and led Silkin to appoint Lord Northfield—former Labour MP Sydney Chapman—to head an Inquiry into this new phenomenon.

P. G. was launched by Peter Hutley, a chartered surveyor with farming interests of his own, including 200 hectares in the south of England, 2,800 hectares in Australia and a fruit and vegetable enterprise in the Seychelles. It was launched with the powerful support of such eminent and erudite businessmen as bow-tied, bespectacled Mark Strutt, senior partner of land agents Strutt & Parker, as well as a director in the 8,400-hectare family farming business in Essex and Suffolk. Dr Charles Williams, another land agent with 520 hectares of his own in Bedfordshire; Sir Oliver Chesterton, Vice-Chairman of the Woolwich Equitable Building Society, a land agent and a Crown Commissioner with control and experience of the vast Crown Estates. E. W. Phillips was Chairman, and doubled up with the positions of managing director of merchant bankers Lazards, and Chairman of the Friends Provident and Century Insurance Group. With Warwick Thompson as Agricultural Fund Manager, it presented a powerful team, backed by Strutt & Parker as managing agents, Lugg & Gould as consultants, Lazards, Barclays and the National Westminster as bankers, with Savills appointed as independent valuers.

The basic conception was a £250 Bond which was in effect a single premium investment in a Life Assurance Policy issued by Property Growth Assurance Company; additionally there was offered larger farmland shares at £100,00 each. Farms are purchased, largely by invitation of the present owner, and investors have the benefit of Savills annual independent valuations, reflecting the value of the Bonds which, although linked to life cover, are readily negotiable at a known bid price.

Agricultural Land Share Investments

ALSI was launched from the West End penthouse apartment of Michael

Jackson-Stops, head of the land agency firm Jackson-Stops & Staff in March 1972, which was a little late to arrive upon the scene. It has always seemed like the poor relation of Property Growth, but it had the sixth Earl of Bradford, CLA President 1955–57 and owner of seventeenth-century Weston Park Estate, Shropshire, as Chairman. For support it acquired the County Bank Ltd (a merchant banking subsidiary of Nat-West). Far from the affluence of the West End, it established itself at The Bury, in rural Chesham, with the land management organized from the Northampton office at Jackson-Stopp & Staff.

The units are offered in £10,000 blocks, and the variation from the P. G. Scheme is in the concept of syndicate ownership of specified farms; at least the investor can lean on the farm gate and look at his money occasionally. It was designed to buy tenanted farms, or even lease-back properties, and primarily became involved in the acquisition of its farms by a personal knowledge of prospective insolvency. It does not bid at public auctions.

The amount of money subscribed has not been disclosed, but by May 1974 it had established seven syndicates owning 1,151 hectares in eight counties, half in Wales or the Welsh borders, one in Scotland, and the remaining three in Suffolk, Lincolnshire and Kent. A wide territorial spread, with an average hectarage of only 160 each. One let farm in Yorkshire was added in 1975.

Although progress has been minuscule, ALSI does offer a financial lifeline to farmers, and indeed one hard-up chap, having sold his farm to a syndicate, then used some of the proceeds to re-purchase shares in his own farm. By this method he had released the locked-up capital inherent in his land, and gained the prospects of sleeping easier in his bed at nights. This scheme varies from others, and does allow a capital injection when it may be required for expansion or taxation purposes. It has not as yet made much progress, but represents another aspect of the growing trend towards outside investors.

Matthews Wrightson Group

'Around 350 comfortably-off people have become armchair farmers, or foresters under the Matthews Wrightson Land Umbrella.'

'Evening Standard', 20 December 1973.

If Matthews Wrightson is unknown in farming circles, then its subsidiary, Fountain Farming, certainly is not. The parent buys the land, hives it off in £25,000 stakes, grants a tenancy to FF, who do the farming and hand over the cash to the parent. As such, the land they have acquired is normally vacant possession, as opposed to both PG and ALSI. Ironically, the farming empire has achieved more success, and more importance, than has the scheme to promote 'armchair land-ownership' for investors.

Matthews Wrightson is essentially a major insurance group, involved in shipbroking and underwriting at Lloyds, as well as air broking, and with a rural land division. Situated in an undignified and bleak skyscraper block in crowded Fenchurch Street, hard by Liverpool Street Station, named Fountain House, the company dates back to 1901, but in 1967 a merger between the shipbroking interests of Matthews Wrightson and Galbraith Pembroke & Co had created Galbraith-Wrightson Ltd. A further merger with Bray-Gibb & Co. Ltd in 1971 created the Matthews Wrightson Group, which came on to the Stock Exchange in 1971.

In launching its Land Investment Scheme, MW stressed the performance of land, as indeed have the other instigators. Said Brian Malyon: 'Since 1950, agricultural land has appreciated five-fold, while equities have only trebled . . . ownership of good agricultural land is one of the safest forms of investment. It is a natural resource which on this crowded island is constantly becoming scarcer.'

Investors were offered the choice of buying a whole farm (which they could have bought with professional advice anywhere, any time, without MW's help), or an undivided share. Another bait was dangled: 'The investor's sole commitment is to become landlord of the property *which may well include a house in the country, or a surplus cottage and valuable shooting and fishing rights'.* (My italics.)

MW has increased the farming estate of Fountain Farming, but the snag to its scheme was that under the Agricultural Holdings Act 1948 it would immediately devalue any property bought with vacant possession, once a tenancy was granted to FF. It circumvented this problem by inserting a clause requiring MW to repurchase at any current vacant possession price.

The figure of 350 investors quoted above (if correct) embraces the Forestry Section, which covers 40,000 hectares, but this is managed forestry and not land-ownership. Today FF is farming in excess of 8,000 hectares, and apart from the stagnation period, 1974–5, its expansion was phenomenal. The main farming project was launched in late 1971, and Nigel Dyckhoff headed the team. A high-powered and influential list of names for the notepaper was not needed, but Anthony Rosen was co-opted. The success of land-ownership for investors was not commensurate with the farming activities of FF, which set about building an empire on its own. Initially it could only find land to farm if it could find investors to supply the massive 'land-locked' capital required. It acquired the 530-hectare Hedge End Farm in Dorset, as tenants of the Prudential, and although it bought the 1,000-hectare co-partnership estate at Boreham in Essex at an advantageous price, it passed the whole estate on to a single pension fund investor. A farm in Hampshire is rented from another insurance company, and probably only just over half its farmed land has been reinvested by armchair farmers.

Part 2

Pressure and Politics

12 Farming Pressure and Politics

Farmers and politicians

'Nothing seems to me more certain in politics than that British agriculture will be neither subsidised or protected.'

The Land and its People (Ernle, 1925).

'The terrible havoc wrought by the war and the shortages in the aftermath persuaded politicians of all parties to support home agriculture as they had never done before.'

The British Genius
(Grosvenor and McMillan, 1973).

'Politics is perhaps the only profession for which no preparation is thought necessary.'

R. L. Stevenson

What is the influence of farmers upon the politicians, or conversely, how much does political influence interfere with farming? Certainly, with only 2½ per cent of the population engaged in agriculture, or relying upon it for their living, the electoral influence of the farming vote is very low. This compares adversely with the farmers' influence in countries with an agriculturally orientated economy, such as New Zealand, but even on the Continent such industrial giants as the West German Republic have 9 per cent of their work force engaged in farming. In Austria the numbers have halved since 1951, but still amount to 16 per cent of the work-force.

In some countries there are specific 'farmers' parties' represented in the national legislature, or very powerful agricultural pressure groups. Farmers here cannot expect to exert any direct or massive influence upon the manifestoes of the political parties, although high, even disproportionately high, emotion about countryside affairs is engendered within most political parties.

Even in Britain, and despite their relatively small numbers, farmers have sought to wield an undue influence on agricultural policy, and have largely succeeded in doing so; the small number of voters is supplemented by a traditional feeling for the countryside. This must affect the political attitude of the parties towards farmers.

In a world where food has become of greater importance as a political issue, the farmers are in a happy position, while home-grown food reduces the import bill.

Farming influence cannot be directly equated with the percentage of rural voters, and for farmers the ultimate industrial weapon of strike action would be largely self-defeating. British farmers have used the weapon of mass public demonstrations, and traffic disruption with tractors, to a far less degree than in many other countries. With the notable exception of a nationwide farm demonstration in 1974, there has been little industrial action of this nature.

Out of the 635 seats in the House of Commons, remarkably few, perhaps under ten, could reasonably be said to have a predominant agricultural vote. Although the agricultural vote may be significant in many more constituencies, it is still one which must be equated to the non-rural vote in any policy statements or canvassing by individual candidates. It is certainly not strong enough to influence the political thinking of the major parties.

However, at the lower echelons—in the county councils, district councils, and many other local public bodies—the farming influence is greater, as farmers with well-organized 'agro-businesses' participate in public work. If the farming community can now produce articulate speakers and conciseness of presentation, it is because the Young Farmers Clubs have made public speaking an important part of training. It was this lack of participation in affairs beyond the farm gate, and the isolationism of farming, which was partly responsible for its neglect in the inter-War years. Additionally, the insidious pressure of the National Farmers Union has achieved for itself, and for farming, a unique place.

Farming affairs have not been the subject of a major political issue for over a century. Despite the emphasis in both 1974 General Elections upon Britain's recent entry into the EEC and its effect upon food prices—with the whipping up of enthusiasm to make it a 'farmer's election'—this did not in the event become a major issue, the later Referendum still less emphasizing the farmer's role. Farmers, then, have wielded some degree of influence upon politicians, but to a lesser degree than in many other nations. What has been the influence of politicians upon farmers?

For over three decades farming has been a quasi-nationalized industry; under the 1947 Act it was required to consult with Government annually. This provision has, however, ensured that the farming voice was heard.

For thirty years from 1947 there has been an unparalleled period of Government support to farmers, ostensibly at the price of supervision and regulation, which has in the event proved to be minimal. There are some constraints upon farmers' decisions, and some complicated structures for the co-ordination of marketing, although these have had to exercise care to avoid the accusation of monopoly, and the attention of the Monopolies Commission. For instance, a quota upon the hectarage of potatoes levied by the Potato Marketing Board is guided by a Government dictate which assesses production against demand, and is designed to save taxpayers' money. There are contracts from the British Sugar Corporation on sugar-beet plantings, and Government manipulation of the milk price paid by the Milk Marketing Board, but generally speaking, individual farmers have gained a remarkable amount of public money, for a minimum of control. It is debatable whether the subsidies that hold down the housewife's price of food are preferable to paying money to farmers who could not produce at the prices housewives are accustomed to paying. Food subsidies, phased out in the late 1960s, and almost totally abolished by the Conservatives with Jim Prior as Minister, were reintroduced by the Department for Prices and Consumer Protection under Mrs Shirley Williams when Labour returned to power, and found food prices rocketing, in 1974. These were unequivocally consumer subsidies, and proved such an embarrassment that they later began to be phased out again.

The liaison with Government has been a double-edged sword, to be used with infinite care, as both farmers and politicians have sought the same aims: to ensure adequate food-supplies and to expand home production, or UK farmers' share of the market. Until the UK entry into Europe in 1973, this liaison between State and soil was conducted entirely within the UK, even though New Zealand butter, Danish bacon, and Caribbean sugar were the subjects of contractual arrangements which shared the market. But the Common Market transferred much of the power of price-fixing from Whitehall to Brussels. If any change was noticed, it was that the chaos was multiplied.

The partnership between farm and politician has a history of ineptitude and urban complacency, dating back to early Victorian times, and which it took two World Wars finally to eradicate. Now, with thirty years of security, and a record of expansion greater than that of industry—plus the changed world food situation—it would seem that political influence upon farming will remain of paramount importance. For twenty years up to 1970 the world seemed bursting with food stocks, but the Russian Grain Raid in 1972 dramatically emphasized that the world was changing to a position of food-shortages. Once more just in time, British farming was protected, and its importance re-emphasized. The politicians cloistered in the Palace of Westminster might not see the green fields, but they were not allowed to forget them. This secure position reinforced the political case for supporting agriculture against the growing tide of urban interests. To have withdrawn support from an industry which had by this time become highly mechanized, highly sophisticated and very capital intensive would have created a traumatic effect far in excess of the numbers of people involved.

When Fred Peart returned to office in 1974, after four years in Opposition, he discovered that there was no longer any cheap food left in the world, and had the unpalatable task of convincing his colleagues, and Labour supporters throughout the country, that food prices must rise: hence the movement by Mrs Williams to remove some of the sting with food subsidies.

The Agricultural Economic Development Committee ('Little Neddy')

The National Economic Development Committee was the brainchild of Harold Macmillan, and came into being in 1962. Its immediate objective was to persuade the trade unions that the Tories were not really such bad chaps after all.

However, it also had a more serious motive: to devise, for the first time, some form of pre-planning and structural organization by which the tripartite sides of industry—Government, industrialists and workers—could get round the table and forecast the economic and strategic direction in which industry should be going. For the first time, as a side effect, it started to erode the totalitarian and isolated position of the Treasury. When the Tories lost power George Brown became Minister of a new ramshackle Department of Economic Affairs, under which Wilson also set up a rival Ministry to hive off some of the Treasury's power, but when the DEA folded in July 1966, after a life of only two years, the NEDC continued. Within this general framework 'Little Neddies' were established for about forty industries to study in depth the problems and projections; some of these have faded into oblivion, the triangular contest in the given industry proving too bitter. The Agriculture Little Neddy has never suffered from this, and has been unquestionably one of the more effective of the committees. Its long run and its harmonious accord have shown in the multitudes of reports which have emanated from Millbank Tower, facing on to the river Thames just west of the Palace of Westminster.

Although set up by the Government, and with its main Council presided over by the current Chancellor of the Exchequer, the NEDC is anxious to proclaim that it is not a Government Department or agency. It gets its cash from the public purse, but it is not involved in implementing Government decisions. Its role is to examine the problems closely, to make recommendations if possible, and to hope that Government will accept its conclusions, and stimulate action. That this does not always occur is no fault of the Neddy Committees, but their reports are more closely aligned to practical problems, and often to practical solutions, than are many of the studies emanating from the ivory towers of the universities.

Agriculture's Little Neddy might have occupied a very minor role among the multitude of other similar Neddies, but for a curious set of circumstances which raised it to a level of importance in national eyes that was above the level of an individual industry. It was in June 1968 that the publication of one of its earlier reports was scheduled, entitled 'Agriculture's Import Saving Role'. One would have expected for it an undistinguished career, when suddenly farming reached a level of national importance that radically increased the impact of the report, and raised the status of the parent body. Sir Nigel Strutt takes up the story[1]:

> At a suitable time before the Minister of Agriculture was persuaded to answer a PQ, warning Parliament that it was about to be inflicted with a major report by the Agriculture EDC. The yawns in the bars of the Palace of Westminster were deafening.

[1]Strutt & Parker *Property Review* 1978, pp. 6–9.

Then suddenly there occurred to the country a balance of payments crisis of such dramatic proportions that nobody could talk of anything else. Our report descended on this scene of panic with a big bang. We were like a new influx of German tourists on the jellyfish in the sea.

The report was timely; there were no more yawns; most MPs hustled to get on the bandwaggon. I have never seen such bi-partisan enthusiasm for agriculture either before or since.

As Britain's entry into the EEC loomed ever nearer, the Neddy Committee constituted a Common Market Sub-Committee under the Chairmanship of Sir Gwilym Williams, and this dissected each aspect of farming, producing a glossy booklet showing the impact which the EEC would have, and the prospects for various farming sectors. The collected booklets form a brilliant diagnosis of British agriculture at that period, and in 1975 the AEDC decided again to conduct a major study of UK agriculture, to examine the stumbling-blocks, and to point the way ahead to the early 1980s. It stated unequivocally that its reports were not directed entirely at the Government, but to highlight the fact that past predictions had not been fulfilled, and that this was not entirely due to the weather. In its report on the financial strategy and structure of the industry it came out firmly with the opinion that farming was over-taxed; this was a frequent plea from the CLA and NFU, but now it was given a semi-official status, and broached at a session of the parent NEDC presided over by Dennis Healey, the Chancellor who had created these punitive taxes. It might have been an embarrassing experience for him, but then politicians' skins are notoriously thick, and Healey's ruddy complexion bore no signs of getting redder.

Membership of the Agriculture EDC at May 1977
Chairman
His Grace The Duke of Northumberland KG, PC, TD, FRS
Members

S. L. Aldous	District Officer, Agricultural Section, Transport and General Workers Union.
Sir Alex Alexander	Chairman, Imperial Foods Limited.
S. T. Beach	National Economic Development Office.
R. N. Bottini CBE	General Secretary, National Union of Agricultural and Allied Workers.
Professor D. K. Britton	Professor of Agricultural Economics, School of Rural Economics and Related Studies, Wye College, University of London.
Dr W. O. Brown	Department of Agriculture for Northern Ireland.
S. Campbell	Past President, National Farmers Union for Scotland.
G. H. B. Cattell	Director-General, National Farmers Union.
J. A. Davies	Council Member, National Farmers Union.
F. C. de Paula CBE, TD	Managing Director, Agricultural Mortgage Corporation.

J. M. Douglas	Secretary-General, Country Landowners Association.
D. Evans	Ministry of Agriculture, Fisheries and Food.
Sir Roger Falk OBE	Former Chairman, Central Council for Agricultural and Horticultural Co-operation.
W. H. Gilliland	General Secretary, Ulster Farmers Union.
B. Gordon	Department of Agriculture and Fisheries for Scotland.
B. Hazell CBE, JP	President, National Union of Agricultural and Allied Workers.
Professor J. P. Hudson CBE, GM	Former Director, Long Ashton Research Station.
Sir Henry Plumb	President, National Farmers' Union.
J. G. Quicke	President, Country Landowners Association.
Sir Nigel Strutt TD, DL	Chairman, Advisory Council for Agriculture and Horticulture.
J. J. Waterman MBE	National Union of Agricultural and Allied Workers.
Professor A. Winegarten CBE	Deputy Director-General, National Farmers Union. (He became Director-General in February 1978, when Cattell went to FMC.)

Three unions

> *'And straight against that great array*
> *Forth went the dauntless Three.'*
> Macaulay

The tripartite interests of agriculture are represented by the landowners, the farmers and the proletariat. Although many farmers are members of both the landowners' and the farmers' organizations, the Workers Union stands somewhat apart. To emphasize the togetherness of the Country Landowners Association and the National Farmers Union, both Sir Henry Plumb, President of the National Farmers Union, and his Deputy, Richard Butler, are paid-up members of the Country Landowners Association. Since almost all landowners are also practising farmers today, it follows that successive Presidents of the Country Landowners Association have been members of the National Farmers Union.

Although the Presidents of the three Unions—CLA, NFU, NUAAW— represent the industry, both on official social occasions and in Government negotiations, their jurisdiction extends only to England and Wales. There are separate organizations for all the Unions in both Scotland and Northern Ireland, with even a break-away Farmers Union of Wales which is an acute embarrassment to the NFU.

The affinity between the NFU and the CLA does not mean that there is always harmony, and the NFU has the more difficult role in promoting policies to suit its

The Rt Hon. Jim Prior, MP, Minister
of Agriculture 1970–2
*Photo The Ministry of Agriculture.
Crown copyright reserved*

Lord Peart, the longest-serving
Minister of Agriculture in recent times
*Photo The Ministry of Agriculture.
Crown copyright reserved*

Bert Hazell, President of the Farm
Workers Union 1966–78; its doyen,
and a former Labour MP
*Photo The National Union of
Agricultural and Allied Workers*

Sir Nigel Strutt, Past CLA President,
and the Minister's confidant
*Photo Country Landowners
Association*

tenantry, as well as a joint policy that will suit the livestock farmer demanding cheap grain, and the cereal farmer hoping for price rises. It must also promote ideas to please its tenantry, which may on occasion involve anti-landlordism.

The affairs of the NFU have been dominated for thirty years by the annual Price Review, and its objectives have been of necessity more short-term than those of the CLA, whose obsession with forestry, deer parks and capital taxation problems contrast with the 'milk and muck' interests of the NFU. The difference between the two is that the NFU is concerned with making money, and the CLA with keeping it. However, there is a remarkable degree of unanimity, which even extends to the NUAAW, which actually campaigns for better prices for farmers, knowing that higher wages can only come from this source. Since many bosses are working in their shirt-sleeves alongside their employees, and in some cases even earning less, the improvement of wage-levels can come only from better farm-gate prices. The NUAAW is almost alone in the trade-union movement in this enlightened attitude, and this emphasizes the tripartite approach of the three unions towards a common goal: the prosperity of the countryside, and all who dwell therein. This enlightened attitude of the NUAAW puts it out of step with other unions within the TUC. As Wilson once said, 'One man's wage increase is another man's price increase': the campaign for high food-prices strikes at the living standards of all other workers.

The NUAAW has also a passionate obsession with farm safety, but it has not over-emphasized training, taking the view that the Agricultural Training Board is paid for by the farmers. Incessant cries that wage-levels are below those in other industries, policies for the nationalization of land and the battle to abolish the tied cottage constitute the major planks of policy for the Union. It welcomes the amalgamation of farms, which will create larger businesses, doubtless making farmers wealthier; it even welcomes the intrusion of the institutional pension and insurance funds into the buying of farmland. This latter policy is working towards the abolition of private land-ownership, and after all, a farm owned by a pension fund is one owned by the savings of other members of the proletariat. Larger farms should ensure fewer 'family farms', and give more job opportunities, giving higher-class machinery and worker facilities for their members. Such operations as Fountain Farming have been welcomed as they provide a larger staffing ratio than in many smaller businesses, and provide a ladder of advancement for their workers to climb: something that is impossible on a farm employing only one or two men. The word 'labourer' has now been abolished and superseded by 'employee' or even 'farm technician'.

The tied-cottage battle was a direct conflict between the NUAAW and the combined weight of the NFU and CLA, but the Inheritance of Tenancies Act 1976 highlighted the conflict between the NFU and CLA. The owner/occupiers, now representing just over 60 per cent of all farmers, can be, and often are, members of both organizations, but the CLA is in favour of a system of landlords and tenants, which may on occasion be anti-tenant. Certainly, tenant farmers are not eligible for membership of the CLA, although the problem of rent-increases considered exorbitant by the tenant are not decided by the NFU or CLA, but by the independent Land Tribunals. This removes a major personality clash which could inhibit future relationship between landlord and tenant, who will often live in close proximity to each other, or even drink at the same pub.

The Inheritance of Tenancies Act extended existing life tenancies of farms to the second generation, as well as widening the scope of inheritance to include other relatives. This was stoutly resisted by the CLA, although its sister organization, the Scottish Landowners Federation, commented that 'The system has worked well in Scotland, the tenant has security of succession whilst the landlord has the knowledge that the value of his holding will be reduced for tax purposes on his death'—small comfort indeed, but it then added that landlords could circumvent the law by going into partnership with their tenants, thus leaving the landlord in sole possession when the tenant died.

They did not add that it had been introduced as an extension beyond one lifetime in Scotland in 1949, repealed in 1958 and reintroduced in 1968.

The NFU could not afford to antagonize 40 per cent of its members, even though they might not be contributing 40 per cent of the subscription income (because tenant farmers tend on average to be smaller-scale). Its dilemma extended to the larger estate-owner with tenants who, because he farmed land directly, and was a member of the NFU, probably paid well above the average subscription (based upon the land possessed). This larger NFU member also could not be antagonized, and he was bitterly opposed to creating virtually hereditary tenancies.

In the event, the NFU sat neatly on the fence, declaring that it was totally opposed to 'automatic succession', drew attention to the reluctance of owners to grant tenancies, blamed the 'penal level of taxation on private landlords' and bogged itself down in the minutiae of the details and operation of the new Act.

While NFU – CLA relations remain harmonious on the surface for the purpose of presenting a united front against the Minister of Agriculture, and often against consumer groups and other factions, this unity has had its minor fissures; but each group is anxious to keep to its own preserves, and not tread over a delicate dividing line. The essence of this policy is enshrined in the basic question: 'Does the industry need two powerful and sometimes parallel organizations?' Although at face value the NFU is numerically three times as strong as the CLA, it has been fighting a rearguard action with the contraction of agriculture in the UK, to keep up its strength. A problem that has also faced the NUAAW, which has added 'allied' workers to its title, and embraces roadmen (another dwindling band of men), factory workers in poultry plants and forestry workers.

Conversely, the CLA has been increasing its membership each year as the number of owner-occupiers grows; it has promoted itself vigorously into the limelight, widened its sphere of influence by the experts it employs in legal and taxation matters, and has grown more respected with each of the post-War decades. The influence of its members in the House of Lords, or at local-government level, is greater than that of the NFU, and it cannot be lightly dismissed, or amalgamated into the NFU. Despite the phenomenal rise in the lobbying power and influence of the NFU, the CLA has done even better, although it virtually started from outer darkness.

The NFU membership at 135,000 is three times greater than the CLA, at 45,000 but it costs four times as much to run, and the average member (arrived by dividing the total subscription income by the total membership), gives a figure of £33, against £20 for the CLA, while farm workers pay £12 per head. Until 1972 the average membership subscription of the CLA was actually below the subscription rate for membership of the NUAAW, with the proviso that the workers all pay a uniform flat rate, whereas the landowners' average figure is calculated from a very wide range.

A comparison of the membership of the NFU and the CLA from the subscription figures reveals that Mr CLA Average falls into the 104–138 hectare bracket, whereas Mr NFU Average has 37 hectares. Obviously, the larger owners are to a man members of their trade union, whereas the smaller farmers are not. Similarly, the NFU figures approximate to the average UK farm size. But the growing work-load of the CLA has shown a subscription rise from an average of £4.22 in 1966 to £19.56 ten years later—a far steeper rise than NFU members have been asked to meet.

There are almost an equal number of workers and farmers in British agriculture, but the NFU membership is 65,000 higher than that of the NUAAW, which stands at 70,000; but both unions have lost 30,000 members in the decade from 1965. This contraction is excused by the NFU as being no more than a $2\frac{1}{2}$ per cent compounded drop, and balances the Ministry of Agriculture statistics, which reflect the number of farms and farmers going out of production, as bricks and concrete take over, and the continuing amalgamation of farms.

During this period, when the two major unions have been steadily losing their membership, the CLA has been growing numerically stronger each year, rising to a total of 45,000 and gaining 5,500 members in the same period that the NFU and NUAAW each lost 30,000. The CLA now admits a new class of professional members, without any land but with vested interests in ancillary lines, such as estate agents, solicitors and accountants, while the NFU includes in its membership vicars with glebe land, and many Members of Parliament representing rural constituencies. The NUAAW has also had to widen its membership to sustain a viable level. It is a paradox that during this same period of numerical loss the farm lobby has gained immeasurably in strength.

Merger

The breakaway Farmers Union of Wales has long been a painful thorn in the side of the NFU, and peace overtures have been made from time to time. It is true that it gives the rebel Welsh farmers an independent voice, but the NFU has sought to appease the Welshmen by adding a 'Council for Wales' among its 29

Committees, and an office in the Principality. Nevertheless, there is still a duplication of services and representation.

This does not apply in the case of the NFU and the CLA. Both fulfil separate roles and preserve separate identities. There has been encroachment in one area, though, in recent years: the NFU has been claiming credit for increases in electricity and other service pole rentals to cover transgression. The NFU could not afford to be left out of this one, although it had been a private preserve of the CLA, and is a matter solely concerned with the landowner. Many a tenant suffers the inconvenience of poles or towers across the land he farms, but the landlord takes the compensation.

Although the respective Presidents keep up a close personal relationship and discuss joint matters, they have never met officially to discuss a merger.

It is a moot point: from which organization would a farmer resign if he had to make a choice? Many are active members on both NFU and CLA Committees in their home counties. The NFU represents the bread and butter, but the importance of the work of the CLA has grown as land prices have rocketed, and capital taxation has become more penal. Farmer subscription rates to the NFU are between three and four times higher for the same-sized farm. The problem of which membership to cancel would thus present a neat dilemma; certainly the NFU is the more expensive, yet through an intense loyalty to class barriers, the majority of farmers would support it, if the choice had to be made.

There is another reason in favour of the NFU: it also creates allegiance through the NFU Mutual Insurance Society, operated through its local secretaries, who spend most of their time as insurance agents, getting most of their salaries from insurance commissions. This also gives them a 'union presence' on the farm at regular intervals, strengthens the contact, and makes resignation after a local row more difficult. Since insurance through the NFU is restricted to members, this ensures an additional service of direct financial benefit to the farmer.

Although a NFU–CLA merger has never been deeply discussed or seriously contemplated, the Buckinghamshire branch of the CLA put forward a resolution to the CLA Council in October 1975. It was quietly withdrawn before it was debated, and might have proved an acute embarrassment if the matter had leaked. The resolution read as follows:

> Being concerned at the large number of different organisations involved with agriculture, the Buckinghamshire branch urges the CLA's Executive Committee to investigate in depth terms for amalgamation with the NFU which preserve the unique political, fiscal and legal services which the CLA provides for its members.

If this merger failed, Bucks suggested that the CLA should sponsor a single organization to represent all aspects of rural land ownership in Great Britain, and should amalgamate with the Timber Growers Organisation and the SLF and Scottish Woodlands Owners Association.

The most cogent argument seems to be that whilst private land-ownership still exists there is a need for a Country Landowners Association, but if total nationalization ever occurred there would be no landowners, nothing to defend, and no members, but even in that Shangri-la there would still be farmers, so the NFU role would continue.

Despite the general amity between the two unions, and the common objectives, relations between them descended to open warfare in November 1976, when an angry NFU Council sent a brusque telegram just round the corner from Knightsbridge to Belgrave Square CLA headquarters, bitterly condemning the CLA for allegedly advocating a cut in the milk price at the forthcoming 1977 Price Review. Since the CLA had not exactly said that, and had in any case used the same arguments at a Select Committee of the House of Lords the previous July, publicly releasing its statement, this seemed as if a belated arrow was wide of its target.

What the CLA had advocated was wrapped up in a later explanation given by CLA Economics Secretary, William de Salis. He was concerned that the milk surplus in Europe was being kept high by high prices, but that since UK milk-producers were more efficient and often operated on a larger scale than their counterparts in the EEC (average in Germany nine dairy cows, France eleven cows), the UK dairy farmer had a great advantage. It was a complicated argument, that was based upon the landowners' prime consideration that capital grants should continue on dairy farms.

However, the *Farmers Weekly* was more blunt:

> Embarrassed, the CLA explained that it did not recommend that the cut should apply until UK producers were receiving the same cash for their milk as their continental colleagues.
>
> This explanation may have appeased the NFU. But I fail to see how any cut in the milk price, either now or in the future, can be achieved without hitting the farmer in the pocket.
>
> The CLA, many of whose members are dairy farmers, should choose their words more wisely, particularly when their remarks are addressed to the people who help to decide the size of the milk cheques.

But most rows are swept under the carpet.

Organize and reorganize

While the Rt Hon. Peter Walker, Supremo in the Department of the Environment, was reorganizing the ancient counties, the NFU also was preparing to redraw its own organizational map of the country.

While Walker's reorganization of local government, the first for over eighty years, was ill planned, rushed through and years later still suffering from teething troubles, the NFU plan was the result of three former plans, and was hacked out with much misgiving, yet diligent and intelligent constructive thought. It evolved from the Cowan Plan of 1969 and the Wilson Plan 1971, and finished as the Cattell Plan of 1972. It was intended to streamline the Union, and to remove the fading jingoism of a chronically outdated system of management. The timing was perfect, and the results helped the office-holders of the NFU to get on with the new job; surely an aim in the best Churchillian tradition. It enabled the NFU to concentrate upon the outward-looking objectives of the whole industry within the pattern of the new nine nations of Europe, and put an end to time-wasting internal strife.

The eventual objective of the Union shake-up was to reduce the 58 County Branches to a more uniform size, since some had as little as 400 members, and others over 3,000. This would be a money-saving exercise as well, and money-supply was in a chaotic state in the Union. Each Branch was autonomous, and its financial contribution to Headquarters in London was only that money left over after local commitments had been met. London never quite knew how much it would get, and budgeting was a hair-raising experience.

The new plan asked for a reverse situation. All the money was to be paid into central funds, and dispersed to the new Branches for their salaries and expenses. This was the easiest clause to get through the active NFU Council, and was approved in principle in 1971. What was more difficult was getting rival counties to talk to each other with a view to reducing local pride. The other changes were concerned with reducing the number of Union Committees in London, and with such duplications as a separate Milk Producer-Retailers Committee as well as a Milk Committee, it was high time that these were amalgamated. In the end six Committees were axed from the original total of thirty-two, although today another three have been added, as each sector of the specialized farming industry seeks full representation with its own HQ Committee.

At an important meeting of the NFU Council on 18 May 1972 the biggest shake-up in the history of the Union was approved, although there were painful decisions to come. Mr (later Sir) Henry Plumb said afterwards, 'Doing this has laid the foundations of an exciting future, a future suited to the 70s and to the years ahead in Europe.' What was not decided was to change the name of the Union. This was a fundamental question which has never been resolved.

The background to any such name-change was the Tory ill-fated and later repealed Industrial Relations Act, passed in August 1971—an Act which inflamed the trade-union movement, and did little to enhance the Tories' popularity with the trade unions in Britain. The NFU had been certified as a trade union as long before as 1913, but after the passing of this Act it lost its status because, though formed on the principles of trade unionism, it had seldom attempted any form of industrial action, was an association of independent businessmen, and by the 1970s was an industrial pressure group, and one with an impressive record in that role. As a trade association and the principal employers' organization of the farming industry, it had little in common with other trade unions, though its multiplicity of local committees and branch offices was more characteristic of a trade union than of an employers' organization. This smaller grouping throughout the country enables contact with a widely dispersed membership to be maintained, thus ensuring that democracy starts at the grass roots. Despite these discrepancies, the title 'Union' still exists, although the NFU is no longer certified as a Trade Union.

The other strong motive for NFU reorganization was Britain's impending acceptance of EEC membership, with its constraints and obligations. With this in mind, and with the probability that Britain's farmers would be more affected, and more quickly, than any other sector of British industry, the NFU sought to lead a united farming front into Europe. The European Collective Farmers Union was called COPA, and later Sir Henry Plumb himself became President of it from 1974–7.

County Branch amalgamations went on apace. In November 1972 Central Southern was formed with nearly 3,000 members, resulting from an amalgamation of West Sussex, Surrey and the former Middlesex Branches. Cumberland and Westmorland got together, but others stuck out for their own independence. In East Anglia Norfolk remained independent, and the rugged West Country independence of Devon was maintained. Devon could only have amalgamated with Cornwall, which with its own form of Celtic independence was the only county to have its own private Mutual Insurance Company, and was almost on the point of refusing to admit to being part of England at all. In the Midlands the smaller counties got together amiably, and in the end the redrawn map of Britain became an effective backdrop for sustaining the hierarchy in their London citadel.

Neither the CLA nor NUAAW had felt the need to radically revamp their organizations, but then both of them had always been in charge of the cash, while the NFU was patently in the weakest position. The CLA subscriptions are paid direct to the London HQ (mainly by banker's order, which befits the more affluent members of the farming society), and the NUAAW subscriptions are collected by local enthusiastic members in the evenings. With only incidental local expenditure, the major portion is swiftly in the grasp of the central organization.

The thirty-one organizers of the NUAAW largely work from their own homes, as befits the origins of the Workers Union, which, before it acquired Headland House in Grays Inn Road, was organized from George Edwards' dining room. Today there is a 'proper' office in Norwich—a not unexpected location, for Norfolk has supplied the succession of leaders to the Union, was in the vanguard with Lincolnshire in its formation, and remains a county with a larger number of farm workers in proportion to farmland than almost any other county. The other 'proper' office is at Maidstone, Kent.

The 'District Organizers' of the NUAAW have their counterpart in the CLA, as 'Regional Secretaries', who also work from their own dining-room tables, an abundance of retired Army officers, and even one Baronet, Sir Philip Duncombe (Beds—Bucks—Berks and Oxon). With eighteen part-timers from the ranks of the semi-retired, these Regional Secretaries look after the forty-seven Branches, which are still largely based on the historical county boundaries. This contrasts with the NUAAW's thirty-one District Organizers, who look after no less than

2,900 Branches, mostly based on a village scale, where meetings are never called and the membership is kept informed through the *Landworker*.

The NFU still has a double tier system with local Branches orientated upon the market town, and a county, or bi-county, structure, with its delegates from the Branches, with its 'Executive' and a proliferation of committees covering the subdivisions of farming: pigs, sugar-beet, dairying, horticulture, etc. These are all feeding the national committees covering the same subjects, and although duplication results, at least complaints can be democratically heard. Nevertheless, one gets the feeling that the leadership in London is leading and instructing the membership in the country, and not the membership pushing the leadership. However, any body of men can ultimately only be led in the direction they want to go, while the NFU is often bogged down considering details like the price of baling string, when the more important fundamental aspects of the world food-supply situation could have more profound effects upon farmers' income. The leadership attempts to preserve the balance.

The wide disparity between this triumvirate is emphasized in the governing structures of the three organizations; the NUAAW is run by a band of thirteen 'brothers', the NFU needs an imposing if austere Council Chamber inside its monolithic Agriculture House at the corner of Knightsbridge to house its 100-plus Council Delegates, while the numerically smaller CLA has a massive Council of 150 who meet in the heart of London Clubland and fashionable St James's at the Royal Overseas League (founded as the Empire Society in 1910, just as the Empire was starting to wane, by Sir Evelyn Wrench). It is here, in the 'Hall of India', that the CLA Council meets, beneath the names of long-dead Maharajas, Barodas and Princes of India whose names are carved into the walls. The comparison between an empire on which the sun has finally set, and the waning power of feudal dukedoms as their sun sets, is all too apparent; still, Brooks, Whites and Boodles are nearby.

The annual get-togethers of the three Unions vary considerably in format; in fact, three more diverse ways of showing the annual flag would be difficult to imagine. For a start, the workers only meet biennially, choosing a seaside resort (Clacton-on-Sea 1974), or the Winter Gardens at Malvern amid the Worcestershire hills in 1976, when little more than a hundred brothers become card-voting delegates, listen to nineteenth-century speeches inflaming the workers against the tyrannical bosses, and drop into secret session when the in-fighting starts. Truly, of the three unions, the workers are the most out of touch with reality of modern life, although the NFU can at times plead poverty when such is patently not the case. The seaside jamboree of the workers lasts three or four days, and among the attendance it is difficult to find a genuine farm worker who was driving his tractor or milking his cows the previous week, and is utilizing part of his holiday to show his loyalty to the Union. The delegates are roadmen, union officials, ex-farm workers, and even others with no current connections, like the one who said, 'I used to work on a farm about twenty years ago, and I joined the Union. I haven't worked on a farm for a long time, but I keep up my membership because they're a friendly lot and I like coming'!

While the workers manage with three or four days, the squires get by in about two hours, with the future President (they change every two years) already decorously decided four years previously. There is an annual jocular report from the President—often resembling an end-of-term report from the Headmaster— and a distinguished speaker such as the Minister of Agriculture, or Shadow Minister if the Tories are in Opposition, and the Shadow Tory Chancellor of the Exchequer (to be briefed about landowners' tax problems). They then settle back for another year in the knowledge that the landowners' trade union is in splendid hands. Since all 45,000 members are invited, since about 200 turn up, and since this fills the afternoon of a quarterly Council Meeting, the audience is composed of the 150 Council Members, a galaxy of ex-Presidents and some reporters. It all passes the time, but rarely makes the headlines.

If the CLA keeps it mercifully short, the NFU combines longevity and boredom in the most effective manner. The most attractive feature of the two-and-a-half-day proceedings can be said to be the Annual Dinner, which is usually at the plush London Hilton. Here in 1953 Sir Winston Churchill peered over his half-spectacles at the serried ranks of ruddy-faced farmers in dinner-jackets and bow ties, to remark in Churchillian fashion, 'I see you are all in your normal working clothes.' Prime Ministers, foreign Prime Ministers, Ambassadors and Royalty (Prince Charles in 1977) have provided an audience for top deck influential speakers.

Ministers of Agriculture are entitled to a free Annual Dinner for life. This is the only time in the year when most of the living ex-Ministers get together; that is, if you discount the row of photographs in the Ministerial Suite in Whitehall Place.

Yet as a sounding board for farmers' current anger, or as a policy-making forum, the AGM is muffled by the process of debating composite resolutions on twenty-nine different committee subjects, and an inspired opening speech from the President. Since the Meeting is as dead as the dodo, the following day's headlines appear in such terms as 'Oh, how dull at the Farmers' Meeting!' Typical of the reports is the following:[2]

> In half an hour less than the scheduled time, this year's Annual General Meeting of the National Farmers Union plodded its way, paragraph by paragraph, through 109 pages of its Annual Report. On the way, it debated 32 resolutions (condensed from an original 77), and commented upon many more matters of concern.
>
> But it never really came alive. One northern delegate raised hopes when he loudly announced his intention to put life into the Meeting, but sadly it only brought one of the more cliché besprinkled contributions of the day.

Even Sir Henry Plumb calls it a Conference, and in recent years it has provided a platform for him to lash the Government (cheers), and to quip 'not all the jobs are Plumb ones' (laughter). It provided an opportunity for turkey-farmers to present him with a well-dressed fat turkey as publicity for the EEC Directive on New

[2] *Farming Industry*, 29 January 1977.

York Dressed, and for Plumb to quip again, 'I was wondering who gets the bird.' It's all very matey, as cups of tea are passed along the top platform, and as the ranging rural accents of England and Wales ring out in nervously delivered, stereotype speeches, a breath of simple countryside honesty rings through the air. (They are all hoping to be caught by the TV cameras and find a spot in the report on the following Sunday lunchtime, when the local lads will really believe that he went down to London and 'put it straight to the Government'.). It is always politicians and Government who can take the kicks, or get the laughs. But as an effective, or even entertaining, spectacle, it comes out a pretty miserable bottom of the poll.

It all takes place as 400 farmers descend upon London in the third week of January every year. The venue is that Victorian Methodist citadel, Central Hall, Westminster, where amid the surroundings of Evangelical discomfort even the chairs in Central Hall are harder than usual. However, Central Hall seems a good place to air the pleadings and anger of farmers, rather than the plush if garish opulence of the London Hilton, where the NFU removed itself for the January 1974 Conference during the three-day week, electricity cuts, scarcity and disruption as the miners held the country to ransom. Perhaps the Hilton seats were softer, for they returned there in January 1975, but the price of the coffee and the incongruity of the surroundings brought criticism that the wrong image was being created by hard-up farmers. So they returned to a redecorated Central Hall the following year.

Agriculture House

Ask a London cabbie to take you to 'Agriculture Hall', and you will finish up in far-flung Islington. Ask for 'Agriculture House' and you will arrive at the Knightsbridge HQ of the NFU.

The Royal Agricultural Hall in Islington is perhaps better known, but today has no farming connections. It remains as a derelict example of nineteenth-century Victoriana situated in rather less salubrious surroundings, and its redevelopment has been mooted many times. Built in 1861 to house the Smithfield Show, its most striking feature is the arched roof of iron and glass which remains an outstanding achievement of Victorian engineering, and measures 117 metres by 82 metres.

Derelict today, the Royal Agricultural Hall has had a chequered history; in addition to Agricultural Shows, it was the first home of the Royal Tournament, it housed the Motor Show in pre-War days, and has even been known to stage revivalist meetings and bull-fighting, walking and cycling marathons, and Cruft's Dog Show, which was held here from 1891 to 1939. During the War it was requisitioned by the Government in 1943 following a fire at the Mount Pleasant Sorting Office. Inland and overseas parcel services were transferred, and the overseas parcels sorting remained here until 1971. After that the complex (which covered two hectares) was sold into private hands, and has remained empty ever since.

Agriculture House is a vibrant and hustling hive of activity. It is flanked by St George's Hospital on the one side, and the plush Berkeley Hotel on the other, with the spring daffodils of Hyde Park across the streaming traffic. Outside, the pavement is wide enough to allow a parking lot for the Presidential car, once a Humber, now a Ford, with its cherished number plate NFU 1, which symbolizes the Presidency of a powerful section of Britain's small businessmen. The building's pseudo-Georgian architecture was bitterly criticized on its erection in 1956 as unrepresentative of contemporary architecture.

It was also criticized by the farmers, who paid for it, as ostentatious, and no proper image for the Union. However, it symbolized in 1956 the growing influence of the NFU, which was being revitalized by the then Jim Turner (now Lord Netherthorpe). The defence replied that ground-floor rentals from a bank and the NFU Mutual Insurance Society would reduce its liability to members. In the event, Agriculture House has proved the best investment ever made by the Farmers Union, but it remains anonymous to the casual passer-by, with only a small plate at its entrance, while the ground floor lettings blazon their names across the façade. As Anthony Sampson wrote,[3] 'Agriculture House does not look much different from other industrial headquarters; no sheep in the corridors, no big men in boots: only a view of Hyde Park as a rural reminder.'

Inside, the roar of traffic permeates even the Presidential office, on the fifth floor of the right-hand corner, where the leather-bound books add a more gracious air to an otherwise utility appearance. The remainder is far from plush, or even spacious, passages and dingy offices give rise to a feeling that the HQ staff, or elected office-holders, must never feel too comfortable, or too secure, and that the degree of convenience must be brought down to a humble farmhouse level: if, indeed, it achieves that.

Agriculture House is not just an imposing London home for the farmers; it also houses many of the offshoots of the Union, such as the British Farm Produce Council, and other bodies which emerged with NFU backing, such as the Agricultural Credit Corporation. Dozens of other erstwhile autonomous bodies exist within Agriculture House, and the Fatstock Marketing Corporation lives next door, although another NFU prodigy, Agricultural Central Trading (ACT), the commercial arm of the Union (which sometimes causes it pride, sometimes embarrassment), has been exiled to Chesham in Buckinghamshire.

The Treaty of Knightsbridge

From the noisy traffic-strewn Hyde Park Corner to the solemn surroundings of Belgrave Square is a short step, and here the CLA resides in a real Georgian home, where the ceiling fell down on Secretary-General James Douglas's desk soon after

[3] *The New Anatomy of Britain* (Hodder & Stoughton, 1971)

it moved in. (He was out of the room at the time.) No. 16 Belgrave Square is a smaller but more comfortable lodging than Agriculture House, and the CLA has a sixty-year lease, taken out in January 1974. The Government-sponsored Nature Conservancy Council is almost next door, at Nos. 19 and 20. Belgrave Square provides a more congruous pad for the CLA than did its tenure of 7 Swallow Street, in a dark alley near Piccadilly Circus. Here it rested on the upper floors, behind a door which announced 'Canning Town Glass Company'. Any connection between the two was purely coincidental, and Canning Town Glass was an unknown company until it achieved notoriety from its Chairman, Lord Brayley.

By moving to Belgravia the CLA cemented its links with the NFU in the proximity of its premises, and although few CLA members ever visit the HQ because the Council Meetings are still held at the Royal Overseas League, the move coined the togetherness phrase with the NFU: 'The Treaty of Knightsbridge'.

Headland House

The workers' London HQ is far removed from the other two organizations. At 308 Grays Inn Road (which is a long road), it resides in one of the less salubrious areas of London, north of the City. The NUAAW office moved from Norfolk to London to occupy Headland House in 1919, and it has held its permanent site longer than either of the other two unions. The NFU occupied 45 Bedford Square before moving in 1956. Their HQ was just north of busy Oxford Street, off the Tottenham Court Road, but flanked by the quiet solemnity of the British Museum. At that time, the Young Farmers Headquarters was in adjoining Gower Street, before they removed themselves to the Royal Showground in Warwickshire.

Headland House was formerly the office of the National Union of Railwaymen, and the original office was demolished in 1965. It was on 20 July 1966, exactly sixty years to the day from the Union's inaugural meeting, that the then Secretary-General of the TUC, George Woodcock, opened the new Headland House.

It has no pretensions, though the name 'Headland' derives from the outer swarth or end of a field. (Any parallel is too difficult to draw.) It occupies a corner site, and the interior would be easily beaten by any branch of Woolworths. The NUAAW, however, seems satisfied, and probably more comfortable in Gray's Inn Road than it would be in Belgrave Square, or even Knightsbridge.

13 The Men who Lead

Farming leaders

'Men are made by nature unequal. It is vain, therefore, to treat them as if they were equal.'

J. A. Froude

The farming leadership in the UK is today epitomized by Sir Henry Plumb, who has become a national figure, and a household name. His frequent TV appearances, to comment on farming, and on the repercussions on farming of political action, have brought the farmers into the public view. Britain's entry into Europe emphasized even more to the urban public the problem of food prices: their explosion derived ultimately from escalating world food-prices, but to the average Briton the EEC is the common agricultural policy, and the CAP is the European Economic Community.

Perhaps Plumb's reign as President of the NFU coincided with the need for a national figure for farming. It is symptomatic of the changing power structure of the UK that Government consultation with the sectionalized pressure groups— consultation, instead of confrontation is now part of practical politics. In this changing power scene, the farmers have not been left behind; the NFU is a pressure group with an immense lobbying capacity. Sir Henry was made for the job of leader. In contrast, his deputies, the leaders of the other unions and the many other important figures in the agricultural scene, are unknown outside the industry. He alone holds the banner aloft. To the outsider he seems a blunt Warwickshire farmer with command of the English language, and a grasp for putting over the best case to further farmers' interests; more important, he knows just how far to go. Although Plumb has used his own forceful personality to create an image of the jolly farmer, his mantle descends to him from Jim Turner (now Lord Netherthorpe). The latter was the dominant personality during his Presidency of the NFU from 1945 to 1960, and built up a painstaking image of tough bargaining as the giant among the four post-War Presidents.

Before the War the Presidency of the NFU was a sinecure, held by a succession of able and public-spirited farmers who came and went; one was Roland Robins, whose son Lionel now sits in the Lords as a Life Peer, and was Chairman of *The Financial Times* 1961–70. Farming in the pre-War period lacked leadership, and it lacked articulate public speakers—something the Young Farmers movement recognized in its early days, placing great emphasis upon 'Public Speaking Competitions' which, even today, put the Young Conservatives to shame.

In 1936 Reginald Dorman-Smith became President of the Union, an old Harrovian MP who later became Minister of Agriculture: although he did not occupy both offices at the same time, it was nevertheless an exchange of roles that would be quite impossible today. It is the closest connection the NFU has ever had with the power-house of Government. In the last year of the War J. K. Knowles became President at the age of forty. James Turner was elected Vice-President. Knowles's term of office lasted only a few months, and upon the resignation of the General Secretary, Sir Cleveland Fyfe, Knowles took over a job which was to occupy him for the next twenty-five years. He was the power behind three successive Presidents of the Union, and was described on his death in 1974 as 'The architect of the modern National Farmers Union'.

Knowles was a farmer. He started farming at Ilkeston, Derbyshire, at the age of twenty-one, became a member of the NFU Council in 1933, and led the Derbyshire Delegation to a London meeting where the NFU took its historic steps towards the formation of an organized marketing system for milk. The end-result of this was the birth of the Milk Marketing Board. Knowles swiftly went up the Union ladder, and became Vice-President in 1943. Although young, he was of a new breed of professional Union men; it was a symptom of the changing times. After his retirement in 1970 he became Executive Director of the Agricultural Credit Corporation, a body he was instrumental in creating in 1959. During his time as General Secretary of the NFU from 1945 to 1970, the organization went through peaks and depressions, but the world had moved on, and after his departure his successor, George Cattell, came without any farming background or qualifications, a man with business experience and in industrial relations, who came from the Department of Employment and Productivity, and had also been employed by Rootes Ltd.

Lord Netherthorpe

'On one occasion a politician was provoked into referring to him as "the sacred bull of British agriculture".'
                    'Farming in Britain Today' (Donaldson and Barber, 1969).

'When he retired in January 1960, he left behind him a structure that was relatively free from inessential scaffolding.'
                    'We Plough the Fields' (Tristram Beresford, 1975).

The NFU was born in 1908; so was Lord Netherthorpe. Thirty-seven years later he became its President. In the fifteen years of his tenure Jim Turner dragged farming from the dark ages, created and consolidated the role of the NFU as a powerful force to be recognized by successive Governments, and successive

Ministers of Agriculture, of which he dealt with four during his time: Tom Williams, 1945–51; Sir Thomas Dugdale, 1951–4; Heathcoat, Amory, 1954–8; John Hare, 1958–60; one Labour and three Tories. His rasping oratory and incisive Yorkshire bluntness induced in farmers a new confidence, and in Government a new respect. No longer was the farmers' champion a pawn of Westminster. Turner had arrived, and the NFU was about to enter a new era, one that would put it in the forefront of the nation's activities, and leave behind for ever the rough treatment and attendant poverty of the pre-War depression.

Tom Williams (later Lord Williams of Barnby) has always been regarded as the major architect of the thirty years of agricultural stability, and the 1947 Agriculture Act as the bedrock of that stability, although the world and the nation at that time were receptive to a planned food-production programme. Williams was the right man for the right occasion, and Turner (co-architect of the 1947 Act) again was the type of farmers' champion who suited the times in which he operated (this is in no way to denigrate his magnificent achievements!).

Lord and Lady Donaldson[1] wrote:

> It is difficult to decide whether Mr. Turner was made for the NFU or the NFU for Mr. Turner. Certainly, he stamped it as much as Lord Reith stamped the BBC. Mr. Turner is typical of many Englishmen in high positions in that he is much cleverer and much more subtle than he seems. It is necessary for Trade Union Leaders from time to time to make resoundingly stupid statements for the consumption of their members, because if they did not, they would soon cease to lead. Mr. Turner was adept at making re-assuring replies to resolutions from the Branches. In reality he is a strong man, a phenomenon much rarer than is sometimes thought, and he held his Council in check by a benevolent dictatorship, while keeping up unrelenting pressure on the Government.

Today Turner goes under the title Baron Netherthorpe of Anston. This is the village where he was born, in the West Riding of Yorkshire, and close to the boundaries with Nottinghamshire and Derbyshire. He was almost a three-county child, and was born on his grandfather's birthday. Turner was not a hard-working peasant farmer. His years in active farming were remarkably few, but he brought to his leadership of the NFU a professionalism that would have been difficult, or impossible, for a dyed-in-the-wool farmer. The secret was in his family background and upbringing.

For many generations the Turners were quarry-owners, and the house in which James Turner was born was named Stoneleigh. No one could have known that many years later the Royal Agricultural Society (in which he has played a commanding role) would establish itself at another Stoneleigh in Warwickshire. The Turners became farmers by a quirk of fate, or a family characteristic. In the early nineteenth century they received an order for stone from their quarry for the restoration of the Houses of Parliament, and Lord Netherthorpe must today be the only peer sitting in the Palace of Westminster to feel that his family actually helped to build the place. Those nineteenth-century forebears could not

---

[1] *Farming in Britain Today* (Penguin, 1969).

have imagined the influence to be wielded by one of their distinguished descendants in that place where their stone was transported. The order was for 30,000 tonnes, and because the James Turner of the day decided he was being over-charged for oats and hay for the team of horses to transport this commission to London, he safeguarded himself by producing his own provender. Turners exercised vertical integration long before the phrase was coined.

Anston stone from the Turner quarry was supplied for the never-ending renovation and repairs to the rambling Palace of Westminster until the 1930s, but James's father Albert was also a man involved in public works. As Vice-Chairman of the West Riding County Council Education Committee, Albert Turner had been instrumental in creating a grammar school in Yorkshire with a bias in its curriculum towards farming subjects, and due to young James's intense interest in everything connected with farming, he was sent to this school. Jim Turner read Agriculture at Leeds University from 1925-8, but already he was developing as a robust sportsman.

Young James achieved fame on the back page of the *Daily Mail*, showing him fighting in the final of the Inter-University Christie Shield. Unimpressed, his father sent him the following letter:

> Dear James,
> Your mother and I are deeply distressed to learn from this morning's Daily Mail that you have been indulging in the degrading pursuit of boxing. We blessed you with an umblemished physique, and here you are subjecting yourself to barbaric onslaught. Please desist forthwith.
> Your affectionate father.

After University, Turner came home to look after the family farm, but with a public-spirited father he soon became involved with the politics of farming as Secretary of the Worksop Branch, and the Local Agency of the NFU Mutual Insurance Society. Although this was a temporary assignment, it became permanent, and gave young James Turner the taste for farming politics. He was a militant member of the Union's Sugar Beet Committee in the pre-War period.

Referring to his sporting activities, the *Daily Sketch* agricultural correspondent wrote on the day he became President of the NFU:

> A few years ago 'Jim' Turner had a great reputation as a rugby footballer and got County Caps for both Derbyshire and Yorkshire. His fearless love of tackling is nowadays applied to Ministers and other people in high places, and farmers everywhere have great confidence in his courage and tenacity as well as his shrewd commonsense.

Almost ironically, on the day Turner was elected to the Presidency, he was absent. He was in fact leading a mission to Quebec which resulted in the formation of the International Federation of Agricultural Producers. The IFAP remains one of the greatest single milestones in his Presidency, and it symbolized his interest in the world scene, where agricultural producers were in fact food-producers—a relationship that is often forgotten. The IFAP is now permanently based in Paris. Modestly, Lord Netherthorpe calls himself a 'creature of circumstance', for the sudden departure of Knowles precipitated him into the hot seat at the age of thirty-seven.

It was as a mark of the growing professionalism of the farmer, and an awareness that the days of the amateur were over, that in 1946 the NFU Council decided to pay its President a regular salary of £5,000 a year—then a princely sum, although in 1946 farming was on a high plane in the aftermath of the War. Union Presidents still receive a salary, although this does not always keep pace with inflation. The £5,000 paid to Turner in 1946 remained a constant figure until 1969, when it was raised to £7,500. The present level is £9,000, while the Deputy President gets £4,500, and the Vice-President £3,600. A flat in London is also provided today for the more relaxed social entertaining which befits the President of a large national organization. The move from 45 Bedford Square to the new Agriculture House was also part of the new image which Turner created. He was given his knighthood in 1949, and as Sir James led the NFU until he became a Baron ten years later. His knighthood also symbolized the growing importance of farming, and its association with the Government power machine. It was received by the farming industry as a sign of the influence which Jim Turner had been wielding, and it came long before knighthoods and life peerages were being dished out to any and every trade-union leader. During his Presidency of the NFU he became a member of the main Board of Lloyd's Bank Ltd, one of the 'Big Five' banks. This was a unique honour, which enabled him to bring agriculture into the environment councils of the City.

After Lord Netherthorpe had received his title in 1959 he retired, thinking perhaps that a fifteen-year stint in a top and demanding job was enough. He had already established himself in a house on Hadley Common in Hertfordshire, a Wren house in peaceful gardens, and had little active farming connections. Uncharacteristically, but with great perception and generosity, having pontificated upon every facet of the farming scene in major speeches for fifteen years, he became relatively silent, and refrained from speaking on farming matters, so as to avoid usurping the role of his successors. He went on to the uncommitted cross benches of the Lords. It would have been a fatal mistake to have allied the impartial and non-partisan NFU to a political party, and since Netherthorpe was still thought of as the NFU the organization would have been seen in a different light. He now sits on the Conservative Benches.

At the age of only fifty-two, and with an outstanding record, he began a new life. Despite continuing heavy involvement with many organizations within farming, his next major job was to become Chairman of Fisons Ltd. Sir Clavering Fison must have rejoiced to get the most powerful man in British agriculture as Chairman of the Fisons Board, and to make Fisons and farming synonymous in the public mind. Netherthorpe sits on many other Boards, and has engaged upon an industrial business career, as well as an unstinted record of devotion to unpaid Governmental jobs, but he did an eleven-year stint as Chairman of Fisons before he retired again in 1973. None of his three sons has followed him into farming; they are all involved in banking or business, and his heir, Andrew, has strong agricultural connections in the business field, as Chief Executive of Dalgety Ltd, the worldwide merchanting and meat company with its Antipodean origins.

Netherthorpe strode the agricultural scene like a giant; with his rotund appearance and massive frame (he must surely be the heaviest member of the House of Lords) he must be the biggest man British agriculture has ever seen.

Lord Woolley

When Netherthorpe retired from the NFU he was fifty-two; he was succeeded by the man who had been his stalwart Deputy for many years, and of whom Netherthorpe later said, 'Harold Woolley, who never once sought to advance his own legitimate claims for office during the years of my Presidency, but rather gave his unstinting support'. Woolley was fifty-five when he succeeded Netherthorpe.

If the NFU was looking for another Jim Turner, it was disappointed; indeed, there could only be one. But in a different way, Woolley fulfilled the office for the next six years, and it was not until his successor Williams had been displaced from office by a vote that Henry Plumb wore the crown which Netherthorpe had graced, and which no one else seemed fit to wear.

This is not to minimize the contribution of Harold Woolley; he also received his knighthood after four years in the Presidency, and, like his mentor, joined the House of Lords, although not until he had relinquished his Presidency.

Woolley was President 1960–6, a time when farming's groundwork period after the War was coming to an end. Things were changing, and Woolley first served at Agriculture House when Soames, as Minister, was proving very unpopular. He also saw the first one and a half years of Peart, when the latter was a new boy in a new Labour Government, returned to office after thirteen years in the wilderness. Woolley also presided during the time of Britain's first, rejected application to the EEC.

The benevolent dictatorship of Netherthorpe was now transmuted into the democratic age of Woolley, and within the NFU the vacuum left by such an outstanding man was filled by a Committee. The President's Council was created from the main office-holders and two of the Committee Chairmen. Woolley's influence upon the farming scene was less pioneering than that of his predecessor: but then the pioneering was already done. He toured the country, banging his fists on the table at farmers' meetings, and remarking, 'I forgot myself banging the table here, it's the sort of treatment I always save for Whitehall.' The farmers loved it, and responded by re-electing him for the next six years. By this time the Presidency was subject to an extraordinary rule that the President could only be re-elected annually on a rising percentage of votes. It requires only a 60 per cent majority to get elected President of the NFU, but this soon rises to 80 per cent, and eventually the President must command 100 per cent. There had been few revolts in the time of Turner/Netherthorpe, but it was a rule that was to unseat Woolley's successor.

Woolley's tenure at Agriculture House coincided with the first serious movements by the UK to gain membership of the EEC, and although De Gaulle eventually vetoed this application, the debate raged throughout the country for several years. Woolley was adamantly against entry, and travelled about saying that it would be a bad thing for farming; while this did not sway the political thinking of the day, it certainly had some impact upon both public and politicians. He certainly influenced many people against the EEC. He had the farmers behind him, but solid information was unreliable and scarce; even after Britain joined in 1973 the real impact upon farming remained unknown, and by 1978 the green-pound muddle had still left farmers confused and questioning any real benefits.

However, Woolley worked hand in hand with the Minister, Peart, who was also at that time anti Common Market. Peart later changed his mind, and so did the NFU.

Woolley retired from the job in 1966 to join the Conservative Benches in the Lords, to make frequent appearances in the House, and to make many more speeches than Lord Netherthorpe. A dairy farmer from Cheshire, his contributions today mainly concern matters affecting his native county.

Sir Gwilym Williams

Woolley retired from the Presidency at sixty-one, and was replaced by the 53-year-old 'Bill' Williams, still a year older on succeeding to the top job than Netherthorpe had been when he retired from it. While Woolley was a tub-thumping, barn-storming blunt farmer, Williams had more panache and diplomacy. His style was more sophisticated, and perhaps more timid. It was an unfortunate set of characteristics to combat the times that were ahead. Williams remained President for four years, from 1966 to 1970.

The days of food-shortages were over, and the battles which Netherthorpe had fought with the Tories over successive Price Reviews were nothing when compared to the new era which had arrived with Wilson's first Government in 1964, and the advent of an ex-schoolmaster, Fred Peart, to the Min. of Ag. Times had changed, and the men around the top table had changed with them.

Woolley had dealt with the 1965 Price Review, Peart's first, and it had been a salutary experience to farmers to find themselves so unwanted. Although many Price Reviews in the past had been disputed, and there had been belligerent voices raised, it was nothing to the new militancy and anger which Peart had aroused.

In 1965 farmers advanced upon Westminster after the controversial Farm Price Review had been announced. At a Commons Division it was passed by only eight votes. This new spring in the air was symptomatic of the times, and followed the 'fair deal campaign' of 1964. The sixties were certainly proving more troublesome for farmers than the fifties had been.

Peart was replaced by Cledwyn Hughes in 1968, but farming was no longer the favourite industry of the British nation, and Hughes had to be escorted by plain-clothes police at an Exeter meeting when six hundred rebellious Devon farmers passed a vote of censure on him and created a Farmers Action Committee. Milk, and its poor price, was the main problem. During the next two years, from 1968 until the Wilson Government lost office in 1970, farmers had a rough deal from an unsympathetic Minister. The NFU President, Williams, fought desperately to keep his members in order. Tough words were no substitute for action, cried the farmers, and urged Williams to lead a march through the streets of London. He could not agree to such personal participation, and as 1970 approached, with its February Price Review determination to be agreed, the farmers mounted an unrelenting twelve-month campaign in advance. Continual pressure was promoted as the best policy to retrieve the farmer's sliding incomes.

Clifford Selly[2] takes up the story:

> By any standards the Union fought an impressive campaign. It came too late to save the neck of the Union's President, who was voted out of office at the General Meeting before the Review. The award of a Knighthood, just before the Meeting, had not helped.

Williams retired defeated, and the farmers found a new champion in the tradition of Jim Turner when they elected Henry Plumb. Williams has fulfilled an auxiliary role in agricultural affairs ever since. He was Chairman of animal-feed manufacturers Crosfields and Calthorp, and served on other influential advisory bodies for agriculture.

Sir Henry Plumb

When young Jim Turner was starting his marathon in 1945 Henry Plumb was only nineteen. Turner had succeeded to the NFU at the age of thirty-seven. Plumb arrived in 1970 at the age of forty-four, with a distinguished career behind him.

After the 1960s, the seventies soon brought a General Election and the Tories back in power, together with Heath's passion to join the EEC. There was a new broom in the Agricultural Ministry, Jim Prior, and so a dramatic change of personalities, and of the job to be done. Plumb was faced with safeguarding British farmers' interests under the new association with Europe. This gave him a mission to fulfil his abundant energy, and his zeal. The problems of the seventies were different from those decades which preceded them, and the NFU was lucky, or wise, to find a man like Plumb to hold the banner.

[2]*Ill Fares the Land* (André Deutsch, 1972).

To be re-elected President requires an 80 per cent majority of the Council Delegates at a private meeting in Agriculture House on the day after the AGM. Although the voting is secret, it can be safely assumed that Henry Plumb in his unassailable position receives 100 per cent support every year. The standing ovations he has received on the preceding days ensure the security of his position.

Apart from new faces at the Ministry, the new team at Ag. House consisted of Richard Butler, son of R. A. Butler, MP (now Lord Butler), and this partnership has continued for many years. In previous Presidencies the second in command has changed with monotonous regularity, but in the seventies a unique partnership between the two men was achieved.

Plumb has kept up his farming interests, and his feet firmly on the soil, in a way which Netherthorpe did not achieve. It has not only given him a first-hand knowledge of current problems, but it gives the members a feeling of affinity with their President. Unlike Netherthorpe, who graduated at Leeds University, Plumb was taken out of school at the age of fifteen to help milk forty-six Ayrshire cows on his father's farm in Warwickshire. This background and an early involvement through the Young Farmers Club movement, where he met his wife, Marjorie, whom he married in 1947—has provided an education in the grass roots at all farming levels. In 1976 the Young Farmers made him their National President. Marjorie Plumb (née Dunn) also milked her father's cows and looked after the sheep, before taking a course in domestic science. Since he now has such a public life, his son John today looks after the family farm, but at weekends Plumb returns to stump his 187 hectares, and become involved with his dairy herd, a herd built up since he left school. A number of feeding pigs, plus cereal crops to feed the livestock, give him a neatly balanced mixed farming system, typical of the middle range of farming.

At the age of thirty-three he became a Vice-President of the Union, and a five-day-week Londoner, but his involvement with his own farm has never flagged, and it has been his strength.

Like Netherthorpe's father, Plumb came from a family with a record of public service: 'My father brought up his family in a tradition of public service. He was on about thirty-five Committees when he died', says Plumb. He rose through the NFU hierarchy, from the Animal Health Committee of the NFU, and was Deputy President to Williams. His knighthood came after three years as President, a year sooner than any of his predecessors.

His success in projecting the farming image to the outside world, and in uniting the farming community, has been phenomenal. He has provided a secure base, and has also widened the scope into the realms of Europe. His involvement, and the establishment of an NFU office in Brussels, are part of his wide vision and his perceptiveness. In 1976 he was even tipped as the next agricultural overlord of the EEC, and as one of Britain's candidates for its two seats on the Common Market Commission. Already President of COPA, the all-European alliance of twenty-four major farming unions, his knowledge of the Commission's routine, and Europe's pressing farm problems, was almost unrivalled. Plumb did not get the job—it went to a Dane—and British farmers were relieved that their champion was not to be lost to them.

Plumb's oratory is only matched by his serious dedication to alleviating the plight of farmers, and although he can make a witty speech, his firmly held conviction about farming prospects does not allow humour to enter into this dedication. It is perhaps unfair to say that he has but one message, and the message is 'Farmers are hard-up; Britain's food prospects are in jeopardy; more cash for farmers.' His pugnacity in fact springs from a deep conviction, that at this moment, and at this moment only, farmers face the deepest crisis of their lives. He believes it, the farmers believe it, and they love him for it.

On a radio programme with arch interviewer Robin Day, Plumb faced an antagonistic questioner who suggested swapping him with the then belligerent miners' leader, Joe Gormley. Plumb looked strictly deadpan, and answered firmly that he was not sure whether the idea was intended to benefit the farmers or the miners.

He defends farming interests with a sincere and deep conviction. His public appearances, on TV, radio, or at packed meetings (where his success is automatic), makes nonsense of the judges who adjudicated at Plumb's Young Farmers Club when he made his first speech. The subject was 'Citizenship and the Farmer'. Plumb finished up firmly at the bottom of the list with the advice to stick in future to things that were proper to the understanding of a Young Farmer.

The confident ring of his voice today is paralleled by the confident march of his feet, and he can walk into the Lord Mayor's Banquet as if he owned the Mansion House itself. His versatility, with Prime Ministers and with pig-farmers, is undoubted, and despite the rigours of commuting back and forth to Brussels, or fulfilling weekend public engagements, he always looks as if he is fully in command, and enjoying himself. This comes to the fore particularly at the NFU Annual General Meeting where his bubbling, effervescent personality prompts him to interject wisecracks after every speech, and his ability to remember names and thank the speaker as if he was a very old personal friend endears him to the entire farming community.

At such an occasion as the AGM, he deliberately confuses words such as exports and experts, and adds that he'd like to get rid of experts sometimes, glancing at the General Secretary of the Union, and quipping: 'Well, some of 'em anyway.' After a militant Devonian farmer had spoken he countered that he hadn't been asked for his passport the last time he went there. It is this informality and his approach to serious problems that enhances his reputation. After one crisis period in farming he had a delegation of farmers to tea on his lawn at Coleshill in north Warwickshire, where in the sunshine, with sleeves rolled up, he talked man to man. Meeting the Prime Minister or visiting agricultural personalities, presiding at the Royal Show, catching planes, Plumb keeps on top of the job.

CLA Presidents

'Some men are born to lead, others to be led.'
Anon.

'I describe not men, but manners; not an individual but a species.'
Henry Fielding

The CLA's electoral procedures differ from those of the NFU, and their Presidents arrive for a biennial term of office, then quietly depart from the scene. This does not mean that they are sunk without trace (quite the contrary), but the short period of high office hardly allows time for a personality to become a household name, or indeed for the President to become known to the rank and file of his own organization. It is a transitory occupancy of a national office, but it would appear to be a stepping-stone to greater things.

They are all to a man the product of either Eton, Harrow or Winchester, have all been to Oxford or Cambridge, and have served in a good regiment. Nevertheless, the meritocracy is taking over from the aristocracy, and one recent President, Tim Heywood from Gloucestershire, confided that he only came into farming, and land-owning, by accident, although as one would expect, these Presidents mostly have large chunks of inherited English acres. Another recent President, Sir Nigel Strutt, confided, 'I believe I did own about twenty acres when I was President.' This rather meagre land-holding qualified Sir Nigel for the job, although he omitted to mention that he is managing director of his family farming empire of 9,583 hectares. But since the CLA is all about owning land, it follows that its leaders should own sizeable tracts.

Surprisingly, the average land-holding of the more recent CLA leaders is only about 833 hectares, well below the scale of many of the surviving hereditary land-owning class, but well above the 354 hectares which is the CLA average (although they boast that 50 per cent of the membership own less than 42 hectares). These leaders may have aristocratic connections, but few are from the peerage.

While leadership of the NFU often leads to a life peerage, and then to be put out to grass, the most obvious distinction between the NFU and CLA is that the two-year stint of the CLA projects their leaders into the inner circles of the Appointments Bodies, the power-houses of the land. Rarely have they left their backwoods for the bright lights and returned home again afterwards. What makes them interesting is the jobs they have fulfilled after they relinquished office, rather than the build-up towards it.

The CLA has adopted a more open approach to its affairs, and far from staying in the shadows has come out into the bright lights. It was Sir Richard Verdin, a Cheshire landowner and President from 1959 to 1961, who set the CLA on this track. Ex-Harrovian Verdin, a barrister, was Chairman of the ill-fated Pig Industry Development Authority (PIDA) for six years after he relinquished his CLA job, and was Deputy Chairman of the Meat and Livestock Commission from 1967 to 1973.

Sir Ralph Verney

'A man of wide learning and experience.'
P. H. S. Wettern, Area Chairman, Sand and Gravel Association;
(Speech at Hollingbourne, Maidstone, 1976).

Sir Ralph Verney (President 1961–3) has become an authority on the aggregates business. He received his knighthood eleven years after leaving the CLA Presidency, so it could hardly have been granted for the job he did in that capacity, but it came within weeks of the death of his father, from whom he inherited a baronetcy, so from plain Mr Verney he became Sir Ralph twice over in a short time at the age of fifty-nine.

The 'Verney Report'[3] set out the problems of a nation avid for sand and gravel extraction to sustain its everlasting construction campaign, and yet bound to preserve some of its farming. Verney's 'Sinews for Survival' presented to the United Nations Conference on the Human Environment in Stockholm, June 1972, is on the same theme. He has also served on the BBC Advisory Committee for Agriculture; has an estate in mineral-laden Buckinghamshire where the pressures of a bursting urban population are acute, and was for seven years a member of the Milton Keynes New Town Development Corporation. Verney's experience on both sides of the fence has given him an insight into the problems of containing the urban population, but has also ensured that a genuine and experienced rural voice has been heard in the citadels where urban sprawl is a paramount preoccupation.

Lord de Ramsey

Lord De Ramsey succeeded his grandfather to the Abbotts Ripton Estate near Huntingdon when he was only fifteen. An estate of hard, heavy land, it has become nationally known as the home of Fisons Heavy Land Experimental Farm, which although it only occupies 33 hectares, has achieved nation-wide acknowledgment, and also provides a private experimental farm, on his own Hanslop-soil type, for his lordship.

De Ramsey's forte is water, and he has become an acknowledged expert on water resources. The problems of heavy-land farmers are normally to remove as much water as possible by an intricate drainage system rather than to acquire more; but certainly, he has all the experience in his own backyard to gain a wider knowledge of the interaction of water and soil. He became first President of SAWMA,[4] won the RASE's Bledisloe Gold Medal in 1974, and also received a knighthood. Perhaps even to a peer letters after your name have more merit than inherited prefixes.

---

[3] *Aggregates, The Way Ahead.* (HMSO, 1976).
[4] Soil and Water Management Association.

Sir Nigel Strutt

'The "Strutt" Report on the Soil was a masterpiece that is on almost every farmer's bookshelf in the country.'

Farm (The Ford Motor Magazine),
Spring 1973.

Sir Nigel Strutt has earned the title 'The Minister's Confidant', and it comes from his position as Chairman of the Advisory Council, which is not another of the fifty or more Ministerial Advisory Bodies on every diverse aspect and section of agriculture, but a special body which is the Minister's Liaison Group (as opposed to the Ministry Liaison Group). When Sir Nigel was appointed to this unique and influential body, close to the Minister's ear, he said that he would only accept the job if he could have direct access to the Minister himself.

The permanent civil servants did not like this break from the traditional procedures, but with his characteristic forthright, and even arrogant, confidence, Strutt replied that unless he could go direct they could get someone else to do the job. Strutt got his own way, and thus holds probably the most powerful behind-the-scenes position in British agriculture today.

Ostensibly formed to co-ordinate the research and development of agricultural thinking, the Advisory Body has been charged with specific tasks, but it was its initial brief to study the impact of the effects of modern farming upon the soil that earned Strutt his niche in the top echelons of power, and his place in the annals of our time.

President of the CLA from 1967 to 1969, Strutt has endowed it with a new image, and he occupied the Presidency during a period of change. Peart was his first Minister, and Hughes followed. It was this latter Minister who appointed him Chairman of the Special 'Advisory' Council. His meteoric rise has been accomplished through an intimate knowledge of the workings of Whitehall, yet he keeps his feet firmly on the ground, with command of 9,583 hectares of the Strutt and Parker and Lord Rayleighs Farms Inc. He is managing director of both. Clearly Strutt has travelled far since his days leading the CLA. After the 'Strutt' report in 1971 came a well-earned knighthood, and he has kept up with go-ahead agricultural thought through the 'Little Neddy' Agricultural Organisation.

He has a quiet approach and a firm, clear and logical mind. A short, dapper man who lost an eye in the Western Desert in the War, his black eye-patch makes him appear formidable. A product of Winchester, and a bachelor, he lives amid the pleasant oak-filled countryside of Essex, and among the renowned Terling and Lavenham Friesians, with which his family have been successful in sweeping away prizes at the Show Rings.

Strutt's committee was charged in 1978 with examining the water requirements of British agriculture—a subject that had previously been ignored.

George Howard

'I write "landowner" rather than "country house owner" for nearly all such houses in England are an integral part of an agricultural estate.'

'Destruction of the English Country House' (Howard).

George Howard is one of the largest men in England, with certainly the largest house in England, Castle Howard in Yorkshire, and he followed the dapper Strutt. Although he married a Duke's daughter, and had as his forebears the earls of Carlisle, by a quirk of family peevishness he inherited the vast Castle Howard Estate, and enjoys a life-style that goes with it, but remains untitled himself.

Howard epitomizes the major landowner who is certainly not the average CLA member, but his ungainly shape and rolling gait belie an incisive brain, and an inherited idea of what leadership is all about. He instituted the 'President's Circus' during his term of office as he travelled around England and Wales with his fellow office-holders in a fleet of cars to bring the Presidency to the people. It was enormously successful.

After his CLA work, Howard became a Governor of the BBC, then was Chairman of the Meat and Livestock Commission (1974–7); three busy years when one sector or another of the livestock industry was in trouble. Howard, as you would expect, is also a keen protagonist for the preservation of historic houses, and he was also a co-founder of Agricultural Forum in 1971.

Charles Graham

'. . . Mr. Graham, a charming and elegant man, to whom not even an Italian could take reasonable offence.'

'British Farmer and Stockbreeder', December 1972.

To follow in the bulky footsteps of George Howard, the CLA found Charles Graham, a baronet's son whose father was also President of the CLA 1941–3: to date this is the only father-son succession in an organization that could have been imbued with nepotism, but strangely isn't. Geographically, he is the most far-flung of the CLA leaders, a hill farmer, landowner, and descendant of one of the ancient families of the border country.

The Grahams have been known in the border country since time immemorial. Their locale was previously Cumberland, but is now part of Cumbria. Graham's estate at Netherby covers 1,666 hectares, through which runs the border Esk, and he has a considerable area of hill land. During his presidency the CLA published a Discussion Document highlighting the problems of the uplands of Britain; certainly Graham has a vested interest as well as an intimate knowledge of the rigours of farming in the hills.

However, Graham also represented the new breed of active landowners who without sentiment have embarked upon high-pressure modern farming enterprises. He had a 12,000-hen battery unit, a contract hedging and fencing business, woodlands and planting and management service, a company supplying sand and gravel from the estate, and another enterprise selling ready-mixed cement. Horticultural produce produced on the Netherby Estate also includes about 40 tonnes of tomatoes a year; chrysanthemums and freesias, as well as the production of horticultural peat.

Coming from the further reaches of the border country, Graham broke the rule that most of the important people in agriculture live near London, or within a few train-hours away. Later, John Quicke from far-away Devon also made it to the top of the CLA tree.

A tall, gangling man who lopes, rather than strides or walks, Graham and the taller Quicke both have the same attribute as Howard, they couldn't look tidy if they tried. Both have hair perpetually awry, and a lean frame, and yet a tremendous air of confidence and command. Like many other CLA leaders, Graham is an Old Etonian.

Tim Heywood

'He is not, he insists, running a club for well heeled country gentlemen in the West End of London.'

'Farmers Weekly', 14 June 1974.

The ascent of Tim Heywood to the top job in the CLA was a distinct departure from that organization's tradition of hereditary and ancestral landowning. His background was in engineering and accountancy, but he inherited the 750-hectare Haresfield Estate in Gloucestershire as the fortunate godson of a wealthy landowner. His background was in the Long Range Desert Group during the North African campaign, and perhaps his most enduring claim to fame is in giving Popski's Private Army its name. The real name of Popski was Vladimir Peniakoff, but his signallers were getting into trouble, so Heywood created Popski.

A quiet, hesitant man with a stammer in his speech, Heywood looked the most unlikely candidate to head the CLA at a time when it was expanding its membership and widening its sphere of influence. Jim Prior had been replaced by Joe Godber as Minister of Agriculture, and somehow the two men seemed made for each other. However, he then became Chairman of the European Landowners Organisation, and he continued in this role after ceasing to be CLA President.

Like Graham, Heywood represented a working estate-owner, anxious to make his hectares pay their way in a practical farming manner, and when he started farming he joined both the NFU and the CLA. It is a feature of CLA leaders that they have already served on other outside bodies with distinction, and Heywood was no exception. He had been Chairman of the Severn River Authority, and of the Gloucestershire Agricultural Executive, as well as a Governor of the Royal Agricultural College at Cirencester.

John Quicke

'With his tall, angular, scholarly figure John could be mistaken for a kindly Oxford Don.'

'Country Landowner', June 1968.

John Quicke of Newton St Cyres, Devon, followed Heywood. An Old Etonian and a product of Oxford, he returned there after war service to read Agriculture. No longer could the son of a landed squire afford to spend his life as a playboy! Quicke followed this with work as a farm pupil before taking over the 1,062-hectare family estate.

He is a practical farmer, with 540 hectares used for a large dairy herd producing both milk and cheese; these, with his other typically Devonian enterprise of sheep with pigs and some cereals, make up a mixed and varied farming pattern. Nevertheless, with his 166 hectares of tenanted land, he could also see the problems of traditional landowners—dealing with tenants. Typical also for this damper, if warmer, end of the British Isles are 354 hectares of productive forest: the CLA has often been accused of looking too much like a forestry organization. An earlier President, Lord Bradford, has indeed become President of the TGO (Timber Growers Organisation).

Following in the tradition of working farmers and men of the soil was Quicke's successor, Roger Paul.

Roger Paul

'19th century Ipswich merchant.'

By comparison with many of his predecessors, Roger Paul, with his 333-hectare farm in Suffolk, is almost a *nouveau riche*. His family were Ipswich merchants specializing in barley and malt for the brewery trade. 'The beerage', not 'the peerage', although Paul is connected by marriage with the Duke of Devonshire.

The Paul family fortunes are now embodied in the modern company Pauls and Whites Ltd, and the Paul family now have large farms, or estates, in many parts of their Suffolk homeland—a far cry from the early nineteenth-century George who started it all.

Paul (President 1977-9), tall, flaxen-haired, articulate and polished, got an OBE for his political work for the Conservative Party in the Eye Constituency, and also carries on the new and more active leadership in the tradition which

Strutt started a decade earlier, and which successive Presidents have furthered to a greater or lesser degree.

The workers' leaders

'Men, my brothers, men the workers, ever reaping something new;
That which they have done but earnest of the things that they shall do.'

Tennyson

The NUAAW has a President and a General Secretary at its pinnacle, neither of whom seem to change very often; in fact, this bastion of democracy seems the least democratic of the three Unions. With the massive inbuilt support which the CLA can command in the Lords, and the close liaison which the NFU keeps with members of the Commons, the NUAAW has nearly always had one representative in the Commons, although down the years the list is a small one: Norfolk seems to have been most successful in getting these people into Parliament. It has been the cockpit of the Workers Union's politics. They also had two members in the Lords: Hilton and Collison. Bert Hazell became President in 1966, but the succession in the NUAAW seemed far from clear, till at Southport in May 1978 Hazell retired and a Yorkshire forestry worker John Hose became President. Joan Maynard was a bad second.

Joan Maynard, MP Sheffield (Brightside), is the only member at the present time, and sits for a largely urban constituency. Before her, Hazell, Gooch and Hilton were not sponsored Union representatives in the same sense as some constituencies with, say, a preponderance of miners supporting the local Labour Party can secure the selection of their own nominated candidate. This can only occur where one occupation is paramount, and although a handful of constituencies have a heavy rural vote, there is no single area in the whole country where farming, or farm-workers, can be considered paramount or dominant. That is unless you look at the politics of Norfolk.

General Secretaries

It is common within the trade union movement for the principal, full-time, fully paid organizer of any union to be elected by the membership rather than appointed, even though the lower echelons, down to the lowly typists, are, of course, appointed and protected in their employment. This security does not extend to the leadership, and it is because the General Secretary is an active leader almost on a level with the President that he must be elected by a democratic procedure; although the full workings of the democratic machine may seem less democratic when closely examined. Certainly the Secretary-General of the CLA or the Director-General of the NFU do not come in for election, as does the NUAAW General Secretary.

Brother Collison, who became General Secretary in 1953, and held the job for sixteen years until 1969, became a member of the House of Lords in 1964 when Wilson achieved power. Collison by the strength of his personality and his length of tenure raised the status of the Farm Workers Union, and by this personality enhanced his own reputation.

A farm-worker on a farm in Gloucestershire for nineteen years, starting when he was twenty-five, having previously worked in an office in London, he worked his way through the ranks, becoming the Organizer for Gloucester and Wales in 1944. He was succeeded in 1969 by Reg Bottini, a rotund, bespectacled man, not unlike Eric Morecambe, with a soft, almost cultured accent that contrasted strangely with the rich Norfolk tones of his working partner, President Hazell. Bottini retired in 1977. He had never been a farm-worker, although he could clock up thirty-three years as a full-time official and eight years as General Secretary; but in 1940 he had joined the Union while employed as a land drainage worker by the River Nene Catchment Board. In 1944 he left his land-drainage job on medical grounds, and went into Head Office as an official in the Legal Department. Bottini became a trade-union hero when he organized a strike of poultry workers whom the NUAW were seeking to recruit, before they expanded their title to the NUAAW. It has always been a bone of contention between other trade unions and the farm-workers to recruit those in fringe industries, whose subscriptions could quite legitimately go in either direction.

Bottini's successor was Jack Boddy, elected on 18 January 1978, a Norfolk man to work with Norfolk-born President, Hazell. It was the massive support of Norfolk, with its large farm-worker membership, which put Boddy into the hot seat. He had been a cowman, later a pig man, then a farm foreman, and he joined the Union staff as a District Organizer in Lincolnshire in 1953.

Boddy's election recorded a 46·6 per cent poll, and gave him 11,065 votes, his nearest opponent, Jim Watts of the Legal Department, receiving 9,810 votes, and there being three other candidates in the field. Boddy was elected by 31 per cent of the votes cast, and it meant that for the first time in the history of the Union two Norfolk men held the top posts. But the method of election was later questioned in the *Land Worker*.[5]

> Three County Conferences felt the system was not as democratic as it should be.
>
> Members do not get ballot papers. One paper goes to each Branch Secretary, who fills it out after a Branch Meeting on behalf of the whole Branch.
>
> This, Dorset delegates felt, was not good enough. They wanted every member to get a ballot paper signed by the member.

Yorkshire was concerned that once a General Secretary had been elected it was a very cumbersome process to remove him, and Wiltshire wanted to bring back the situation before 1972, and re-create an elected post of Assistant General Secretary. At least they did not advocate going back to an elected Vice-President.

[5] 1 February 1978.

They had only succeeded in removing Joan Maynard in 1972 by abolishing the position.

Lord Hilton

'His subsequent route to Westminster and his present position there reads like a modern fairy story.'

'The Land Worker', May 1966.

Albert Hilton succeeded that indefatigable campaigner for the downtrodden farm-workers Alderman Edwin George Gooch, a stalwart of the old school who started life as a blacksmith, became a journalist, and Chief Sub Editor of the *Norwich Mercury*, and was an MP for the North Norfolk seat from the Labour landslide in 1945 until his death, just before another Left Wing surge swept Wilson into power in 1964.

Hilton had won the adjacent South-West Norfolk seat after a road accident killed the sitting Socialist Member, Norfolk farmer Sidney Dye, who had sat in the Commons from 1945 to 1951, had lost his seat when the Tories came back under Churchill, and regained it later.

After spending the War years as a Labour Party Agent for another of the rural Norfolk seats (East Norfolk), Hilton became an official of the NUAAW after the War finished. He went into Parliament on Dye's death in March 1959. A Methodist lay preacher, he ironically lost this traditional Labour seat in 1964, to a cattle auctioneer from Swaffam, Tory Paul Hawkins. The uncertainty of political swings in East Anglia has affected the NUAAW membership in the House. East Anglia, and Norfolk in particular, can always be relied upon to vote in the opposite direction to any national swing.

Hilton lost by a narrow margin of only 53 votes, and paradoxically it was by that exact number that Bert Hazell won the North Norfolk seat left empty by the death of Gooch. At the same 1964 Election the NUAAW had lost its long-standing President by death, and its acting President lost his seat, but Hazell, a stalwart of the Union, gained a seat. Thus the representation in Parliament remained.

The vagaries of politics can be as uncertain as the weather, and if Hilton was expecting to emulate the long run of Gooch in leading the Farm Workers Union, he was to be disappointed. However, Hazell was now in Parliament, and before Hilton could be ratified in the job he had been promoted and Hazell took his place.

The seatless Hilton, after a lifetime of service to the Labour Party (which was now in power with a wafer-thin majority) was an obvious candidate to strengthen Labour's position among the peers. To risk a by-election was courting trouble, and Hilton became Baron Hilton of Upton in May 1965. He was not the first 'peasant' to be created a peer. The General Secretary had already become Baron Collison of Cheshunt in 1964. Hilton had already been given a seat as a Government Director on the Board of the British Sugar Corporation, and was a part-time member of the Eastern Gas Board. In promoting the President (acting) Prime Minister Wilson had in just over one year granted two life peerages to the NUAAW, but then Labour had been out of power for thirteen years.

Wilson appointed Hilton as a Lord in Waiting (one of three Government Whips in the Lords) in 1966, and in this capacity he was ineligible for the top Union job. So from an eviction from his father's tied cottage on a Norfolk farm, Albert Hilton rose to be a Government Minister in 1966, which was also the Diamond Jubilee Anniversary of the founding of the Union. He died in 1977.

Bert Hazell

'The fact is, that output per farm worker has increased by 6 per cent a year during the past decade–double the increase in industry.'

Bert Hazell, speech at Tolpuddle Rally,
20 July 1975.

Norfolk politics swung in Hazell's favour when he beat a local farmer, Frank Easton, by 53 votes in 1964. Two years later, when Wilson swept to a majority of 97 in the House of Commons, Hazell beat another Norfolk farmer, Ralph Howell, by 737 votes. Politics are uncertain, and four years later Howell captured the seat for the Tories and held it again, even when Heath lost power in 1974. By this time Hazell had become firmly entrenched as President of the Union, but he was now out of a job.

It was a neighbouring North Suffolk farmer, Jim Prior, who now wielded the patronage at the Ministry of Agriculture. He gave Hazell a job as a member of the Potato Marketing Board, and shortly afterwards he became Vice-Chairman of the Agricultural Training Board.

Despite his pronounced Norfolk accent, Hazell has lived in York for over forty years, and served on the West Riding War Agricultural Committee from 1939; he had fought unsuccessfully to get into Parliament twice before gaining North Norfolk in 1964, but had preceded Hilton as the Labour Party Agent for the East Norfolk seat in 1933. Despite his exile to York, Hazell's roots are in this wind-swept part of East Anglia, jutting out into the North Sea, and bordered by the flat wastes of the Wash. He started life as a farm-worker, and came from the solid stock of Norfolk farm labourers who had founded the Union, and who have played a leading part in it ever since.

Hazell speaks softly as he peers benignly through his glasses, but the soft voice can conceal an evangelical passion. Collison is a tall man, but Hazell's short stature reminds me of a labourer, impeded in growth by toil. However, it is a long time since he was a farm-worker; apart from being President of the NUAAW, and having a six-year stint in Parliament, he has also been a J.P. for York City since 1950, was Vice-Chairman of the Leeds Regional Hospital Board, and Chairman of the Area Health Authority. Hazell and the General Secretary who followed Collison in December 1969, Reg Bottini, are moderates in the trade-

'The Sacred Bull of British Agriculture', Lord Netherthorpe
Photo National Farmers Union

Lord Woolley, NFU President 1960–6
Photo National Farmers Union

Sir Gwilym ('Bill') Williams, NFU
President 1966–70. Voted out of office
Photo National Farmers Union

Sir Henry Plumb: forceful farmer's
champion
Photo National Farmers Union

union movement: perhaps they represent faithfully the moderate attitude of their members, but as a practical and practising pair of operators, they achieved great strides at the negotiating table, and can justifiably take credit for raising farm-workers' pay from the lowest industrial levels to something slightly above the lowest. This moderate leadership did not inspire even the Socialist political masters to remove the long-felt Union sense of injustice over tied cottages. That was left to a very militant Left Wing lady.

Joan Maynard

'Miss Joan Maynard, Labour MP for Sheffield Brightside, and a Member of Labour's National Executive, is well known for being as far to the Left in the Labour Party as one can get without actually falling off the edge. This conjures up a picture of a sort of North Country La Pasionaria, or Sheffield's answer to Rosa Luxemburg.'

Andrew Alexander,
'Daily Mail', 5 May 1976.

Collison was a farm-worker for twenty-one years, and General Secretary for sixteen years; his successor, Bottini, came up through the Legal Department of the NUAAW, but Joan Maynard was a farmer's daughter. It is true that her father only had a rather small Yorkshire farm, but he was still a farmer, and not a farm-worker. She represents a militant Left of Left attitude in a minority, if vociferous, wing of the Union, wields little power and is an acute embarrassment to the leadership; yet when projected into Parliament at short notice she used it as a platform to harry her own Party into abolishing the farm tied cottages. This was staple Union policy, which had received lip service only from the Labour Party for some time. It was her personal triumph to abolish the tied aspect of workers' accommodation.

Joan Maynard's translation to MP came unexpectedly, when the sitting Labour Member for the Brightside constituency of Sheffield, Eddie Griffiths, was ousted by his own party because of his right-wing views. With only a few weeks to go before the second General Election of 1974, in October, Maynard was selected, and certainly there was no doubt about her left-wing views. Griffiths stood as 'Independent Labour', and polled over 10,000 votes. Maynard, as the official candidate, won, but split the Labour supporters, ending up with a majority of 7,926, a considerable drop from the 20,000 majority that this seat had previously enjoyed. A short, middle-aged matronly figure, with a slow and pedantic form of speech, she chooses her words carefully, and then punches them out in a broad, if rasping, Yorkshire accent. Anyone less like a firebrand of the militant left wing would be hard to imagine. Hers is not the intellectual Fabianism of the Socialist girls from Oxford, but more like that of the rather dogmatic grandmother who has got to the age in life when she always gets her own way.

She helped her father on the family farm at Easingwold, and later at Thornton-le-Street, but he was an ardent Socialist and instructed his children in the dogma. Joan was a willing pupil, and she decided to dedicate her life to the Labour Party, joining it a year before she joined the NUAAW, and was a full-time paid agent in the Tory stronghold at Thirsk and Malton. Before she became an MP she was already a member of the powerful National Executive of the Labour Party.

Her militant stance—of which she is proud—is at considerable variance with the moderate attitude of the placid Hazell and the smooth Bottini; she is always encouraging the workers to strike, although the only strikes in the NUAAW are almost historical, and she roundly castigates both Hazell and the other members of the Union Executive for a lack of leadership.

Maynard became Vice-President of the Union in another unexpected and surprising manner: firstly surprising, since she was a woman amongst a band of brothers, and unexpectedly because there were plenty of stalwarts for the position. In fact, the choice became so wide that she slipped in as the outsider. Although this let a breath of fresh air into the somewhat stolid Union Executive, it became rather too fresh for her fellow-travellers. In secret session at the 1973 Biennial Conference the delegates found that the only way to remove this embarrassing woman from her position was to abolish the office itself. On the pretext of saving £300 per year, they decided to have no Vice-President at all; at that time the Union had an overall deficit of £50,000, and so the £300 saving was an excuse.

At Biennial Conferences her rabid denunciation of the popular Hazell, and her advocacy of measures which are clearly out of tune with the membership, has seen her motions and resolutions defeated time and time again. She goes against the popular tide, but never gives up, and never seems to learn that the exercise of power is contained in the title of R. A. Butler's autobiography *The Art of the Possible*. She challenged Hazell's position as President in 1975, and got only 26 votes to his 69; but then the Norfolk Communist Wilf Page got only 4 votes.

Dedicated to her cause, wedded to an implacable hostility towards the 'bosses', she at least admits that the farm workers are much more content than most other people, and adds with irony, 'But that, of course, militates against me.'

14 The National Farmers Union

The greatest single weakness of the NFU is that it has no definite policy for agriculture.'

Enough is Enough (Young, 1969).

'The NFU is regarded by the Ministry of Agriculture as a highly competent organisation.'

Report of the Commission of Enquiry into Industrial and Commercial Representation. CBI 1972.

The NFU was founded on 10 December 1908, and resulted from the Lincolnshire Farmers Union, created in 1904 by nine farmers. The first President was Colin Cambell, and he held this position until 1917. Of the three major unions to cover agriculture in England and Wales, the NFU is the youngest. The CLA had been formed as the Central Landowners Association in 1907, and the Farm Workers Union dates from 20 July 1906, with a formative meeting at the Angel Hotel, North Walsham. Thus the origins of all three date within a very short period of each other. The Scottish Farmers Union was founded in 1913, and the breakaway Farmers Union of Wales in 1955.

The NFU's greatest problem has been to steer a middle course between the larger and wealthier farmers in the east and the numerically stronger, but smaller and poorer, livestock farmers in the west. Since the livestock farmer is often the customer of his arable brother, buying cereals for cattle, pigs and poultry, and even transporting hay and straw from east to west (as occurred on a massive scale during the two dry summers of 1975 and 1976), it follows that half the farmers agitate for higher grain prices, while the other half want them lower. Even seed produced by one farmer is purchased by another, and the NFU has to tread delicately between these opposing interests. Somehow it succeeds. Although obviously concerned with advancing price levels, it keeps itself fairly aloof from mundane commercial activities, although there have been some sadly abortive attempts at involvement in the past.

There have been three major direct commercial forays in recent years: Fatstock Marketing Corporation Ltd (1954), NFU Seeds Ltd (August 1961), and Agricultural Central Trading (January 1962). The first is now a public company in which the NFU, through its nominee, the NFU Development Trust Ltd, acquired a 73 per cent share after a bitter take-over battle with International Meat Company, Thomas Borthwick & Son, in 1977. NFU Seeds Ltd has disappeared under the title 'National Farm Seeds Ltd'. It is now part of Agricultural Holdings Company Ltd, operated by an old-established Essex seed merchant, Hurst's, and Agricultural Central Trading has been banished to a pretty village in Buckinghamshire.

Over the last fifty years the NFU has made a number of unfortunate excursions into the commercial world, but these have proved abortive and very expensive. The rumps of these ventures were assembled in a now defunct body called Farmers Central Trading, which inherited the losses made by the earlier attempts, and in acute embarrassment they were not disclosed until years later.

Direct commercial involvement is today strictly not for the NFU, although there is lip service paid to co-ordinating orderly marketing through ACMS Ltd[1], which is the latter-day successor to a 1971 link-up between the marketing and commercial department of the NFU and the independent Agricultural Co-Operative Association. ACMS costs the NFU £74,000 per year, and provides an intelligence system of market prices. It does not operate in any direct commercial sense, and although housed in Agriculture House, Knightsbridge, it has its own offices and its own staff. The Agricultural Credit Corporation is in the same building, and although created by the NFU, it is only a back-up financial institution for farmers who are so much in the red that their own bank managers, or the AMC, will not entertain them. Beyond this the NFU involvement in commerce exists only through its ownership of a majority holding in FMC (Meat) Ltd. There are two major reasons why the NFU does not become commercially involved.

Firstly, the Monopolies Commission would never allow farmers to 'pool' their produce or hold the nation to ransom in the way that French farmers sell their produce to their own Co-Operatives, who market this in bulk. Such a stranglehold upon the consumers would not be permitted in Britain. Secondly, the job of marketing is in any event already being efficiently carried out by the statutory Marketing Boards for major commodities like milk, while for purposes of bulk buying, groups of farmers have got together, either under the wing of a local merchant, or under the NFU-sponsored Agricultural Central Trading Ltd. Besides this proliferation of marketing organizations there are the Farm Co-Operatives which compete with the private agricultural merchants in a typically British way.

This leaves the NFU with the role of a political, if non-partisan, pressure group to lobby and negotiate in the broader spectrum of Governmental policies. This it has become adept at doing, and it has built up an enviable reputation for the subtleties of its approach, its success being envied by the most militant trade unions in the country.

[1] Agricultural Co-operation and Marketing Services Ltd.

The Union was ensured a hearing under the terms of the 1947 Agriculture Act, and it was appointed the Official Representative Body with which Government could discuss the Annual Price Review, although it was not given power to negotiate. The NFU developed and exploited this position in its own favour, but with Britain's entry into Europe the UK Minister of Agriculture became subordinate to the EEC Commission in Brussels. With this removal of the price-fixing centre from Whitehall, with the added wider basis of European prices, the NFU stood to lose a lot of its power, and much of its glamour. This has also been eroded by the new terms for agricultural representation to the UK Minister in the run-up period before he flies off to consult the Agriculture Ministers of the 'Nine'. It was not only the CLA and NUAAW that were added to the consultation list, but also a selection of bodies such as the Transport and General Workers Union, and the Food and Distribution Industrial Council. The days of the NFU's single-handed role in attempting to influence prices have gone, as indeed has the UK prerogative to fix its own.

After Britain's accession a five-year transitional period was fixed to cushion the effects of food prices upon the British housewife; this, with the mass of 'small print' that had not been scrutinized or publicized in advance, gave the NFU a new role in fighting regulations unacceptable to British farmers. Many of these were embodied in the Treaty of Rome, but others have evolved as 'regulations' through the Brussels Commission; nevertheless, as we move into the 1980s the NFU will have to find a new and positive role if it is to preserve the reputation from which its power derives.

The NFU involvement in commercial activities, or even commercial advice, is minimized by its designation as a 'Employers and Trade Organization'. Under the Restrictive Practices Act 1956 it is banned from 'market-rigging', this Act in fact setting out to protect the unsuspecting customer from 'rings' or over-charging; but in the case of the NFU the law has proved to be an ass, and not for the first time.

During 1970 the troubles in farming unseated the affable Bill Williams from the NFU Presidency, and propelled the tougher Plumb into the top job, while the NFU advised its members to boycott the markets for one week by not sending any animals for sale. A later court action declared that this was illegal advice, but it could be given when an exemption was applied for; unfortunately, the NFU was ineligible to apply. In 1972 the Barker Report on Marketing was published. This met with general disapproval. The NFU had for years been trying to co-ordinate the haphazard schemes for marketing farm produce, yet Barker advocated precisely what the law forbade. With the accession into Europe looming closer, with its troubles at home, and with discontent raging among farmers, the NFU wanted to put itself into the same powerful position of some of the Continental farmers with their co-operatives. A situation arose over bacon contracts and supplies.

The British Bacon Agents, operating on the London Provision Exchange (where the weekly bacon prices were worked out), found they could not fix the price against those of their competitors, but could only quote 'reported' prices from various markets. The British Bacon Curers Federation, another stage in the pig marketing set-up, was also hamstrung because it had advised farmers to cut back their pigs by 10 per cent. The Registrar issued a strong warning to them, that they were not allowed to advise their members nationally how to achieve a target of 265,000 tonnes, which the Minister of Agriculture had suggested was their quota. A Government Ministry was laying down a strict tonnage, yet the BBCF could not advise its members how to achieve this target. The NFU had been asked to comment upon the National Bacon Pig Contracts in 1971, but was banned from even issuing a statement. The anomaly went yet further. The Wisbech and District Growers Association in Cambridgeshire wanted to discuss with merchants and processors various ways of stabilizing the strawberry and plum crops. Earlier it had negotiated basic prices and quantities with the merchants, and had achieved some stability in a highly volatile market. The Registrar of the Restrictive Practices Court issued a warning, and the whole patient process which had been built up by the Wisbech Growers was destroyed.

In 1973, as the NFU was struggling to reshape the structure and organization of British farming to meet the EEC criteria, it suggested a Federal Cereals Seeds Marketing Organization, which would aim to meet the stringent quality and marketing requirements. It was set up to follow precisely what the Barker Committee, and the Government, wanted. Montague Keen takes up the story[2]:

> It will come as a surprise even to those inured to the follies of Government and the eccentricities of our Courts to discover that in the eyes of the law this could well constitute a huge conspiracy to defraud the public. The activities of such an organisation would be promptly placed in the same category as those sinister price rings which it was the very reasonable object of the Restrictive Trade Practices Act, 1956, to attack.

The NFU came in for warm praise in Lord Devlin's Report[3], but then the redoubtable Jim Netherthorpe was a member of the six-man Committee of Enquiry set up by the CBI to look at the differences between trade and employer organizations and Chambers of Commerce. It praised the set-up whereby each farmer member is not only a member of his local branch, but also of his county branch, and is also automatically a member of any specialist groups such as Poultry, Horticulture, Seeds, etc., which often have a separate branch operating within a county framework. However, the Devlin Report highlighted one of the basic problems in the highly organized realms of modern farming: that there were too many organizations jostling with each other to find a role, and in consequence overlapping. It cited, for instance, the fact that while the NFU negotiated milk prices, the Quality Milk Producers Ltd negotiated the premium

---

[2] *British Farmer and Stockbreeder,* 6 January 1973.
[3] Report of the Commissions of Enquiry into Industrial and Commercial Representation commissioned by the Association of British Chambers of Commerce and the Federation of British Industry in January 1971. It set out to review the current states of industrial and commercial representation and was chaired by Lord Devlin.

for quality milk from breeds such as the Jersey or Guernsey noted for their cream. In another example the Report said:

A leading example is the British Poultry Federation. As vertical integration in the industry has extended from production through to marketing, there is an overlap in membership and services between the NFU and the BPF.

But if the farming industry is a jungle of overlapping and double representation, (of which the poultry industry is by far the most confusing), then other industries in the UK have similar or worse problems. Thirty-two different organizations were to be found in the combined agriculture–fishing and forestry sector, but the textile industry had 129 organizations; food, drink and tobacco 128; and the construction industry was a maze, with no less than 393 various bodies and organizations.

The NFU shop window

The Annual Motor Show is the shop window of the motor trade, and is organized by the Society of Motor Manufacturers and Traders; paradoxically it also has a hand in the annual farmers' 'Smithfield Show'. Other industries have their own Shows, Trade Fairs, Conferences and shop windows, etc. The CLA, quite in character, has its own 'Game Fair', to present shooting, fishing and country sports, but the NFU organizes, quite strangely, a Horticultural Fair and Conference called, again quite strangely, 'British Growers Look Ahead', which takes place in a hotel in Harrogate. With the plethora of County Agricultural Shows operating independently, and the mighty Royal Show organized by the RASE (whose role in agriculture is more significant than at first sight), the NFU has little left to organize as a shop window for farming. Nevertheless, a Tomato Show in a Victorian monstrosity seems far from the dignified role of the Union at its political nerve centre in London. It does, however, promote British food through an affiliated body ensconced behind the façade of Agriculture House, laboriously labelled 'The British Farm Produce Council', which runs on a pathetic contribution.

The BFPC is, however, not the sole baby of the NFU. It was created in 1960 by a combination of the NFU, Marketing Boards, FMC and a few others, with the objective of extending the consumption of farmers' produce. Its backing is proportionate to the ability of its sponsors to pay. The Council was headed for many years by Sir Richard Trehane until his retirement from Chairmanship of the MMB in 1977, but the guiding light and Chairman is an Essex farmer from Clacton-on-Sea, Charles Jarvis, a Sassenach who quotes Burns with gusto, and has become an indefatigable protagonist of the British way of eating, who travels the country proclaiming the virtues of home-produced food with an evangelical fervour. The Board of eight members is made up of representatives from potatoes, meat, milk, eggs, an ex-President of the Scottish NFU, and even a watercress-grower. The NFU has one representative, a lady.

The BFPC has no counterpart abroad, and claims to be the only body dealing generally with the promotion of British food, although such bodies as the Flowers Publicity Council and others occupy a specialist role. In a nation which is a major food-importer, farmers are forced to fight paradoxically harder for a share of their own markets. Within the life of the BFPC since 1960 the percentage of home-produced food consumed in the UK has gone up from 51 per cent of the whole to 53 per cent, which has thus widened the gap over imports to 6 per cent. Since a 1 per cent swing equals almost £100 million, it is substantial, even if the BFPC cannot claim the full honour of achieving it.

With the financial assistance of the MMB, and three large industrial companies, the NFU launched yet another food-promotional campaign in 1977, entitled, quite inexplicably, 'Help Yourself'. This time the £40,000 campaign was contributed by BOCM/Silcock (part of the Unilever Group), Massey-Ferguson (UK) Ltd, and ICI. All of these have substantial vested interests in promoting the prosperity of their customers—the farmers.

Commercial interests

> *'Why is it that the NFU, a superbly effective body in so many ways—as deft as a ballerina when conducting its political affairs—is given to treading on banana skins when straying into commercial fields.'*
>
> Derek Barber, in 'Power Farming', December 1975.

> *'No nation was ever ruined by trade.'*
>
> Benjamin Franklin

NFU Seeds Ltd

After the establishment of the FMC in 1954, a new spirit of commercial development was sweeping the NFU after Netherthorpe's retirement. In the autumn of 1961 the NFU decided that it could usefully set up an organization, purely commercial, to market pedigree strains of seeds. It is not a major field of farmers' purchases, or even sales, but it represented an area which could be an experiment with a product that was being sold by one farmer and bought by another. 'Cut out the middleman' was the cry. In the event it was bungled, came as a bombshell to both the trade and farmers, was bitterly criticized by most of the farmers whom it had been set up to assist, and today has been quietly washed away under another name, and is part of a commercial company.

The formation of NFU Seeds Industries Ltd came like a bolt from the blue; the NFU through its Development Company had a commitment of £125,000, which farmers seized upon with indignation, fearing that their subscription funds were being misused in this manner. An assurance that the money did not come from subscriptions did little to assuage fears that this was the thin edge of the wedge. Farmers felt that NFU involvement in commercial activities of this kind sullied it, a strange and almost inexplicable attitude.

The idea had originally come from Lincolnshire farmer Henry Burtt, and had it had a happier birth it might have been the forerunner to a deeper NFU involvement in commercial fields. But the whole affair was chaotic. Originally conceived as a co-operative venture between the NFU and three trade partners, with the blessing of the Seed Trade Association, two of the traders withdrew in embarrassment even before the first Board Meeting. They were Dunns and Townsends, leaving only one trade partner, Hurst, Gunson, Cooper Taber Ltd, an old-established Essex company with roots going back to a Mr Field and a Mr Child in 1560. Hursts honoured its committment at the risk of being boycotted by other members of the STA, and indeed by its own farmer customers. NFUSI did become a brand leader in herbage seeds, but it never became a real force in the seed trade.

Agricultural Central Trading Ltd

Operating under its 'Action' label, ACT has become a trading force in the UK farmers' field, even if its catalogue today looks more like that of a mail-order store, and containing such essential farmers' requisites as a deep freeze, and nice woolly jumpers. It is in essence a bulk buying group which cuts retail prices by hawking around the market-place, and by collecting its money in seven days. One of the problems of farm finance that bedevils farmers' trading is that farm produce, being the primary product, is sold at wholesale prices, whereas farmers' inputs are all purchased retail.

To knock significant holes in retail prices requires wholesale bulk orders, and pre-planning; something farmers are not good at. The collection of sufficient individual orders, and the bulking of the purchase for good discounts, requires more planning than farmers had been accustomed to, but ACT, although it has never achieved its predicted turnover, has achieved a considerable degree of bulk buying organization to the benefit of its farmer customers. Early payments are worth some discount, and since delivery charges are part of retail sales—including after sales service on some items—this new organization cut out much of the service, at the expense of the discount. Orders are delivered to a central farmer whose neighbours collect their individual orders themselves.

Between 1958 and 1962 many farmer buying groups sprung up as they sought to cheapen costs; the abolition of Retail Price Maintenance by Edward Heath, many years before he became Prime Minister, still lay ahead, but farmers discovered that they could get remarkable savings on such items as barbed wire and tractor batteries (up to 40 per cent discount). The war of the High Street Supermarkets and the advent of Green Shield Stamps was yet to come, but the farmers were trimming their costs. These fragmented farmer groups which had sprung up all over the country, at a truly miraculous speed, were finally co-ordinated under one umbrella. This was Agricultural Central Trading Ltd, which was set up in 1962. It was never envisaged at the outset that the NFU could go it alone; it formed an alliance, described as a 'shotgun wedding', with the existing ring of farmer-controlled co-operatives, which, in no way linked to the ÑFU, or even to each other, were felt to represent a farmers' voice. The co-ops saw this as a threat to their own existence; although both parties put up £5,000 in January 1962, by July they were taking divorce proceedings, and they separated in August. Sir Miles Thomas, Chairman of the ACT Board, gloomily described the intervening period as 'my uncomfortable months'. The partners were incompatible, the groups wanted to buy direct from the manufacturers; and the co-ops, seeing this as an extension of their own activities, wanted the goods supplied through them.

Sir Miles Thomas, former Chairman of BOAC, was conscripted by NFU President Woolley into the farming scene at the same time that Lord Netherthorpe was being wooed by Sir Clavering Fison to go in the opposite direction. Thomas was not a success, and he soon left the scene; created a life peer in 1971, he still hides his embarrassment at this débâcle by omitting any reference to his period as Chairman of ACT from his entry in *Who's Who*.

ACT was launched with grossly unrealistic optimism concerning its attraction to farmers, and without any hint of the antagonism it would arouse in the private trade. Farmers had been well served by local agricultural merchants for many years, and despite the movement towards co-operatives, joint marketing schemes and bulk buying, the vast percentage of all farmers' trade still goes through the private sector. When ACT was launched it was set a target of taking £400 million of the farm trade from the existing establishments within five years. When that period was reached it had achieved a paltry £14 million, and in its eleventh year it was still at that same turnover. By the eighteenth year it had jumped to £25 million—still a far cry from £400 million, its target when launched. It lost a massive £58,174 in its first year of trading, and although this was reduced in later years, the first five-year period showed an accumulated loss of £3,500. Its chequered history since showed losses around 1970, when the National Postal Strike cost it £40,000, and in 1971 the livestock business was wound up, reducing its turnover by over £3 million, but reversing a loss into a modest profit.

After the co-ops withdrew in August 1962 ACT moved into new offices in Basil Street, London, just behind Harrods, and in that month Sir Miles Thomas, looking to the future, said, 'ACT is now rapidly becoming a vigorous trading organisation instead of a rather heated debating society.' It was to be a long road before ACT achieved stability and a solid reputation, or was accepted as another weapon in the farmers' armoury.

After ten years the NFU withdrew from ACT completely, and today there are approximately 700 groups of farmers looked after by about 50 local offices of ACT. Each group member receives a monthly newsletter from his local ACT office, telling him the place and time of the next meeting. Meetings are held in farmhouses, and there is a pyramid-style democratic organization. The range of goods has been curtailed; the originally visualized market of 5,000 new tractors and 2,000 new combine harvesters bought annually by British farmers remained only a mirage. The manufacturers and dealers decided resolutely that they would not supply ACT, and both sides have settled down to recognize that these machines need an after-sales service which ACT cannot give.

FMC Ltd

'We have been struck both by the Trust's lack of knowledge of FMC's activities and the lack of any dialogue since 1971.'
Monopolies Commission Report on NFU bid to take over FMC 1975.

'The hopes for FMC as a public company in 1962 have not been justified by events.'
Document to FMC Shareholders in relation to NFU takeover bid 1974.

Founded as the Fatstock Marketing Corporation in 1954, and now known more simply as FMC Ltd, this multi-million-pound meat organization was the brainchild of the NFU. It was owned and controlled by thousands of small farmers with five-shilling shares, went public in 1962 when the NFU lost control, has been the subject of two bitter takeover battles and a report by the Monopolies Commission, has seen bitter wrangling between its NFU masters and its directors, with sackings and resignations, was the cause of a scandal that rocked the Heath Government in 1973, and has, as a paradoxical result of an abortive takeover bid by Borthwicks in 1977, now come back under the NFU wing with a 73 per cent stake in its shares.

To call this NFU control is not strictly true. FMC was created by the NFU Development Trust Ltd, which was formed in 1953, and is thus one year older than FMC itself; but the Trust has become an important auxiliary of the NFU, and not least because its original investment of £20,000 has turned into a cool £3 million. The original objectives of the Trust were vague: 'To assist in the expansion of agricultural production and to promote and develop co-operation in agriculture,' which could mean anything and everything. Its registered office is at Agriculture House, although it is not strictly owned by the NFU. FMC Ltd occupies a neighbouring modern glass structure abutting on to Agriculture House in busy Knightsbridge, but is further away in its outlook, and the two organizations have been at loggerheads with each other more than once. It is a baby which outgrew its parent and started kicking rather hard. Exactly who does own the £3 million is open to dispute, and the original 94,000 five-shilling farmer subscribers (of whom only about 70,000 actually came up with the cash, and whose identity is not easily ascertainable anyway) would have a strong claim in the event of any winding-up procedures.

It all started as the ration books were being discarded, and food-rationing ceased, though the Government still retained a separate Ministry of Food, amalgamated into the Ministry of Ag. and Fish in 1954. In 1953 the NFU had been pressing for a Fatstock Marketing Board, but there was strong opposition from the butchers, livestock auctioneers and even some farmers. The following year the NFU decided to go into direct business as a competitor to the traditional, entrenched set-up with its own company. The Fatstock Marketing Corporation was born. It bought the basic farm animals, cattle, sheep and pigs, and paid a dead-weight basis in a new way to which farmers were unaccustomed. Normal sales prior to this time were through the auction ring on a live-weight basis, without weighing machines, and subject to guesswork. FMC put a bottom in the market, and gave farmers a new and welcome option. Floated on a minimal capital, it was able to finance itself through the fact that butchers paid cash on delivery, and the farmers had to wait a few days for their money—a situation in which many companies operate with skilful advantages to themselves.

After eight years the Marsh and Baxter Group came on the market. This contained the Harris of Calne bacon-curing factory in Wiltshire, also the Dunmow Flitch Bacon Company, so that now FMC Ltd is responsible for the Flitch that is presented annually to the married couple who can prove they have not had a row for a year. Then, in order to continue to expand, the NFU Development Trust Ltd had to put the shares on the open market. Although many farmers never forgave them, it was the only method of raising cash, and indeed many farmers were among the share subscribers when FMC went public in 1962. Since that time Marsh and Baxter has been a less reliable partner, and the vagaries of pig marketing in the UK have been fully responsible for this cyclic situation. ACT found its operation more profitable when it jettisoned its Livestock Division, and indeed Borthwicks, whose abortive bid for FMC in 1977 finally restored the NFU dominance, has shown that life can be either meat, money or muck. Borthwicks record shows that it made a profit of £9 million in 1972, lost £13 million the following year, and jumped back to a £4·6 million profit in 1974. But in all this expansion of FMC could be seen the figure of Sir John Stratton.

The original Trust had been formed by the NFU, and also by the Scottish and Ulster Farmers Unions, but when it became public the Development Trust was re-formed as Trustee for the 94,000 farmers, and there was an unresolved attempt later to transfer this power to a seven-man Board. The complexities of the exchange of shares and the purchase of the Marsh and Baxter Group removed the Trust from direct control of FMC Ltd, and it then placed nominated Directors upon the Board. When the Trust was re-created Sir John Stratton (who had been appointed FMC Chairman in 1957, four years after its creation) wanted to be Chairman also of the Trust Board. NFU President Sir Harold Woolley made it a condition of Union support that the Trust Chairman should be appointed by the NFU Development Company.

Despite Woolley's opposition, Stratton was appointed Chairman of the Trust, and with both chairs under his control, he was reappointed to these dual and often conflicting roles, for many years. As farmers saw it, FMC represented the trade, and the Trust represented the producers. It took until 1970 to remove Stratton from the Trust and replace him by an NFU man.

A short white-haired man who died in 1976, Stratton was a shoe-manufacturer, Chairman of Dolcis for ten years until 1957, when he became Chairman of the original Fatstock Marketing Corporation. He was both Chairman and Chief Executive, and became President in 1974 after a seventeen-year reign, but his time in office had put a firm stamp of success on a business that can be highly volatile. Only in two years of its history has it lost money; in 1963/4, and again with a smaller loss in 1966/7. Stratton sold off £61,000 worth of his own shares in FMC Ltd in 1971—an action which was hardly commensurate with his own confidence in the company, although he declared that the sale was for domestic reasons. Any hint that he was selling out was dispelled by the next year's figures, which showed a massive jump in profits.

In fact, the figures were so good that he received a bonus under the terms of his contract of a £315 rise per week. This was announced in 1973, when Heath was trying to stem the tide of wage increases. It incensed the lower wage earners, and undermined the pay restraint talks being hammered out between the Government and an unwilling TUC. Stratton was asked by an NFU, embarrassed at the adverse publicity, to hand back his £16,000 bonus. In the event he kept it, saying, 'It was a modest bonus which I think I deserve. I am a most helpful and generous-minded person.' He could certainly not be described as a very diplomatic person. In the end the Inland Revenue, of course, took most of it. The NFU Development Trust eventually replaced Stratton by the bluff David Darbishire, Vice-President of the Union, and the number three man after Plumb and Deputy President Butler. (Vice-Presidents come and go fairly regularly, and usually without much trace. John Coussins, a Dorset dairy farmer, succeeded Darbishire as Chairman of the Trust when he stood down from the Vice-Presidency in 1977).

A firm of stockbrokers, Greene & Co, reported in 1972 that of thirty-three companies in the FMC Group, eight were making losses, but added that under the forthcoming Common Agricultural Policy FMC should do well, suggesting that it might even venture into Europe to buy up a few meat businesses. FMC has not done this, although it does have a company in New Zealand (Denny's, the meat-exporters), and there is a string of eleven companies in such by-products as skins, hides, wool, even meat and bonemeal and tallow. There is also an involvement in Ireland. The growth potential mentioned by Greene's set the takeover rumours going, and the NFU got worried. It only had a 37 per cent stake in the Ordinary Shares, though it built this up to 40 per cent two years later when it put in a takeover bid itself. Although it was strictly a commercial company, and not completely controlled by the NFU, the FMC still had a bias towards the British farmer: something it feared might disappear if a newcomer entered the takeover battle and was successful. The patriotic sympathies could wither away rather sharply. So the NFU had to bid.

The 1974 takeover battle

The NFU Development Trust made an offer of 65p for the FMC shares, a price which was the same as that at which they had been floated twelve years before—obviously not a good investment. This was a capital bid worth £3·7 million, but the FMC shares had seen a chequered career. Just after flotation in 1962 at 65p, they shot up to 102p, and everyone was very happy, but a few years later they fell to only 22p, by 1973 going back again to over 100p. By 1974 they were down to 39p, so that the NFU bid was a realistic one in relation to their cash value on the open market. It was estimated that the Trust and private farmers owned 70 per cent, although there was a total of 14,000 shareholders. By this time, after twenty years' existence, FMC had acquired 26 per cent of the pig market, and only 12 per cent each of the cattle and sheep slaughtering business. There were no rival bidders, and the assets were estimated at £10 million. Pre-tax profit stood at £3·6 million, and the annual turnover was a massive £244 million. The Socialist Minister of Agriculture, Fred Peart, became a Director of FMC Ltd after losing his job in the Government when the Socialists were turned out of office in 1970, but left the FMC Board in February 1974, when Wilson returned to 10 Downing Street again. It was on the day of the second General Election of 1974 (10 October) that the NFU bid was announced.

Said the *Farmers Weekly*[4]: 'Farmers started the meat business that grew into FMC. They sold it, for reasons which looked good at the time. Now they want to buy it back.' But the FMC Board rejected the takeover, although there were NFU representatives on it, including past NFU President Sir Gwilym ('Bill') Williams. They unanimously rejected the bid on the grounds that the criticism of FMC performance was unjustified, and that in any case the 65p bid was far too cheap: it should be at least 135p.

Two weeks later three of the Directors changed their minds. They were John Jenkins, Cambridgeshire farmer and past President of the NFU of Scotland, who had been placed on the Board by Plumb himself; W. Watson Peat, another Scottish farmer; and J. G. Farbon. The last two had been Directors of the NFU Trust only that year. It seemed that someone had put some pressure on someone else. The farming industry was divided about the merits of this takeover anyway. Predictably, the NFU organ[5] backed the bid, and Peter Bell wrote:

> It should be emphasised that the move will in no way affect the present crisis in the livestock industry. But a successful outcome could go some way to prevent another such crisis through the development of contracts and a consequential stabilising effect on the market.

But John Cherrington in the *Financial Times*[6] was more explicit:

> What farmers do not seem to understand in their quest for better marketing is that what determines the price of food is neither quality nor who handles the meat, but supply and demand.

[4] 18 October 1974.
[5] *British Farmer and Stockbreeder.*
[6] 25 October 1974.

And he concluded:

> As far as FMC is concerned, the NFU might just as well save its money.

The Trust refused to increase its 65p per share bid, and by the end of October acceptances of 1·6 million shares had been received. This increased the NFU stake to 56·7 per cent, but suddenly the whole matter was referred to the Monopolies Commission, and a six-month stalemate developed. The Trust Chairman, Darbishire, hit out at the Secretary of State for Prices and Consumer Protection, Shirley Williams, and said at Broadway in Worcestershire:

> It seems quite incomprehensible that when farmers try to help themselves with their own money, and when the livestock industry is going through the most ruinous and catastrophic period in its history, the Prices Secretary, Mrs. Shirley Williams, should refer the Trust's takeover bid for FMC Ltd to the Monopolies and Mergers Commission on what appears to be the flimsiest of pretexts. Meanwhile, the Minister of Agriculture, Mr. Fred Peart, has been for years encouraging producer controlled marketing and set up the Central Council for Agricultural and Horticultural Co-Operation to assist this development.

The NFU was forced to hand back the acceptances, and stalemate prevailed. The NFU told the Monopolies Enquiry that it should not be adjudicating upon the matter at all, and Darbishire's plea that Mrs Williams had used the 'flimsiest of pretexts' weemed valid. A merger was between two organizations trading in the same field—which could produce a monopoly—but the NFU Trust was a non-operational organization. Quietly the sitting Commission evaded this issue and continued to collect its evidence. The report was due for publication in May 1975, but it was delayed for nearly two months. When finally announced it roundly castigated the childish attitude of both FMC and NFU.

> To an outsider, the prospect of two large organisations, both dependent on agriculture, and whose Headquarters buildings stand side by side overlooking Hyde Park, allowing such a rift to develop at all seems incredible. But, in many walks of life, rows between close neighbours often tend to become quite deep seated and bitter.[7]

However, the general opinion of the report was that it might be less harmful to prohibit the merger, and therefore permission was given. But by this time the NFU had other things on its plate, and was adopting new tactics.

In January it had raised again that hoary old chestnut, a Fatstock Marketing Board, although these were more delaying tactics while the FMC bid was in the refrigerator. At the FMC Stratton had been replaced the previous year, and a minor civil servant from the backwoods of the Ministry of Agriculture, Anson Payne, had taken over as Chairman, while Stratton was pushed upstairs to be President of the Company. Payne was a failure, and moves were made to replace him as a vital ingredient to a shake-up in the operation of FMC. As Stratton's bonus payment had been a headline-hitter, so was Payne's. He was

---

[7] Peter Bullen, *Financial Times*, 17 July 1975.

given £205,000, which included £35,000 for 'retirement benefits', and there was a £170,000 public pay-off under his contract, which ran until he reached the age of sixty-five, seven years later. This sort of expensive dismissal was described in the *Financial Times* as 'very much a feature of life at the top of FMC'. His place was taken by David Darbishire, but Jack Clarfelt came back as Chief Executive and Deputy Chairman. Clarfelt had been Managing Director from 1954 until FMC went public. He had a family meat wholesaling company, Clarfelt & Co., which had been the basis for FMC when it was created. After leaving Clarfelt became head of animal feed and meat wholesaler Smithfield and Zwannenberg, who were duly taken over by commodity traders S. & W. Berisford. The company Clarfelt returned to after a fifteen-year absence was very different from the one he had left. But the battle to put newcomers on the Board meant sacking some of the others, and they did not like it. However, a new bidder for FMC was around the corner, and his intervention would ironically achieve for the NFU the majority holding which it required. The Monopolies Commission Report had banned the NFU Trust from acquiring anything other than nominal parcels of shares in any one year; it was not empowered to go to the Stock Exchange and buy up every share that became available.

The Borthwick Bid

Borthwicks were until 1976 the fourth largest private company in the UK, but in that year (not a good year for taking companies to market) they went public in a rather badly subscribed issue. They had become established as an importer of New Zealand lamb towards the end of the nineteenth century. The company was owned by seventy-odd shareholders, but if one left out family trusts, they were really only forty shareholders, all of them third- and fourth-generation Borthwicks, with seven of them on the Board. The international headquarters of the company, which Tom Borthwick had moved from his prosperous Liverpool to Stall No. 367 on London's Smithfield Market in 1892, was now tucked away behind the bleak façade of Smithfield Market, opposite the even bleaker back end of Barts Hospital, next door to one of the ancient gates to the City of London, St John's Gate, and facing the lovely Chapel of the Knights of St John.

Borthwicks had a turnover of £292 million, and FMC one of £327 million, but Borthwicks were strong throughout many countries of the world, and weak in the UK, where FMC were major operators. It looked like a suitable marriage that would benefit both companies. But the FMC, although entirely independent of the NFU, and with the NFU Trust as its largest single shareholder (though a minority shareholder) were adamantly against such a move. FMC had originally gone public in order to finance the takeover of the Marsh and Baxter Group. This removed control from the farmers, and they were determined that this should not happen again; indeed, the policy was still to gain full control, though at their modest share-buying programme this would be impossible till well into the 1980s.

It was all over fairly quickly. Borthwicks announced their bid on 15 March

1977, and withdrew from the battle just over three weeks later, on 11 April. They had opened the bidding at an equivalent price of 101p for the FMC shares that the NFU had bid 65p for three years earlier. The NFU Development Trust put up an offer of 97p per share, and Borthwicks came back the same day with a bid of 125p. This pushed up the Stock Exchange quotation to 117p, and effectively blocked the Trust's offer. Borthwicks were offering £12·5 million in the face of a £9·7 million counter-bid, although the Trust owned so much that it did not require to buy as many shares.

The Trust remained determined not to sell; although there had been talks between the two companies in the previous November, John Coussins, now in charge of the NFU Development Trust, and Jack Clarfelt, sentimentally attached to this baby he had nurtured in its infancy, bitterly rejected all the arguments put forward by Borthwicks. In the face of strong opposition from the FMC directors, Borthwicks gave up the battle. In the course of three weeks Borthwicks had bought a 9 per cent stake in FMC, and this was sold to the NFU Development Trust for £805,000. It gave them a 56 per cent stake, and finally brought back control to the farmers after a fifteen-year gap.

The NFU Trust had offered to buy any FMC shares which were on offer, and although they paid Borthwicks £805,000 for their 9 per cent stake, they were in fact offered considerably more shares, and finished up owning 73 per cent of FMC. It had firmly put the direct control back into the hands of the farmers, but it took an overdraft of £2,700,000 to buy the offered shares.

For the company there were still troubles to come, and in December 1977 Bill Newton-Clare resigned his directorship, explaining that his 'profit-orientated views were not acceptable to some Members of the Board'. The NFU commissioned a report by the Manchester Exchange and Investment Bank on all its commercial interests, including FMC, and in a shock announcement two months later in February 1978 the NFU appointed its own Director-General, George Cattell, as the new FMC managing director, with a brief to raise falling profits.

The National Farmers Union Mutual Insurance Society Ltd

> *'Down went the owners—greedy men whom hope of gain allured;*
> *Oh, dry the starting tear, for they were heavily insured.'*
>
> W. S. Gilbert

> *'Agriculture is especially vulnerable to damage through arson or incendiarism.'*
>
> '60 Years of Service to Farmers and Growers' (1970).

While farmers who are not members of the NFU can send their cattle for marketing through the FMC, or can buy cut-price goods through ACT, they cannot insure with the NFU Mutual. It exists only to serve the members of the National Farmers Union (although this does extend to the Scottish and Ulster Unions), and making it the only organization in British agriculture to cover the whole of the United Kingdom; not even the Ministry of Agriculture itself can claim that.

It represents a tie-up to the various farmers' unions, and while not contributing substantially to Union funds, it makes it more difficult for a member to resign, and means he must rearrange all his multifarious insurances as well. There is an added side-issue: its competitive premium rates are a strong argument in any recruiting drive, emphasizing as they do that part of the subscription will be covered by the benefits of joining the allied insurance company, a point which both the CLA and the FUW realize. The CLA offer insurance services through Boulton & Co., and the FUW realized at the outset of their break from the NFU that loyal adherence becomes stronger when backed by cash. They allied themselves quickly to another 'mutual' insurance company.

The Society's link with the NFU, apart from only taking members' business, is a far more practical one. The Branch Secretaries could not expect to show a 'Union presence' in market towns throughout the country on the pittance which the NFU pays them as a salary, neither could many of the Branches support an office of their own. A happy partnership has therefore evolved, through the appointment of local Branch (but not County) Secretaries as collecting agents for the 'Mutual'.

The NFU Mutual was formed by farmers, is run by farmers, and supported by farmers. There is a Board of Directors composed entirely of farmers or horticulturalists, including past NFU President Lord Woolley, but not including either Netherthorpe or Williams. There are fourteen Branch Offices, including Glasgow for Scotland, Belfast for Northern Ireland, and Llandudno on the tip of North Wales. England is divided into eight areas, each with a local Board of prominent, or formerly prominent, local NFU men. Boards also cover Scotland, Northern Ireland and Wales. The wholly owned subsidiary the Avon exists to cover the insurance requirements of farmers' families, or of wives who may not themselves be named as NFU members, and it also has offices in Birmingham, Manchester and London. These last are hardly market towns where farmers quaff their ale, but the Mutual itself is centred amid fine farming country, in the heart of England at Stratford-upon-Avon. With the NAC established only a short distance away at Kenilworth, it would seem that leafy Warwickshire has become the heart of the farming body, as well as the heart of England, even though in both national and farming terms London remains a strong contender.

In the insurance world the NFU Mutual is pretty small fry. It rated no. 16 in the 1976 league tables of UK insurance companies[8], with a non life premium income of £39 million against the top company, the Commercial Union

* *The Times* 1,000. 1976 1977.

Assurance, which has an income of £922 million, just 23 times larger than the NFU Mutual. It does, however, deal with life assurance itself, as does the Avon.

Another unique feature of its operation links it to the farmers. It employs local farmers as fire assessors or other claims valuers for smaller claims, although the local farmer might work with a professional valuer in a larger claim. While fire damage is readily assessable, many farming claims are complex, specialized and even purely local. These local farmers with their up-to-date knowledge are invaluable in keeping claims in check. Setting one farmer against another in this way mitigates the more excessive or less genuine claims. One could wish that the car insurance companies could devise a similar method of reducing excessive garage repairs, which might reduce the premiums.

At Stratford the NFU Mutual rests amid the old-world charm of Shakespearian England behind a charming façade of Queen Anne windows which abut on to Church Street, and where you walk through an archway emblazoned above with the facsimile of a wheatsheaf, the Mutual's emblem (the Avon uses a swan), and behind is a functional modern office block with its glass exterior and open-plan interior, packed with electronic data-processing equipment. It is a stark contrast to the unsophisticated calm of the river or the municipal gardens, or even the uncompromising solidity of the Memorial Theatre itself, than which even the modern Hilton is more appealing. It was in a tea shop in Stratford where the NFU Mutual was born in 1910, just as George V was crowned ruler of a nation and an empire.

By 1910 the NFU itself had still not celebrated its second birthday, but in April 1909 the Stratford-upon-Avon Branch was formed. Later that same year seven tenant farmers sat down in that unmarked tea-shop to find a way of strengthening the newly formed Branch. They founded The Midland Farmers Mutual Insurance Society, and started in a farmhouse at Clifford Chambers. In 1911 the society moved into Guild Street, using one room and allowing the caretaker the remainder—free of rent. Five years later, in the middle of the First World War, as farming fortunes were rising, it moved to Bridge Street, and in the aftermath of that war, in 1920, to Church Street, its present home.

In closely packed and highly inflammable farm buildings the problems of fire are acute, and with less precautions prevailing than today, it was nothing short of miraculous that at the first Statutory Meeting of the new insurance company the members were congratulated on having no fires! Had it foundered at that time, no doubt someone somewhere else would have started a similar organization at a later date. But it didn't. In 1921 drought brought a rash of fire damage to farms and crops, but by this time the society had embarked on heavy reinsurance, and its financial strength had grown apace. In the 1967–8 foot-and-mouth epidemic which swept across Britain the Mutual paid out £1·5 million in insurance claims. It proved that they had gone a long way from humble beginnings.

The old 'Midland Farmers Mutual Insurance Society' lost its identity when the NFU Mutual came into being in 1919. Already it had thrust its roots beyond the Warwickshire countryside where it began. In 1923 the Scottish Farmers Union linked itself to the Mutual. The Avon was created in 1925. Ulster joined the happy band in 1930, when the Mutual bought out another farmers' company covering some of the northern counties of England, and named the 'Northern Farmers Insurance Society'. In 1928 the Mutual signed its first Life Assurance Policy, and two years later pioneered the idea of a 'family policy'. It had thus widened the scope of its insurance business, and widened the area to cover the United Kingdom, except for the Celtic extremity of Cornwall. It took sixty-six years, till 1976, before the Mutual became the officially recognized NFU insurers in this bastion of nationalism.

In 1919, when the NFU was looking for one insurer to serve farmers in every part of the country, it was wooed by a number of existing companies. The Midland Farmers Mutual was the smallest of them all, but they were on a winner when they declared, 'Choose us, and we will offer what nobody else can; we will insure only members of the NFU, and our policy holders will be our sole owners, thus ensuring that we shall work only in their interests.' Among the treasures of the Mutual is a set of glasses, each etched with a picture of a wild animal native to East Africa. They were a parting gift from the Kenya NFU for the help which the Mutual gave to establish insurance facilities in Africa. In 1946 the Mutual provided for the Rhodesia National Farmers Union a complete insurance cover, copied from the UK pattern. A Branch was opened in Salisbury, which at one period also served Zambia and Malawi. Business was written for farmers in Kenya, Uganda and Tanganyika, but operating conditions in the bush were unlike deals with British farmers, and this was later withdrawn.

If the Society was successful abroad, the problem of Cornwall remained—that is, until 1976. The Cornish farmers had been covered by the Cornish Mutual Assurance Co., which was the official insurer of the NFU in Cornwall, and this was having effects upon the progress of the 'official' Mutual in neighbouring Devon. The break came as a result of the loss-making straw-trek operation mounted by the Cornish NFU to bring fodder from the eastern counties to avert a winter shortage in 1975.

Many Cornish farmers claimed that this assistance was given in return for transferring their business to the NFU Mutual from its Cornish counterpart. The straw-trek operation lost the Cornish NFU a sum of over £60,000, and the NFU Mutual gave them £10,000, allegedly as a contribution from the goodness of its heart, but undoubtedly to woo this breakaway faction into the fold. Accusations were made of poor payments to the Cornish NFU Secretaries, who relied upon their agency fees to supplement their income, but after the break only three out of seven local secretaries accepted the NFU terms.

It was ironic that a unique example of farming togetherness which inspired the movement of fodder to the stricken areas should have been responsible for breaking the power of the Cornish Mutual and confirming after sixty-seven years the monopoly of the NFU Mutual. It can now truthfully be said to be all-embracing throughout the United Kingdom.

The Farmers Union of Wales

> *'One road leads to London*
> *One road leads to Wales*
> *My road leads me seawards*
> *To the white dipping sails.'*
>   John Masefield

> *'The all-powerful policy makers at Agriculture House cared little for the*
> *problems of Welsh farmers ... they came from flat, rich land which swept as*
> *far as the eye could see.'*
>   'Y Tir.' Journal of the Farmers Union of Wales, November 1965.

The NFU covers England and Wales, but the Farmers Union of Wales also, and obviously, covers Wales. Lucky Welsh farmers, they have two Unions to represent them. Since Scotland and Ulster have always been independent of the NFU, but Wales within its orbit, the presence of a 'rebel' or breakaway movement in the Principality is a considerable thorn in the NFU side.

Nevertheless, the FUW, born in 1955, continues to flourish, is financially healthy, provides a focal point for patriotic endeavour for around 14,000 Welsh farmers, and carries out many of the services which the NFU provides at about half the cost of an NFU subscription. It gives the poorer and smaller Welsh farmers an independent voice. There have beeen many moves through the years towards a shotgun wedding, merger, takeover, or even surrender, but the position remains stalemate, and there is deep distrust and acrimony on both sides. The NFU cannot break the power of the rebels, and the breakaway union cannot persuade the NFU to abandon its jurisdiction over Wales. On many subjects the two unions are united in their policies for Welsh farming. On a few, such as the devolution issue, they are at variance, but the NFU in London will not give up its territorial claims over Wales. It would be tantamount to defeat, and a reduction in its administrative area would weaken its standing for bargaining purposes. The result of all this is that the NFU leans over backward to give Wales a special place in its affairs, and the Welsh farmers probably get the best of both worlds.

The NFU set up a special 'Committee for Wales', disbanded it in January 1971, and created a rather grander 'Council for Wales' with Welsh representative Idris Davies, a Pembrokeshire farmer, as its Chairman. Davies had a place on Copa, the Central Body of European Farm Organizations, led a Welsh team in the Price Review Talks, and sat on other bodies as a Welsh spokesman to placate his fellow-countrymen. In 1976 the Chairman of the Council for Wales was given a place in the inner circle of the Union. He certainly ranks as a more powerful figure than the other Committee Chairmen.

Davies retired in 1974, and his place was taken by David Carey-Evans, with 240 hectares in the incomparable Snowdonia area. Plumb makes a 'Presidential' trek to Wales twice every year, and the Welsh Council make sure that he goes to the loyalist branches on a strict rota system. This royal progress makes the Welshman feel he is needed, but the membership of the FUW continues to rise. It is even stated that some farmers are members of both unions. Yet this 'wooing the Welsh' policy has produced little tangible togetherness, and the FUW, head held high, resolutely goes its own sweet way.

It all started in Carmarthenshire on 3 December 1955, but there had been severe discontent and dissatisfaction for many years before that. This arose from the status of Welsh agriculture (which after all is pretty insignificant within the context of the whole of England and Wales); the NFU had treated the Welsh representatives on its Council, and the affairs of Wales, in an indifferent manner. The Welsh complained that they had no representatives on the then powerful and influential Price Review team; they had fewer representatives on the various Marketing Boards than some of the Home Counties.

Resolutions from Welsh counties to the NFU were either ignored or swept under the carpet. The Welsh delegates who had trekked to London looked upon their visits as a complete waste of time. They were getting the brush-off, and there was a sense of injustice that the policies of the NFU were designed for those who were already the 'fattest' farmers. At that time (1955) other controversies were coming to a head: attempts to get the NFU President to Wales to address farmers' meetings were nearly always unsuccessful; a request for a special conference to discuss Welsh problems was rejected. When the NFU increased its subscription rates the Welsh farmers complained that the 30-hectare farmer was being asked to pay the same increase as the 800-hectare farmer.

On a rare visit by a top NFU man to Wales, the Vice-President of the NFU, Mr Harold Woolley, spoke in Anglesey. When questioned about the lack of a Welsh representative on the Price Review team, Woolley retorted that they were not going to discard good men on the team to put Welshmen in their place![9] This treatment of the nationalistic Welsh farmers was the spark which created the Farmers Union of Wales.

In 1955 the Welsh set up the rival organization, and held their first Welsh Conference at Aberystwyth in 1957. They also set up an insurance link to give their members the same service that the NFU Mutual gives to English farmers. In the first fifteen months of their existence they acquired an income of nearly £20,000, and today are in a healthy financial state. The breakaway union established itself in Chalybeate Street, Aberystwyth, but in 1963 moved to its present headquarters at Llys Amaeth, Queens Square, Aberystwyth. In its early days the FUW had as its Assistant General Secretary John Morris. Morris was elected Labour MP for Aberavon in 1959, and became Secretary of State for Wales in 1974, an office which Harold Wilson had created in 1964. Morris has been a powerful ally to his previous employer.

[9] *Y Tir*, November 1965.

The FUW, which exists today as a breakaway faction, is secure, and seems unlikely ever to disappear; but it is not the first attempt to establish an independent union. Another was created in 1918, and collapsed four years later, in 1922. Its objectives bear a striking resemblance to the policies of the FUW. What is really wanted is special treatment for Wales, and if the objectives have not changed, it would seem that the anomalies still exist. The early union eventually amalgamated with the NFU on terms which promised some degree of independence, but which in the event brought little of the sort of independence the Welshmen were after. It took thirty-three years to recreate another independent Union, and the year after it was created the only Welshman ever to be President of the NFU, Mr Tom Williams of Forden, Montgomery, said that such a union should not be formed until Wales had its own Secretary of State. He died in 1964, just seven days before Wilson named James Griffiths as the First Secretary. By this time the FUW was ten years old.

During the livestock crisis in 1974 both FUW and NFU members stood side by side in picket lines to prevent the importation of Irish beef into Anglesey, but when in the same year Kent farmers donated 5,000 bales of hay to the fodder-stricken Welsh farmers, suffering from a disastrously wet summer, the manner and operation of the support to Welsh farmers was carried out by the NFU, and not the FUW. Brecon and Radnor NFU received hay at the new Severn Bridge, and it was stored on the Royal Welsh Showground before distribution. The FUW did not complain, and accepted, though grudgingly, that the gift was a deal between two NFU Branches, and that they had little to say in the matter.

Attempts have been made continuously to heal the split, but this is not entirely an England versus Wales issue; even the loyalist Welsh farmers are angry at times with the FUW, seeing it as a split voice. Fuel is added to the fire from time to time, as tempers flare and discretion goes out of the window. In 1973 a rather undiplomatic NFU official at Rhayader described all non NFU farmers as 'the Shylocks of agriculture'. This was hardly a conciliatory statement, and it moved FUW Vice-President Rhydwen Pughe to retort, 'Such statements reek of bitterness and rancour', and suggested for his part that one might as well call all non FUW members 'lepers'. On the subject of devolution, the NFU opted to oppose it, on the incomprehensible grounds that it would 'harm' Welsh agriculture. The FUW said that anything less than a full Welsh Assembly with legislative powers would be a waste of time and money.

Although Wales provided one Minister of Agriculture, Cledwyn Hughes, recognition of the FUW has been notoriously slow, though in 1977 in the Jubilee Honours List the FUW President, Thomas Myrddin Evans, became a CBE, and declared, 'The decoration is recognition of the Farmers Union of Wales.' He was at that time just completing his twelfth successive year leading the FUW. Evans is a director of Carmarthen Farmers Ltd, and a member of the Welsh Agricultural Organisation Society; he is also a small farmer, running a 20-hectare intensive milk and poultry holding in the centre of the village of Pencader, Dyfed. In the same List a leading member of the NFU in Wales, Verney Pugh, got an MBE.

Certainly, Wales now gets more favourable treatment, and its farmers more services: with two overlapping unions, both wooing the farmer to their cause, it would seem that Wales today has an adequate representation and a strong voice in the affairs of agricultural politics. In the end, though, the Welsh farmer still tills a more uncomfortable and unrewarding furrow than does his English counterpart.

15 Landowners and Workers

The Country Landowners Association

'I never cease to marvel at the cool effontery of the Country Landowners Association.'

J. P. Pickering,
(Letter to 'Financial Times' 4 April 1973.)

'Although less noisy than the NFU, the Association is no less astute in representing its members' interests.'

Hugh Clayton,
'The Times', 8 September 1975.

The Country Landowners Association started life in 1907 as the 'Central' Landowners Association. Ten years later it boasted that half the members of the House of Lords, and over 100 MPs, had joined it. The 'landowner' image is one that it has been trying to play down ever since, and it stresses more strongly today the fact that 90 per cent of the membership have less than 200 hectares, 75 per cent less than 120 hectares, and half the 45,000 members have less than 40 hectares. But then, since its inauguration, the whole pattern of land-ownership in the UK has changed, as the large, hereditary aristocratic estates have been fragmented, opening up a new class of landowners who as farmer/owner-occupiers, have taken over from the tenantry of yesteryear. In 1900 only 10 per cent of the land was thus occupied. Today nearly 60 per cent is owner-occupied.

This figure conceals the fact that the 'playboy' landed aristocrats of the nineteenth century started their decline as their rent-rolls diminished in the agricultural depression from 1875 onward, and have now become down-to-earth farmers, as were their ancestors in the seventeenth century. Thus some of the change-over shown in the land-ownership statistics is a cover-up for the direct involvement in farming on the part of the hereditary owners. The figures may imply that the landed estates have been halved in the twentieth century, but this belies a change of occupation in many cases.

The CLA has changed its image in keeping with the changing times, but while a lot of smaller farmers have been roped in, the membership also includes such vast landowners as the Church Commissioners, the Duchy of Lancaster, many of the County Councils with their considerable land-ownership for statutory smallholdings and Green Belt farms, and even the new Pension Funds and institutional landowners. These are regarded by the CLA as part of the 'private sector', and have joined; while the largest private members are reputedly Lord Barnard of Castle Barnard and the Duke of Northumberland. Since the truly vast territorial 'kingdoms' are in Scotland, their owners are members of the Scottish Landowners Federation. But despite the advent of hordes of very small landowners into its ranks, the CLA is still largely controlled in its Local Committees, and at its Central Council, by the larger landowners. Even the NFU has difficulty in exonerating itself from the charge that it is run by the larger farmers. Quite often they are the only ones with the time to spare to participate.

Today the CLA boasts that it covers over 6·8 million hectares of land, out of a total of 11·2 million hectares in England and Wales; but the CLA does go out of its way to actively recruit new members. It employs a para-military sales team in addition to the ring of Regional Secretaries, who cover the country. These recruiters work in conjunction with the Regional Secretaries, but are self-employed, and live (pensions apart) on the first year's subscription of any new members they can enrol. It is a system that pays handsome dividends; the NFU in contrast has lost 30,000 members in recent years, but it employs no recruiting techniques. This remains a mystery, since there may be about an additional 100,000 farmers, under one guise or another, who are not members of the NFU. Anyway, the CLA continues to increase its membership annually.

While titles abound in the higher echelons of the CLA, it is noticeable that despite the vested interest of the hereditary aristocracy, with its strong land-owning links, very few of them take an active or leading interest despite a dire need to improve their finances by direct involvement in farming. The CLA hasn't had a peer at its head since 1965, and in today's socio-democratic world, may never have again. This lack of leadership by the aristocracy in the agro-field is a perplexing phenomenon; for instance, The Farmers' Club has only had one peer as its President since 1842.[1]

The policy of the CLA remained unchanged since its inception in 1907. It is to protect the interests of agricultural and rural land-ownership; thus by definition it is not an organization to fight for the interests of urban landlords. As part of its original incorporation, the extent of this battle for the landowners interest was defined as being 'only as far as is consistent with the interests of the nation, which are above those of any industry or any individual'. This high-minded philosophy emanated from the patriotic days of Edward VII.

Defending landowners against taxation is one thing, defending against the threat of compulsory purchase for a New Town, new reservoir, or local-authority requirements, is another; but defending the indefensible against all encroach-ments into the countryside is yet another. Caravan parks, leisure centres, sporting grounds, opening the family mansion, sideshows in the park, fishing in the lake, or even hiring out the old homestead for a 'pop' festival in the summer

[1] Lord Bledisloe, 1923.

could hardly be construed as 'promoting the industry of agriculture', although they may be the lifeline of an impoverished owner.

The rush towards joining the CLA has been strengthened by successive Government attacks, through the insidious backdoor nationalization of the land through taxation. As the screw has been turned it has made landowners—and even the new owner-occupiers—see more clearly the need for a body concerned only with the ownership aspect, and each minor alleviation of the harshest clauses of a Finance Bill has been claimed as a success by the CLA.

But how do you defend the private inheritance of land against the inroads of capital taxation, when land is worth £2,500 a hectare and 10 per cent of the CLA's members are probably millionaires, some of them many times over? The CLA strives valiantly to sustain its policy, but keeps strictly to the dictum that 'tax avoidance is legal, but tax evasion is not'. Advice on the best way to mitigate the tax bill forms a valuable part of the CLA service to its members: the problems of succession and the future of the family farm have not only been exercising its legal and taxation expertise, but have given it a positive role. It has risen to the challenge, though the outcome represents a tactical withdrawal rather than a resounding victory.

In pursuance of its policy the CLA has monitored the changes in land values. This seems a natural procedure for the CLA, but it took the violent 1972 Land Boom before it started this service. It was instituted to prove that not all land was worth the massive figures being headlined, and to prove, for the purpose of probate valuation, that average prices were much lower. The Scottish Landowners Federation took another five years to follow suit, with its own survey of Scottish land values. The CLA instituted a 'Capital Investment Survey' in 1975 6 to prove that the threat of penal taxation was producing a complete lack of confidence in the future, and forcing owners to stop investing in new buildings. The tied-cottage legislation in 1976 temporarily stopped the building of new farm cottages. The CLA Surveys have proved the point, and there was no other body within UK agriculture which could have done it. Annually the CLA writes to the Chancellor of the Exchequer (in common with hundreds of other organizations), proffering advice on the items which should be incorporated into the coming Budget. The CLA letter gets longer and longer as the list of demands grows, but is often ignored when Budget Day arrives; but then that happens to most of the other advice proffered by interested bodies. Chancellors of the Exchequer have a traditional habit of listening only to themselves.

With its highly articulate 'top brass' and with its County Chairmen influential people in spheres other than the farming world (county councillors, JPs, etc.) the CLA can work behind the scenes to great effect, and while the NFU concentrates upon keeping in touch with MPs throughout the country, the CLA widens its net, not forgetting that if occasion arose it could still probably muster a majority in the House of Lords. The 'top brass' hold regular meetings with what they call 'leaders of opinion' throughout the country, and regular dinners are arranged to cement liaisons on many sides.

The NFU can claim that Britain's countryside should be protected for its food-producing, and import-saving, capacity. The CLA dwells upon the beauty of the countryside, and the protection which landowners can give as its keepers. Thus the design and siting of new buildings, the preservation and planting of hedgerow and other trees and public access to the land itself are the salient points of the CLA policy. CLA President John Quicke[2] said:

> Up until about 150 years ago, I believe there was accepted by owners of land a much greater degree of public access than has been usual in our lifetime. I am not advocating a return to those days of almost unrestricted public access; but I think it is politically essential for us to be seen not to be against the reasonable extension of it.

This displays the neat balancing trick which is the CLA, and also its awareness of the general public demand to penetrate the private portions of the land.

Farm Buildings Award Scheme

'The most glaring weakness on British farms is the high proportion of obsolete and dilapidated farm buildings.'

'Farming and Food Supplies'
(Bramley, 1965).

In pursuance of its aim to beautify the British countryside, the Farm Buildings Award Scheme was instituted in 1969. Said the CLA, congratulating itself: 'With growing public awareness of the value of country landscape and the contribution that farms and their buildings can make to the rural scene, the CLA Award Scheme has won wide approval.' From England and Wales, in its inceptional year, it attracted 92 entries, but quickly declined to only 42 two years later; boosted by splitting the country into four regions, the entries went up to 137, and boosted again by £2,000 prize money from the British Steel Corporation (later superseded by £1,600 from the Asbestos Cement Manufacturers Ltd), it makes a contribution towards the greater congruity in the design and siting of farm buildings.

Despite this scheme, the majority of new buildings on farms are strictly functional, tightly costed, and pay little or no allegiance to the question of blending into the countryside. The advent of dark-toned asbestos has helped, but the freedom from normal planning restrictions leaves the whole matter open to considerable criticism.

Although the CLA scheme is better than nothing at all, it cannot be said to have become a major influence upon farmers' intentions. In 1971 the Financial Times Industrial Architectural Award was bestowed for the first time on a farm building. This was Lee Abbey Farm at Pretty Lynton in North Devon, but the

---

[2] President CLA 1975 7, speaking at the Annual General Meeting. 27 October 1976.

judges made a barbed comment in their assessment:

> We ... make the award to it because it demonstrates that farm buildings using standard components can be placed without offence in a landscape of great beauty—a rare enough demonstration to be of national significance.

But awards of this nature to farm buildings are indeed rare.

In France, however, the CLA scheme was copied in 1972, when the French Government and the Agricultural Credit Organisations put up no less than £60,000 for the project. Half was spent on producing a book to describe the need for planning farm buildings, in order to preserve the beauty of the landscape. The remaining money went on the award itself, and the whole of France was divided into three regions. With the Continental flair for incentive, it was decided that the winning buildings would also qualify for loans at a low interest rate—a philosophy that would never get past the starting-post in England without the smear of 'slush-money' or corruption. Unfortunately, we do not expect to pay in order to create incentives.

Prize-winning buildings in the CLA Scheme are not given too great an accolade, and the judges in some years have been scathing in their comments. In one year there was no national award at all, because none of the entries was sufficiently outstanding. But after the 1976 judging there were particular criticisms. Said those who judged the Western Region: 'We set a high standard, but nevertheless were somewhat disappointed that the quality of entries was not higher.' The Eastern Counties judges said: 'In some cases the appearance of good buildings was spoilt by poor detailing of doors, windows, guttering and painting.' Those who judged the Southern Region said in similar vein: 'The plain fact is that with modern materials, design know-how, and practical commonsense, farming with livestock doesn't have to be the mucky, cold, tedious, wet job it was 50 years ago. Yet the user will sometimes introduce all these old deficiencies on units designed to avoid them.'

The buildings ranged from a sheep-handling system in Derbyshire costing £4,200 to a complete dairy complex in Cheshire which cost the farm-owner £73,250. The winning building for the Eastern Counties had been the subject of considerable local controversy, and had been labelled a 'trouble barn'. It had been erected on a prominent position, amid considerable local opposition, and the judges commented:

> The location of the farmhouse and main yard in an exposed position on high ground made it inevitable that the new 140 feet x 127 feet building with a penthouse rising to a height of 50 feet would have a great impact on the environment. That impact could have been disastrous.

Situated on a commanding height facing the lovely Stour Valley, which runs as the boundary between Essex and Suffolk through Constable's country down to Flatford Mill, the building is visible from a great distance; from the penthouse (large enough to garage four cars at once), you can see four churches. The judges commented, 'The impact could have been disastrous'; the locals thought it was.

The Game Fair

*'Any student of the British would have noticed in the early days of the event
(CLA Game Fair) some remarkable examples of what is loosely called the
county set.*
But democracy has now set in . . .'

John Cherrington
'Financial Times', 31 July 1976.

Apart from being unique in concept and format, the CLA's Game Fair is also the
only example of an itinerant event left within the UK farming scene, apart from
some of the specialized technical demonstrations which are in a different
category. It has gone totally against a wind of change which either wiped out
completely many County Agricultural Shows or forced the survivors to go
'permanent', but the Game Fair (which only came into existence in 1958, by
which time most of the County Shows were celebrating their centenaries), has in
the 1970s shot its attendance figures up to nearly 80,000 people for a Friday and
Saturday event at the end of July.

The difficulties facing the County Shows were in the expense of moving
around each year, and the attendant difficulty of finding suitable sites, but the
Game Fair has more exacting requirements, which include not only good road
access but a piece of parkland for its standholders, plenty of oak-trees to make
the shooting more difficult, plenty of space to prevent the spectators being shot,
and a useful stretch of water for the fly-casting and the gun-dog retrievers. A
strict set of criteria, and one which becomes increasingly more difficult to meet.
Modern farming has ploughed up many of the ancient parks. The Fair goes to
Scotland once every five years in conjunction with the Scottish Landowners
Federation, who by this tacit agreement promises not to set up a rival event. Even
if it did it is doubtful if the Game Fair would suffer, such has been its success. The
Game Fair makes a profit, and it brings kudos to the CLA, but only a small
proportion of those attending are in fact members of the CLA itself.

Gamekeepers—of which there are more left in England than butlers—
shooting clubs of working men with urban occupations, followers of Izaak
Walton and the local population, arrive by the busload. Smart dress has for the
most part disappeared, bowler hats have gone, to be replaced with shirt-sleeves
and open necks. Nevertheless, well cut tweeds abound and in the car-park that
classless badge of the true sporting countryman, the Range-Rover, is still much
in evidence.

The success of the Game Fair has been phenomenal (if only the NFU could
have hit upon such an ideal) and from the first Fair at Lord Ellesmere's[3]
Stetchworth Estate near Newmarket, it took the CLA by surprise.

When 8,500 visitors instead of the expected 2,000 stretched resources beyond the
modest limits provided, it was obvious that the CLA had not only instituted a sporting

[3] He became Duke of Sutherland in 1963.

success, but also a new form of public entertainment. Moreover, it set a precedent of vital importance at a time when the fusion between town and countryside was becoming more marked, and understanding between the two more blurred.'[4]

From its initial surprising start, it doubled its numbers at Hackwood Park, Basingstoke, in the following year, 1959, and peaked in 1966 at the Duke of Devonshire's incomparable Chatsworth, nestling amid the Derbyshire hills. The site itself under the shadow of the great house was constricted, and fragmented on a narrow and unlevel strip between the walled gardens and the river below, but 48,500 people came, and they went back there again in 1975, when 76,000 created another record. The Scottish attendances are always lower, and numbers dropped by 20,000 at Blair Drummond in 1968, the second time the Fair had been there. It was another ducal home that provided a boost in 1974, when the Game Fair went to Stratfield Saye. This was the home of the eighth Duke of Wellington, and the Fair received the accolade of royal patronage when the Queen came to bestow her blessing upon it.

Stratfield Saye had been purchased by the first Duke when a grateful nation voted him the money for a home and estate befitting a great national hero after his triumph at Waterloo. The eighth Duke, his great-great grandson, who had only succeeded his father in 1972, two years before the Game Fair arrived, faced the taxation problems of many owners. Already a director of Massey-Ferguson Ltd, and later President of the Farm Management Association, he opened the 'Wellington Country Park' in the same year, and at the Game Fair opened his home to the public for the first time in its 344 years of existence.

But there were problems. Stratfield Saye lies midway between the M3 and M4 Motorways, not far from Basingstoke, in a part of Hampshire that is almost into Berkshire. Despite the police traffic controls, the totally unexpected crowd stretched as far as the M4, and in the heatwave of the second day the traffic pile-up even affected the access to Heathrow, much to the chagrin of airport passengers. But the Game Fair had really arrived. It then went back to the Cavendish family home at Chatsworth, then to beautiful Glanusk Park in South Wales, just across the new Severn Bridge, and nestling in a beautiful, leafy Welsh valley. The public came swarming in to the tune of 78,400. There was no stately home thrown in, it had been pulled down fourteen years previously, but the Prince of Wales was the royal patron and visitor.

The Game Fair is not an exhibition but a participatory event, with sporting expertise to be displayed. The whole gamut of the British way of sporting life is on show: archery contests, the deadly strongbow, falconry (not so participatory), Pugs and Drummers, which takes its delightful if mystifying title from old Berkshire traveller's slang for ferrets and rabbits. Then there is game-rearing, the establishment of a good shoot, and that other allied sport which complements the off-season and has its own 'close'—fishing. The apparent contradiction to the non-initiated between shooting and conservation, and the true spirit of the

[4] CLA Press Release.

countryman, is epitomized at the Annual Game Fair in a totally different way from any other event in the UK calendar. This is certainly not a farming show.

The modest row of standholders would not compare numerically with a minor County Show, but they swarm with enthusiasts lovingly fingering hand-made guns costing thousands of pounds, they talk knowledgeably about the fishing gear, and comment expertly about the clay-pigeon shooting as targets whistle through the air from high towers erected with scaffolding and corrugated iron platforms to protect the launchers. Sporting prints, old books, oil-paintings of pheasants and weatherproof clothes for shooting and fishing make up a galaxy of interest. The main worry facing its sponsors is the organizational problem that comes from success. Nevertheless, it amply demonstrates that the British have an inherent love of their countryside, and all things pertaining to it.

It is also peculiarly British that while we have swept away so much of our heritage in our ancient town centres, decimalized our money, and displayed a twentieth-century outlook upon the world, radically changing everything in sight, the game laws have survived through several Socialist Governments intact, and little changed from feudal times. Poaching offences can still bring a stiffer penalty than baby-bashing; though otter hunting is banned, the preserves of many esoteric blood sports seem inviolate. This is not only a feature of the British way of sport, but it does provide two major rewards.

Because of the legal protection upon the shooting and fishing seasons, and the stiff penalties which preserve the private ownership of both game and fish, it is possible for owners to expend considerable sums in fostering and nurturing these creatures for the sport they will yield. This not only means that the participant can expect to come home with a bag, there is also considerable value in both shooting and fishing rights, which supplement many an Estate income to the tune of several thousands of pounds annually. In most of the Continental countries, and in the United States, anyone can shoot at sight, with certain rather weak provisions; consequently, nothing is preserved, the slaughter is indiscriminate— and there is no 'Game Fair'.

The Workers' Trade Union

'Joining a Trade Union remains a somewhat untypical activity for the farm worker; many more vote with their feet each year.'
'The Deferential Worker' (Newby, 1977).

'. . . The person in this country who is in the most strongly entrenched position next to the King, is the Trade Union Official.'
Aneurin Bevan

Up to 1974 there were a total of 491 affiliated and unaffiliated trade unions in the UK; at the peak in 1896 there were 1,358, and even in 1945 there were 781. Amalgamations and regroupings have reduced the fragmentation and independence of many breakaway unions within industry, while at the same time increasing the power of the trade unions, and their militancy. With a membership of the NUAAW of 70,000, representing less than 50 per cent of the number of full-time farm workers, it is in a manifestly weaker position than either the NFU or CLA to sustain its claims to represent the industry.

The NFU claims to have the allegiance of 85 per cent of the farmers, and the CLA records about 60 per cent of the land; thus the weakness of the NUAAW position is immediately apparent.

The membership of the NUAAW was at its peak in 1958, and remained high until 1966, since when it has shown an erratic decline. It is not the only union to suffer thus. The National Union of Railwaymen lost half its membership, 175,000 members going between 1957 and 1975, as the Beeching Axe reduced the number of railwaymen. While the decline of the NUAAW can be attributed partly to lesser numbers of workers on the land, there is also a greater problem in collecting subscriptions or fostering enthusiasm for the Union, due to the fragmented position of farm-workers working in ones and twos throughout the whole country.

The NUAAW claims 85 per cent of the workers in Lincolnshire, and says that its highest other counties are Norfolk, Essex, Kent and Wiltshire. Although it claims to be the voice of the industry, it is a salutary fact that only 75 per cent of its members are actually farm-workers, and since the Transport and General Workers Union also has an agricultural section, with a membership of around 10,000 farm-workers—which covers, moreover, the farm-workers in Scotland where the NUAAW does not trespass—it would seem that this fragmentation of the brotherhood is a weakness for the larger body.

Finance is a serious problem, and for many years the NUAAW has run at a deficit; it is more difficult to put up the workers' subscriptions and still retain their loyalty when these subscriptions are collected on the doorstep by local union volunteers. Neither farmers nor landowners are as likely to lose members if the subs go up, and the Workers Union is well aware that an increase will bring resignations. This prevents it raising its subscription to keep up with inflation, or to provide the same level of service.

The NUAAW, allied today to the Labour Party, started its life with strong Liberal connections, although its chief ally could rightly be said to be none other than the NFU itself; in presenting a case for higher wages (which must inevitably bring higher food prices) the Union has found the NFU the better ally. In the trade-union movement as a whole, NUAAW membership represents less than 1 per cent; yet although it is among the smallest unions, and even one of the quietest, it has still gained substantial increases in the wage-levels of farm-workers, its greatest success being the abolition of the tied cottage in 1976–7. There is a lack of militancy in the Union policies, and it has not called a strike since 1923. Agricultural wages are fixed by a statutory Wages Board on which the NUAAW has five seats, and the TGWU three. These eight members oppose the NFU representation with eight seats, and it is left to the five independent members to make the decisions when the other two sides are locked in unresolved conflict. Since the enemy in the 1970s has been the wage freezes and constraints of both Tory and Socialist Governments, the workers, as in many other industries, no longer see the farmer as the nigger in their woodpile. The NUAAW has a conflict with its own District Organisers, who have a trade union of their own to assist in the improvement of their pay and conditions; they have been at odds with the leadership more than once, and within its policies the NUAAW treads a narrow tightrope in advocating larger farms (which should provide more jobs), and at the same time encouraging the statutory smallholdings. A worker who becomes an independent small farmer could well change his allegiance, and the matter is not pushed; the union cannot ignore this right of workers to personal betterment.

'Allied' was added to the title in 1966, making the name the National Union of Agricultural and Allied Workers, as a rearguard decision to retain Union independence. The TGWU has made overtures with a view to merging; these have been firmly rebuffed by the NUAAW, but a declining membership and financial problems may mean that independence will one day disappear. The Union today lays claim to be the successor of a union founded in 1872 by a Liberal lay preacher and later MP: Joseph Arch.

Arch was born in 1826, eight years before the Tolpuddle labourers were to go into the history books. He was a roving hedge cutter who travelled the country and punctuated his speeches with quotations from the Bible and Shakespeare. Arch was an inspiring orator; under a giant chestnut-tree at Wellesbourne in Warwickshire[5] in 1872 he led the disgruntled farm-workers into forming their first real union. He pulled no punches, reminded them of the hours they worked, and the medieval serfdom of their conditions. After the meeting a Committee was formed, and then the Warwickshire Agricultural Labourers' Union came into being. Arch stood for Parliament as a Liberal in 1880. He lost, but when the labourers were given the vote he won, and was elected three times, finally retiring from public life in 1902, dying in the house where he was born at Barford in 1919. He had championed the cause of the farm-workers, and in his homespun suit he proved a doughty warrior in Parliament, but was often criticized by the workers because of the many difficulties of the original Union, and was labelled a Liberal Party poodle. Another quotation from the period savagely slated Arch: 'drinking his bottle of whisky a day, but hardly opening his mouth for any other purpose'.

The original Union had among its rules the following:

> Its object is to elevate the social position of the farm labourers of the country by assisting them to increase their wages; to lessen the numbers of ordinary working hours; to improve their habitations; to provide them with gardens or allotments; and to assist deserving and suitable labourers to migrate and emigrate.

Emigration was considered in those days to be the panacea for the downtrodden workers, and the only opportunity to escape. Arch himself visited Canada in 1873, eighteen months after the founding of his Union (which had quickly

---

[5] Wellesbourne is now the home of the National Vegetable Research Institute.

changed without much foundation into the 'National Agricultural Labourers' Union'). It had within that eighteen months achieved a membership of 71,835 and over 982 branches, with a weekly journal called *The Labourers' Chronicle*, yet there were still separate unions in Kent and Sussex, and a Lincolnshire Labour League with its own headquarters and weekly journal. But the times were bad for farming, and in 1874 the farmers began to fight back against the new collaboration spreading among their men. In Suffolk the men asked for a shilling a week rise. It was refused, and a lock-out was instituted, covering nearly all central England. More than 10,000 men lost their jobs, and were turned out of their tied cottages. It broke the Union, and put the whole path of progress back for thirty years.

Refounded in 1906, in the same period which saw both the CLA (1907) and the NFU (1908) founded, it has been continued since that time through various name-changes and amalgamations. It cut its ties with the Liberal Party in 1911, and the following year there was a 'National Agricultural Labourers and Rural Workers Union' founded by George Edwards in Norfolk, the title somewhat portentous for what was in reality a local union. There were others, such as the Lancashire 'Farm and Dairy Workers Union'. In Herefordshire and Shropshire there was 'The Workers Union'; although this was an urban-based industrial union, it hived off many agricultural workers. In 1919 the NALRWU moved to London, and by the following year it had a membership of 93,000. The Agricultural Section of the Workers Union had 120,000 members, but the Norfolk-based, now National Union, was to cut its membership to 25 per cent of its 1920 figure in the coming three years, as depression hit the farming industry, and indeed the whole country. In 1920 it became the 'National Union of Agricultural Workers', although two years later another breakaway union, 'The National Union of Land Workers', was formed under the aegis of the New Agricultural Party, which had been launched as the only example in British politics of a direct political party to represent the countryside, and pledged to return MPs with their hearts wedded to the protection of British farming.

All these unions and counter-unions, name-changes, and disorganized foundation-building for the modern union were carried out during times of depression and civil political insurgence as Britain came out of the blood-bath of one war, and staggered uneasily towards the next. During this time the farm-workers went on strike. It was 1923, and with strikes such a permanent feature of the British way of not working in the 1970s, it can be recorded that the farm-workers' last official strike took place in the historical days of that year.

Although there has been no strike since that time, this does not mean that the heavy stick of industrial action has not been shaken, but the 1923 strike nearly bankrupted the Union, and provided a salutary lesson to the Union officers, a lesson they never forgot. With the old guard now gone from the scene, it would appear that the trauma of the 1923 strike is now forgotten, leaving the field clear for the farm-workers to indulge in a massive show of strength.

It is doubtful, however, if they would ever call an effective strike, or one which would not in the end break their own power. In the 1923 Débâcle, 20,000 strike notices were sent out, but only 5,000 men stopped work. In five weeks, two years' subscriptions vanished in strike pay, and the Union faced a financial crisis. The strength of the TUC today, and the brotherhood of working-men, has often seen one union supporting another in times of acute crisis, and other unions would doubtless come to the assistance of the farm-workers.

Farm-workers, although protected by their union, and receiving pay-rises in keeping with all other sections of the working community, live and work in isolated communities, where militant talk and rabble-rousing is impossible. There are no lunch-time mass meetings in the works canteen, no factory-gate haranguing, no possibilities of excommunicating the more moderate members, and no opportunity to pressurize the lingerers. It is a basic weakness of the NUAAW case, and they recognize it. Even in the old days, there were twin problems about any strike; firstly, that the workers largely lived in tied cottages, from which they could be evicted by a vindictive farmer if they struck, and secondly that to be effective a strike must be timed to coincide with either the harvest or the seed-time. The more regular livestock farming could be carried out by the farmer himself, without excessive disruption, but if the harvest were left rotting in the fields the Union would get an extremely bad reputation, and it would be physically impossible for the employers to pay their wages when they returned to work.

The tied-cottage aspect has now disappeared, but the reduction in the numbers of workers to a situation where there is basically one employee to every employer means that the personal bond between the two would be difficult to sever for any industrial purposes. In any case, the employers could negotiate any private wage settlements between master and man unbeknown to either Government or Union, and remuneration can be supplied in many different forms, such as free petrol, free fuel for the central heating system in modern farm cottages, as well as the normal perks such as free milk on a dairy farm, potatoes on an arable farm. All this increases the problems of stirring up a sense of injustice sufficiently to bring the workers out on strike. Any serious move would require the active participation of the distributive lorry-drivers with their milk tankers, who could stop the flow of produce from the farms, but since the Government has taken over the collective bargaining role, and has imposed nation-wide, across-the-board sanctions, the target for strike action is no longer the farmers but the Government. In this sense, the NUAAW wisely campaigns for better prices for the farmers, in the hope that some of it will rub off on to the workers.

NUAAW policy statements

In the bleak Great Northern Hotel near King's Cross Station the Union launched its third policy document since the War on an October morning in 1976, when the whole of Britain was enveloped in the most serious drought for two centuries. It had taken the Union eleven years since its previous statement of ideals, and this compares favourably with political parties which rewrite their manifestos for every General Election, or Presidents of the United States who deliver an annual 'State of the Nation' address to keep themselves, one suspects, going in the same direction. If the NUAAW would appear to be single-minded and inflexible, it only proves that its original objectives have still to be fulfilled.

Health and wealth under our feet was the first Union policy document after the 1945 War, and was issued in 1953, revised three years later, and stood the test of time for nine years until *Farming for the Future* was released in 1965, again in the inauspicious surroundings of the Great Northern Hotel. *Outlook for Agriculture*, the 1976 glossy policy statement, extended to 103 paragraphs, and dealt at greater length with the Common Agricultural Policy than it did with wages. But it set out the aims of the Union on many questions, even though these aims could appear to be conflicting. Even on the subject of land-nationalization (now politely called 'Public Ownership'), the Union has maintained a favourable position since 1954, but in 1952 it had actually voted against it, and the emphasis today is tepid rather than tempered with violent militancy. With a reduction of 120,000 English and Welsh farm-workers in the decade between the two policy documents, the Union has to struggle hard to justify its existence. It emphasizes that with a reduced labour force, productivity increased at over double the rate of performance of industrial workers throughout the nation, though discreetly ignoring the farm evolution from men to machines, with the substitution of capital for labourers.

The Tolpuddle Rally

> '*As the people of rural England move into the darkness of the industrial age, some rays from the setting sun of an older England fall across the scene and light up for us to see six men who laboured in the fields.*'
> *Sharpen the Sickle* (Groves, 1948)

Ringing with the symbolism of rural deprivation, the name Tolpuddle conjures up visions of bearded, oppressed farm labourers with baggy trousers tied below the knees with string; however, Tolpuddle is not situated on a bleak northern moor but eleven kilometres east of Dorchester, in Dorset. Each year its village street revives to the sound of a silver band, and marching men carrying banners as the NUAAW stages its Annual Rally to immortalize the memory of the battle which the six men of Dorset, the Tolpuddle Martyrs, fought and lost in 1834.

Colourful banners, and up-to-date placards, proclaiming the latest injustice which the Union is fighting, provides a backcloth to leading Government Ministers (when Labour is in power) as they arrive to address the faithful. By comparison with the Miners' Galas in the North of England, it is all pretty small beer, but it reminds one of the fear and oppression of those early martyrs, and hints that, given half a chance, the wicked Tory farmers would cut the wages and oppress the labourers once more. Which all proves just how much out of touch with reality the union movement is.

It was in 1834, three years before William IV died and a young Victoria came to the throne, that six farm labourers from Tolpuddle were chained, manacled and deported on a convict ship to Australia. They had been sentenced to seven years' transportation, but two years later they were all pardoned, although it was 1839 before the last man returned to England. The first five, after returning to England, emigrated to Canada, and the last, James Hammett, died at Tolpuddle in 1891. He was blind, and went quietly into the workhouse to die. Said Reg Groves[6]

> When they buried him in Tolpuddle Churchyard, the Squire stood by the grave to make sure that no-one spoke for or on behalf of Trade Unionism.

The whole episode was overblown, and out of all proportion to its real severity, although it crystallized the whole problem of farm-workers at that time. It made a chapter in the struggle for the legal protection of trade unions, and for the respectability which the NUAAW has created by its responsible attitude.

The Tolpuddle Martyrs' 'crime' was that they had formed a 'Friendly Society of Agricultural Labourers', but they were charged with taking unlawful oaths under an Act of 1797 that had been rushed through Parliament to quell a naval mutiny in that year. The Tolpuddle rebellion was inflamed by a local Bench who had ruled that labourers must work for any wages the farmers were willing to pay. Since wages had dropped from 10 shillings per week to 7 shillings, and it looked as if 6 shillings was around the corner, the workers were understandably incensed. A hurried trial before a picked jury and a hostile judge on 19 March 1834 finished the case as far as the Dorset farmers were concerned, but the issue attracted national attention, and was used by the embryonic trade unionism of the time for an all-out attack upon employers and Government. It became a test of strength, and symbolized a struggle that was emerging in every village cottage or slum street in the country. The rebellious work-people saw the dramatic contrast between their own poverty and the wealth gap with the employers. Perhaps that outlook persists to this day.

Apart from its Annual Rally, and its biennial conference, the Union, seeking solace in its history, and pride in the struggle of the early leaders, sought to perpetuate this in a massive Rally in 1972 to celebrate the centenary of the Union created by Joseph Arch.

Less than four hundred farm-workers, including wives and children, came to commemorate Arch in the Warwickshire village of Barford, his birthplace. Highly political speeches, and a slashing attack upon the Tory Industrial Relations Act by Michael Foot, plus a new wage demand from General Secretary Bottini, roused little enthusiasm, and the stage was stolen by an unknown actor. Bearded, and wearing a nineteenth-century-type check suit, he was dressed up to resemble the picture of Arch on the banner behind the speakers. He delivered an

---

[6] *Sharpen the Sickle: The History of The Farm Workers Union.*

extract from one of Arch's speeches just a hundred years old. He at least captured the mood.

The tied cottage battle

'When tied cottages are the subject for discussion, you can be prepared for argument which is liberally garnished with ingrained prejudice and political opportunism. Frequently, I have observed, it is not over-burdened with facts.'
'Farmers Weekly', 25 January 1974.

'The Labour Party has been intending to act on farm workers cottages since 1945.'
John Fryer, 'The Sunday Times', 5 January 1975.

'For well over 60 years, the Union has been calling upon successive Governments for the introduction of legislation to remove from the agricultural scene the greatest social iniquity that has ever bedevilled the country's most basic and important industry, and from January 1st, 1977, the tied cottage system as we have known it for so long, will cease to exist.'
'The Land Worker' (Bottini, 1977).

A major plank of the NUAAW policy was always its bid to abolish the 'tied' aspect of farm-workers' cottages. They called it a social injustice, a relic of feudal times, and an iniquitous anomaly that hit at the downtrodden workers. Although the abolition of the farm-workers' tied cottages had been part of the Labour Party policy since 1945, it took over thirty years to bring it about, and the battle was a bitter one. It marked, however, perhaps the greatest triumph in the history of the Union, even though it only affected a very small minority of the farm-workers themselves.

The NUAAW publicity machine had always recorded with mounting horror the number of evictions from tied cottages which occurred every year, and although the numbers represented less than 1 per cent of the total number of workers housed in accommodation on the farm provided—largely free—by the farmer as an added incentive to attract labour, yet the Union campaigned strongly and bitterly against this injustice.

Today around a half of Britain's farm-workers live on the job in cottages or houses supplied by the farmer; in remote areas this is a *sine qua non*, and means that there are little or no travelling expenses to work. For stockmen with irregular hours it is an obvious boon, and in the period after 1945 a vast modernization programme of old cottages was embarked upon by farmers in general. It is estimated that there are 100,000 houses owned by farmers and land-owners which are occupied by their workers. Thirty years ago only one-third of the workers were so housed, but as the labour force has continued to diminish, the percentage in tied accommodation has risen. As a subsidized housing stock for the nation, it is a not inconsiderable contribution to the cheap food policy. The remainder of the farm work-force live mainly in council houses supplied by the local authorities in the nearest village. Tied accommodation of this nature is not unique.

The greatest parallel with the traditional method of housing farm-workers can be found among miners, although there are distinctive differences between the two situations. Farm cottages tend to be owned in ones and twos on individual farms, and as the labour force has declined many have been sold off at enhanced prices for weekend cottages or to other commuters. When a cottage becomes empty the farmer naturally wishes to see it vacated, and reoccupied by the successor in the job. This does not apply to the mining industry. When the National Coal Board came into existence in 1947 it inherited about 140,000 tied houses which the private coal-owners had built in the pit villages, many in isolated places, to attract and retain a labour force.

The coal industry has declined in a similar way to agriculture, inasmuch that from 1958 to 1971 the numbers of miners shrank from 700,000 to roughly one-third of that number (285,000). The rate of pit-closures was averaging one each week between 1965 and 1969, but all the houses were owned by one body, and there were no problems of eviction of the elderly or retired. In twenty-eight years the NCB disposed of about 70,000 houses, but it also built about 23,000 new ones. It estimated that about 40 per cent of its houses were occupied by miners' widows or disabled or retired miners, and the rents are low. It also estimated that only about 20 per cent of the miners live in NCB houses. Disposal of this expensive luxury has been put under way by the NCB, which on completion will have received well over £300 million. In one year alone £5 million net profit was made after paying interest charges, and in 1976 the Board put up their remaining stock of 85,000 houses for sale at roughly half market values, estimating that if sitting tenants refused to buy they would be offered to local authorities or housing associations. Failing this, there was always the open market, retaining only a very small number of houses near collieries for pit rescue workers. This emphasizes that there are more problems with owning houses than is often appreciated.

The Shelter Report[7] estimated that there were in Britain about 1 million tied houses, and that farm-workers occupied only about 10 per cent of these. Thus there went up the cry: 'Why single out us?' when the abolition of the tied cottages became a burning issue between the farmers' organizations and the Government and NUAAW.

The list is endless; hotel workers naturally and normally live on the job, and vacate their accommodation when the job ceases. Over ten thousand of the Church of England clergy live in parsonage houses which are tied to the job, and from which widows have often had to move incontinently if their husbands died. Many caretakers, teachers, nurses, policemen and firemen live in tied cottages (as does the Prime Minister himself), but when the Labour Government were

[7]Shelter *Report on Tied Accommodation* (November 1974).

returned with a wafer-thin majority in February 1974 Harold Wilson decided to retain his house in Lord North Street, and use No. 10 Downing Street as an 'official office' without moving in. The unedifying sight of Heath's grand piano on the pavement outside Downing Street was featured in many newspapers, and brought home the ruthless eviction procedure which accompanies a change of Premiership in the UK. At an earlier time the cameras had caught Sir Alec Douglas-Home departing via the garden gate, while the incoming Prime Minister faced the TV cameras at the front door. All this is in contrast to the more leisurely way in which some other countries accomplish their change of government. For instance, in the United States the President wins his election in November, but takes over two months later. Even if Wilson did not move into Downing Street, the Labour Party Manifesto had already stated unequivocally that when it was returned to power it would abolish the agricultural tied cottage. It was the plainest and strongest way in which this problem had been faced by the Labour Party, although it had been part of their Manifesto and a plank of policy since 1945.

In the 1964 Election, when Labour were returned after a thirteen-year period out of office, George Brown, MP (later Lord George-Brown), gave what became known in the NUAAW as 'the Swaffham Pledge', when he stated, 'If elected to office, the Labour Party would ensure that there would be no eviction from a tied farm cottage without suitable alternative accommodation first being available.' It was a step, but not sufficient for the NUAAW, and in the period up till 1974, various tinkering with Rent Acts did not materially alter the fact that when a farm-worker lost his job he would also lose his home. Various delaying procedures had been introduced to soften the blow, but the basic position remained as it had for centuries. The NUAAW embarked upon a sustained campaign, and for a union of their modest size and influence they achieved a significant triumph. (It must also be noted that the vociferous Joan Maynard became a Member of the House of Commons in the October Election of 1974.)

The tide was already turning, and in the previous year no less an institution than the *Farmers Weekly* had instituted a survey and embarked upon a heated debate. The Survey was published in January 1974, only five weeks before the general election which would give Labour its power.

The main finding of the *Farmers Weekly* Survey suggested that the greatest benefit of a supply of houses was in its attraction to make farm work more competitive with other employment, and to maintain the regular work force. But the Survey threw up other interesting facts: the cottage supply represented £195 per hectare over the sample; nearly 23 per cent of cottages had been built since 1947, but about two-thirds were more than fifty years old, and many were built during the golden age of British farming, from 1875–1900. There were also wide variations in the cottage stocks throughout England, Scotland and Wales, and nearly a third of the respondents in this Survey had been forced to take legal action at some stage to evict workers, though in many cases this only involved a solicitor's letter. Legal action was rare in Scotland, but more prevalent in south-east England, where a higher proportion of new workers insisted upon a cottage with the job. Although it did not come to any final conclusions, the Survey added grist to the mill, and highlighted the whole matter as a prelude to the battle to come.

Bert Hazell, NUAAW President, replied to the Survey, stating:

> The British farmer will ultimately have to face the fact that he cannot go on relying on obtaining labour without competing on equal terms with other industries. But given comparable wages and working conditions, which can only come about with the abolition of the tied cottage system, the drift from the land can be reversed.

It would seem that the social injustice of evictions was not the only reason, and that freeing the tied cottages could be used as a bargaining weapon in wage negotiations; no longer would the employers be able to point to a hidden subsidy in the form of free housing, which was in any case only being distributed to half the workers.

The Labour Party Manifesto for the February 1974 Election had stated, 'The Labour Government in its first period of office will abolish the agricultural tied cottage,' and with Wilson safely ensconced in Downing Street once again, the NUAAW looked for instant action. It was to be frustrated once again, and it was to be nearly three years before the abolition became a legal fact. With so slender a majority in the House of Commons, and a Government that was only to last seven and a half months, there was little scope, or indeed priority, for such a measure, when other more important tasks had to be tackled. Dick Crossman became Minister of Housing, and while expressing platitudes did little. Fred Peart, again Minister of Agriculture, found himself too busy to attend the Biennial Conference held at Clacton-on-Sea, and apologized at the last moment. Summer came, and the workers began to be disillusioned; the General Secretary, Reg Bottini, got a CBE in the Birthday Honours List.

But the pressure was building up, and in the period of 1974–6 no less than seven major reports were published on the subject of farm-workers' tied cottages. They were:

November 1974 Shelter *Report on Tied Accommodation*, by Moira Constable.
February 1975 *'The Views of Fountain Farming Employees on Tied Cottage Accommodation.'* Employee Decisions Ltd. An independent survey carried out for Fountain Farming Ltd, which showed that 84 per cent were 'very content' or 'quite content', and only 8 per cent were 'very discontented'.

The NUAAW stated in reply to this publication that at the time of its introduction one of the company's employees, a married man with three children, was at present under notice to quit his tied cottage, although, it alleged, three cottages stood empty on that particular farm.

April 1975 *Rural Housing: The Agricultural Tied Cottage*, by Alwyn Jones, for the Social Administration Research Trust.

A Survey which set out the history of the various Acts relating to tied cottages, and added some conclusions in the form of case histories.

June 1975 *Tied Cottages in British Agriculture,* the Tavistock Institute of Human Relations.

This was a Survey that was welcomed by the NUAAW as a massive vindication of its policy. The NFU also welcomed it, as dismissing many of the myths surrounding the problem, and Vice-President John Cossins said, 'There is nothing in this Report which justifies abolition of the agricultural service house system.' The CLA also thought the Report favourable, and confirmed—as the Shelter Report had already conceded—that the tied cottage was not the problem, but rather a general shortage of houses to let in the countryside.

August 1975 *Abolition of the Tied Cottage System in Agriculture.* Consultative document from the Department of the Environment and the Ministry of Agriculture, Fisheries and Food.

The Minister, Peart, thought this document so inconsequential that he was not present at its introduction, but left the matter to his Parliamentary Secretary, Gavin Strang. Nevertheless, for the first time it showed the position of tied houses on farms in various Continental countries. Belgium and the Netherlands, with a family farming background, had little need for tied houses, and the farm-worker was eligible for State loans. There was some tied accommodation in Ireland, a little in Denmark and West Germany, but regulations governed rents and termination of tenancies, while workers had been given encouragement to buy their own homes. France had no legislation, and very little discontent, but in Italy all regular farm-workers had a free service house as part of their contract. There had been dissatisfaction, and some problems.

September 1975 *An Alternative to the Abolition of the Tied Cottage in Agriculture,* an informative document on licensing, by Moira Constable (The Arthur Rank Centre and the National Agricultural Centre).

This was an independent survey, which pointed out that total abolition would have an adverse effect on farm production, and that only 5·3 per cent of farm workers interviewed who were living in tied cottages were in favour of total abolition, but it highlighted the fact that the main concern of the workers was the insecurity offered by the current system. With a guarantee of council rehousing as an alternative to abolition, and a licensing system, it concluded that complete abolition was not the only solution, although the problem of rural housing remained.

February 1976 *Significance of the Service House for Milk Production,* by Ruth Gasson (Department of Land Economy, University of Cambridge).

This emphasized the fears of dairy farmers that their cottages were not to be available for workers, although there was more anxiety among the owners of large herds in the south-east. About 75 per cent of all dairy workers were stated to be living in tied houses. Where the pressure on housing generally was less acute the farmers were less worried, but a large number stated they would give up milk-production if their houses were redesignated without the 'tied' aspect.

After the February 1974 Election the NUAAW quickly wrote twice to the Secretary of State for the Department of Environment: they received only a

printed postcard acknowledgement. Things were moving slowly, and after the
October Election of that year the Union looked forward to real action, but
expressed disappointment once again that no reference to the Government's
intention was voiced in the Queen's Speech. The Union put on the pressure when
meeting Ministers, and the DoE consultative document in August 1975 was a
result of the work and lobbying that was going on behind the scenes, and in the
House of Commons from Joan Maynard. Certainly the Government at that
time, and probably Peart himself, saw this as a minor pinprick, although at a
later stage Peart was to embrace wholeheartedly the concept of abolition
(although in that speech he was addressing the NUAAW Biennial Conference at
Malvern in 1976). Letters to the Prime Minister from the Union did little good,
but in the Queen's Speech in November 1975 it was reaffirmed that tied cottages
would be abolished during the parliamentary session. Registering the cottages
and creating an interchangeable system with council houses was discussed, but
the NUAAW was adamant. It wanted complete abolition, irrespective of its
effects upon food-production, and irrespective of any mitigating clauses which
might protect the farmers. The workers had waited sixty years, and this had been
part of Labour Party policy for thirty years, and they were not going to be fobbed
off once again. In December 1975 coach-loads of farm-workers converged on the
House of Commons to lobby MPs; armed with posters and led by their
President, General Secretary and Miss Maynard, they made their point.

Evictions had only been running at 13 per year, but the Union had defended
over 500 cases annually, and many occupants had found alternative accommodation before the bailiffs moved in. Although many farm-workers were quite
happy with the situation, one former Labour MP, past Parliamentary Secretary
and Essex farmer John Mackie[8], stated that the tied cottages should not be
abolished. On his farm he employed twelve workers, all living in tied cottages.
John Mackie had built them within the previous twenty years, and his workers
agreed that better houses and better conditions had altered the situation. 'If the
tied system is abolished, there is no question that the men would be worse off;
there is no way I would dream of paying them that much more a week,' stated
Mackie unequivocally.

But the tide was running out, and on 12 April 1976 the Rent (Agricultural) Bill
was presented to the House of Commons. It was the start of another major battle.
It lasted all summer, was mutilated in the House of Lords, only managed its
passage through the Commons by a guillotine measure, and when finally on the
Statute Book had a flaw which required the introduction of an Amending Bill
before it could be enacted.

The basis of the method of abolition was to give tenants a security equivalent
to a Rent Act code: this required farmers to need their cottages to provide
alternative houses, or the local authority to grant the dispossessed householder a
council house 'in the interest of efficient agriculture'. But since local authorities

---

[8] Parliamentary Secretary, Ministry of Agriculture, 1964–70.

always had long waiting lists, the practical problems which this would involve were small consolation to the farmers.

In May 1976 Gavin Strang said that the Bill would bring social justice, and the CLA Secretary-General, James Douglas, replied, 'The Bill of Agricultural Tied Cottages will disrupt the farming industry and have an adverse effect on food supplies.' At the same time the Government had put down a clause in the Agriculture (Miscellaneous Provisions) Bill to give security of tenure to tenant farmers. The two controversial measures severely upset farming progress.

Peart went to Malvern in May, and called the abolition of tied cottages 'an historic Bill'. He came down firmly on the side of the workers for the first time. The following month at Keelby Church Rally NUAAW President, Hazell, anticipated stiff opposition in the course of the Bill through the Commons, and declared, 'Throughout the years farm-workers who have occupied tied cottages have always been fearful—or anyway nervous—about their future.' There was still this emphasis upon the feudal oppression of the tied cottage. Also in June 1976, in the heart of the NUAAW country, at the Royal Norfolk Show, Strang said, 'It will end with one fell swoop the quasi-feudal relationship which many workers in the countryside have with their employers and landlords.' By September Bottini was saying that the end of the system was in sight. The Bill, having passed all its stages in the Commons, was about to be debated by their Lordships, and he threatened:

> I am reluctant to believe that this non-elected body will on this occasion devalue the country's democratic arrangements as they have too often done in the past, by indulging in sectionally motivated blocking tactics. If they do, it could amount to a hollow victory. As it would inevitably add fuel to demands for the radical reform, if not abolition, of the Upper House.

From the outset of the Labour Government's return to power, the position had not been whether the tied-cottage system would be abolished—that was sacrosanct to their policy but when this would come about, and how the resulting problems could be overcome. One of these was still the inability of local authorities to house workers needing to be replaced, and both NFU and CLA drove home the points that more pressure should be put upon the local authorities. The Bill had also stipulated that in order to enjoy its protection, farm-workers would have to be in possession for two years. The CLA wished this period to be doubled.

Wilson had retired in March, and Callaghan had taken over. Peart had left the Ministry of Agriculture for the ermine of the Lords in September, and lawyer Silkin had taken over. The Government majority was tiny, as by-elections went against it, and the House of Lords, with a rare show of spirit, rejected or hamstrung five major Government Bills. These concerned the nationalization of the shipbuilding and aircraft industry; the Dock Work Regulation Bill, another contentious issue; the Education Bill abolishing grammar schools; the National Health Service Bill, which set out to abolish pay-beds from the Health Service; and the Tied Cottage Abolition Bill itself. Perhaps this one might have been passed without a tottering Government majority in the Commons, but it added to the disruption which the hereditary Upper House was determined to implement. The procedure was a delaying one only, and on its return to the Commons in November 1976 it was passed. It received the Royal Assent on 24 November 1976. But another problem was already arising.

Under the Act's provisions the Committee structure was to have a new tier— yet more of the massive Committee ramification throughout the agricul- tural industry—called Agricultural Dwelling House Advisory Committees (ADHACs), and set up to advise local authorities on the true agricultural need for the outgoing worker. The battle then became a matter of getting workers' representatives rather than farmers on these Committees. On 1 January 1977 the Act came into force, and on New Year's Eve came the first test case. It was a conflict between NFU President Plumb and his herdsman at Southfields Farm, Coles Hill, Warwickshire. The herdsman, Bob Salisbury, had left his job managing 120 dairy cows and 200 young stock. He had acquired a job in a light engineering factory, and was willing and anxious to move into a new home, but the local district council had not provided one. It was to be an initial test case, but only a few days later a Conservative spokesman in the Commons pointed out that due to the amendments made in the Lords, and the guillotine procedure used to rush this Bill through Parliament, it contradicted itself, and in parts was gibberish.

The NUAAW had won its major battle (although forestry workers were not included in the new provisions at that time), and in launching the ADHACs the new Minister, Silkin, wished the members well, and laid out a series of guidelines instead of issuing statutory regulations or directives. The guidelines were worked out with the backing of the whole industry, and seemed very reasonable. Peace was restored among the three unions within the UK farming industry, and the new Committees settled to adjudicate upon the agricultural need for repossession of a cottage. Nevertheless, the position remains that ex-farm workers can obtain employment in the local town and still occupy a farm cottage that was built and designed to house a worker in close proximity to his stock and his workplace. The net result was a complete stoppage of the building of any new cottages on farms.

16 The Ministry of Agriculture

'Superficially, British agriculture seems an unlikely candidate for the close attention of Government.'
     The State and the Farmer (Self and Storing, 1962).

'Today the farmer may complain that the Ministry concerns itself too closely with his affairs, that its officials come too often to his farm; but he will at least agree that with this development has come a very considerable concern to support him and to provide him with help to run his farm profitably.'
     'The Ministry of Agriculture, Fisheries and Food' (Winnifrith, 1962).

'To a far greater extent than any other, the Ministry discharges almost all the functions of Government in relation to its major industry.'
     Sir Arton Wilson. Report of the Committee appointed to review the Provincial and Local Organization and Procedures of the Ministry of Agriculture, Fisheries and Food, 1956.

Properly entitled a 'Ministry', it has remained remarkably inviolate over a period when Ministries have become 'Departments', when conglomerates have been created by amalgamation, and when new industries such as North Sea Oil and Gas have been given Ministerial status and responsibility. In the past there have been Ministries of Mines, Munitions, and of Aircraft Production, wartime expedients created to meet a peculiar situation. Amid all changes, the Agriculture Ministry remains aloof in its virtual autonomy.

Farmers take pride in the fact that theirs is the only single industry in the UK of sufficient importance to warrant its own special Ministry, and reflect that this must emphasize the importance in the national economy of agriculture. Nationalized industries such as railways, electricity and coal and steel have grown from fledglings to adults, and have left the Government behind; they are now almost uncontrollable. Not part of any Government Department, and accountable to Parliament, many of them go their own sweet way. They have become as strong as the power which created them. Government intervention into the realms of private industry has been more by way of throwing a lifeline to ailing giants such as Rolls-Royce or British Leyland. The forays of the National Enterprise Board have been along these lines. Ours may be a capitalist society, but it has been liberally dosed with Government intervention in trade. Money, it seems, still holds the strongest key to unlock doors; and still talks.

Farming falls between the categories of a directly controlled nationalized industry and one that is left completely to its own devices. Today's agriculture dates from the wartime emphasis upon food-production, and from the 1947 cession of the rights of self-government by the farmers, in exchange for guaranteed prices under the Act of that year. There is little compulsion by government, although the industry is supported by Government cash. Since the phasing out of the well tried and trusted support system in favour of the EEC protection from import levies, the direct involvement of the Ministry with farmers' incomes has been less.

Food subsidies were introduced by the Labour Government, and would be difficult to withdraw completely; they are under the aegis of the Department of Prices and Consumer Protection, and the farmers do not bear the stigma of obvious subsidy, although the cost is in fact included in the Ministry of Agriculture estimates.

The pin-striped, bowler-hatted, civil servant image down on the farm has largely gone, and the amount of form-filling has been reduced; it was a necessary requirement of a vast bureaucratic machine that was dispensing many millions of Government funds, but the Ministry realized that part of its unpopularity was from the form-filling image, and it has done its best to reduce the chore. By June 1973 the number of Census Forms had sunk from 700,000 to 350,000—a reduction of 50 per cent in five years, with the Ministry's comment: 'The Ministry is as pleased to be rid of this mass of forms as farmers must surely be, especially as the saving has been achieved with no significant loss of information and has resulted in staff and cost economies.' It continued that instead of a return for each farm holding, this has been replaced by one for each farming unit, and with the amalgamation of farms farmers were being forced to complete a separate form for what had been once upon a time an individual holding. The same has applied to O.S. numbers of erstwhile and historical field boundaries, which in practice are now small areas in the middle of vast prairie tracts.

The phasing out of subsidies also removed the necessity for an inspectorate to descend, unwelcomed, upon the farm, or worse, to spy over the hedges and satisfy themselves that farmers' field returns were accurate. When cereals were being given large deficiency handouts it was standard practice for there to be a check upon the accuracy of farmers' returns. Nowadays the returns are made annually, and give a national statistical picture, but since no cash is involved an inspectorate is unnecessary. In this context only the Potato Marketing Board employ snoopers to look over the hedges and 'fine' farmers who are growing more than their allocated quota of potatoes; but the PMB is not the Ministry.

The man from the Ministry is largely down on the farm at the farmer's invitation, and far from a coercion of the peasants, the spirit is one of co-operation. There are virtually no cropping restraints upon UK farmers, with the exception of the zoning of some vegetable seed production, where cross-pollination could be disastrous. This lack of compulsion on the British farmer stands in contrast to the Danes, where the growing of winter barley was banned in an attempt to eradicate disease. It is perhaps in the field of animal husbandry and diseases where the Ministry plays its most important part, and its team of vets can be deployed in the event of a foot-and-mouth outbreak among cattle, swine fever or SVD in pigs, Newcastle Disease (fowl pest) in poultry; the dreaded Colorado Beetle, common on the Continent but rare in Britain, can also get the man from the Ministry excited.

Farming's claim to be a quasi-nationalized industry is hardly substantiated, and the Ministry is no longer unpopular. This has largely been achieved by the free services of the local ADAS offices, and the facilities of the Ministry for diagnostic analysis for everything from soil nutrients to animal health (although there is now a system of charges for some of these items). The personalities of the local ADAS man and of the characters inhabiting the Ministry farms (experimental and not research) have given the Ministry a good image among the farming community, with such men as Ralph Bee at Drayton and Paul Harvey at Boxworth. No local conference is complete without an ADAS speaker, whether organized by a local discussion group or by a commercial interest, and the Ministry co-operates with the multi-national industrial giants who have strong commercial links with the industry. It used to give the accolade of respectability to the Ministry to be invited, but now this goes to the organizing authority, and the farmers will quote ADAS statistics, ADAS figures, ADAS results, with great authenticity and relevance to their usefulness in practical farming terms.

While subsidies were in force farmers received cheques from the Reading Computer of the Ministry and filled in claim forms which might be subject to error, although the cases of deliberate fraud were few. One particular incident involved over-claiming on the now defunct lime subsidy, and farmers have been fined for not completing their Ministry Returns.

The MAFF today administers grants and subsidies, which are partly historical relics of the pre-EEC days; it acts as a catalyst of political opinion, and as the vehicle for political parties in the enactment of those policies (which in reality are more changes of emphasis than fundamental departures). The keynote of all political policy is expansion, and the farmers' attitude towards successive Ministers has been governed by the Minister's acceptance of the expansionist possibilities for home agriculture. All Ministers pay these lip service. The MAFF powers to determine price-levels have been curtailed, and the decision-making transferred to Brussels, but like all Government Departments, it is a highly complex administrative machine, and exists to put into practice the ambitious policies of the Cabinet, to carry out EEC recommendations; as such, it is run by the civil servants and the computers.

The Ministry has a far wider role than just farming, having, as its title implies, responsibility for both the fishing industry and Britain's food-supplies. Beyond this also there is a multitude of odd crops which have been gathered together under the Ministerial wing, including Kew Gardens and the Royal Botanic Garden in Edinburgh, even though the MAFF does not include Scotland or Northern Ireland in its ambit. The Scottish agricultural affairs are administered by the Secretary of State for Scotland, but his duties covers a very wide range of activities, and in reality the MAFF calls the tune. The Fisheries Department is largely for the purpose of creating regulations, or collecting statistics, but it achieved some fame with the extension of off-shore fishing limits, and in particular during the protracted Icelandic Cod War. It also deals with wine. An all-embracing industry, from herrings to hams, and known as the Ministry of 'Fish and Chips'!

The Ministry of Food

Food-prices are the prerogative of the Department of Prices and Consumer Protection The MAFF is involved with ensuring that the supply of food arriving at the docks balances the home-grown production of a nation which needs to import 46 per cent of its total food requirements. The negotiation of food-trade agreements is the prerogative of the Foreign Office, and is part of an East-West strategy for balancing power. As such, the role of the MAFF in its Food Division would seem subservient to the others. In reality it acts as a statistical and forecasting agency, and controlling only the health aspects of food which may be unloaded from foreign ships. Its actual power to import, export or negotiate is fairly minimal; for instance, New Zealand butter, Australian lamb, Canadian wheat and Caribbean sugar are being limited in favour of the EEC where local supplies are possible, and the Trade Agreement on Danish bacon has incensed the British farmer for many years, reducing his chances of expanding pig-production, while sugar-beet was not given the green light for expansion until 1976, when world sugar-supplies looked less assured. The involvement of the Foreign Office in this respect received considerable prominence, with the complete renegotiation of our food trade agreements, and although Joe Godber had stamped the country as the Shadow Minister of Agriculture in the pre-1970 period before the Tories came to power, in the event he did not become the Minister of Agriculture but went to the Foreign Office as a Secretary of State, charged with the express duty of renegotiating many of our food trade agreements.

This division of responsibility for food-supplies, and what appears to be a fragmentation of the nation's interest, has a historical background. In the past there have been two Ministries of Food, both essentially wartime creations.

In the First World War the purchase and distribution of food was largely free from Government control, and in the hands of private industry; but the Board of Trade was given powers to requisition stocks if they were being unreasonably withheld, and the public held to ransom. These powers were never used, although the Board issued lists of recommended retail prices. A Food Department was created at the Board in 1916, with Lord Devonport as Food Controller; in effect, a Minister of Food. It thus took over two years to create a Ministry of Food, and the rationing schemes for sugar were abolished in November 1920, with the Ministry becoming defunct on 31 March 1921. Thereafter its powers were transferred to the President of the Board of Trade. By contrast, the second Ministry of Food was already in embryonic form even before war broke out on 3 September 1939. It had been foreseen that a submarine blockade could seriously disrupt food-supplies, and from 1936 onwards a Department within the Board of Trade was established. W. S. Morrison, who as Chancellor of the Duchy of Lancaster had been responsible for the food defence plans, was appointed Minister of Food at the outbreak of war, and what had been a Department of the Board of Trade achieved its own importance and Ministerial status.

During the War years, it became the world's largest trading organization, with an annual turnover of £1,000 million per annum, and it administered schemes for rationing and price control. Increased home production and careful rationing reduced the food imports from 22 million tonnes down to half that figure, but even before the War was over it was apparent that food shortages would continue. It seems ironic that neither bread or potatoes were rationed during the 1939–45 war, but that the world shortage of wheat in 1946 led to a rationing of bread and flour until 1948, and the failure of the 1947–8 potato crop brought forth an instant system of potato rationing. Truly the problems of fighting Hitler had left many more problems in their wake. All this necessitated the continuation of a separate, and highly influential, Ministry of Food.

Although there had only been six years of war, nine years of food rationing followed, although by 1953 the work of the Ministry of Food was quietly reducing, and food rationing was expected to be abolished by mid-1954. Nevertheless, it was also obvious that there could not be a return to the pre-War situation, when food had been a minor department of a minor Ministry. By this time the Ministry of Food was also operating some of the schemes for providing farm price guarantees. Britain had to face up to the post-War problems of the disastrous drain upon her financial reserves, and the fading away of an empire, and in this context food was now a more important subject than it had been previously. The boffins were proclaiming world food-shortages, but Britain's standard of living was rising. Harold Macmillan as Prime Minister was later to sum this up in his catch phrase 'You've never had it so good.'

The problem remained of what to do with the Ministry of Food. This could have been decimated, and replaced under the wing of the Board of Trade, but this was itself a rapidly growing Department: there were now the complex Trade Agreements with other countries, there was future policy to be considered, and also the more strongly enforced Food and Drugs Legislation. The real explosion of sophistication in Britain's eating habits was yet to come and canned food or frozen products were not yet so popular. But clearly food was fast becoming an important, as well as emotional, topic.

There were still memories of the wartime shortages in Ministerial minds, and it seemed wrong to fragment an efficient set-up completely. Weighty arguments were advanced for splitting the work up between a number of Departments on the pre-War lines, but equal arguments were advanced that there should be 'a Minister free to speak for the consumer', which would no longer be possible if it was swallowed up by Agriculture. On the other hand, the growing importance of the farming lobby and the relation of food-requirements to overall farm production was a great argument for integrating food into the Agriculture Ministry. The decision was taken, and the Minister of Agriculture and Fisheries (Heathcoat-Amory) doubled up as both Ministers, prior to taking over the joint post in 1955. He continued in that role for another three years, and successive Ministers have embraced both titles.

To the farmers it has often seemed an incompatible situation, and the Minister has been labelled as either 'Food' or 'Agriculture'. It has seemed the greatest insult that could be given to a Minister to label him 'now he looks like a Minister of Food', and farmers have roundly castigated several Ministers for wearing their Food hat, which appears in conflict with their Farming one. There has never been any serious attempt at the political or Whitehall level to divide the two Departments. They remain inviolate under one umbrella, and although there has never been any sustained campaign by the farmers it remains a niggling point.

Successive Ministers have defended their position. The Food addition creates a larger edifice and gives them more personal status, and they contend that the farmers are better served with a joint Minister at the Cabinet table, who can see both the farming and food-supply or housewife problems at the same time. It is better, they argue, that any decision affecting both sides, or incompatible with either, should be decided in the calm of the Ministry rather than at the Cabinet table. In the event of a Minister of Agriculture and a Minister of Food (one or both of whom might not rate Cabinet status anyway), being completely at loggerheads with each other, the final arbitrator could well be another Cabinet Minister, or the collective Cabinet which, they continue to argue, could not possibly have all the inside information and weigh up all shades of opinion. It would seem that for better or worse the MAFF will retain its identity, unless another outbreak of conflict between nations, and another submarine blockade, makes it imperative for a Ministry of Food to be established.

Ministers of Food 1939–55

1939–1940	W. S. Morrison	1946–1950	John Strachey
1940–1943	Lord Woolton	1950–1951	Maurice Webb
1943–1945	Colonel J. J. Llewellin	1951–1954	Major Gwilym Lloyd-George
1945–1946	Sir Ben Smith	1954–1955	Derick Heathcoat-Amory

The origins of the Ministry

'Agriculture in England is dead, and the Board's business is to bury it decently.'

Henry Chaplin.
First President, Board of Agriculture, 1889–92

The Ministry which exists today owes its direct origins to the Board of Agriculture which was created in 1889, but an earlier Board had been created in

1793, when Pitt was Prime Minister. It lasted twenty-nine years, and there was to be a 67-year gap before another Board was created. Its re-creation was more in the nature of salvation for an ailing section of the community than for any purposes which related to its sophisticated role in the machinery of Government today.

The first Board was formed twelve years before Trafalgar, and lasted until eight years after Waterloo. It was vigorously opposed by Fox, Sheridan and Grey, and was finally constituted by Royal Charter, being carried in the House of Commons by 101 to 26 votes. Its objective was 'the encouragement of agricultural and internal improvement'. The first President was Sir John Sinclair, but posterity owes more to its £400 a year Secretary, Arthur Young. The President got a salary of £2,000, which by today's standards must have made him a very wealthy man. Arthur Young travelled the country, and has left behind his incomparable surveys of the state of farming at that time. He wrote the *General View of the Agriculture of the County of Suffolk* (1797); *County of Lincoln* (1799); *Hertfordshire* (1804); *Norfolk* (1804); *Essex* (two volumes 1807); *Oxfordshire* (1809). From this early Board came to be founded some years later the Royal Agricultural Society of England (RASE). It was supported by an annual grant from the Exchequer, something of which the latter-day successors of the RASE might be envious.

Although agriculture was not represented by any separate official board within the Government structure for over half a century, this did not mean that it was ignored. A succession of Acts such as the Tithe Act 1836; the Enclosure Act 1845; and many more such as Peel's infamous repeal of the Corn Laws in 1846 (ruinous to agriculture), all held significance for farmers. Cattle plagues were a feature of the mid-Victorian period, and a Cattle Plague department was established in 1865, under the President of the Council, to deal with a serious epidemic of cattle plague or rinderpest which began at Islington in June 1865, and by the end of the year had spread throughout Great Britain, 70,000 cattle being attacked on 10,000 farms. The Cattle Plague Department was a branch of the Home Office, but was transferred to the Privy Council in 1866, and the name changed to the Veterinary Department in 1870. By 1879 the various administrative bodies concerned with farming were severely fragmented.

Cattle diseases came under the jurisdiction of the President of the Council, whose main responsibilities were for art, science, education and religion. Agricultural statistics came under the Board of Trade, whose main interests were in railways and ships. Woods and forests came under a separate body of Commissioners, and agricultural holdings were in the charge of the First Lord of the Admiralty. It was said that a request to the Privy Council for a supply of the orders relating to cattle plague had been met by the dispatch of a parcel of forms of thanksgiving by the Archbishop of Canterbury for a bounteous harvest! From 1874 onward, the depression struck hard at agriculture, and by 1880 it was acute. This led to a greater interest in the haphazard way in which the country's greatest industry was being administered. In 1881 Sir Massey Lopes moved in the

Commons that a Department should be set up to co-ordinate the agricultural responsibilities. In his speech he said that the matter had been 'carefully considered by successive Governments for the last twenty years'. Previously it had been suggested that the Minister should be of Cabinet rank, but provided this clause were dropped, Gladstone felt it would be possible to agree to the establishment of the new Department. At that time the USA had a separate Department of Agriculture, and many other countries had also hived off their farming departments. Gladstone agreed that the administration of animal diseases should be attached to the new Department, and Joseph Chamberlain, President of the Board of Trade, considered that the time was now ready to go ahead. It was not *carte blanche* for a massive Ministry, but the Veterinary Department was allied to the Agricultural Department of the Privy Council in 1883, and the agricultural returns were taken away from the Board of Trade. The first detailed statistical tables were published in 1884, although in 1966 the MAFF published *A Century of Agricultural Statistics*. The movement was gaining strength, and with the collection of the powers into a separate Ministry an Act was given the Royal Assent on 12 August 1889 to establish a Board of Agriculture for Great Britain. The Ordnance Survey Department of the Commissioners of Works was transferred, also the Agricultural Department of the Privy Council Office and the Land Commissioners for England. In addition, the Board was charged with 'making such enquiries, experiments, and research, and collect or aid in collecting such information as they may think important for the purpose of promoting agriculture or forestry', and horticulture was expressly included under the general title.

A 'Board' then did not compare with the modern image of a Minister, plus perhaps a Minister of State and a Parliamentary Secretary, to run the show. The Board consisted of half the Cabinet, and influential Members of the House of Commons or Lords were appointed to it. It started in 1889 with an estimate of £55,000, which was £7,000 more than the cost in the previous year of the Land Commission and the Agricultural Department of the Privy Council. (It still compares rather favourably with the £1,157 million[1] which the modern Ministry now clocks up rather regularly.) It had a staff of 90, which was one less than before amalgamation, and compares with the 15,000-plus staff of the Ministry today. This figure works out at roughly one civil servant for every ten farmers, but still compares favourably with the Ministry of Defence, which employs 306,000 backroom administrators to look after 373,600 active members of the armed forces (although boasting that at one time there were more administrators than soldiers, sailors and airmen).

The new Board allocated £5,000 for agricultural and dairy schools, and the first President was Henry Chaplin. The son of a country parson from Rutland, he was a Victorian squire and lived until 1923, dying at the age of eighty-three, when

[1] *Net expenditure Agriculture, Fisheries and Forestry. Appropriation Accounts 1975–76*. HMSO.

The Times said, 'Lord Chaplin had become something of an institution. He undoubtedly owed a great deal to his good looks.' Said to own 12,127 hectares at Blankney in Lincolnshire[2] with a rental of £30,317 per annum, this Old Harrovian with an Oxford degree was an MP for forty-seven years, and created a viscount in 1916. He had been Chancellor of the Duchy of Lancaster before becoming President of the new Board, but had been a member of the Royal Commission on Horse Breeding. He was a Steward of the Jockey Club, a Master of Foxhounds, and was married to the daughter of the third Duke of Sutherland. His daughter married the Marquess of Londonderry, but an earlier romantic escapade went against him, although he gained financially as just retribution.

Chaplin was engaged to Lady Florence Paget in 1864, but in July Lady Florence made a dramatic elopement with the Marquess of Hastings, via the Oxford Street entrance of Marshall and Snelgroves. Three years later Hastings ruined himself by betting £100,000 against Chaplin's horse Hermit to win the Derby. At odds of 66-1, the horse won by a neck.

In the Fish Act 1903 Fisheries was added to Agriculture, and in the same year the Royal Botanic Gardens at Kew were transferred to it from the Commissioners of Works and Public Buildings. The Royal Botanic Garden in Edinburgh was transferred in 1889 to the original Board. It claims to be the second oldest Botanic Garden in Britain, dating back to 1670, although it was established on its present site at Inverleith in 1820. The oldest Botanic Garden in Britain is that at Oxford, founded in 1621.

Contrary to public belief, Kew Gardens is more a scientific institution than a public park. Its main function is the accurate identification of plants and plant material, and it serves as a centre for the distribution of both decorative and economic plants.

The soil at Kew, extending to 120 hectares, is largely impoverished sand and gravel, which with an average rainfall of under 600 millimetres per year, is not prone to the fostering of prolific growth. Kew, originally commenced as a small botanic garden of $3\frac{1}{2}$ hectares by a Princess of Wales in 1759, was handed over to the nation eighty-two years later, in 1841. Various additions came with successive monarchs, and now it is one of the finest Botanical Gardens in the world, with a reputation that is unsurpassed. As a plant quarantine station, Kew acts as a halfway house, in which plants passing from one country to another may be held in heated glasshouses designed for the purpose. The MAFF took over Wakehurst Place, near the South of England Showground at Ardingly, as an adjunct to Kew in 1968. This, the property of the National Trust since 1965, had been left to them by Sir Henry Price, onetime Chairman of the National Liberal Council, and was previously owned by Gerald Loder, Lord Wakehurst. Rainfall at Wakehurst is heavier than at Kew, and the soil more retentive; it is the right complement to Kew, and a onetime private garden has been created into a modern botanical miracle. The Elizabethan mansion with its weathered

[2] *Return of Landowners*, 1873.

stonework and large windows has been extensively refurbished, and its character retained. Wakehurst, like Kew and the Royal Botanic in Edinburgh, represents the more unusual interests of the MAFF.

At one time the national stud was under the wing of the MAFF.

Supporting the Ministry

The various Departments of State are nowadays headed by a 'Secretary of State' as opposed to a 'Minister', although they are normally all Ministers. The original Board of Agriculture became the 'Ministry' in 1919; perhaps the word 'Board' had Victorian overtones reminiscent of the boards for the deprivation of the poor, although one anachronism survived for many years in the 'Board of Trade'.

This birth of the Ministry was more in the nature of an accident than a deliberate change of policy, such as the transition in the 1960s of Ministries into 'Departments' on the American system. After the poor harvest of 1916, a separate Food Production Department was established, within the Board; its Director-General was directly responsible to the President. The Ministry came into being through a Private Member's Amendment to a Bill passing through Parliament. This Bill was concerned primarily with other matters, but with peace things were changing, and the establishment of the Forestry Commission in 1919 relieved the Department of its statutory responsibilities for forestry matters.

The transition into a Ministry was almost unmarked. The existing President of the Board, Lord Lee of Fareham, continued in office throughout this period, and is best remembered for his gift of Chequers to the nation as an official residence for the Prime Minister.

(Chequers, with its famous collection of Cromwellian portraits and relics, became the PM's residence on 1 January 1921. Lee later added 280 hectares of land to this gift of a Tudor mansion, set in the Chilterns five kilometres from Princes Risborough.)

In 1927 Francis Floud[3] wrote with great pride:

> Agriculture and Fisheries are the two oldest industries of the human race, but with the exclusion of the Air Ministry, the MAFF is the youngest of the Departments of State. They are also the only industries to have a Cabinet Minister to represent them in the Government.

Throughout the inter-War years from 1918 to 1939 the Ministry was concerned with various Acts to help the depression that had hit farming as severely as many other industries. The former policy of free trade became more protectionist. Wartime shortages and the creation of a separate Ministry of Food was followed by the 1947 Act, which gave the farmers the stability of guaranteed prices, and the NFU a positive role in the price-fixing structure. It also added to the importance and fame of the Ministry, but the advisory services were also building up, and the

Permanent Secretary MAFF, 1919 27.

bureaucratic intervention in farmers' lives was becoming plainer. In the wider context of the nation's affairs, the continual emphasis on the import-saving ability of British farmers to produce food in a world where it had become a scarce commodity enhanced the importance of the MAFF. The policy switched again, to advocate membership of the EEC, with adherence to its Common Agricultural Policy. This, coupled with the sudden jump in annual inflation and its effect on food prices, brought both the Ministry and its chief into greater prominence again. The number of questions addressed to the Minister in the House was greater in the early 1970s than in the entire decade previously.

The emphasis was upon national and international affairs being conducted by the Minister, while the subsidy system touched heavily upon farmers' incomes and increased their contact with the Ministry. There nevertheless remained a grey area in between, which has been filled by a rash of committees.

The Minister's advisers

'A camel is a horse designed by a committee.'
Anon.

'Advice is seldom welcome, and those who want it the most always like it the least.'
Lord Chesterfield.

Today the MAFF is supported by a vast committee structure with over fifty 'Advisory' Committees on every subject and aspect, from the Food Additives and Contaminants Committee to the Consultative Panel on Badgers and Tuberculosis. The old 'War Ags.' (CWAEC) have finally been disbanded—although it took nearly thirty years of peace to accomplish the feat—and Regional Panels have been established nation wide to provide the cars of the Minister 'down on the Farm'. At the head of the committee structure of the MAFF is the 'Advisory Council', chaired since its inception in 1972 by Sir Nigel Strutt, and the only committee responsible directly to the Minister himself. Boards, Authorities, Panels, Committees and Councils are part of the democratic structure of the non-corruptible, participatory British society at the end of the twentieth century.

In this proliferation of committees agriculture is not alone, neither is it top of the league, as was revealed in a series of Parliamentary Questions in 1977 about QUANGOs (Quasi-Autonomous Nationalised Government Organisations). The table overleaf shows the rating from which it will be noted that among the paid appointments the MAFF employs the most but pays the least, and that as usual Scotland seems to live in a world of its own. Prime Minister Callaghan refused a request by MPs for information on the extent of 'patronage' exercised by Ministers.

The influence exercised by the Minister of Agriculture is nevertheless considerable, whether on paid or unpaid jobs, which may result in fringe benefits.

Paid Positions	Number of Positions	Salaries Expended
Agriculture	354	£165,000
Education	136	£200,000
Employment	161	£300,000
Energy	151	£835,000
Home Office	127	£310,000
Prices and Consumer Protection	104	£232,394
Trade	54	£341,278
Scottish	716	£700,000
Unpaid Positions		
Agriculture	988	
Prices and Consumer Protection	978	
Home Office	2,673	
Trade	237	
Scottish	4,000	

This is a symptom of the massive edifice which has been erected, and of the complicated system of semi-autonomous boards which nowadays hold considerable sway over the industry, over everything from the administration of the new Covent Garden at Nine Elms to the Red Deer Commission in Scotland, nominations for the Eggs Authority, the Meat and Livestock Commission, the Home Grown Cereals Authority, and the Central Council for Agricultural and Horticultural Co-operation. Many of these bodies are not controlled by the Minister, but a number exist with the benefit of Government grants and subsidies, and if the patronage of the Minister is important, this patronage is also wielded by the NFU, CLA and NUAAW. The composition of these various committees is unlikely to include representatives who have not been appointed by one or other of these bodies, except that academics and university representatives can also be found among their ranks. The real farmer participation is therefore limited, which may or may not be a good thing.

The Agricultural Executive Committees (now superseded by Regional Panels) go back through the mists of time to 1916, when it was realized that as farmers are virtually a law unto themselves, it would require their co-operation to increase food-production in wartime. In the First World War the War Agricultural Executive Committees (WAECs) had power to enforce full and efficient use of all land, with the power of dispossession. In 1939 again they reappeared with wide powers to direct farmers and landowners to plough up their grassland, and were administered ruthlessly; they also set up their own gangs of men and machinery pools to take over and to farm directly land which was being under-utilized. It was a ruthless procedure, as it had to be. The Committees relinquished their hold with peace, but successive Ministers were reluctant to disband them. The 'War' prefix in their title was dropped, and they continued, though in a fairly negative role.

The Ryan Committee in 1949 reviewed the organization of the Ministry of Agriculture and Fisheries in general, and of the AECs in particular. Five years later the Arton Wilson Report contended that the AECs could be harnessed admirably for the purpose of cementing the partnership between State and the industry, and even included a recommendation that sanctions might still be necessary 'where farmers will neither help themselves nor help to reduce the burden of agricultural subsidies', though concluding 'we expect these individuals to remain a small minority'. This raised the spectre of a quasi-nationalized agricultural industry, without complete freedom. Nevertheless, British farmers do enjoy as much freedom, if not more, as their counterparts in many other countries, while few industries or sections of industry exist in the UK today without some measure of State intervention.

Defining the Ministry's role

'Butchers have called for a separate Minister for Food. They say the Minister of Agriculture, Fisheries and Food, Mr James Prior, has a bias towards the farmer.'

'Farmers Weekly', 14 April 1972.

The work of the Ministry with regard to its executive responsibilities to farming varies according to the political climate, but other spheres also provide an ever-changing scene, and the MAFF by no means covers the entire orbit of agricultural and rural affairs.

Agricultural education comes under the Department of Education and Science. Farm safety is now within the competence of the Department of Employment, through the Health and Safety Executive. The Forestry Commission, though grant-aided by the Ministry, was established by a Royal Charter, and is certainly not a Department of the MAFF. Agricultural research comes under the Privy Council, within the five research bodies. The Nature Conservancy Council and the Countryside Commission are part of the Department of the Environment, and planning, which concerns land and farming, is under the Minister of Housing and Local Government, although at its fundamental levels it is now the responsibility of local district councils. All this means that there are different authorities governing the various aspects of the countryside. But farming itself is the sole prerogative of the MAFF.

In October 1976 the CLA called for an all-embracing Ministry of 'Rural Affairs'. Its call was stimulated by a document from the DoE entitled *The Countryside—Problems and Policies*, which the CLA said was designed to encourage conflict rather than co-ordination in countryside affairs, the DoE underlining divergences between the need to expand food-production and other countryside uses. It did not give food-production a priority. The CLA suggested that one centralized Government Department should be set up, to work closely with farmers and landowners on all matters affecting rural land. The Forestry Commission, Nature Conservancy Council and Countryside Commission, as well as the Development Commission, should come under the wing of the MAFF.

When the Forestry Commission was reconstituted under the Forestry Act 1967 ten members were appointed by the Queen for a period of office. Nevertheless, the Forestry Commission is responsible to three Government Ministers: the Minister of Agriculture, the Secretary of State for Scotland and the Secretary of State for Wales. It is required to make an Annual Report to Parliament, and its funds are provided in part by the Treasury. The staff are civil servants.

The Nature Conservancy Council comes under the wing of the National Environment Research Council, and overlaps the Forestry Commission inasmuch that it maintains woodlands and nature reserves, and promotes the study of biological sciences. It also conducts research into the uses of timber at the Forest Products Research Laboratory at Princes Risborough. It is perhaps less in conflict with agricultural production than is the Countryside Commission, which is more concerned with using rural tracts for leisure activities.

Agricultural research is administered through the Royal Charter which established it in 1931. There are five such bodies engaged in research in the UK: Agriculture, Medicine, Science, Natural Environment and Social Science. They received their funds by a Parliamentary Grant-in-Aid through the Department of Education and Science, with a small part coming from the sale of livestock and produce by the Council's Institutes. There is an Advisory Board for the Research Councils, but they are essentially unconnected to their respective industries or professions.

Agricultural education was transferred from the MAFF to the then Ministry of Education (now the Department of Education and Science) in 1959. It relinquished its consultative role on planning problems in 1973, and unwillingly lost its Safety Department to the Department of Employment in 1977. While education, safety and farm training might seem allied subjects, they appear now to be deployed among three Ministries. The Agricultural Training Board gets its money from the MAFF, but it is essentially an autonomous body.

The process of withdrawing education from the MAFF started with the 1944 Butler Education Act, and the transfer of local responsibility from agricultural to education committees, although the inspection of farm institutes and part-time instruction courses was made on behalf of the MAFF by the Ministry of Education. As a result of the De La Warr Report responsibility for agricultural education provided by the County Councils was finally transferred from Agriculture to Education in 1959, and the DES assumed responsibility for the grant-aided agricultural colleges in 1964.

The consultative role of the Ministry on planning matters was never enshrined in the original 1947 Town and Country Planning Act, but through the years the Ministry had been used by farmers to push their case for the requisite planning permission for agricultural houses (most farm buildings not being within the orbit of the planning laws anyway). The Ministry sought to protect the best agricultural land from new housing estates or urban development, and could always furnish technical information on soil-type or the fragmentation of a farm.

It acted as a watch-dog, though it was rarely successful in halting the march of 'progress' which swept concrete and houses over vast areas of former farmland. However, planning authorities did at least consult the Agricultural Land Service of the MAFF, although they were not obliged to accept its advice. In the case of a complete deadlock the Land Commissioner could refer the matter to the MAFF in Whitehall, where it could be a subject for debate with the Ministry of Housing and Local Government.

The Ministry also consulted other Departments where land use was involved. Under the 1963 General Development Order the planning authorities were under the obligation to consult the MAFF before refusing permission, or imposing conditions. They did not have to consult when granting permissions, and until 1973 the MAFF had a role to play in planning.

In that year a new Order came into force whereby the planning authorities were no longer required to consult the MAFF; with some 400,000 planning applications being registered each year, just under 3 per cent came from farmers for developments in conjunction with their farming activities, or for development of a more general nature. The Ministry had been involved in about half of the farmers' applications, which were mainly for dwelling-houses, with about 5,000 cases to deal with each year. This procedure came under the new broom of Jim Prior, that was sweeping away many of the established roles within the Ministry; but this removed a safeguard for the British countryside.

Farms are inherently dangerous places—perhaps more so than the average factory—and there was therefore already a long history of Acts regulating and controlling aspects of farm safety. There was a Chief Safety Inspector in the form of John Weeks, an enthusiastic exponent of the unforeseen dangers on the farm, but with the passing of the 'Health and Safety at Work' Act 1974 the collective problems of safety throughout industry were collated under a new body, 'the Health and Safety Commission'. The Bill had originally been placed before Parliament by the Tory Government which went out of office on 28 February 1974, and it excluded agriculture from the concerns of the Commission. The Labour Government which followed reversed this ruling, but following intensive lobbying of MPs by the CLA the situation was again reversed, and responsibility returned to the MAFF.

Amendments had been put down by the Conservative spokesman on agriculture in the House of Lords, Earl Ferrers, and by the Chairman of the CLA's Legal and Land Use Committee, Lord Middleton. Passed by the Lords, the Bill returned to the Commons, and although the Labour Government tried to reverse the agriculture provisions yet again, it was defeated by a combination of Conservatives, Liberals and other parties. At that time the CLA considered it essential that safety and such other matters as training should be under the MAFF. This was July 1974, just before Parliament went into its Summer Recess, and there was to be another General Election on 10 October. In September a consultative document was published by the Government, from the Employment Department of Michael Foot. It again reversed the position, and brought agriculture under the wing of the Commission, and away from the MAFF. Roger Paul, Chairman of the CLA Agricultural Policy Committee, accused Michael Foot of carrying out the instructions of the NUAAW. Foot countered that if one argued that he was acting on union instructions—which he of course denied—the CLA could well be accused of negating the will of the Commons by persuading the Conservative majority in the Lords to act on *its* instructions. The CLA called this 'a blatant flouting of Parliament', and the NUAAW came back that implementation of Foot's new reversal would require a Commons majority, so the CLA would have another opportunity to persuade its friends in the House of Lords to reverse the decision of an elected Parliament.

This was inevitable with a Socialist majority committed to the idea that health and safety would be transferred eventually to the new Commission. But farmer's son John Weeks, who had joined the MAFF in 1946 as Machinery Inspector for the West Midlands, kept his top job with the new body. The change was delayed by a Government financial cutback, but was eventually passed in 1976, and by 1 March 1977 the reorganization was completed. An Advisory Committee was set up under the Chairmanship of the Director, John Weeks, with twelve members: four from the NUAAW, three from the NFU, with one from the National Farmers Union of Scotland, one each from the CLA and the Tree Growers Organisation (representing private forestry employers), and two from the Transport and General Workers Union.

Grants and subsidies

Throughout the world it would seem that farming cannot support itself without the assistance of State cash. Although this may be the result of a controlled society, and the withdrawal of free market forces, the essential is to ensure the continuance of steady food-supplies. Any political party which cannot feed the nation adequately is soon in trouble, even though notions of 'adequacy' vary so widely in the world.

The support system for UK farming still rests upon the 'cheap food' policy of the nineteenth century, although the realities of world food-shortages and escalating prices have to be faced. It seems ironic that the oldest profession in the country is unable to sell its goods at a price which could ensure security for its producers. Within this context, the MAFF designs and administers a series of grants to promote and encourage various sectors of the farming industry. Subsidies as a direct alleviation of the cost to the housewife have not largely disappeared under a revolutionized world food trading situation, and are concealed in a complicated system of threshold and intervention prices which are part of life with the CAP. Individual nations exercise nationalistic priorities towards farmers, priorities which when examined closely bear great resemblance to a weird form of social security. Indeed, the philosophy of keeping sectors of the farming community above the breadline—if only just—must be considered a social benefit and an equalizer to level out the vicissitudes of climate and soil.

Among the multitude of grants are those for farm amalgamations. These follow in principle the methods with which the original member countries of EEC faced these intractable problems: today UK farmers can get a grant for amalgamating one farm with another. Naturally, the procedure is wrapped up in considerable red tape and form-filling, but at least in the UK corruption is almost unheard of. Grants at a higher level are given for farmers in the hills as opposed to those in the lowlands, and they receive better prices for their sheep and cattle. Understandably, many hill farmers would be unable to survive financially without these grants, but they also help to produce food from unpromising sections of the nation's land.

The social advantages of keeping the hills alive have led to debate, balancing the productivity of this land of wool and lambs as opposed to its yield if afforested. The real future must surely lie in an amalgamation of the two functions, which can provide shelter belts in the winter for the animals, add to the aesthetic value, and yet produce some timber in the more distant future.

Farm buildings have been grant-aided for many years, with amounts which started at one-third of the estimated cost, went up to 40 per cent, and in two steps went down again to only 20 per cent. The Ministry lay down strict tendering procedures, and also have a system of 'standard costs', by which a farmer can do the work himself and claim on the 'standard costs' basis. Corn merchants erecting grain silos on their premises do not get grants, but farmers, erecting the same buildings on their farms, do. It has long been seen as an injustice by the merchants.

There are schemes for the raising of farm productivity, such as the FHDS[4], which came into operation on 1 January 1974 and is due to end on 18 April 1982. The FHDS has already been the subject of minor changes, and this will undoubtedly continue, so that by 1982 it will hardly resemble its appearance at birth. Nevertheless, in essence it is a scheme based on the income per labour unit, and where the income for the farmer and his men, including some part-timers, is below an overall figure (after various complicated deductions), then grants are payable.

These are no more than the various grants which Government has given to industries as an incentive to expand and redevelop in the designated development areas of the country where unemployment is the highest. Farming grants are given the nation over, providing they fulfil the criteria, with the exception of the unconditional hill farming grants.

Beyond these, there is an ever-changing scene of support which often results from a disastrous market price, like the pig subsidy given in 1976 to distraught pig farmers which was later declared illegal and banned by the EEC. The Dairy Herds Conversion Scheme was instituted to pay farmers to go out of cows and into beef. It set up useful payments, which would compensate a farmer going out

---

[4] Farm and Horticulture Development Scheme.

of milk-production for the wastage of his specialized dairy buildings, his grass leys and his farming disruption—but he had to guarantee to produce beef as a substitute for the over-production of milk that was bedevilling the EEC farming policies. These schemes are devised to push and pull the agricultural industry in various directions, but are all voluntary.

The Whitehall HQ

'The sentinel on Whitehall Gate looked forth into the night.'
Macaulay

As the Palace of Westminster is the political nerve centre of the nation, so nearby Whitehall has grown into the administrative and executive centre. Adjacent though the two centres are, they often seem further removed from each other in the spectrum of policy-making and its execution. In principle, Westminster makes the decisions and Whitehall carries them out.

Whitehall Place, where the MAFF resides, runs from Whitehall proper to the confluence of streets at Charing Cross Bridge by the Embankment. The MAFF buildings occupy the east side of Whitehall Place, and it is here that the shop-window of the Ministry is situated. In the confines of this modest street it is estimated that over ten thousand farmers gathered in a mass demonstration in 1970 before moving off in procession across the river to the car-park of the Royal Festival Hall to embark in taxis for the individual lobbying of influential people and bodies.

The newer of the two buildings in Whitehall Place is the west block which was built in 1952, and occupied by Agriculture and Fisheries, to be joined by Food two years later. Inside, the foyer is stark and comfortless, and the Enquiry Desk tucked away beside the staircase is indistinguishable. At first impression the building is cold and uncomfortable, and represents the utility of the stringent times of 1950 when it was commissioned.

The ground floor houses the Press Department and the Ministry Library; in the basement are large freshwater fish tanks, giving a real meaning to the Fisheries responsibilities of the Ministry. (There is apparently no roof garden to indicate the agricultural connection.) Upstairs is a Conference Room, the Ministerial Suite containing the photographs of successive occupants, and on every floor the inevitable standard Civil Service notice-board. The Ministerial floor has a display cabinet of silver trophies, and a large teak urn. The building itself is impressive for its façade; if architecturally uninspiring, it at least blends with its neighbours. It is not in fact a large building. The U shape gives it an inner well, and from the offices there is a view across to a back street where an Army recruiting poster beckons.

The east block is dark and the stonework fading, although around this corner many buildings have revealed a greater charm with the new methods of cleaning up London's shabby stonework. It was built in 1913–14 for the then Board of

The farmer's London home: Agriculture House in Knightsbridge, which stands on the site of the old Alexandra Hotel. It was a much-criticized building when erected *Photo National Farmers Union*

Through these doors has walked every Minister of Agriculture for nearly thirty years.
The impressive entrance to the Ministry in Whitehall Place, London
Photo The Ministry of Agriculture. Crown copyright reserved

Agriculture, but the Board never occupied it, for the First World War broke out and the War Office requisitioned the building. It became the main HQ of the new Ministry of Agriculture that was created in 1919, but twenty years later, when another war was declared, the War Office moved in again, and made it the QM General's Department. It suffered bomb damage during that war, and was not made habitable for the Ministry until 1954, two years after they had occupied the newly built west block.

From Whitehall Place the Minister can be within the confines of the Palace of Westminster, and in the House of Commons, in a very few minutes. It is in essence his private suite and his private office; it houses the head of the Whitehall Civil Service Department, but the administrative section of the work goes on in a modern tower block in Horseferry Road along the river near the Westminster Hospital.

Much of the work of the MAFF is, however, distributed throughout its other locations. The Central Veterinary Laboratories are at Weybridge in Surrey, the Plant Pathology Laboratory at Harpenden in Hertfordshire, and in March 1972 the Pest Infestation Laboratory was taken over from the Agricultural Research Council and combined with the Tangley Place Insect Department. The archives are stored at Hayes in Middlesex, and there is a Fisheries Research Laboratory at Lowestoft in Suffolk. Tolcarne Drive at Pinner produces the publications and staff training. Wellington House near Buckingham Palace deals with tropical foods such as tea, bananas, coffee and sugar. Rat problems are dealt with on the Toby Jug site at Tolworth near Surbiton in Surrey, and there is a neat division between the advisory service to farmers and the pest service, which, although occasionally advisory, in fact deals with chiefly indoor pests, such as rats and grain beetles in cereal barns. It is a happy thought that as the DoE is responsible for Buckingham Palace, the Ministry of Agriculture is responsible for the rodents that may infiltrate the building. Beyond this the Ministry presides over seven regions that cover England and one for Wales, with 26 Area Offices and a multitude of lesser centres where the staff can get closer to the farmers they represent and the industry they are administering.

1889–1903	Board of Agriculture
1903–19	Board of Agriculture and Fisheries
1919–39	Ministry of Agriculture, Fisheries and Food
1939–54	Ministry of Agriculture and Fisheries
1954	Ministry of Agriculture, Fisheries and Food

Permanent Secretaries to the MAFF

1889–91	Sir George Leach	1936–45	Sir Donald Fergusson
1892–1913	Sir Thomas Elliott	1945–52	Sir Donald Vandepeer
1913–17	Sir Sidney Olivier (later Lord Olivier)	1952–9	Sir Alan Hytchman
1917–19	Sir Alfred Hall	1959–67	Sir John Winnifrith
1919–27	Sir Francis Floud	1968–72	Sir Basil Engholm
1927–36	Sir Charles Thomas	1972–	Sir Alan Neale

Twelve Permanent Secretaries during the MAFF's political life have served thirty-four Ministers. They were quiet, behind-the-scenes administrators; few did anything after retirement, and only one later became a peer, although the knighthood went with the job. Floud, Vandepeer and Engholm were the only inside appointments, having served in the Agriculture Board or Ministry previously, and Neale, Winnifrith, Hytchman and Fergusson all came from the Treasury. Fergusson had been Private Secretary to successive Chancellors of the Exchequer for sixteen years, and he is the only one who transferred to another Ministry after leaving Agriculture. He went to the Ministry of Fuel and Power from 1945–1952. Winnifrith and Neale started their Civil Service careers in the Board of Trade, and although few of them achieved anything after leaving, Floud later became UK High Commissioner in Canada 1934–8, and chaired the Agricultural Wages Board, 1943–7. Vandepeer had been Private Secretary to nine Ministers between 1922 and 1934, when he left Agriculture for eleven years, during which time he led the backroom boys to the League of Nations in Geneva in 1936. But he came back in 1945 to steer the Agriculture Act 1947 on to the Statute Book. At that time he had as an Assistant Secretary Engholm, who by a rare inside promotion later achieved the top job, although this took him twenty-one years, and he only kept it for four years before retiring. Winnifrith has certainly to date achieved greater fame, emerging from behind the cloak of anonymity with which the Civil Service is wrapped. After his 'retirement' he bacame Director-General of the National Trust from 1968 to 1970, and later a member of the Hops Marketing Board. He emerged as a rabid anti-Marketeer in the 1975 Referendum, and wrote the Labour Party Agricultural Policy Statement. He became well known for advocating that the British buy their food cheaper outside Europe.

It was a mark of the growing pressure of Britain's European involvement and its farming spin-off that in 1973 the MAFF was accredited with a new post of Second Permanent Secretary. It went to Freddy Kearns, who had been a member of the official UK Delegation during the negotiations for membership of the EEC, and was later knighted.

The Farmers Advisory Service

'It is a primary purpose of ADAS to develop new technology and disseminated it amongst farmers as quickly as possible.'
Dr Keith Dexter, 7 January 1977.

Within the UK agricultural industry there is another industry: the advisory industry. It consists of a vast army of men and women, experts in their respective fields, who can be called upon by farmers with a problem. Commercial companies involved with animal feeding stuffs have an army of nutritional experts and diagnostic laboratories to provide a back-up service. Agro-chemical manufacturers have advisers, fertilizer companies can test soil requirements and give advice. They all have a wide-ranging brief that is designed for the promotion of their products, and the protection of their reputations. Amid this plethora of advice the farm-machinery manufacturers stand aloof, trusting their machines and leaving the rectification of faults to the local mechanics.

Beside the commercial advisory set-up is the official Ministry body, labelled today the Agricultural Development and Advisory Service, which incorporates the whole spectrum of agriculture and horticulture. It was created in 1971 by combining the old National Agricultural Advisory Service (NAAS), the Agricultural Land Service (ALS), the Animal Health Division and the Land Drainage and Water Supplies Department. It has a team of architects labelled Architects in Agriculture, founded in 1975, has provided socio-economic advice since 1974, has its own string of twenty-four Experimental Husbandry Farms and Experimental Horticultural Stations and employs 5,000 of the 15,000 staff of the MAFF.

The sophisticated advisory service which has been evolved through the years, and which escalated in the 1970s, is nothing new; it has always been recognized that off-the-farm knowledge could be useful, although during the pre-1939 depression hard-pressed farmers poured scorn on the 'advisers' who were attached to the County Agricultural Colleges as men who had failed at farming themselves, and yet sought to make other farmers bankrupt by telling them how to do it. Agricultural Colleges were labelled as places where a farmer's son might go to learn all about the mistakes his father had made while earning enough money to send him there. The cynics had a field day, and the advent of wartime control and directives to farmers—often by ex bankrupt farmers—did not help to promote the idea of NAAS, which was created in 1946. It was a slow, patient haul to the modern counterpart which was born in the 1970s.

The original concept was to drag farming into the new era of the post-War period and a chain of farms were established which were both experimental and usable for demonstration purposes. In no way were these envisaged as centres of fundamental research, nor have they evolved in this direction. The first farm came into being in 1947, and the chain was quickly built up. The farms were on the pattern of the Norfolk Agricultural Station at Sprowston, which had been in existence for a long period, and which epitomized the Norfolk farmer's soil-type, climate and geography. Therefore, in selecting the NAAS farms localities were chosen where the land would provide uniform conditions for field experimentation, while the horticultural stations must obviously be situated in an area where farmers would be interested. Although embracing the whole of the British Isles, they are essentially for husbandry and horticultural purposes, and are not greatly concerned with animals, other than their practical management, plus the stimulation of grassland, or its upkeep and feeding potential.

In order to build up NAAS's reputation, and despite traditional Civil Service anonymity, its top men became well-known personalities in the farming world. They were prophets and leaders, and followed the pattern of progress by urging the benefits of greater grassland usage (still vastly under-used in the UK), forage farming, specialization, and the keeping of proper accounts. Sir James Scott-

Watson, a farmer's son from Dundee, and Chief Education Officer to the MoA before it lost its education role, was Chief Scientific and Agricultural Adviser, becoming Director-General of NAAS in 1948, and guiding it for the next six years. Among the backroom boys who emerged was a Welshman who had been head of the Welsh Department of the Ministry: Emrys Jones. He became Director of NAAS in 1961, and six years later Chief Agricultural Adviser to the Ministry. Jones worked at the unification of the fragmented Ministry services, and was the virtual creator of the Agricultural Development and Advisory Service (ADAS).

A management consultant's report commissioned by Cledwyn Hughes when he was Minister in 1968 was conveniently fulfilled when the new broom, Jim Prior, became the Tory Minister of Agriculture in June 1970. 'Modern line-management methods' was the new trend, and the modern ADAS was created. It opened for business in March 1971, but ironically three months earlier Prior had announced drastic cuts in the advisory service staff, and a shake-up of the whole Department. This was to be reversed in 1974, with Peart back at the Ministry.

The Prior cuts involved reducing the total Ministry staff from its swollen figure of 16,125 in October 1970, with a loss of 1,065 jobs by April 1974. It meant cutting 512 office workers and 150 technical staff, and reducing the advisers by 400. The Institution of Professional Civil Servants—the ADAS advisers' 'Union'—accused the Minister of harming farming by such cuts, and claimed that there was no outside organization able to provide a quick diagnostic service for pest and disease problems. It also emphasized that farmers needed impartial professional advice, and concluded: 'Private industry appears to be in no position to replace Ministry advice.' Prior moved from the MAFF in November 1972, and Godber took his place. The cutback continued, and due to the Government's financial stringencies a system of charging for certain services was instituted. In February 1974, when Peart returned, one of his first moves was to reverse the concept of line-management, which had resulted in situations where a veterinary surgeon could find himself at the head of other professionals. The specialists were being moved around willy-nilly, and morale was bad. Resentment and redundancies, with early retirements, had taken some of the top men prematurely away, and Peart sought to reverse this policy.

Within three months of Peart's return to Whitehall Place the Ministry were advertising for sixty new Advisory Officers to specialize in dairy husbandry, general agriculture and horticulture. The four hundred retired ex-members of ADAS were offered the chance of rejoining under conditions which included repaying a proportion of their redundancy payments. Very few accepted.

Sir Emrys Jones

'When the NAAS was formed in 1946, he swept through the Far West like an evangelist preaching the Gospel as provincial Grassland Officer.'

John Winter, 'Farm'

A fast-speaking Welshman, with a disarming smile and a bubbling enthusiasm which reveals itself in his robust rendering of Welsh hymns, accompanied by his wife on the piano, Emrys Jones became the first Director-General of the newly shaken up ADAS. His background as Director for Wales and later in the Ministry HQ gave him an eminence in the industry which reflected the organization he created.

Jones's breadth of vision concerning the direction of British farming sets him down as a visionary; he is labelled 'Jones the Grass', but his far-sightedness goes beyond the present. In an interview he once said, 'By the year 2000 I visualize family farming and contentment in the west; company farming and ulcers in the east.' He rhapsodizes about the hills and uplands of Britain as its greatest untapped agricultural asset, but his enthusiasm for his job was damaged, and in August 1973 he suddenly resigned, having been knighted in 1971, to become Principal of the Royal Agricultural College at Cirencester. 'I shall be a hundred miles nearer to my beloved Wales,' he declared. The Ministry had lost its most flamboyant protagonist, but the RAC had gained a national figure.

Erlam Dobb

There were two Deputy Directors under Jones, Erlam Dobb and Walter Smith; the first the archetypal civil servant with the administrative capacity, the second a flamboyant figure in the Jones tradition, who had become well known to the farming community, spoke pugnaciously on public platforms, and had travelled the length of the country. Perhaps it would have been too much for the mandarins in the background to have had such another extrovert as Jones. Smith left London for a Welsh posting, and Erlam Dobb got the job.

Dobb also had served as a provincial Land Commissioner in Wales, was a professional associate of the RICS, a qualified surveyor, and had served in the War with the Fourth Royal Welch Fusiliers. His was a stop-gap appointment; he was sixty-three at the time, replacing the 58-year-old Jones. In under two years he retired, and Keith Dexter took over.

Keith Dexter

If Jones' resignation was a surprise, then so was the appointment of 47-year-old Dexter after Dobb. A slightly balding man, with a boyish face, tall and soft-spoken, he is in contrast to the flamboyant Jones, but symbolizes the changing scene of farming. Dexter had his background in economics, and he had been in various Ministries prior to obtaining the top job. The son of a Leicestershire farmer, he has his roots in the soil.

Dexter senior had a mixed farm in Leicestershire, and as a boy Dexter suffered backache when ploughing with a team of horses. He spent the freezing early hours of winter mornings delivering reluctant calves with a block and tackle, but his academic talents blossomed at Nottingham University in the Economics Department working on milk-production costs. He went to the University of Illinois on a Fulbright Scholarship, and obtained his Doctorate in 1953. He was a backroom economist in the Ministry, but became an adviser on farm management.

If Jones was a grass enthusiast, then Dexter is a champion of the small farmer at a time when they are disappearing rapidly, or being cast into oblivion by the expansionism of their neighbours. Dexter acknowledges that large company farms are here to stay, but he champions the small man, who he says can extract more crops per hectare, more meat and more milk from a cow. But his role is to oversee the industry, to prophesy its direction, to point this out to farmers, and to keep a satisfactory relationship with his Minister. Whitehall is the source of assistance for British farmers, while the relatively young Dexter has to keep up with the changing farming scene.

Presidents of the Board of Agriculture and Ministers

Henry Chaplin	9 September	1889 – 17 August	1892
H. Gardner	31 August	1892 – 29 June	1895
Walter Long	4 July	1895 – 11 November	1900
R. W. Hanbury	16 November	1900 – 28 April	1903 (died)
Lord Onslow	20 May	1903 – 30 September	1903

Board of Agriculture and Fisheries

Lord Onslow	1 October	1903 – 16 February	1905
Sir Ailwyn Fellowes	14 March	1905 – 10 December	1905
Earl of Carrington	11 December	1905 – 23 October	1911
Walter Runciman	24 October	1911 – 5 August	1914
Lord Lucas and Dingwall	6 August	1914 – 26 May	1915
Earl of Selborne	27 May	1915 – 11 July	1916
Earl of Crawford	12 July	1916 – 12 December	1916
Reginald Prothero	13 December	1916 – 26 July	1919
Lord Lee of Fareham	18 August	1919 – 8 January	1920

Ministry of Agriculture and Fisheries

Lord Lee of Fareham	9 January	1920 – 13 February	1921
Sir Arthur Boscawen	14 February	1921 – 24 October	1922
Sir R. A. Sanders	25 October	1922 – 22 January	1924
Noel Buxton	23 January	1924 – 6 November	1924
Edward Wood	7 November	1924 – 3 November	1925
Walter Guinness	4 November	1925 – 7 June	1929
Noel Buxton	8 June	1929 – 12 June	1930
Dr C. Addison	13 June	1930 – 24 August	1931
Sir John Gilmour	26 August	1931 – 30 September	1932
Walter Elliot	1 October	1932 – 2 November	1936
W. S. Morrison	3 November	1936 – 1 February	1939
Sir Reginald Dorman-Smith	3 February	1939 – 14 May	1940

R. S. Hudson	15 May	1940 – 3 August	1945
Tom Williams	4 August	1945 – 31 October	1951
Sir Thomas Dugdale	1 November	1951 – 21 July	1954
D. Heathcoat-Amory	29 July	1954 – 6 January	1958
John Hare	7 January	1958 – 27 July	1960
Christopher Soames	28 July	1960 – 15 October	1964
Fred Peart	19 October	1964 – 5 April	1968
Cledwyn Hughes	8 April	1968 – 18 June	1970
James Prior	19 June	1970 – 5 November	1972
Joseph Godber	5 November	1972 – 28 February	1974
Fred Peart	29 February	1974 – 10 September	1976
John Silkin	10 September	1976 –	

N.B. Page 303 gives details of addition of 'Food' to ministry's title.

17 The Ministers

'This is very true; for my words are my own, and my actions are my Ministers',

Charles II

One died in office (Hanbury, 1903), one resigned abruptly (Dugdale, 1954), two returned to the same office (Noel Buxton and Peart) and none ever became Prime Minister. Heathcoat-Amory went on to be Chancellor of the Exchequer, the highest office attained by any past Minister of Agriculture after his translation. Soames went on to be the UK Ambassador in Paris, and an EEC Commissioner. Peart and Prior became the Leader of the Commons, and most ended up in the House of Lords, exchanging their Ministerial role for relative obscurity. One might therefore deduce that the Minister of Agriculture is a sinecure in the patronage of the Prime Minister for long and trusted service, rather than a proving-ground for higher office to come. The post rated eighteenth place in the Ministerial pecking order in the Heath Government, and fifteenth in the Callaghan administration, 1976.

Up to and including Silkin in 1976, there had been 34 incumbents of the office; for only ten years four months of this time was the post occupied by a peer, and the last was Lord Lee, over fifty years ago, even though it is still not unknown for a senior Ministry to be held by a member of the Upper House.[1] The position normally takes a seat in the Cabinet, although there have been three periods when it was downgraded. Surprisingly, Prothero was not in the Cabinet during his tenure of 1916–19, even though for most of this period agriculture was basking in the sunshine of importance though the exigencies of wartime. In the next War it happened again, and from 1939–51 for a period of twelve years during the wartime Coalition Governments and the succeeding Socialist one, agriculture was not given the accolade of a Cabinet seat. For a short period in the Wilson Government, when Cledwyn Hughes became Minister (1968–70), the position was not of Cabinet standing.

The average length of tenure in the office of Minister has been thirty months, with three lasting under a year, the shortest being the five-month caretaker period of Lord Crawford from July to December, 1916. But in 1905 Sir Ailwyn Fellowes lasted for only nine months, and Noel Buxton only a few days longer during the short-lived Labour Government of 1924, although he returned for a slightly longer period five years later.

[1] The thirteenth Earl of Home was Foreign Secretary before he renounced his peerage to become Prime Minister as Sir Alec Douglas-Home in 1963.

Incumbent for the longest time has been Tom Williams, who was Minister for six years three months during the entire two administrations of Attlee, until the Labour Government's defeat in 1951. Williams, moreover, had a total of eleven years within the political framework of the Ministry, having served as one of Hudson's Parliamentary Secretaries from May 1940. Peart would have liked to equal Williams's record at the Ministry, but for various reasons missed it by three months, although his tenure was split; but the Earl of Carrington (later Marquis of Lincolnshire) holds the second longest record with his continuous five years ten months from December 1905. Peart apart, the longest-serving Minister in the post-War period has been Soames.

Today the Minister is supported by a Minister of State in addition to a Parliamentary Secretary. This office was added in April 1972 as a mark of the importance of agriculture, with the EEC in mind. Anthony Stodart, who had been Prior's Parliamentary Secretary, moved up into the new position, and when Labour returned to power Edward Bishop was appointed Minister of State. When the Minister, as an MP, came from the Commons it was considered appropriate that one of the two Parliamentary Secretaries should come from the Lords, and even in the long period of Socialist government from 1945 to 1951, with Williams as Minister, this practice was continued, with first the Earl of Huntingdon and then the Earl of Listowel. In the earlier days, when a peer was President or Minister, the Parliamentary Secretaries provided a voice in the Commons. Twice Dukes have occupied this position. During the First World War the Duke of Marlborough acted as unpaid Parliamentary Secretary, and in the Second World War, with Tom Williams in the Commons under R. S. Hudson, a lordly presence was provided by the Earl Marshal the Duke of Norfolk; a ducal bedfellow for the miner's son Williams, who was to become a successful Minister. Wilson broke the lordly tradition in 1964, and both the Parliamentary Secretaries came from the Commons: John Mackie and James Hoy, who served in tandem for the full period of Wilson's two Governments, firstly under Peart, then under Hughes.

Only four men who eventually became Minister had served as Parliamentary Secretaries in the Department as part of their training for the job. Sir Arthur Boscawen had been PS to Lord Lee when the Board was translated into a Ministry in 1919, and after Lee retired he was immediately appointed as Minister of Agriculture and Fisheries. In 1930 Dr Addison became the Minister after working under Noel Buxton in the Coalition Government. Addison had 365 days as a PS, and 438 days as Minister. When Attlee became Prime Minister in 1945 the vast experience of Tom Williams at the Ministry during the wartime period made him the only possible candidate from a Labour Party traditionally short of agricultural experience. The last of the four was Joe Godber, who was a PS to Soames from 1957 to 1960, but it was twelve years before he became Minister, and he had served in various other capacities in the interim. There has only been one woman at the Ministry: Peggy Fenner, who became an MP for Rochester and Chatham in 1970 when Heath unexpectedly toppled Wilson from power.

Housewife Mrs Fenner was Parliamentary Secretary at the MAFF, 1972 to 1974, and it was the apparent connection between rising food prices and farm production that encouraged Heath to appoint a woman to the job. From 1889 to October 1974 there twenty-three General Elections and at fifteen of those the ruling party lost. With thirty-four Ministers of Agriculture during the period it would seem that half of them were replaced—for diverse reasons—during the term of a Government in a reshuffle.

In the last forty years there have been eight Tory Ministers and only four Socialists. It is ironical that the Labour Party, in the persons of Williams and Peart, have appeared to be greater friends of the farmers than have the Tories. In general farmers admit that they are usually better off under the Socialists, although they continue to vote Tory almost to a man.

Hudson was called a dictator, Dugdale a tragedy, Hare arrogant, Soames worse, Prior insensitive, and Godber dull; only Heathcoat-Amory was obviously liked. Of the Socialists, Williams was venerated, Peart pragmatic, Hughes forgotten, and Silkin smooth. The least successful is usually considered to be Soames.

Sir Reginald Dorman-Smith

Dorman-Smith, who died in March 1977, was Minister of Agriculture for a short period in the closing months of Chamberlain's Government, which fell in 1940. He had been invalided out of the Army after the Afghan War in 1919 at the age of only twenty. Dorman-Smith settled in Surrey, got involved in local politics and took up farming. Through his local NFU Branch, he became a member of the Council, and in 1935 he was elected Unionist MP for the Petersfield Division of Hampshire. It was as an MP that the farmers called upon him to lead them as their President in 1936. In January 1939 Chamberlain appointed him Minister of Agriculture in succession to W. S. Morrison. Said *The Times* in its obituary[2]:

> When war came in the early autumn, a slow start had been made to put agriculture on a war footing. The response from the farmers to his appeal to plough up at least 2 million acres of grassland had been excellent. When in 1940 Winston Churchill became Prime Minister, Dorman-Smith was succeeded at the Ministry of Agriculture and Fisheries by Mr R. S. Hudson. The retiring Minister promptly rejoined the Army.

He went to Burma as Governor in succession to Sir Archibald Cochrane, but the Japanese invasion of 1942 soon overwhelmed his administration, and although he stayed in Burma until 1943, he was in imminent danger, and spent the rest of the War in Simla. He retired as Governor after the War until August 1946, when he resigned on grounds of ill health, and lived his remaining thirty years in Hampshire as an English country squire.

Tom Williams

R. S. Hudson cajoled and bullied the farmers of Britain into expanding their

[2] 22 March 1977.

food production as the submarine blockade nearly starved Britain. Grassland was ploughed up, and in 1943 the greatest area of wheat was planted that the UK had ever seen; not until the 1970s was the record reached again. Farming politics had only one message: to produce more food at any cost. The farmers did well, and the War Agricultural Executive Committees, set up and operated by Hudson, were hated. As the atom bombs dropped on Japan Churchill felt that a General Election should be called, and in August 1945 the National Coalition Government which had sat since 1931 was defeated. Hudson also lost his job. The Labour newcomer was Tom Williams, who had served under Hudson, and who for the quarter of a century since his period of office has been venerated by the farmers as the saviour of British agriculture. He came at a period when the need for food rationing was paramount, but the farmers were popular idols for having saved the nation's bacon. If the farmers could do no wrong, neither could Williams, and he fixed in farmers' minds the belief that they were always served better by Socialists than by Tories.

The 1947 Act safely on the Statute Book was accredited to Williams, although it was the culmination of policies that had been slowly evolving throughout the War years, and was in the event supported in the House of Commons by the Tories also. A miner's son, representing the Don Valley in Yorkshire, Williams was a distinguished figure with his head of immaculately waved silver hair, and his adherence to a white stiff wing collar, already almost a museum piece.

Sir Thomas Dugdale

It is standard procedure today that any Government Department which wishes to dispose of agricultural land that has been compulsorily acquired, however long before, must first of all be offered to the original owner, who if he refuses to buy it has to allow it to be offered for auction. This ultra-democratic procedure is now enshrined in the hearts of the Government Departments which hold agricultural land, and is known as the Crichel Down procedure. It resulted from the affair known as the 'Battle of Crichel Down' and the dramatic resignation of the Minister, Tommy Dugdale.

A bluff Yorkshire squire and farmer, Dugdale had occupied various Government offices in the pre-War period, including a spell as Parliamentary Private Secretary to Stanley Baldwin in 1935. He was Chairman of the Conservative Party for two years, but resigned through ill health in October 1944. During the Attlee Government Dugdale became the sparring partner of Tom Williams as the Opposition Spokesman on agriculture, and when Churchill commenced his second period as Premier in 1951 Dugdale was the obvious choice as Minister of Agriculture. It was almost one of those rare occasions when the Shadow Minister has indeed become the substance.

Dugdale became Minister in November 1951, and in 1953 the newspapers were blazoning forth the injustice being meted out to a Commander Marten from Dorset. The story went back to the wartime period when, under the aegis of directives and dispossession orders, the Ministry had acquired over 77,000 hectares of farmland for direct farming purposes. Under the 1947 Agriculture Act an Agricultural Land Commission was created to manage and farm this land, and although the Tories were against the more harsh disciplinary powers embodied in this Act, and against nationalizing farming, Dugdale took a passive line and followed its spirit while looking carefully at some of its more socialistic ideologies.

Pressure was being brought by a body called the Farmers and Smallholders Association, one of many phantom organizations operating with a small staff in three rooms in Austin Friars, committed to the abolition of subsidies and controls, and of the substantial powers still held by the Government as a relic of the War emergency. The Commander Marten affair was an ideal vehicle for a campaign, and the CLA also were wondering why a Tory Minister was being unduly slow in reversing Socialist policies.

Crichel Down extended to 290 hectares, which before the War was mostly sheep grazing, with a small amount of arable land. It had been compulsorily acquired by the Air Ministry in 1937 for a bombing range, and although acquired from Lord Alington (who had died in 1940), it was left in trust for his daughter, who married Lieutenant-Commander Marten. Of the 290 hectares, the Air Ministry had taken 131 hectares, but by 1949 it no longer required a bombing range, and the land was transferred to the Ministry of Agriculture, which entrusted its management to the Agricultural Land Commission; it was then delegated to the Land Service Department, and farmed in co-operation with the Dorset Agricultural Executive Committee.

Although it had been used as a bombing range, Crichel Down was still agricultural land, and the Ministry officials pondered its future. They suggested letting blocks to neighbouring farmers, equipping it as a single farming unit, and finding a tenant; while although this was not considered, the Minister was empowered to sell it under Section 90 of the 1947 Act. However, the British public were not going to see the freedom of an individual to retain his own property filched away: the public supported Commander Marten. He became a public figure, writing letters, invading the Ministry, and complaining personally to the Parliamentary Secretary; he enlisted the support of his MP Mr Crouch, convened meetings and hit the headlines. The gallant wartime Commander was being victimized by petty officialdom, and the public did not like it. Dugdale had been advised to let the land in its existing condition, and although Marten had been one of the earliest and most persistent applicants, the tenancy was negotiated privately, while Dugdale agreed to sell Crichel Down to the Commissioners of Crown Lands. Marten secured an interview with Dugdale, who was unresponsive, and the owners of 66,800 hectares which had been taken from them in similar circumstances petitioned for a full Inquiry. It is doubtful if Dugdale even knew of his officials' actions in the early stages of this 'battle', but in the glare of publicity he was forced to submit to a public inquiry. Sir Andrew Clark, QC, was appointed for this purpose.

Clark's inquiry was published in June 1954, and it was a devastating condemnation of petty officialdom; it criticized various civil servants, and said that they had deliberately sought to deceive the Minister, Dugdale. Although corruption was ruled out, there was overwhelming evidence of obstinacy, smugness and incompetence. A report to Dugdale was 'riddled with inaccuracies', and Marten had been considered a nuisance by the civil servants who were determined not to let him succeed in his plea to regain his wife's land. In the debate in the House of Commons in July 1954 Dugdale firmly asserted that his staff had not wilfully deceived him. As befitted this bluff Yorkshire squire, with his transparent honesty and honour, he accepted the full responsibility, even though he had not been aware of the situation, and resigned. It was the last occasion that a Minister of the Crown has resigned because of the incompetence of his advisers, the civil servants.

Dugdale remained an MP for another five years, and then became Lord Crathorne in 1959. He was later Chairman of the Political Honours Scrutiny Committee, and was involved in the furore over the Wilson resignation Honours List a year before he died on 26 March 1977, ironically only six days after Dorman-Smith. He kept his agricultural connections, and as Crathorne played a leading part in the RASE, and was a director of Massey-Ferguson Ltd.

Heathcoat-Amory; Hare; Soames

Churchill promoted Amory from Minister of State at the Board of Trade to the Agriculture Ministry, where he remained until becoming Chancellor of the Exchequer three and a half years later in January 1958, after the Chancellor, Peter Thorneycroft, in company with Nigel Birch and Enoch Powell, resigned over proposed expenditure cuts. Macmillan then called upon Amory to lead the Treasury. Said Macmillan: 'He was rather hesitant, but accepted.'[3] This tall, quiet, modest, unambitious, slightly stooping bachelor from a farming constituency at Tiverton in Devon, although not a farmer himself, set about clearing the debris left behind after the Crichel Down mess, which *The Times* had called a 'sorry and tangled tale'. Amory supervised the amalgamation of 'food' back into the Department, and worked to evolve the pattern of the Annual Price Review ritual which was becoming a major focal point in the public policy of the Government, and the work of the Ministry. Wrote Macmillan:[3]

> Although the estimates for 1956–7 had in the main been settled before I became Chancellor, there was one formidable exception. . . . It was known as the Farm Price Review. This Annual Debate was carried on with almost Byzantine deviousness, based upon a series of figures which few could understand, and all challenged. In later years, I was to become accustomed to the Alice in Wonderland method of calculation by which the final charge to the Exchequer at the end of the farming bore little relation to the sum estimated.

[3] Harold Macmillan, *Riding the Storm, 1956–59*

The 1956 Price Review was the subject of an unprecedented claim of £41 million by the NFU. Behind the scenes the Government decided to offer £17 million, hoping to finish up somewhere near £22½ million. In the event it finished up with £24 million, and Macmillan wrote:

> I don't think the farmers will launch a violent campaign against the Government because Sir James Turner is too clever not to realise that, in the present economic climate the public will think an extra £24 million a year is pretty generous. The example of an 'imposed' settlement will be very healthy.

Nine months after Amory became the Minister, Churchill finally retired in April 1955, and Eden took over, for a short and traumatic period. He resigned in January 1957, after the Suez débâcle, after only twenty-one months as Prime Minister. Harold Macmillan succeeded him, and Amory stayed at the MAFF. He saw the 1957 Agriculture Act on to the Statute Book, which set farming on a new expansionist course, set limits by which the guarantees for farm products could be reduced in any one year, and instituted a grant system of 30 per cent of the cost of new farm buildings.

John Hare, a Suffolk farmer from the village of Little Blakenham (he later became Lord Blakenham), and a son of the Earl of Listowel, married a daughter of Lord Cowdray, an aristocrat with experience at the Colonial Office and the War Office. Hare followed Amory as Minister in January 1958. He held the post under Macmillan until 1960, when he became Minister of Labour. His reign was inauspicious and inconspicuous. The Tories were in power for thirteen years, and neither General Elections nor changes of Prime Minister were valid reasons to change horses in the various Ministries. He departed in a Government reshuffle.

Christopher Soames, Churchill's son-in-law, and with a farm in his background, took over for a four-year stint that was to end when Wilson won the 1964 General Election. Soames was in hospital with a broken leg during the Election, but retained his Bedford seat, although he could not appear in his constituency during the campaign. However, when he did appear during the 1966 Election he lost.

From 1960 to 1964, Soames faced a very different situation from that of his predecessors. Food was now more plentiful, memories of farmers' wartime efforts were fading, and the crunch was on. There had been a massive escalation in the Treasury liability under the Price Review procedures. In the late 1950s it had been around £250 million, but in 1961–2 it suddenly shot up to £342 million. Soames had the embarrassing task of explaining to the House why the deficiency payment on fat cattle had nearly quadrupled since the previous year. Lamb prices had plummeted, and the Treasury cash pay-out had escalated to compensate for this under the system which was the payment of a 'deficiency' in the actual market price against the price 'guaranteed' under the Annual Price Review procedures. Soames set about curbing the Treasury liability, and the Government's embarrassment. He was the victim of circumstances in a changing world, but whereas Williams had cashed in on the circumstances of his times to ingratiate himself, and his party, with the farmers, Soames had the different task of steering in the opposite direction.

Unfortunately, he was unpopular with the farmers. In the 1964 General Election, which threw out the Tories, many farmers voted Socialist for the first time in their lives. It was a reaction against the policies which Soames had been promoting.

Fred Peart

'The Cobdenite Gnomes of Whitehall have poor Mr Peart locked firmly in their Gladstone Bag.'

William Rees-Mogg
'Sunday Times', 1976

'In a curious way, this immensely shrewd politician has become a part of agricultural lore.'

'Power Farming', Derek Barker, 1976

Sir Alec Douglas-Home lost the 1964 Election and Wilson marched triumphantly into Downing Street; and a man from the largely industrial constituency of Workington in Cumberland became Minister of Agriculture. The thirteen years of Tory rule had ceased, and there went with it the succession of Ministers with farming backgrounds. Here was a complete newcomer to the scene, and an ex-schoolmaster to boot.

Perhaps the Tories had more farmers in their Parliamentary ranks to choose from, and the Socialists less, but Dugdale was a Yorkshire squire, Heathcoat-Amory a Devonian landowner and son of a baronet, Hare, the brother of the Socialist Earl of Listowel, was a Suffolk farmer, and Soames ran his father-in-law's Churchill's farm at Chartwell in Kent. They also were men with previous Ministerial, if not Cabinet, experience. At a later stage Prior was to be propelled from obscurity to the Ministry of Agriculture in one jump, but Peart became Minister in October 1964 from the obscurity of the Back Benches, with the only testimonial that he had been PPS to Tom Williams up to 1951; at least that was a modicum of agricultural experience, although the world had moved a long way in the intervening period. In appointing Peart, Wilson was also appointing untried men to other posts. The party had been in Opposition for so long that those who had served in the Government prior to 1951 were now old or dead.

Wilson, relatively inexperienced himself in the ways of Government, came into office with a dramatic 'one hundred days' policy for revolutionizing the Government structure and reshaping the future of Britain. He alienated the City, assuming they would be Tories, whereas in reality there was a lot of sympathy for him there. The City was prepared to let the new Labour Government flex its muscles before it passed comment. The farmers too were prepared to let Peart have a honeymoon period; after all, he had replaced the much maligned Soames, and anything seemed to them better. In the end Peart rode to triumph, but in the beginning he was a highly unpopular Minister, probably the most unpopular ever to sit over the farmers. Who misjudged whom will be a historical debating point; it suffices to say that despite Soames's unpopularity and his introduction of the 'standard quantities' which had set cash limits on the size of deficiency sum which the Treasury were prepared to pay, Peart engendered such hostility with his 1965 Price Review that the farmers were heard to say, 'Come back, Christopher, all is forgiven!' The 1965 Review was an utter disaster, and the honeymoon over.

Tall, with patriarchal forehead and heavy lips, pragmatic Peart survived the farmers' anger after his initial setback to become a sort of rural folk hero. He infuriated his civil servants and close aides by playing snooker at 3 a.m. after an all-night sitting in the House, or at the Brussels Talks in the 1970s. He knew little about farming, and less about farmers when he came into the job in 1964, yet when he returned after a six-year absence for his second spell at Agriculture in 1974 he was warmly welcomed, and when he went to the Lords two and a half years later the farming press rose as one man to acclaim this urban hero who had become the farmers' friend. Few men can have had the opportunity to read such glowing praises, of a quality usually reserved for obituaries.

Peart spanned twelve years, from Soames to Silkin, with a brief interlude of Hughes, Prior and Godber, from the turbulence of Price Reviews to the traumas of the Common Agricultural Policy. In 1964 there were cheap food surpluses in the world. Peart, like Soames before him, was a victim of circumstances, just as Williams could do no wrong because he too was a creature of circumstance, but then Williams encountered food shortages, not surpluses. When Peart came back for his second spell in 1974 his first discovery was that all the cheap food had gone. Again he was a victim of circumstance, but this time it was favourable to the farmers.

The 1965 Price Review

Peart was appointed Minister on 19 October 1964. It gave him little enough time to assimilate the problems of his new Department and to size up the farmers' agitation, before the coming Price Review. In those days the Review itself was conducted in the Whitehall Place HQ of the MAFF, and commenced with a happy photograph of the NFU leaders waving their briefcases as they strode up the steps. It also occupied little more than a week or ten days, with an announcement in Parliament a few days later. The whole business was called the 'February' Price Review, and in fact took place within that month.

In 1965 the NFU with their economists had worked out that farmers' costs had risen by £29 million since the previous year. They wanted to recoup these, plus an additional £1 million; a target of about £30 million was the starting-point.

Milk was a problem area, and A. G. Street[4] had been moved to write, 'Nothing

[4] *Farmers Weekly*, 5 February 1965.

less than a rise of 6d a gallon will halt the drift from milk and ensure that there will not be a serious shortage in the foreseeable future.'

Wilson as the new Prime Minister had appointed his team with the criterion that 'Cabinet collective responsibility' was to be the theme; Departmental lobbyists were not encouraged. The previous year Soames had been in trouble with the Cabinet over the size of the Review, but had gone direct to Douglas-Home to win backing before taking it to the Cabinet; at least Soames was developing a reputation for fighting his own figures through the Cabinet, and for pushing the farmers' case around the Cabinet table. This course of action was denied to Peart.

Peart maintained that £30 million was too much, and in the last stage of the talks around the table with the NFU the two sides showed signs of reaching agreement at a figure of £23 million. At this point Peart left the negotiations to get Cabinet ratification. Callaghan as Chancellor of the Exchequer, and George Brown as Minister for Economic Affairs, were not always in unison, but on this occasion both heavily vetoed the junior Peart's proposals. Crossman[5] wrote: 'Coming immediately after the Election we had to cut right back on the Election bribes the Tories had given the year before.' Peart came back from the Cabinet offering an unbelievable £10·5 million. The effect of this sudden about-turn upon the farmers leaders' was considerable; the Review had been scheduled for announcement in the Commons on Wednesday 17 February. In the event it was not announced until 17 March, a month late. New schedules of prices were hurriedly arranged by the Ministry to meet the overall £10·5 million figure, but the farmers were uncooperative and furious. In the Cabinet Peart found himself alone; there was little sympathy for him, and little sympathy for the farmers. The Labour Government was now in office with the economy in a perilous state, and was acting in an ultra-cautious manner. It was unfortunate for poor Fred Peart.

The 6d advocated by A. G. Street and the farmers' leaders resolved into a desultory 1d. The farmers had to absorb £19·5 million of the increased costs from their own pockets, but worse, the fine words of Peart before he became Minister the previous year now sounded false. The comment was scathing. In October 1964 before the Election, Peart had written.

> In the last nine years, the Government has imposed five Price Reviews on the industry, despite opposition from the farming community. The Labour Party is acutely aware there has been, in real terms, a drop in farm income since the Tories took office.
>
> Such a situation cannot possibly continue. There must be a new and constructive policy for the industry which would give a fair return to the producer, farmer and farm worker, and provide, at the same time, food at reasonable prices to the consumer.

Peart had also earlier said that Labour's policy was to establish a prosperous industry. This began to have a hollow ring. The farmers took full-page advertisements in the national newspapers citing figures to show that in the decade 1955–65 manual workers' earnings had risen by 78 per cent, retail food

[5] Richard Crossman, *The Diaries of a Cabinet Minister 1964–66.*

prices had risen by 31 per cent and national productivity per man had risen by 3·2 per cent per annum, whereas farming productivity per man had gone up by 6 per cent per annum. During one period of these increases farmers' incomes (including subsidies) had actually fallen by 1½ per cent. In a debate in the House of Commons on 29 June 1964 George Brown had said, 'Our balance of payments problem would look absolutely impossible but for the tremendous expansion for which the industry is responsible,' and in the same debate Peart himself had said, 'Agriculture makes a major contribution to the economic growth of the country, and plays an important part in the solution of our balance of payments problems.' Another commentator said:[6] 'When the Labour Government returned to power it had the opportunity of winning support, even from Conservative farmers. This opportunity it has chosen to throw away.'

The Price Review had been announced on Wednesday 17 March; the following week-end the long knives were out. Shadow Chancellor of the Exchequer, Edward Heath, speaking at Butlin's Holiday Camp at Clacton-on-Sea, said, 'It is no wonder that farmers are hopping mad. They can now see how far they were led up the farmyard path by the Labour Party at the last Election.'

Lord Collison, then General Secretary of the NUAAW, speaking at Worcester, defended the Price Review because the previous year had seen a massive £25 million added to the farmers' returns. He emphasized that while farm prices had risen during the previous nine years by 45 per cent, the labour bill had gone up by only 14 per cent, and farmers' costs had gone up by only 37 per cent. There were few who defended poor Peart. One MP called it 'another fraud by the Prime Minister', and it was said widely that Peart had been sold down the river by savage attacks made on the farmers by the Prime Minister and by the Chancellor of the Exchequer, Callaghan.

In the Saffron Walden rural constituency in Essex the sitting Member, R. A. Butler, had chosen after the Tories' defeat to opt out of politics in favour of the academic life as Master of Trinity College, Cambridge. Peart was scheduled to be a speaker on the Monday evening. It provided an opportunity for six hundred farmers to swamp a meeting in Saffron Walden Town Hall which would normally have been attended by a dozen loyal (if ancient) Socialist supporters.

That evening in a pre-recorded *Panorama* Peart had faced ten farmers with arch interviewer Richard Dimbleby in the chair. Millions of viewers saw Peart get the bird as Sussex farmer Richard Denny pulled a live 3-week-old chicken from his coat pocket and handed it to Peart before the cameras. Another farmer set off to give live hens away to the Prime Minister, but ran into parking trouble and left the hens in a secret hideaway. The scene was certainly set for a dramatic display of anger by the farmers. In the ancient Market Square at Saffron Walden they burnt Peart's effigy, and the farmers inside the hall provided a hostile audience for him. He insisted that his Review was fair and generous; had he been sympathetic to the farmers' cause and apologetic for the 1965 Review he might

[6] *East Anglian Daily Times*, 20 March 1965.

have got away with it, but his trenchant defence of his actions angered the farmers, and he misinterpreted the nature of their complaints. The mistake was to think of farmers as political animals, whereas in reality they were only concerned with their own income levels, were isolationist in their pleas for a fair deal, and possibly insulated from many of the pressures of life by their rural habitat. The NFU and CLA had never, and will never, pursue a policy of allegiance to either of the main political parties. Peart called them Tories—and it didn't go down very well.

'Why', he asked, 'is it over the last eight years you haven't criticized worse situations? I will tell you; it is because you are here not as farmers, but as Tories. Abuse is no argument, and I know many progressive and sensible farmers welcome my Review. It was a Labour Government who gave you the 1947 Act. It was a Labour Government who refused to go into Europe at the expense of the British farmer.'

He concluded, 'I fully believe the farming industry with my Price Review and its long-term implications will have the opportunity to improve its income. It will benefit the young progressive farmer.' But the farmers didn't believe him. Two days later Saffron Walden went to the polls and returned Peter Kirk as its Member. In another by-election that same day the Conservatives lost a seat at Roxburgh, when a young Liberal won the seat. His name was David Steel.

The following Thursday (25 March) the House of Commons was in uproar as Peart came in to answer a barrage of questions; there had previously been a move to protect him by Labour MPs who had put down a large number of questions that afternoon in an attempt to shield Peart, and to prevent the Opposition Parties from making capital out of the crisis. Peart entered the Chamber smiling, a Conservative MP called 'Bring on the chickens', while a Labour MP retorted, 'You're chicken hearted!' The following week the Price Review Debate in the Commons was heralded by mass lobbying as farmers boarded trains from all over England to descend upon Westminster. The NFU President, Harold Woolley, was ill, and Williams took his place. The NFU launched a campaign, and asked for half a million pounds from the farmers. Harold Wilson invited the NFU leaders to dine at No. 10, and throughout the country tractors and placards formed processions. Drastic action in boycotting markets or withholding milk-supplies was talked about, and at Caxton Gibbet in Cambridgeshire an effigy of Peart was hung from the ancient gallows with the message 'Now cut this down, brother Peart'. A cow draped in black was led through Uckfield, in Sussex, and meetings were attended by well over a thousand farmers at a time. In April the farmers were still seething with anger, but the Price Review passed with a majority of six in the House of Commons, and with Peart roaming the country in an unrepentant mood the situation began to cool down. In any case, the spring weather had arrived, and farmers became too busy at home for mass demonstrations. In June Peart opened a new market at Ipswich, but a well-organized boycott by the farmers with their cattle reminded him that all was not forgiven.

Inflation was really recognized as an ogre in the 1970s; it is surprising how short our memories are. The NFU claimed that its costs had risen by £29 million in the year up to February 1965, but the following year estimated that they had gone up by £52 million. In Peart's fourth and last Price Review, a month before he left the Ministry in 1968, there had been cost increases in the year of £68·5 million. His Review in 1968 gave the farmers £52·5 million, which was a fivefold increase on his first tumultous Review three years earlier.

Peart was promoted to be Lord Privy Seal and Leader of the House of Commons. Six months later he became Lord President of the Council. Cledwyn Hughes had taken over.

After Wilson lost the 1970 Election Peart became the Shadow Minister, and with his reputation he became an influential spokesman for agriculture not only on the Opposition Benches but throughout the country. He remained in that position until February 1973, when Norman Buchan was given the job. Buchan had been a Joint Parliamentary Under-Secretary for Scotland with Special Responsibility for Agriculture in the pre-1970 Labour Government. He represented Renfrewshire West, a widely scattered rural constituency. This fiery Scotsman with the staccato speech did not succeed to the job as Minister when Labour returned to power. 'Shadows' have a habit of doing all the groundwork, and then in the final issue not getting the job. Godber had worked on farming indefatigably, and was snubbed by Heath when Prior was appointed in 1970. Other Shadows come and go, and when Labour returned to power it was Peart, who had been moved over to Shadow Defence, who became Minister of Agriculture again.

Buchan was appointed Minister of State under Peart in his second administration, but resigned after ten months on a clash of personalities. He was succeeded by a little-known MP, Edward Bishop, who had been the number three man at the Ministry. Bishop, an ex-aeronautical designer from Newark, was a Church Commissioner, and had been the Opposition Spokesman for Agriculture for a few months in 1970, but came directly from his position as Opposition Spokesman for Trade and Industry.

Peart came back into office in 1974, pledged to bring back farm subsidies, which had been largely phased out according to the rules for Britain's entry into the EEC. Labour were also pledged to renegotiate the terms, and in particular the Common Agricultural Policy. Food subsidies were to be introduced, Peart reversed the decline of ADAS, and 1974 proved once again to be a year of mass demonstrations and strife, as farmers brought out their tractors, their placards and their leaflet bombardments.

Within days of Wilson's return to power, he had set up Shirley Williams in a new Department of Consumer and Price Protection. She soon dispensed £150 million in food subsidies. Subsidies for cheese, subsidies for bread, subsidies for butter and subsidies for beef for old age pensioners. The subsidy system was back in force, but with a difference. It resulted now from the lack of cheap food to be found in the world, and on 26 April 1974 EEC Commissioner George Thomson addressed the Royal Commonwealth Society in London on this theme. He said:

> It is a modern myth to imagine there are great reservoirs of cheap New Zealand dairy
> produce, of cheap Canadian wheat, of cheap Caribbean sugar, and Australian produce
> ready to flood our supermarkets but blocked by the dam of Community Food Taxes.
> The world price of wheat more than doubled in 1973. Seventy-five per cent of New
> Zealand dairy produce now goes to more profitable markets elsewhere than Britain.
> New Zealand last year under-fulfilled its quota for butter to Britain by 21 per cent, and
> her cheese was about one-third under quota. Whatever the fluctuations in the future,
> Australia, Canada and New Zealand are not going to bind themselves to artificially
> low prices if they can get more on a world market.

Peart addressed the Farmers' Club in May, and told them the same story. He
emphasized that the agricultural industry would have to produce food at prices
consumers could afford to pay, but his insistence that farmers' prices should be
allied to consumer acceptance did nothing to mitigate the fears and worries of the
livestock producers present, and his emphasis upon 'reasonable' prices did not
help to allay the fears that livestock producers were undergoing at the time.
Peart brought in a subsidy on oil for glasshouse producers, and backdated it to 1
January. This was a token gesture to mitigate the worst effects of the Middle East
oil crisis which had pushed up fuel prices, and he instituted a 50p per score
subsidy for pig-producers. But the livestock sector of British farming was in deep
trouble, and he was unable to get them out of it. The 1965 campaign had been
about the under-recoupment of costs, and was largely a battle over the price of
milk. 1974 was inflamed by troubles in beet, pigs and eggs, but the target this time
was the imports that were spoiling the farmers' market. Milk was also in trouble,
and there were threats that the cut-back in production would lead to rationing. In
the event this did not happen, but the whole Pandora's Box added up to an
unfortunate situation for Peart's return. This time, however, he was not the
target of the farmers' wrath. Strangely, there was no massive attack upon Europe
either. While the NFU had been against entry originally, they had supported it
under Heath, and were to do so again in the Referendum. Peart had also been an
anti-marketeer, but had modified his views to a passive acceptance, with the
proviso that while the CAP was not perfect, it was re-negotiable and could be a
useful tool, provided nationalistic policies could be invoked from time to give
sectionalized support in times of crisis. It was a philosophy with which the NFU
agreed. Both farmers and their Minister were on the same side. Peart had learnt
how to handle the farmers.

It was not, however, roses all the way. On his appointment the *Farmers
Weekly*[7] had said:

> Fred Peart's recall to the Ministry of Agriculture puts direction of policy in the hands
> of a man who has worked closely with the industry in an earlier term. As he is a senior
> figure in the Labour hierarchy, farming's hope must be that his selection signals the
> new Government's appreciation of his Department's responsible role and the immense
> productive potential which it can tap in the national interest.

[7] 8 March 1974.

Thus was he welcomed as a politician of considerable strength who with his vast experience would provide a champion for farmers. However, three weeks later[8] the *Farmers Weekly* again wrote:

> Minister of Food, Mr Fred Peart, dealt farming a foul blow at the Common Market Price Review when he ripped market support from under the feet of beef producers. Large investments by market-minded farmers have been turned into gamblers' throws.
> If you sell when the market is high, you win. If you buy calves when the market is high—sorry, but you lose. Name of the game is Peart's Roulette.

Whereas in 1964 Peart had seen the heavy guns of the Cabinet ranged against him, in 1974 it was different. Callaghan, now Foreign Secretary, and with a farm of his own in Sussex, fought for the protection of British farmers in the battles at Brussels, and Wilson was dragged into the act when a letter from Heath drew attention to the state of the country's meat supplies and the difficulties of livestock farmers. At least with the ex-Prime Minister and the new Prime Minister exchanging letters on the farmers' problems the matter could be said to be occupying the highest authorities in the land!

1974 passed, and Peart settled down to re-negotiate the CAP, and to prove a farmer's champion. In February 1975 Peter Bullen in the *Financial Times* wrote:

> It is charm and cheerfulness rather than unremitting intellectual cut and thrust that have brought him success in the EEC Council of Ministers, friendships on all sides of the House of Commons, and the appreciation of his Civil Servants. Even disgruntled farmers find it hard to dislike him, and that is no mean achievement.

Wilson made his surprise resignation announcement on 16 March 1976, and when Callaghan re-formed his Government in April Peart remained as the Minister of Agriculture. During the summer months rumours of his impending departure continued to circulate, but at the same time it was widely known that 'Fred' (as he had become known) wanted to equal Tom Williams's length of service. It would be 10 December when this magical date arrived, so it was said. However, other factors were coming into play, and in September before Parliament returned from the Summer Recess, Callaghan announced a Government reshuffle.

Anthony Crosland as Foreign Secretary had died in office. Roy Jenkins at the Home Office was resigning to take up the Presidency of the EEC in January 1977, and on that date also it was Britain's turn for her Minister of Agriculture to take over a six-month stint as President of the EEC Council of Agriculture Ministers. It would have been unfair to have had a new man in both EEC positions at the same time. Peart left the Ministry to become Lord Peart, and Leader of the House of Lords. His reign at Agriculture was over. In the rash of by-elections Jenkins's Stetchford seat and Peart's Workington one both went Tory in the wave of anti-Socialism that was sweeping the country; only Crosland's Grimsby seat was narrowly held by a TV personality.

Peart's departure—which appeared to be his final departure—was recorded in

[8] 29 March 1974.

the farming press. Said Diane Montague:[9]

> The generality of farmers and traders in the industry, whom Fred Peart has so often
> had to disappoint because of political pressures, may be surprised to learn that most of
> those who have worked closer to him regard him as one of the best Ministers of
> Agriculture we have ever had.
>
> For the second time, Fred Peart is succeeded by a lawyer with no knowledge of the
> farming industry. One can only hope that the second time will be more successful than
> the first.

John Cherrington summed it up in *The Financial Times*[10]:

> When first made Minister, he claimed to be a pragmatist, and this quality was
> demonstrated in his negotiations with fellow Ministers in Brussels.
>
> One could not credit him with any knowledge of the science, practice or business of
> farming. His contribution has been an uncritical, and possibly too trusting support of
> his Civil Servants, and an absolute loyalty to Cabinet decisions. He has, though, it is
> believed, put farming's case very strongly in Cabinet, and has always been accessible to
> advice from Sir Henry Plumb and other farm leaders.

Cherrington concluded:

> But Fred Peart leaves farming as the second most popular Minister since Tom
> Williams. For much the same reasons—because farmers don't believe in shooting at a
> Minister who, like the pianist, is doing his best.

Whatever the reasons for Peart's removal from office, and its timing—and the
coming Presidency of the EEC Agriculture Ministers must have been a prime
reason—he had endeared himself to the farming community and become the
farmers' friend. Geoffrey Rumsey[11] thought he had become too much of a friend:

> The education job done on Fred Peart over the years by the NFU was probably the
> main reason for his sudden removal from the job, in that he appeared to be growing
> over-fond of his farming hat at a time when the food head-piece is fashionable at
> Cabinet level.

James Prior

> *'He has a comfortable porcine look, red face and white hair, and walks into a
> room as if it were a field.'*
>
> 'The New Anatomy of Britain' (Sampson, 1971).

> *'His evangelical upbringing survives in him as an ethical if not as a doctrinal
> force. His spending habits, like his habits or thought, remain much more those
> of the professional than the land-owning classes; he wears a Marks and
> Spencers mackintosh, drives an Austin-Allegro.'*
>
> John Whale, 'The Sunday Times', 22 May 1977.

Prior was at the Ministry for twenty-nine months, from June 1970 to November

[9] *Agricultural Supply Industry*, 17 September 1976.
[10] 15 September 1976.
[11] *Arable Farming*, October 1976.

1972. He came in as a new broom; he became known as 'Honest Jim'; he behaved like a bull in a china shop, and brought a refreshing breath of air to his job; he pulled no punches, and asked for no quarter. In the end the farmers gave him none. Tied to the star of his mentor Heath, he rose with his master, echoed his voice, but did not sink with him in the end. The reverberations he set up in the corridors of Whitehall still make the permanent officials break into a cold sweat, and his translation to higher things was greeted with relief by the farmers also.

Peart later tried to reverse some of Prior's actions, but things were never to be the same again. The end of the Price Review system, the mainstay of farming politics and policies since 1947, was the end of an era; now Brussels called the tune. Peart had started badly, but eventually went out lamented; Prior started bountifully, and thereafter declined. His initial panache appealed to the farmers, but the proof of the pudding was in the cash register, and he unfortunately left office just before both the land and grain booms put big money into farmers' pockets. The sad thing was that Prior gave the farmers what they wanted, was probably the most pro-farmer of all the Ministers, but in the end provided a mixture too strong for farmers' stomachs; such is gratitude.

When the new Prime Minister forms his Government there are hectic days of wheeling and dealing, jostling for position, private secretaries making urgent telephone calls, balancing the left and right of the Party; old and tried friends are often discarded, and placated, and faithful Shadows do not always get the Department they have been shadowing. A new Government is a complete new spectrum, and sometimes all is formulated in a matter of hours. Nevertheless, there was much surprise when Ted Heath announced the appointment of the then unknown, and certainly untried, Jim Prior as Minister of Agriculture. This had every appearance of being an appointment in gratitude for Prior's service to Heath as Parliamentary Private Secretary, friend and confidant in the years of Opposition. Prior stood by him, and thus was rewarded.

But Joe Godber had been travelling about, hawking new ideas at NFU Meetings and on public platforms. He had evolved new and radical policies which were taking some selling to the farming community, but by his patient honesty he had become accepted as the only possible choice for Minister of Agriculture when the Tories returned to power. It had seemed a foregone conclusion. Not only had he been Shadow Minister for nearly five years, but he had strong connections with the agricultural scene. His brother was elected Vice-Chairman of the Farmers Club in December 1969, with the expectation that he would become the Chairman a year later. Said his proposer in 1969, Jim Eve, 'I only hope that when he duly succeeds to office he will have the pleasure of welcoming his brother here as Minister of Agriculture.' It was more than a foregone conclusion. It was a certainty. But Prior got the job and a Cabinet seat, coming straight from the back benches without previous experience. Prior was forty-three, and the second youngest Cabinet Minister in the Heath Government. Peter Walker at thirty-eight was the youngest. But at least Prior was a farmer.

Some politicians buy farms, and some farmers become politicians. Prior belonged to the latter group; he described his advent into farming:[12]

> In between the wars, my father was a country lawyer, and he became Official Receiver in Bankruptcy for the County of Norfolk. As a small boy, in the early thirties, I used to go round with my father and visit some of his clients, although at that time, and for many years afterwards, I thought that there were an enormous number of bankruptcies in Norfolk during the Depression. There were in fact comparatively few; but those that there were certainly made a marked impression upon me, and an even greater impression upon my father, who did his utmost to see that his son should never farm.

Prior continued that if it had not been for the fact that he first of all decided he wanted to become a Land Agent, and then decided to go into politics, he would never have been a farmer. He managed the farm of John Hill, near Southwold on the East Anglian coast. Hill stood for Parliament, and Prior made some speeches to help him. He was elected, and when Prior suggested that he also wanted to embark upon a political career Hill replied, 'One politician on the farm is enough—you had better go and find somewhere else.' Prior left, bought his own farm, and said, 'It was the best day's work I ever did.'

Prior entered Parliament during Macmillan's successful election in 1959, winning for the Conservatives the Lowestoft seat from a Socialist Member, and narrowly escaped losing his seat in the Wilson sweeping victory of 1966. His appointment as Heath's Private Secretary was a balancing act recommended by the Chief Whip, William Whitelaw, who said that Heath would look better if he was flanked by a farmer. It worked, and they became close friends.

Prior had a 150-hectare Brampton Farm in his Lowestoft constituency, with cereals, peas for processing and pigs and beef. Later his own herd was to be slaughtered after it failed its brucellosis test; this sort of thing gave him an intimate knowledge of farming affairs, and made the farmers feel that the Minister was one of them. A few weeks after his appointment he invited the Press to see him driving his own combine; it was a public relations exercise in the best tradition, but caused some ribald comments when the photographs appeared with Prior wearing an Establishment tie and with neatly pressed trousers. But he seemed a colossus in the farming scene in comparison with his predecessors. When he addressed the traditional meeting with the Farmers Club in London he was able to sit on the platform without his Civil Service Chief for support. Hughes only two years earlier had whispered to his adviser to find the answer to every question; not so Jim Prior, who glanced confidently at the audience and smiled at familiar faces. He wise-cracked his way with bonhomie and familiarity.

To Wallace Day he quipped, 'I welcome your reappearance in agricultural politics'; to John Cherrington: 'We are all entitled to ride our own hobby horses', and to recall being questioned as an undergraduate by Frank Garner, sometime Principal of the Royal Agricultural College. His courage in making unpopular remarks and his obvious mastery of the problems gave the farmers confidence that here was a real champion, even if the future was going to be somewhat different from the past.

[12.]Speech to the Farmers Club, 16 December 1970.

The Heath Government was wedded to the philosophy that actions without too many words was the best policy, if only in contrast to the flamboyance of Wilson. Few Ministers were given rope to make provocative speeches or hit the headlines. A 'quiet' period of Government was heralded, but out of this four Ministers did come quickly to prominence. Robert Carr became involved with strike settlements and the Industrial Relations Bill. Peter Walker as a colourful and youthful Minister in charge of the multifarious Department of the Environment caught the public eye, Margaret Thatcher withdrew the free milk from most sections of schoolchildren, and was dubbed 'Margaret Thatcher—milk snatcher', and as food prices suddenly escalated Jim Prior became a national figure on the TV screen. He found himself at the centre of a storm not of his own making, but as a forthright and outspoken man in a silent regime, the new hounds latched upon his every pronouncement. The quotation at the head of this section describes him walking into a room as if it were a field, and he went into the Ministry like a whirlwind. If Godber's policies were radical, then Prior's were revolutionary.

The Report on the reorganization of NAAS landed on his desk, and ADAS was created overnight. He then announced cuts in its staff, and later introduced charges for some of the services which had been free. The Northern Pennines Rural Development Board was quickly wound up; it had been established in 1969 under Peart's 1967 Agriculture Act, and covered some 7,800 square kilometres of the Pennine areas, with the task of dealing with the special problems and needs of rural areas of hills and uplands. The old successors of the 'War Ags' were abolished, and four hundred Committees went with them. Regional Panels were set up. Prior turned down an eighty-clause Bill which his civil servants had prepared for the control of pesticides. Less legislation and not more was his Tory philosophy, and the voluntary system which was working previously still operates. He cut his own élite assistants in the Ministry, having one political assistant, Tony Stodart, instead of the normal two. Including his PPS, his total team of three MPs contrasted with the five MPs at the Ministry under the previous Administration. With all his emphasis on change, he managed with a smaller team, and remarked in honesty and without rancour, referring to his predecessors, 'I can't understand what they all did.' He waltzed through a mountain of traditional Whitehall red tape, and left behind him an unusual calm instead of the chaos which was predicted.

But it was in the field of farming politics where the realities of life lay. Prior had promised 'expansion—right across the board', and it was a remark which led him into trouble later. The Farmers Union of Wales took him literally, and suggested a 10 per cent increase 'across the board' on all farm products. Prior was in an expansionist mood, and at the Treasury Tony Barber was printing money, and boosting the economy as fast as he could go. The expansion policy was seized upon by farmers with glee, but in the last months of Hughes there had been massive inflation of costs, and the farmers were losing out again.

As the campaign for the 1971 Price Review gained an impetus which with a new Government stood some chance of success, Prior jumped in unexpectedly with an interim Review (something quite unheard of) when he added £58 million to farmers' 'guarantees' in October 1970, just a few months after taking office. His high-flying methods took the farmers and the NFU by surprise, but they were not as surprised as the NFU Council, sitting in solemn conclave at Knights-bridge, when the new, intrepid Minister of Agriculture arrived almost un-heralded to speak to them. It was an unprecedented step.

But costs for farmers were still rising rapidly, and the 1971 Review showed an increase of £140 million since the previous year; it contrasted starkly with the £29 million increase which Peart had found so troublesome only six years previously. Prior gained for the farmers £84 million, which made a total of £138 million. Even the *Farmers Weekly*[13] was moved to comment:

> The real battle of the Price Review does not take place between the Ministry of Agriculture and the farmer's team. The decisive action—the shedding of blood, sweat and tears—takes place when a determined Minister of Agriculture, pushing his industry's case to the limit, twists the arm of a tight-fisted Exchequer, and gets some spending money.
>
> Against a hard-line Chancellor who misses no opportunity to trim public spending, Mr. Prior does not seem to have done too badly.

He was in short the farmers' hero. The following year costs had risen by £48 million, and the Review announced increases of £72 million. It was a real boost to farmers' incomes, but Prior's flair for cutting through officialdom was once more displayed in the bizarre manipulations of the announcement of the 1972 Review.

While the matter was largely settled, with only a few details to work out and the traditional White Paper to print, the news of the settlement leaked out. Prior took the bull by the horns, rushed down to the House of Commons, and announced his Review two weeks earlier than scheduled. He could not see why something of such great importance to farmers should be kept under wraps.

'Get your return from the market' was his cry, as he stamped the country, preparing farmers for life under the CAP. Farmers had long agitated that the consumer should pay the proper price for his or her food; they disliked the term 'subsidy', and here was a man promising them a realistic price from the market-place. Yet they had been cosseted by guarantees for nearly a quarter of a century, and the harsh jungle of free competitive enterprise was unknown to many of them. Prior was advocating the high old-fashioned Toryism, and it was now outdated. Far from relishing the cut and thrust of market forces, the farmers (who had voluntarily given up certain freedoms in 1947 for the safety of the guaranteed prices and deficiency payments system) were reluctant to turn their backs and face the unknown world of darkness, or to leave behind the safety which they had built into their affairs for a long time. It was a brave policy, but it misfired.

In April 1972 a Cabinet reshuffle created an additional post of 'Minister of

[13] 19 March 1971.

State' at Agriculture, and Tony Stodart filled this position. A farmer himself, with 320 hectares in East Lothian, at around the 300-metre level, growing cereals and producing lambs, he was an ideal companion to Prior, and like his boss was a farmer long before he became a politician. His post was taken by an ex-smallholder, who had been milking cows regularly eight years previously—Peter Mills, an MP for Torrington in Devon, but then in partnership with his brother, with 110 Ayrshire cows on 144 hectares near Sherborne in Dorset. There was now at the Ministry a team of three farmers. But Prior had been given the job of Deputy Chairman of the Conservative Party, and with two strong men to look after the 'Agriculture' side of the Ministry, his task was leaning towards the 'Food' angle. In that month his star was beginning to fall, despite his favourable Price Review, and his obvious sympathy with farmers, but the reduction of the Farm Advisory Service was less popular than he had imagined, and those remaining shuddered in their shoes with trepidation for the next axe to swing. In November Prior left Agriculture to become Leader of the Commons, and belatedly Godber got the job for which he had shadowed for so long.

After the Heath Government was defeated, and after the maestro himself had been ejected by his fellow MPs, Prior allowed his name to go forward in the battle for the leadership. He collected nineteen votes, and came a very bad third, far behind Margaret Thatcher and William Whitelaw. He admitted afterwards that it was a mistake, but although nothing is certain in politics, and the most unlikely events sometimes transpire, it would seem that as no Minister of Agriculture has yet been elevated to the Premiership, then Jim Prior stands as good a chance as any—but time alone will tell.

Joseph Godber—Big Joe

> *'Compared with Jim Prior's cheery façade, and somewhat (one suspects sometimes deliberate) indiscreet asides, Joe Godber doesn't smile much, and has the thoughtful air of a city banker.*
>
> *Perhaps the breezy air of the Suffolk coast brought out more of the Regency buck in Jim Prior, while Joe Godber's personality has been subdued by the calmer atmosphere of his native Bedfordshire.'*
>
> Graham Rose, 'Modern Farmer', March 1973.

Tearaway Jim was followed by 'honest Joe', and with typically British aplomb Godber was welcomed as the steady older man who had been cast aside in favour of the bright young lad from Suffolk. His eventual succession was welcomed as British Justice. Godber had spent five years working out the new Tory policy, and the technicalities of phasing out the subsidy system, while phasing in the EEC levies. Prior had come along and pinched the headlines; now the hard-slogging architect was being drafted back to pick up the pieces. It was also a just tribute to a man whose roots were in farming, and whose political loyalty had been exemplary. It was to be his last Ministerial role.

Godber took over on Guy Fawkes Day, 1972, and was summarily ejected from office on 28 February 1974, when Heath lost the General Election. He had served in several minor Ministerial capacities at the Foreign Office, as Secretary of State for War for a brief period in 1963, and in October of that year was appointed Minister of Labour in the Cabinet formed by Sir Alec Douglas-Home. His first major appointment had been as Joint Parliamentary Secretary to the MAFF in 1957. Godber's roots had been in the Bedfordshire farming scene, and although he was elected an MP for Grantham (Mrs Thatcher's home town) in 1951, he had still retained an active working interest in the family farming and horticultural business until 1958.

Cast in a vastly different mould to Prior, Godber came from a family where his father had used a legacy in 1910 to buy a house and land at Willington, near Bedford. Four years later Joseph was born, but Isaac Godber had six sons and one daughter. They were a remarkable family. Each was brilliantly successful in his chosen career, and each had gone to the top of his own tree.

Joe apart, his brother George (now Sir George) became the Government Chief Medical Officer; brother Geoffrey became Chief Executive of the new West Sussex County Council after the reorganization of local government. Will was Chairman of the Farmers Club, Chairman of the Governors of Shuttleworth College, and received a CBE for his services to agriculture. Frank won the DFC as an RAF fighter pilot in the war, and followed this with a key job in the Meteorological Service. The last brother, John, made his fortune from the rubber plantations in Malaya, and retired at the age of forty-eight. Neither was their sister idle. Joyce was County Archivist of Bedfordshire until she retired in 1968. Joseph has two sons, and the family horticultural business is in good hands.

Godber lives in the haunted house which his father bought in 1910, and where he was born. With his urbane looks and his white hair, this tall but slightly stooping man always appeared older than his years. His style was low-key, but when he said that he was deeply concerned you knew he meant it, and had confidence in this solid man. He exuded an air of technical efficiency, but expressed his views in a deadpan manner—as a duty. These solid qualities were ideal for the transition into Europe, and as a negotiator he could be tough. The outstanding impression was of a man who would never jump into a thing until he had carefully weighed up all the pros and cons, and run the whole deal through a computer first.

As Godber came into office Britain went into the Common Market, and in the first Farm Review (1973) in which Britain was no longer master of her own fate he had the difficult task of negotiating the Annual Price Review with the farming leaders in London, all the time knowing that it might not be ratified by the EEC Commissioners in Brussels. It was also a year of quite fantastic increases in farm costs; some £217 million in one year, although with inflation running riot the increase was to be an unprecedented £600 million the following year.

Food prices in the shops were spiralling madly too, and Heath, the architect and passionate advocate of Britain's entry into Europe, was determined these increases should not be blamed upon our new European allegiance. In many ways Heath was unfortunate; the Russians had upset the world grain markets with massive purchases which had wiped out the stockpile of grain held in the United States for twenty-five years. Prices had rocketed, and British cereal farmers were on the crest of a wave. Some even admitted, 'It seems almost immoral to accept so much money.'

Godber's task was to cut the limits of the proposed EEC 1973 rises, and he also had to support British farmers. His first Review was hailed as a victory for the British housewife, and a defeat for the farmer; he came under attack from NFU Branches, but it was a pretty low-key affair. The farmers made protesting noises, these were muted.

Godber was Minister for only sixteen months, and his second Price Review in 1974 took place while the General Election campaign was under way. In the event he secured for British dairy farmers an increase of 5p per gallon, when the EEC calculated limit had been only 1·5p. It taught the useful lesson that Common Market rules were made for breaking. The farmers respected his efforts to do his best for them—although he did reduce the capital grants on farm buildings, much to the chagrin of the CLA, and he did withdraw the beef guarantee. It was perhaps fortunate in some ways that Heath lost the Election, and Godber lost his job. He went out a respected man, and Peart came in to face the 1974 demonstrations and troubles.

Godber had been snubbed when he was not appointed Minister in 1970, and he was snubbed again when he was omitted from the list of Shadow Ministers by Heath. Twice snubbed was enough, and he opted for the world of directorships and big business, becoming a director of Booker McConnells, the sugar company with Caribbean interests. He also accepted a consultancy post with the Beecham Group; because of its food interests he was a useful acquisition.

John Silkin

'Our prime weakness as a industry today, therefore, must be the man appointed as our advocate. Determined to make a name for himself by making his contribution to the lowering of the cost of living at the expense of the agricultural industry. . . . Our Minister of Agriculture is the most potent recipe for disaster that we have seen for a very long time.'
                    J. Thorley, National Sheep Association, 23 February 1977.

With Tory Governments and the Tory Party in general, there is usually an heir-apparent to the Agriculture Ministry. The Tories have plenty of rural members with farming interests, although the heir-apparent does not always succeed to the throne as often as might be expected. But in the Labour Party there is a greater problem finding a new Minister with any modicum of knowledge about farming at all. When Peart went to the Lords this void became apparent, but such also are the vagaries of political promotion that if a man is a loyal party member, whether of the Left or the Right, as well as a host of other pressures, determines the choice. The Prime Minister's power of patronage is not always as great as would appear. A lawyer by vocation, a left-wing Tribunite with strong anti-Market feelings, but the son of a Socialist stalwart who had been Minister of Town and Country Planning from 1945 to 1950, was the architect of the Town and Country Planning Acts 1947, and later became Lord Silkin. He had two sons. Sam became Attorney-General in the Wilson Government, and John, having contested three General Elections before finally making it to the House of Commons, became Minister of Agriculture. He had occupied the position held by his father with special responsibilities for land, and had been reappointed by Callaghan in April 1976. Silkin came in as a new Minister with less knowledge of farming than any other Minister since Fred Peart himself twelve years earlier.

With the Referendum firmly behind Britain, and the Government committed to making the best of whatever sort of job they thought it was, the choice of Silkin with his violent anti-Market views was strange. Peart had become a tepid Marketeer, but was determined to make it work. Silkin was committed to its abolition. While Callaghan himself could not as Prime Minister advocate Britain withdrawing from the Market, he could put many spanners in the works in a subtle, underhand way that would discredit the EEC, and in particular the CAP. But Silkin came into office with another problem facing the farmers.

He became Minister on 10 September 1976, when the 1976 'Drought of the Century' was still in full spate. The countryside was burnt up with relentless sun, blue skies followed each other day after day, and rain had become a distant memory. The New Forest was burning, water-rationing was in force, and a 'Minister for the Drought' had been appointed. The weather has always affected farmers' fortunes more than those of politicians, and this was no exception, but it gave the political animal Silkin a taste of the simple, if intractable, problems which faced farmers. The effects of the drought upon farming were serious, and Peart had been photographed in arid East Anglia, standing in a parched field. There was little Silkin could do, and it was an inauspicious start.

Another, deeper, problem was worrying farmers. This was the disparity between the EEC price-levels and the way these were translated into sterling, with a massive devaluation taking place all the time. The farmers had been promised that the transition to the higher EEC price-levels would be accomplished over a five-year period, and this was the fourth. But the ogre of the 'green pound' had widened the gap by over 30 per cent, working adversely on farmers' returns. They had been agitating for a revaluation of sterling, and the Irish actually did it. Silkin, however, proved quite inflexible. He maintained that farmers were not being seriously affected, that there was contradiction in the industry itself, and that it would not assist every farmer. Said Silkin[14]:

> This is not a question of the producer versus the consumer, much as some people would like to say. It is really a question for the whole nation.

[14] Speaking at the Farmers Club, 8 December 1976.

As far as the farmer is concerned, devaluation of the green pound has surprisingly contradictory effects. It would mean higher returns on some commodities, but it would also mean higher costs, and therefore lower returns on others—for example, our Christmas turkey. And in some areas of farming and horticulture the green pound would have no effect whatsoever. What we can be sure of, however, is that it would have an effect upon the cost of living, and incidentally, higher prices can mean a lower consumption of food. We all remember how in 1974 the shortage of sugar put up the price to the housewife, and consumption has never fully recovered since; and the high level of potato prices at the beginning of this year cut the consumption of potatoes by 25%.

His adamant refusal to devalue the green pound was understandable. The EEC was forking out £1·5 million per day as a hidden food-subsidy for the British housewife, and for the British cost of living. The farmers could be upset with impunity when the whole nation was manipulating EEC procedures to such good effect.

But more dramatic events were to take place, and it involved a heavy defeat for the Callaghan Government, which was in any case only surviving as a minority Government with the support of the Lib-Lab Pact.

The background to the events started earlier, and although Silkin was adamantly refusing to devalue the green pound, he did make a strange request to the Farmers Club in autumn 1977 for a platform for a major policy speech in early January. Some cynics observed that perhaps he could not get himself invited to talk to farmers, so he had to make the request himself; in any case, it was an unprecedented move. The Farmers Club preserves its integrity and independence by inviting successive Ministers to address it after taking office. No Minister, unless reappointed after a gap, had ever spoken twice, but Silkin's request was agreed, and a date fixed for 18 January 1978. Notices went out, and in early January Silkin changed the date to one week earlier (11 January). There was speculation about this, but the loyalists of the farming community, some 400 of them, passed dutifully through the dusty portals of the National Liberal Club in Whitehall Court on 11 January.

The major policy speech proved to be a hollow threat; why he requested this platform, why the Farmers Club agreed, and why so many farmers took the trouble to attend remains a mystery. It was a non-event, apart from a motion put from the floor by an erstwhile Socialist and Labour candidate, West Country farmer, Frank Paton, who demanded the resignation of the Minister, which with suitable decorum was neatly sidetracked by the Chairman, Fountain Farming managing director Anthony Rosen.

But things were moving nevertheless.

On the following day in the House of Commons, in reply to a modest and almost unnoticed question from a back bencher, Silkin announced that he would apply to the Ministers of the EEC for a 5 per cent devaluation of the green pound. There was a projected debate in the House of Commons on this matter on 23 January, and since the NFU Annual General Meeting would be assembling in

The NUAAW's inauspicious and anonymous HQ in Gray's Inn Road, in a less fashionable part of London. The 'No Entry' sign is on a post, and not on the building!
Photo National Union of Agricultural and Allied Workers

16 Belgrave Square. The elegant London home of the Country Landowners Association
Photo Country Landowners Association

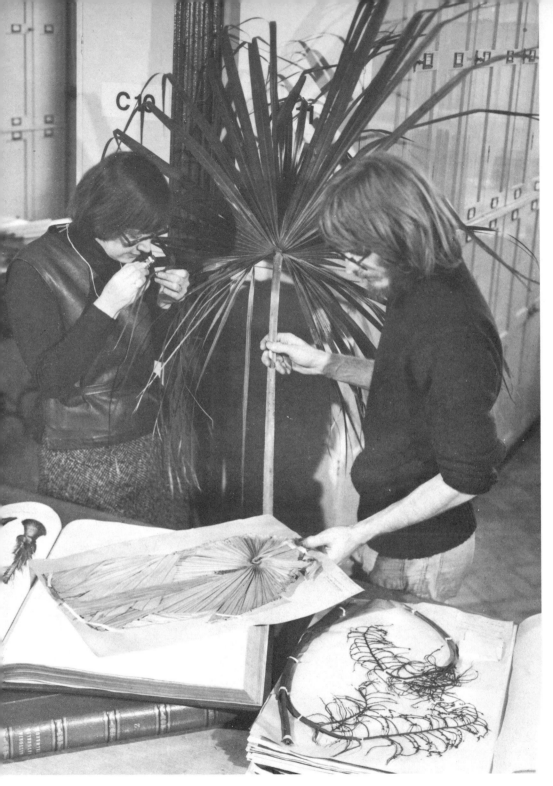

Kew Gardens is an important botanical centre, part of the Ministry of Agriculture.
Here two research workers are busy on rare botanical specimens
Photo Ministry of Agriculture. Crown copyright reserved

London on the following day and listening to a speech from Mrs Margaret Thatcher at its Annual Dinner that night, it appeared that farming was to be subjected to a timetable of political manoeuvring.

Margaret Thatcher spent the weekend on her brother-in-law's farm near Harwich in Essex, and was photographed wearing muddy boots, tramping across a yard and driving a tractor. Callaghan went to his own Sussex farm without photographers. On the Monday, it was doubtful, even before the Commons Debate, if the Government proposal for a 5 per cent devaluation would succeed. The naughty Liberals wanted 10 per cent, and the Conservatives 7 per cent, and with the other fringe parties voting against the Government it proved in the end to be a defeat by 11 votes (291–280), when Members rejected the Government motion. The Tories were labelled as the party of dear food for hard-pressed pensioners, and the Government made political capital out of their defeat. But for the farmers it was a triumph of many months of patient propaganda and pressure. The following evening should have been a pleasant occasion at the NFU Dinner at the London Hilton. With the Leader of the Opposition coming there after a triumphant Governmental defeat, she could have wooed the farmers into the Tory camp for life. In the event, the meeting earlier in the day had still castigated all political parties for not doing enough to alleviate the wide discrepancy between European and UK farmers' incomes. Mrs Thatcher's evening speech was a political harangue which went down badly with the assembled farmers. They were bored at the petty bickerings of politicians, and still wanted a realistic approach to the promises that had been given when Britain joined the EEC five years earlier.

Silkin thus lowered his reputation with the farmers by shaking hands with one hand and hitting them with the other hand. He did help somewhat on the drought, hint broadly that 'averaging' farmers' income over a three-year period would be a helpful action—if he could persuade the Treasury to this line of thinking. Healey's 1978 (and thirteenth) budget broke new tax ground by introducing a two-year averaging of farmers' incomes if there was more than a 30 per cent fluctuation—Silkin claimed the credit and said, 'this reform is one to which I have been personally committed since I became Minister of Agriculture'. He acted unilaterally to give hard-pressed pig farmers a 50p per score subsidy which was later declared illegal by the EEC, and withdrawn. He inflamed farmers by asking them to 'sacrifice'; the sacrifice was to moderate their demands for higher prices. As president of the European Council of Agriculture Ministers, the annual Farm Talks were conducted by the Parliamentary Secretary, Gavin Strang, with Silkin in the Chair.

There was such a low ebb of confidence among the farmers, who thought that the pressure of bringing down food prices was paramount in the Government's policies, and would bring ruin to the farms, that Strang was forced to make a statement at Reading[15] to the effect that farming was not being forgotten. Silkin

[15] 9 March 1977.

had met the farmers in Shropshire and Worcestershire, and had been listened to courteously. He went to Smithfield Market, where the meat traders and porters banged and waved their cleavers in anger.

A Communist millionaire sold off much of the European butter surplus to the Russians, and Jenkins, now the Commission President, suspended sales to Eastern Europe overnight. Silkin, like many other Ministers before him, found that the pressures were of inflation, spiralling food prices, loss of money by farmers. It is a permanent problem which has plagued farm Ministers as well as farmers.

The Cabinet salary list is restricted to seventeen, but Callaghan had nineteen members. Millionaire Harold Lever and well-heeled Silkin volunteered to forgo their £16,000 salaries and worked on an MP's £6,270 plus £3,500 secretarial allowance. Even this was criticized by Tory Peter Walker[16] who said that since Silkin was not working for British farmers but for the Irish and Danes it was they who should pay his salary.

Conclusion

One senior civil servant at the MAFF, who worked under ten different Ministers in his time, confided (anonymously, of course) that he preferred working under a Tory Minister rather than under a Socialist, because the Tories knew precisely what they wanted to do. Labour relied more heavily upon the established staff, and since civil servants are trained to carry out orders, not issue them, his point of view was understandable.

History is a harsh judge, and the two most misjudged Ministers are probably Soames and Prior, who fought determinedly in the Cabinet for the farmers. Yet it is Williams and Peart, the two major Socialist Ministers in the post-War period, who have received the accolade of success, and maybe immortality. Popularity with the customers in the shops often means conflict with regard to farmers' prices, and the divergence between the agricultural and food interests makes the job a dexterous dance along a swaying tightrope.

It is a job which involves, as no other Ministerial brief does, a direct and personal confrontation with the industry, and the Minister of Agriculture makes more speeches, attends more luncheons and dinners, opens more shows, attends more markets, presents more cups, pins on more rosettes, and travels the nation with a fuller diary, than does any of his Cabinet colleagues. It keeps him in very personal touch with his customers.

Since the advent of the EEC he has become a more important figure in the Government hierarchy, and is seen on TV more than was the case a decade earlier. As a household name, the Minister of Agriculture would now be recognized by more people, more quickly, than was the case ten years ago. Food prices, and more importantly food-supplies, figure highly in the national priority

[16] 3 January 1978.

list. It is a far cry from the debate when Gladstone would only agree to the establishment of a Board of Agriculture if the clause to include its President in the Cabinet was dropped.

Either way, in a nation that is heavily urban weighted, where farming has only a low place in the Ministerial pecking order, and not even always a Minister in the Cabinet, it would nevertheless seem that as Ministers come and go they have become more involved than mere figureheads. In this job they have little chance to cogitate in their ivory tower in Whitehall.

Since the Minister is the transient head of the policy-making side of the industry, he has the power to set the political and financial climate, but he cannot control the weather yet. Some individual farmers will always do better than others, and past Price Reviews have often seemed to be 'up corn—down horn' or vice versa. The divisions within the industry itself make a cohesive policy difficult, and with the added complexity of equating the production levels for the whole of Europe, with its consumer demands, there will inevitably be surpluses, or even shortages. The elements will always ensure that nothing is certain until it is safely in the barn.

How real, then, is the Minister's effective power to control events, or to use the carrot as opposed to the stick, and to switch the emphasis from one commodity to another—particularly as Ministers and Governments can go much more quickly than does the farming season? It takes two or three years before a change of direction can transmit itself into lower or increased production.

Within the collective responsibility of the Cabinet, it would appear that the nation's food supplies are more important than farmers' incomes.

Part 3

The Structure and Importance

18 The Structure and Importance

'The best business you can go into, you will find on your father's farm or in his workshop.'

Horace Greeley.

Farming was once described as a way of life; today it is a business, and agriculture is one of Britain's many industries—the largest, with an output in excess of the car industry and the coal-mines added together. As such it is big business, and as individuals many farmers may have an annual turnover of £250,000. Thus while the practical expertise of milking cows or driving a tractor is an essential ingredient for success in an industry with only one full-time worker for every employer, nevertheless financial acumen is also a requisite for the modern agrobusinessman.

There is, of course, a wide diversity between the scope and scale of individual farmers, and of individual farms, and one can only talk about 'The National Farm' in the sense of an average, for making comparisons with other industries or with other countries. The net conclusions to be drawn from any such comparisons must be that British agriculture is more productive than the remainder of British industry, is faster in its projection of new ideas, is more important than most people think, is much larger and more mechanized than the agriculture of most other European countries, and can stand aloft as a shining example, even in a world context.

Yet British farming is tiny in comparison to the size and scale of the Texan feed-lots for beef cattle, or the ranching agriculture of the Argentine or Australia. This is not to say that even by those standards it does not still come out with very high marks, and in particular, despite the hidebound traditions and rural caution, British farmers have been innovators to a degree which is quite unexpected. The British agricultural farm machinery industry bears witness to the support of British farmers, and in the business of pedigree bloodstock it is a satisfying, if salutary, thought that vast areas of the world today are stocked with the progeny of British breeds. Thus British agriculture's strength is world-wide.

In the UK in 1975 there were 93,000 medium- and large-sized farms; it was the same figure seven years earlier, but it disguised the inescapable fact that there had been an increase of 5,000 large holdings, and a reduction of 5,000 medium-sized ones. But in the same period the additional business opportunities of the larger farms came from the disappearance of 22,000 smallholdings, those not large enough to provide work of a full-time nature for one or two men. The movement towards the abolition of the smaller farm businesses, and the enlargement at all levels of those remaining, has been a perpetual feature of the British farming scene for at least thirty years, and during the period 1968–75 no less than 53,000 very small holdings went off the map, or at least left the Ministry statistics.

This trend towards the large farm business is marked by the amalgamation of small farms, additional land being regarded as a lifeline during times of stringency. It is to be noted that this policy of amalgamation has been accomplished, and still continues to be accomplished, without Government pressure (the effects of the Farm Amalgamation Scheme which offered a pension carrot to small farmers who sold out to their larger neighbours has been negligible). The individual farmer has followed his own perceptive nose and discovered the benefits of farming on a larger scale; it must also be a highly relevant factor that intensive livestock systems with automated feeding, and the increase in all forms of mechanization, have enabled farmers to increase their output with the same or even less staff, and that the escalating capital cost of all this new machinery has been justified only when the overheads could be spread over a larger business.

Efficiency and productivity by natural commercial forces have given farming an annual productivity increase that is double the rate for town-based industries, and for years when industry generally was improving its productive capacity by 3 per cent per annum farming was achieving an output increase of 6 per cent. Although farms have increased in size and scope, they are still small units when compared with almost every other major industry in the UK.

Nevertheless, the average size of UK farms is still only 40 hectares, at which level only the most intensive farming operation could be considered viable, or even above a peasant subsistence level. But within the context of the EEC countries, British farms are almost twice as large as those of our nearest rival, which is Denmark (average farm size 22 hectares), and three times larger than the average for all European farms. UK farmers have a larger proportion of the large farms; 29 per cent are over 50 hectares, while France has only 10 per cent over this size. This policy of increasing farm sizes has been accomplished in the UK with freedom from any form of restriction, and with the freedom of the land laws in the UK, which contrast starkly with the rigid regimentation and regulations of the Continental tradition. It has enabled UK farmers as individuals to buy land and expand their farms as they wished.

The progress towards larger farms does not appear equal throughout the UK, and the following table demonstrates that although England and Scotland appear roughly equal, it has only been the quite dramatic advance in Scottish farm sizes between 1968 and 1975 that has displaced the previous discrepancy: even today Northern Ireland farms are less than half the size of those in England and Scotland, whilst the Welsh are also substantially smaller than the English or Scots. This discrepancy can be ascribed to the more progressive thinking of the natives, and arises from the greater prosperity of farming in those regions. It is a facet of human nature that the rich grow richer, and the poor always remain the poor. Human greed could be cynically observed as the base for this progression, but it has enabled a vast re-structuring of the farming industry at its grass roots.

Increased farm sizes

	England Hectares	Wales Hectares	Scotland Hectares	Northern Ireland Hectares
1968	42	27	33	20
1975	52	33	55	24
Percentage increase from 1968–75	25%	22·5%	75%	20%

Concentration of enterprises

'When a man is to be hanged in a fortnight, it concentrates his mind wonderfully.'

Samuel Johnson

The traditional multitude of enterprises on every farm has now given way to a concentration upon fewer lines, and in effect although mixed farming systems still abound, they have fewer individual enterprises than was the situation 20 years ago. This concentration of effort has resulted in greater specialization, and the end result of greater productivity per bird, per hectare, per cow, etc. In extreme cases on arable farms this has resulted in 'mono-culture' of cereals alone, with no other crops and no livestock, and in some cases no regular labour force. A system that may abound in the Canadian wheat belt, but one that is alien to the traditional pattern of UK farming.

In another direction, the 'mono-culture' in the livestock sector reveals the intensive dairy farm devoted only to milking cows and the production of milk; selling its calves off at birth, buying fully developed replacements, making no fodder, but with every hectare grazing direct into the animal's rumen. But more common is the intensive pig and poultry farm which has been vicariously labelled a 'production unit', which is wholly based upon an area of concrete and a small factory of buildings. It is not farming in the romantic image, although this development has been an integral feature of the progress of farming in the UK from being a rather backward 'way of life' to a highly geared industry.

The contraction of British agriculture has resulted in a steady loss of 3,500 farmers annually, precipitated by the losses of farmland to the insatiable tide of urban and industrial development. The Ministry statistics show that there are 166,000 full-time farms but this figure dropped by 18,000 in the five years 1971–6. This number of full-time farms recorded 218,000 full-time and 71,000 part-time farmers, the explanation being that the duplication of 'farmers' occurs where father and son, or wife, work together as partners. Within this contraction the concentration of enterprises, with its concomitant benefits, continues unabated. Today 15 per cent of the farms account for 56 per cent of the output.

This extension of farm businesses in scope and size has resulted in farming becoming big business, and by streamlining their operations and reducing the diversity of their stock and crops farmers have become more vulnerable with the removal of the security which comes from a wider spread. Thus when one sector of farming is in trouble, however temporary—pigs may be taken as a typical example—the specialized pig farmer who has concentrated all his business into this one line of production suffers irreparable damage to his bank balance, while the mixed economy of an arable farm with a pig enterprise on the side, growing and feeding its own grain (which is in effect marketed as pig meat), can provide an insulation for the more violent price cycles. The grain boom after 1973 escalated feeding costs to livestock farmers, and put disproportionate riches into the cereal farmers' pockets, but those farmers who had both interests lost the benefits of the high grain prices but were able to survive a depression in the livestock sector.

In many instances this concentration of enterprises has resulted in a dramatic decision to drop a long-standing feature of the individual farm, and each year nearly 5,000 farmers decide to give up dairy farming, 1,500 potato growers vanish and about 4,000 pig farmers decide that enough is enough. In the five years 1964–8 farmers with egg-producing hens dropped out of the business at a rate of 12,500 every year.

These farmers are those who may only be keeping small numbers of animals, while with crops the potato/sugar beet syndrome has long provided a tug-of-war—particularly near one of the seventeen sugar beet factories in the UK. Many farmers have gone out of dairying when the last, and final, cowman retired or departed, and it is this availability of labour that is an important factor in persuading farmers that the time for reappraisal of the farming system has arrived. This is probably the greatest incentive towards forcing the change, but the other factor that becomes paramount is the 'crossroads' decision when reinvestment of a large capital sum becomes a necessity.

Dairy farming requires a labour intensivity for twice a day milking and a modernized, electronically operated milking parlour. Fifty thousand pounds would not be an untoward sum for the modernization of a unit that had fallen below modern standards, and in the arable world the replacement of expensive sugar beet or potato harvesters, with all the allied equipment required for a very small annual usage, and a large capital sum locked up, means that when the time for replacement arrives the farmer often decides to drop one particular crop, reduce the diversity of his operations, and concentrate his resources into a greater utilization of that machinery which he can more justifiably purchase. The spreading of overheads can only in effect be accomplished by a gradual enlargement of the farm itself, or by an expansion of the lines of production which are retained. Thus the efficiency of British agriculture has been forced upon farmers by the rising tide of inflation, and by a lack of prosperity, rather than by any golden carrot.

There are limits to revolutionary change in the farming system which come from the capability of individual farms to withstand violent changes; thus in the wetter grass-growing counties dairy farming is a more obvious bet than growing cereals, and to attempt to mimic the grass-growing capabilities of the Midlands, North and West in the dry eastern counties is to battle against the dictates of nature and the climate. There are thus obstacles for the farmer who endeavours to concentrate on new lines; nevertheless, enhanced cereal prices and greater mechanization have resulted in cereals being grown in many areas of the country where they are less suited to the soil and rainfall.

Farming means to most people animals, and in urban eyes no farm is complete without them; in fact, 65 per cent of the total output of British farming comes from livestock, and livestock products, yet farming is also the harvest, and throughout any year its prospects and progress put it in the forefront as an important aspect of farming. But the actual return to UK agriculture represented by the grain harvest is only 13 per cent of its total output. In fact, the annual wheat crop is no more important than the production of eggs.

As farmers, of whatever size, seek to streamline their activities by a reduction in the number of enterprises carried out on each farm, it follows that specialization into fewer lines of production creates larger units. One farmer, it appears, is always anxious to take up the slack which another farmer has discarded, and with a freedom of action only curtailed in the contracts for sugar beet, the quotas for potatoes or the registration with the MMB as a milk-producer, British farmers can expand or diminish whatever they choose with no constraints, using their market intuition to assess the profitability of new lines. Haphazard though this system may appear, and with farmers acting in isolation, the end product has nevertheless made a consistent pattern of rationalization and structural planning.

The increasing specialization of farm enterprises has produced the benefits of scale and potential increases in expertise with large-scale economies. Aided by the viability of larger and more efficient machinery to reduce costings, it is a healthy evolution that has by no means been completed, and will continue into the future. The results of this process can be shown in the expansion of dairy herds. In England and Wales the average number of cows in each dairy herd was only 21 in 1960, but had more than doubled, to 46 cows per head in 1975. Scotland now has an average of 71 cows per herd, while Northern Ireland has only 20. The UK national average is 43 cows, which contrasts starkly with the situation in Europe. The average UK herd is twice the size of that of our nearest competitor, Holland; it is three times larger than those to be found in France, Germany or Belgium, and four times larger than in Italy.

The overall production of UK agriculture continues to expand, and cows now produce 450 litres more per head than in 1939. Hens produce 43 extra eggs each year, while wheat varieties have shown a yield increase of 25 per cent in twenty-five years, and the plant-breeders see no reason why this trend should not continue. Grain-production today records an increase of 250 per cent over pre-

War levels, egg-production has doubled, pig-meat production has also doubled, and scientific formulations of feeding rations have increased live-weight gains per unit of food intake for all livestock. Nitrogen and other fertilizer applications have increased grass and arable production, with a consequential increase in stocking rates and crop yields. A dramatic revolution of farming practice yields more food from fewer hectares for more people, and with a lower labour force.

Speaking at a conference on Food and Farming at Coventry Cathedral[1], Edward Bishop, Minister of State, said:

> The average yield per cow is now well over 4000 litres per year, nearly 60% higher than the level just after the war. The area of land needed for each cow has fallen, and because of improvements in milking machinery it is now possible for one man comfortably to milk over 100 cows.
>
> The number of pigs produced per sow per year has risen, while the amount of feed needed to produce one kilogram of pig meat has fallen; but perhaps the most dramatic changes have occurred in the poultry industry, where poultry have to a very large extent gone indoors into environment-controlled houses where cleaning, feeding, watering and egg-collection are mechanized. At the same time efficiency has increased very remarkably.
>
> There have also been interesting developments in arable farming ... thus, on average, one man is now employed on every 81 hectares of arable land compared with five men for the same area 20 years ago ... Yields of many vegetable crops have doubled, or more than doubled, during the last 25 years.
>
> Agriculture now employs less than 3% of our labour force and also produces about the same percentage in gross domestic product. This is an impressive record when one looks at many other countries—and when I travel abroad on agricultural export work I find that it receives wide acknowledgement.

Two days later Keith Dexter, Director-General of ADAS, warned farmers not to become complacent over their superiority in production and efficiency. He said:

> To date, the trade record of UK agriculture is good; in the last 20 years net product has risen by 75% despite a reduction in labour input of more than 50%. Labour productivity has increased by approximately 6% per annum—twice that achieved by UK industry in general over the same period. Recent surveys have shown that our best dairy farmers are as efficient as the best Dutch dairy farmers—long regarded as being the most efficient in the EEC; but our average dairy farmer is not as efficient as the average Dutch farmer, indicating a wider range of performance in the UK.

The UK produces 10 per cent of the agricultural produce of the EEC countries, but has 14 per cent of the agricultural land; thus by this criterion the land of Britain is less productive than on the mainland of Europe, but the explanation is different. The marginal lands of Britain are indeed sparsely occupied by both men and animals, and although seeding from the air, and aerial fertilizer applications, has been perfected, it is little used, whereas with the smaller peasant farmers in Europe there is a more intensive use of what may be termed marginal land. Since there are less farmers in the UK, and the farms are larger, the British

[1] 15 October 1977.

farmer is in a higher income bracket than would be normal for farmers in Europe. The dividing lines between horticulture and 'pure' farming are obscure, with most fruit, both hard and soft, vegetables and flowers being classified as market garden and horticultural crops. Peas are a vegetable, but are grown on large farm scale, and turnips, while also an edible vegetable, are often grown for cattle feeding. Potatoes, while a vital part of the nation's diet, are indisputably not a horticultural crop, but a farm one.

Output of British agriculture

Importance of Livestock and Crop Output (in percentage)		Ascending Order of Importance (in percentage)	
Livestock	**(37)**	Milk and milk products	21·5
Fat cattle and calves	15	Fat cattle and calves	15
Fat sheep and lambs	4	Fat pigs	10
Fat pigs	10	Potatoes	10
Poultry	6	Barley	7
Others	2	Wheat	6
		Poultry	6
Livestock Products	**(28)**	Vegetables	6
Milk & milk products	21·5	Eggs	5
Eggs	5	Fat sheep and lambs	4
Clip wool	0·5	Sugar beet	1·5
Others	1	Fruit	1·5
		Clip wool	0·5
Crops	**(26)**	Sundries	6
Wheat	6		
Barley	7		
Potatoes	10		100
Sugar beet	1·5		
Others	1·5		
Horticulture	**(9)**		
Vegetables	6		
Fruit	1·5		
Others	1·5		
	100		

Feeding the nation

'More than half the people of the world are living in conditions approaching misery. Their food is inadequate.'

Harry S. Truman

'In the 10 years from 1965 the volume of agricultural output rose by 20%, whilst industrial production only went up 13%. Given the right conditions for expansion, British farmers can produce still more food at home, and thus cut our huge food import bill even further.'

'Help Yourself', NFU Campaign for Farmers, 1977.

In the pre-1939 period British farmers supplied 35 per cent of the nation's temperate food supplies. Today, UK farming produces 65 per cent, and the population has risen by 20 per cent in that time; additionally there has been a massive swing in eating habits, with people eating more than was the norm forty years ago. As a percentage of total UK food-supplies, nearly 53% are now supplied from the home base; this is a figure that has risen over the last decade, but in fact reached a peak of 54·6 per cent in 1972–3. It represents an output which is 2·5 per cent of the gross domestic product, employs 3 per cent of the capital formation of the nation, and is produced by 2·7 per cent of the total manpower.

Production of farm output as a percentage of total consumption

	Pre-1939	Average (1975–77)
Milk	100	100
Pork	78	99
Poultry meat	80	99
Eggs	61	98
Potatoes	96	95 (1974)
Barley	46	93
Oilseed rape	12 (1972)	88 (1977)
Beef and veal	49	85
Cheese	24	64
Wheat	23	56
Mutton and lamb	36	52
Sugar	16	29
Butter	9	22

The high level of self-sufficiency in many staple products owes much to the encouragement derived from unrestrictive Government policies but Britain's farmers have complained about the trade agreements which always allowed Danish bacon a large share of the bacon market, hampering British pig farmers in their efforts to increase their market share. Again, not only was butter from New Zealand a traditional import, but the New Zealand economy relied heavily upon its British outlet. In the tariff wall which was erected around Europe by the Common Agricultural Policy, one of Britain's conditions of entry was the gradual phasing out of this source of supply, and not its immediate cessation, despite the over-production of milk and milk products within the EEC. Britain's sugar beet farmers can only produce an annual tonnage which is consistent with the capacity of the British Sugar Corporation's factories to accept and process the crop. For many years sugar has been subjected to international sugar agreements, and it could be disruptive to close the UK to Caribbean sugar. Many nations in that area rely upon their sugar exports as the cornerstone of their economy. The table above illustrates the changing relation of British farm-production to food-consumption, but since there has been a population and an eating increase, the table opposite more accurately illustrates the real expansion of some of the major products of British farming.

Even in a restricted area of land that has declined by nearly 3 per cent, UK farmers' cattle have risen from 8·5 million to 13·5 million and pigs from 4·5 million to 8·6 million, while poultry have nearly doubled from 76 million to 140 million.

**Percentage increases in farm production
from pre-1939 to late 1970s**
(Taking into account food consumption and population increase)

Butter	400
Wheat	300
Cheese	250
Sugar	250
Meat	175
Milk	70
Potatoes	25

Nutritional standards have risen to the point where although it is still estimated that one-third of the world's population are undernourished many nations now consume much more than they need. In Britain the Ministry of Agriculture and Food estimates that the average Briton consumes 25 per cent above his nutritional requirements; taking a base line of 1962 as 100, meals bought and eaten away from the home have risen by 65 per cent, while food prices have only risen by 55 per cent, housing by 72 per cent, fuel and light by 61 per cent and general services by 69 per cent.

Beer consumption rose between 1973 and 1976 from 197 pints to 209, while that of spirits climbed from 4·3 proof pints to 5·1; thus the sophistication of an affluent society is well illustrated, while despite anti smoking campaigns consumption of tobacco still continues to rise. (Unfortunately, statistics on the expenditure for bingo halls are not available!) Consumption of dairy products rose from 25·7 kilos per head in 1973 to 26·3 kilos two years later, and then fell back to the 1973 figure in 1976. Meat-supplies fell over the four years to 1976 by 10 per cent, and potato-consumption dropped in 1976 because the drought had drastically reduced Britain's potato crop; but in compensation flour-consumption, which had been steady at 9 kilos per head, jumped suddenly to nearly 11 kilos per head. Sugar-consumption shows an interesting if illogical pattern. It increased by about 1¼ kilos per head in 1976, after a return to normal supplies from the shortage of 1974, but it was still only 20 kilos per head, and had been nearly 23 in 1973. Thus the consumption of many of our staple foods stopped its steady increases in the period of national stringencies and high unemployment from 1974 onward. Nevertheless, the total spent on food showed a steady decline until the early 1970s, and it is no longer the major item of household expenditure.

Way back in 1900, the household food bill was nearly 90 per cent of weekly wages, and in spite of this, low wage-levels and a subsistence standard of living meant that meat was never eaten by some families, while many also went without shoes. In the social upheaval of the twentieth century the cost of food within the household budget showed a decline, to only 17 per cent in the mid-1960s. (The figures have been distorted by their inclusion under a general heading of 'food and alcoholic beverages'. Alcohol was consumed more, and its price rose more rapidly than food prices, but within this bracket in 1965 household expenditure was 32 per cent of the whole and even with food price rises in the 1970s it had dropped to under 30 per cent by 1976.) Food has traditionally been cheap in the UK when compared to other nations, and despite the emphasis upon spiralling prices it still represents a modest part of the weekly budget.

Percentage of consumers' expenditure for food

	1960	1970	1974	1975
Household expenditure on food	25	20·2	19·2	19·3

Source: Government Statistical Service MAFF, 1976.

The largest industry

British agricultural production is worth more than the combined farm output of Australia and New Zealand, and these are two major agricultural countries. The cereal production of tiny Britain is almost double that of vast Australia, and does not appear insignificant when compared to that of the vast rolling prairies of mighty Canada. In beef-production the Argentine stands the highest, but Britain's production does not lag far behind. In comparison to other UK industries, farm production is greater than that of the motor industry and the coal-mines combined.

Since Britain is an industrial nation, with only 2·7 per cent of its working population engaged in farming, the size and scope of the industry is largely misunderstood; it gets no headlines because of union problems and strikes, it gains no kudos for its export achievements, and in fact rarely hits the headlines at all, despite a perpetual flag-waving exercise by the NFU. The general public barely acknowledges that farming is indeed an industry.

Farmers and their men are often regarded as rustic survivors in a jet set age, and there is a lack of appreciation or even interest, except when formerly the matter of the annual Price Review payments became headlines. When payments were abolished after Britain's entry into the EEC even that doubtful headline vanished. The British have a lack of interest in the subject of food, and although gourmet restaurants are now opening, they represent a special treat rather than a normal daily preoccupation. The motor-car industry, with its stream of strikes but its export potential, comes nearer to the hearts of the massive urban population.

Car factories, coal-mines, steelworks, airports and docks can all be identified with particular towns, but farming exists everywhere, except within the larger conurbations. It is extremely diverse in nature. The NFU boasts that agriculture is Britain's largest single industry, and the only criterion for this statement must be the distinction of the primary industries from those which manufacture, or just assemble, a multitude of products from other industries. To this extent all industries, excepting perhaps coal-mining and quarrying, are substantially dependent upon other inputs, although the water, gas and electricity industries do produce a single product, and the North Sea oil industry similarly. Within this group agriculture has the greatest production in fiscal terms; it is also undoubtedly the largest industry in territorial terms, with its spread throughout the United Kingdom.

In terms of comparison with Britain's other manufacturing and construction industries, the production from UK agriculture (when allowances are made for the deduction of inputs) does rank as the largest industry. The construction industry has a turnover that is in excess of that of agriculture, but it is employing a vast multitude of materials which may have been partly manufactured by other industries, so that its total figure cannot bear a corresponding comparison.

This is not to assert that agriculture is entirely a primary producer, not employing outside inputs. The fertilizer industry contributes heavily towards the output of farm produce, agrochemicals have become big business, farming for all its mechanization is a relatively small user of fuel for energy, but the production of the tractor and farm machinery factories must be deducted from its output. Conversely, much of the output of farming is converted on the farm into another form before it is sold; thus the consumption of grain into meat represents a reduction on average of three times its tonnage, even though the price of the meat product should allow for the home-based inputs. It is estimated that the dependence upon a healthy agriculture by the labour force of the ancillary industries amounts to 9 per cent of the working population, or in other words for every one man working on the farm there are over three others in the back-up industries.

Agriculture in the UK does not monopolize the industrial scene, and since Britain is a major food-importing country, the agricultural industry does not have the same influence as its counterparts in many of the European countries. Even in the USA the farmers have greater power, and the USA is a food-exporter.

Farm exports

'As a net food importing country, our opportunities for direct agricultural exports are, of course, limited.'
'British Agriculture Looks Ahead', NFU, September 1964

'There is no reason why adequate supply capacity to meet export demands should not exist. The export possibilities will be of benefit to producers generally, and also to domestic consumers.'
Report of an Enquiry into Agricultural Exports, May 1976.

Britain is the world's largest food-importing country. Our agricultural productivity has made great strides, but still produces only 53 per cent of our total food requirements. In an import-saving role, the NFU has sought to boost the importance of farming to the national economy, yet paradoxically, British agriculture is also an active exporter.

The value of exports from the agricultural sector amounts only to $1\frac{1}{2}$ per cent of Britain's total annual exports, but it is still greater than the export of shipbuilding and marine engineering, clothing and footwear, and furniture. Despite our dependence upon vast food imports, the trade deficit of farming, forestry and fishing is less of a drain upon our currency reserves than is the deficit from the massive imports of natural minerals.

Apart from direct farm products exported, the additional value from the ancillary industries can reasonably also be considered under this head by virtue of a home market which promotes technological advances and development. Thus the additional value of exports of the farm-machinery and agrochemicals industries make a total contribution of 6 per cent to the vital UK export achievements. Undoubtedly the world-beating UK farm machinery industry owes its existence to a healthy UK agriculture which has stimulated its inventive genius, and provided a giant test-bed for the development of new machines, many of which have become world-renowned leading export lines. British farmers, who are among the most mechanized in the world, have demanded new and improved machines, and have led the manufacturers along the path. The same cannot be said for agrochemicals, which are largely the product of research aimed at a wider market than the UK can provide. The costs of development cannot be justified unless the sales can be multinational.

The parodox that Britain is exporting food while importing at the same time is not quite the result of muddled bureaucratic thinking that it appears. Although nearly 80 per cent of farm exports are in fact food, some of this has been processed, and also include items such as coffee and chocolate which are processed from imported raw materials. Others bear little likeness to the product which leaves the farm.

However, the export-import balance sheet of many other industries shows on close examination that the apparent ebullient salesmanship which produces astronomical monthly figures is not always as clear-cut as it appears. Many machine parts are rough-cast in the UK and shipped to the nearer ports on the Continent, where they are finely ground and closely machined, to be re-imported into the UK in another guise, installed into vehicles, and then again exported. These massive monthly figures often duplicate the same item, even though in a more refined state. But the exports of agriculture rarely come back again, and the coordination which now exists within individual companies operating their own factories on both sides of the English Channel is as logical as producing the various parts in diverse factories throughout the UK, utilizing a major assembly plant in a central location.

The export of cereals is an example of the interchange of products as the export-import business dictates; in total, we consume 22 million tonnes, for both human and animal feeding, but the average British harvest is 15 million tonnes, making an average annual deficit of 7 million tonnes. Yet we export up to half a million tonnes in our best years. This is explained by the variation in the quality and destination of coarse grains. We must import protein meal which cannot be grown in the UK; second-grade malting barley finds a ready market in Scandinavia for the lager-type brewing industry. We export first-class malt to Germany, in competition with the French, and we use our own malt for the production of Scotch whisky, which is a popular export throughout the world. We send wheat and flour to the EEC countries, and British expertise in the formulation of compound feeding-stuffs finds a market throughout Europe.

In order to produce the traditional English white bread-loaf we need a percentage of the hard Manitoban wheat, and even if we became self-sufficient in cereals, this import would still be required. Cereal exports from the UK are mainly to Europe, and are highly volatile: the UK harvest fluctuates by as much as 3 million tonnes from year to year, and this means that the variability in its size and quality requires the free movement of grain from one country to another. The interdependence of nations has been an economic fact for much longer than is normally recognized; for instance, the economic stability of New Zealand had always rested upon the butter market in the UK. The same applies to the cane-sugar producers in the equatorial regions. As proved, UK cereal exports are highly unpredictable, but over a period of years barley, for example, averages 400,000 tonnes, even though this mean is taken over a range of only 51,000 tonnes in 1972 to one of 1 million tonnes in 1975, and again in 1977–8. There has been a narrowing gap between exports and imports in recent years, and although agricultural exports today are 6 per cent of total UK exports, this is a declining figure. In 1965 it represented 8·4 per cent of exports. But in that year imports represented 31 per cent; by 1972 they had declined to just under 20 per cent. The greater growth of other sectors of exporting industry has thus marginally reduced the importance of farm exports, but the greater productivity of the home farm has reduced our dependence upon imports. Agricultural imports were 4½ times larger than agricultural exports in 1963, but a decade later were only three times greater. With the trade in food and live animals the gap is even wider; the ratio of imports to exports fell from 10–1 in 1963 to 5–1 in 1973, and so the agricultural export business remains important in assisting the UK balance of trade.

British bloodstock

Britain has become known for the quality of its bloodstock and although these form a well-known part of our agricultural exports, they in fact amount to only 3 per cent of the total. Eight Jersey cattle from the Queen's Farm at Windsor went to Brazil in 1974 as part of a delivery of a hundred British pedigree cattle of ten different breeds, and worth £200,000. They were exhibited at the International Brazil Show. In 1973 fifty Herefords formed the first part of a 200-head deal with China. Hereford blood is to be found on the pampas in South America and in the beef feed-lots in the USA. Welsh Blacks have been exported to North America.

Pedigree Suffolk sheep have been dispatched to many countries; in 1972, 704 went to six countries, which compared with only 362 in the previous year. France was the main destination, but new markets have been established in Italy and Belgium.

At the 1974 Brazil International Show, Jersey cattle had the largest representation of all breeds, although there were problems in exporting these cattle due to difficulties in obtaining sufficient aircraft cargo space. Canada has imported fifteen heifers from the Luing breed, produced by the Cadzow brothers in Scotland. South Devon cattle have been exported in large quantities, and the British Friesian has gained ground consistently in the USA.

As the British Friesian today is descended from Dutch strains which arrived in this country via South Africa, so today the healthy environment of British pastures are providing a staging point for the world distribution of European cattle. The last outbreak of foot-and-mouth disease in Great Britain was in June 1968, and since that time the longest free period since the turn of the century has been recorded. Rinderpest was eradicated in the UK in 1877, and the USDA[2] recognized Britain's healthiness as a transitory quarantine station in September 1973. It was a mark of recognition that has been a boon to the export of pedigree breeding cattle. Semen has become a major item, and the MMB have dispatched salesmen to tour Australia and promote semen sales from pedigree British bloodstock. (This is not to disparage the efforts that have been made by pig-breeders to secure sales for Landrace Large White and Hampshire pig breeds to many parts of the world, while South Down, Hampshire Down, and North Country Cheviot sheep have also been exported.) It all adds up to a world influence for British cattle, although once beasts are exported their progeny do nothing for Britain's annual import-export accounts.

Despite this emphasis upon the export of breeding stock, it is nevertheless a paradox that the export of commercial cattle runs at double the pedigree rate, and as a vast food-importing nation we still manage to export vast quantities of beef and veal, mutton and lamb, and pork.

The import of New Zealand lamb into Britain sustains the New Zealand economy, and at exhibitions in Paris British lamb-producers have boosted their sales to the French. The 1968 foot-and-mouth outbreak in the UK was blamed upon the import of beef from the Argentine, and as a result only boned beef has been imported into the UK ever since. This created a dramatic drop in Argentinian beef imports, and assisted the British farmer. Similarly, the importation of animals from the Republic of Ireland was restricted to a test for bovine tuberculosis in June 1976, as a protection against introducing TB into the UK national cattle herd. In another sphere potato exports were banned in September 1975, when the Government realized that the dry summer had resulted in a total crop that was unlikely to satisfy normal UK demand. With another dry summer in 1976, the ban remained in force until July 1977, when the

---

[2] United States Department of Agriculture.

forecast of a larger crop influenced the Government to lift the prohibition on potato exports. But in the main exports of British food are unrestricted, and the market free-for-all continues to produce the best results of private enterprise and market forces.

Breakdown of farm and ancillary exports
(as percentage)

Farm machinery	56
Direct farm products	28
Fertilizers	10
Agrochemicals	6
	100

Division of agricultural exports calculated at 1975 figures, but unlikely to vary greatly from year to year
(as percentage)

Pedigree breeding animals	3
Farm and vegetable seeds	4
Commercial cattle	5
Vegetables, fruit and flowers	6
Processed food products	13
Cereals and feeding-stuffs	34
Meat	35
	100

Cattle exports

The export of live cattle from the UK commenced in the summer of 1956, when a shipment of live cattle was sent to Holland on the instructions of the American Army Veterinary Corps. This was an American contract to supply food for Servicemen in Europe. It was a condemnation of the UK slaughterhouses that they did not comply with the US standards, whilst those at The Hague and Rotterdam did, so the animals were transported live across the English Channel. This was an export trade that was in its beginnings quite small, but it attracted attention, and by February of the following year there had been sufficient public outcry for a Parliamentary Committee to be formed. Known as the Balfour Committee, it eventually produced the 'Balfour Assurances' which set standards for the transportation and slaughter of cattle to many, but not all, European countries.

Lord Balfour of Burleigh was appointed by the then Minister, Heathcoat-Amory, and the committee commenced its investigations on 6 February 1957. Its members were four men and one woman, and its brief was to inquire into the export trade of live cattle. In addition to Lord Balfour, there was a Tory MP, Lady Tweedsmuir, who was later to be given a Life Peerage in her own right, and was at one time a director of Cunard. Then there was a Socialist MP, Arthur Champion, who had been Parliamentary Secretary at the Ministry for seven months in 1951, losing his job when Churchill won the General Election. The quintet was completed by a vet, G. N. Gould, and the last member, Clyde Higgs, a businessman turned farmer from near Stratford-upon-Avon, a confidant of Jim Turner (then NFU President), but an irascible and energetic anti-marketeer who died ten years before Britain finally joined the EEC in 1973. The Balfour Committee must have set a speed record for any Government inquiry, either before or since. It was set up on 6 February, and reported back on 15 April, just ten weeks later, whilst many Government Inquiries sit for years. In its whistle-stop tour the members visited the east-coast shipping ports in both England and Scotland, followed the animals being exported to Holland, Germany and France, and inspected the port facilities and the slaughterhouses in Marseilles and Bordeaux. They took oral evidence from twenty-eight people, and written evidence from fifty-seven others. The end result was to establish that an alternative carcass trade was not feasible, and that the sea or air journey to the Continent was not sufficient reason for imposing a total prohibition, although they did suggest that certain improvements could be made. The Report emphasized the nature of the problem:

> Cruelty to animals is often the product of ignorance, sometimes of mere brutality — at its worst it is the result of the combination of both. Such instances are, we pride ourselves, rare in this country, yet there is no room for complacency in this matter. The evidence put before us reveals that our standard of humanity in the treatment of cattle for slaughter is not always everywhere equally high.[3]

The Balfour Assurances were summed up in four points:
1 Cattle shall not travel more than 100 km from the port of disembarkation to the place of slaughter.
2 The animals shall be adequately fed and watered during transportation and lairage.
3 The animals shall be humanely slaughtered only by the captive-bolt pistol or electrical-stunning systems.
4 No animal exported from the UK for slaughter shall be re-exported by the importing country.

These stipulations were signed by France, West Germany, Belgium and the Netherlands in 1957, while in 1964 the countries were invited to extend the 'Assurances' to exports of cattle from Northern Ireland and to exports of sheep and pigs for immediate slaughter from the UK. France refused to sign, but the following year Italy gave the Balfour Assurances for cattle, sheep and pigs. Despite humane conditions apparently assured by the Balfour Recommendations, an illicit trade was conducted, partly through Southern Ireland, and the promises were not always being kept. Another wave of sentiment swept across

[3] Para 38, Report of the Committee of Enquiry into the Export of Live Cattle to the Continent for Slaughter, April 1957.

the British nation in 1972, led by the RSPCA, who had investigated many cases of cruelty, and had produced weighty evidence that the export of live cattle was an inhumane trade. The Balfour Assurances were being circumvented or ignored, and there were not adequate safeguards to prevent this, it claimed. In addition, some of the rules were becoming outdated; a series of campaigns developed to halt the export of live food animals.

On 12 July 1973 the House of Commons debated the subject of animal welfare and the export of live cattle; despite a brave rearguard action by the Minister, Joe Godber, a Government Amendment was defeated by 285 votes to 264 votes, and a complete ban on live-animal exports was imposed the following day. In the debate it had been announced that another inquiry into the trade would be instigated, and fourteen days later the members were appointed. As Lord Balfour had been a banker, and Chairman of Lloyds Bank, so the new Chairman, Lord O'Brien of Lothbury, had been Governor of the Bank of England from 1966 until his retirement only a few weeks before this inquiry was set up in 1973. It took slightly longer than the Balfour Committee to report, and delivered its recommendations in February 1974. Meanwhile farmers and their leaders were angered at the arbitrary and, they claimed, ignorant way in which the House of Commons had accepted emotional arguments.

The O'Brien Committee reported that the Balfour Assurances had indeed been broken, but its energies were directed towards the welfare aspect of the animals, and it said:

> We took the view that although the live trade is of importance to those in the industry who are affected by its operations, it is of small economic significance to the United Kingdom as a whole.[4]

It did, however, set out the economic arguments and the apparent contradiction of an importing country being concerned with exporting:

> It has also been argued that it is illogical that the UK, as a net importer of meat, should export live food animals, particularly when some of those animals may have attracted Exchequer subsidies. We would not regard this as a particularly telling argument for several reasons.
>
> Firstly, the argument could be applied with equal force against the export of carcass meat which is the alternative normally advocated. Secondly, as a trading nation the UK is involved in the export of many products in which she is less than self sufficient, but it is generally recognised that the advantages of free trade outweigh these peripheral results of it.

Soon after the O'Brien Report was completed on 7 February 1974 Heath plunged the country into a General Election, and throughout 1974 and until after the second Election of that year the O'Brien Committee Report lay pigeonholed. Animal exports continued to be banned, although Cheshire farmers had threatened to challenge the legality of the House of Commons vote as contrary to the Treaty of Rome, which envisaged free interchange of healthy stock between

[4]Report of the Committee on the Export of Animals for Slaughter, 1974, para 21.

member countries. An export deal worth £600,000 between Welsh farmers and Greece for 6,000 calves was reported lost because of the regulations governing export licences. Young livestock was still available for exporting, but not cattle for immediate slaughter. The ban remained in force, and in early 1975 the House of Commons finally debated the O'Brien Report. It had said in its first recommendation: 'We do not consider that a permanent ban on the export of live animals for slaughter is justified on either welfare or economic grounds.'

And this time the House of Commons, on a free vote, carried a motion to lift the ban on the export of live animals. It was passed by 232 votes to 191, a majority of 41, but interestingly the number of MPs who turned up to vote for the removal of this ban was considerably smaller than those who had voted in the heated debate in 1973. All parties had their supporters; the ruling Socialists, opposition Tories and Liberals and Nationalist MPs, and Conservative agricultural spokesman Francis Pym said, 'There are some 14·5 million head of cattle to feed in Britain, but the supplies of fodder are adequate for only 13 million. It is hard to quantify accurately the loss through malnutrition and starvation, but some estimates are as high as 1,000 head a week.' The Secretary of State for Wales, John Morris, in the final speech concluded, 'While welfare is the main consideration, the resumption of exports will benefit British agriculture and balance of trade.'

The live cattle trade resumed, and it might have been assumed that the battle had been won, but just over two years later, in 1977, the RSPCA mounted another massive campaign. In a rash of somewhat emotional advertisements in the national press it depicted a calf on its knees, and issued an impressive booklet parading again its arguments against the cruelty of shipping live animals. This problem may never be resolved. The importance to the agricultural industry of this traffic is not very great, but currently the slaughtering facilities in the UK are not of the highest standards. One of the problems arises from the unknown destination of the animals; large fat cattle are obviously destined for the slaughterhouse; young calves, however, may be exported to be reared on the Continent, although some may be killed early as veal or baby beef. There is no organization to monitor the future progress of these animals.

Farm machinery exports

The achievements of the farm machinery industry in its export battle may not appear to make a major contribution to Britain's economic survival, but nevertheless are far more important than is shown by the figures, or than the public suppose. The total exports in any year show the British farm-machinery industry to be tiny compared to the giant exports of the mechanical engineering, chemical or electrical industries. But agricultural machinery exports amount to the same value as the export of motor-cars (which is not to be confused with the exports of the motor industry, including spare parts). Farm machinery exports are considerably greater than is the export of alcoholic beverages, and have become a truly purposive export business. Without world-wide sales the British farmer would undoubtedly suffer from an inferior range of machinery.

Seventy per cent of the total production of the British farm machinery industry is exported annually, which compares with 53 per cent in West Germany (1974), although that figure was only 28 per cent in 1964. The UK is the second largest exporter of farm equipment in the world; only the USA has a greater record. Within the overall figure of production for export, David Brown estimate that 80 per cent of their tractors go for export, and indeed tractors form a major part of farm machinery exports, with 78 per cent of the total output going for export.

In terms of the balance of trade—imports against exports—the UK agricultural engineering industry ranks fourth. Its adverse ratio is only one-third that of the mechanical engineering industry, but this points to the loyalty of British farmers in curbing their demands for imported machinery, which would affect the balance of trade. Nevertheless, the advent of strikes at the Massey-Ferguson factories and the shortages of Ford tractors has influenced British farmers to buy imported makes. Today there are tractors on British farms from France, Germany, Italy and even from Russia, though the combined total of all these is very small indeed. It must be admitted, however, that in the combine harvester range British models—mainly Massey-Ferguson—no longer occupy the major place, and the imported Claas from Germany and the New Holland Clayson from Belgium have taken nearly 60 per cent of the total market. In the smaller range of farm machinery, the Scandinavian spring tine harrows stole a march upon the British manufacturers, and have established a significant stronghold on British soil.

Until 1973 British Leyland headed the list of Britain's major exporting companies, but the following year ICI took over the lead from the strike-torn and ailing motor giant. There are four major farm-machinery companies in the 'top 100' exporters list. Massey-Ferguson hovers around tenth place annually, and is the largest exporter, as well as being unquestionably the largest manufacturer, and although Ford are among the top five, their exports are orientated towards cars, even though tractors from their Basildon plant are exported from Britain. In thirtieth place comes the Caterpillar Company, with its heavy crawler tractors. Ostensibly founded as a farm machinery company, with its crawlers used throughout the world, nevertheless it now occupies a major position in the field of civil engineering and earth moving. Ten places lower down the list comes International Harvester, with its range of tractors and farm machinery, and down the list at about number 75 comes the Tractor Division of David Brown, now part of the Tenneco empire with its home base in the USA.

Perkins, a subsidiary of Massey-Ferguson, supply Diesel engines to the Claas Combine Factory in Germany, where either Perkins or Mercedes engines are fitted for world-wide distribution. The cheaper Perkins engine occupies a larger share, and many of these are reimported into the UK in the completed combine harvesters. In other directions there is an interchange and reimportation of certain items, but among the countries which are supplied from the UK it comes as a surprise to find the USA so high on the list, the answer being that the British medium-powered tractor is a world-beater, although the products of the USA have a dominant role with the larger HP tractors and the heavy crawler versions.

Division of farm machinery exports

	Major Exporting Countries	£m	% share
Agricultural Machinery (general)	West Germany, France, Ireland and South Africa.	109	17
Tractors	South Africa, Australia, USA, Turkey, Japan, Scandinavia.	303	49
Tractor parts	USA, Belgo-Lux, France.	151	24
Engines for combines and and tractors	USA, France.	64	10
		£627 m	100

Source: Report of an Enquiry into Agricultural Exports, May 1976, Appendix 2.

Massey-Ferguson

The largest single contract ever won by British industry in Eastern Europe was the deal between Massey-Ferguson and the Polish foreign trade enterprise Agromet Motoimport, representing the Ursus Tractor Group of Companies. It was a £155 million deal to erect a new tractor factory near Warsaw, and in fact embodied the complete reconstruction and modernization of Poland's tractor industries. It was a deal completed together with other British companies such as GKN and CAV, aided and blessed by a consortium headed by Barclays Bank.

Gained against strong opposition from Poland's nearest western neighbour, West Germany, and flaunted in the face of Poland's friends in the Comecon, this coup by Massey-Ferguson gave it an outlet for its own Perkins engines and expertise. The Ursus tractor is now available in the UK, but is very similar to the M-F versions.

Massey-Ferguson, a world-wide company with its origins partly in Canada (Massey-Harris) and partly in the UK (Harry Ferguson), rationalized its combine-harvester manufacture by making only some models at the Kilmarnock factory, while producing others in its factories in France and Belgium; but the export of UK machinery from M-F has included agreements with the Egyptian authorities for a new 2,400-hectare cane development at Kom Ombo Aswan, although this included cane harvesters and cultivation equipment produced by Massey-Ferguson in Australia. It had introduced mechanized cane harvesting to Egypt in the early 1960s, and had been commissioned by the Egyptian Government to study the Kom Ombo scheme on reclaimed land near the Aswan Dam area. M-F also has a strong market in Turkey, and a factory using imported components from the UK.

British Agricultural Export Council

Despite its contribution to the export battle, British agriculture cannot be said to be a natural exporter, and apart from breeding livestock the farmer is not directly connected with exporting. His only interest lies in selling farm products as a means to sustain market prices by relieving the pressure. In this field meat and cereals are of prime interest, but both undergo processing before being exported. If farmers are not passionately interested in exporting, neither have successive governments utilized their full resources to promote exports. The chequered story of the British Agricultural Export Council illustrates the tepid nature of Government interest, despite its continual repetitive cry that Britain can only survive by the volume of its exports.

There are so many Government-inspired bodies with impressive names but little financial strength, and there is always a wide gulf between politicians and businessmen, each despising the other. Within the context of the national budget, the contributions towards export promotion are microscopic. In 1970–1, £6·8 million was contributed by the Government; that figure had dropped to only £3·7 million in 1973 (although it did rise to £12·6 million in 1975–6). The major portion of this was devoted to the promotion of Trade Fairs and Overseas Exhibitions, and the permanent UK Trade Centre in Tokyo.

In addition to the BAEC, there are only four other export councils: the Sino-British, East European, Middle East and Israel, and for a period the BAEC did not receive any Government funds at all. With such a small amount dedicated to the promotion of British products, how can we justify the lip service which politicians pay to this aspect of our trade?

The BAEC was created in 1966 at the instigation of the Government, as a private company limited by guarantee. It had the full support of the Ministry of Agriculture, the Department of Trade and Industry and the British Overseas Trade Board. A Welsh Agricultural Export Council had been formed the previous year, sponsored by the Royal Welsh Agricultural Society, with no paid staff, and provided with services by the RWAS. The BAEC was to be a co-ordinating organization which would be partly funded with a grant from the British Overseas Trade Board, and partly through subscriptions from its members. By 1970 the BAEC was receiving £10,000 from the BOTB, and had a membership of 152 trading companies or organizations. During that year twenty-three new members joined, and twenty-six resigned. The following year the grant was increased to £25,000, but in 1973 it was withdrawn in a fit of Government economy. Later that year its future was tentatively secured with an agreement that a contribution of pound for pound would be granted, with a minimum grant of £20,000. Members' subscription was already at that level, and the Council then had an assured income of £40,000.

In July 1975 the Minister of Agriculture, Fred Peart, asked his Advisory Council to look at the contribution of exports. This reported in 1976 that there was a potential for the increase of exports, but that more money would need to be injected. It considered that £150,000 would be sufficient for an initial year, but that to be effective this should quickly rise to £500,000. A levy on the agricultural industry was one proposal which did not find favour among the farmers, and the farm machinery manufacturers thought that they were doing a good job on their own. This report sparked off a debate, and highlighted the fragile existence of the BAEC, which was barely able to survive. It pointed out that in Germany, for instance, the promotion of agricultural products was sustained by an annual expenditure of £5 million.

From the outset the BAEC had been a baby of the NFU, with its office inside Agriculture House in Knightsbridge. Its Chairman had been from 1968 an expatriate German businessman, Sir Rudy Sternberg, later to become Lord Plurenden; but in 1973 Sternberg became its President, and an ex-President of the Board of Trade, Michael Noble, a Scottish landowner politician, became its new Chairman. Noble retired from the Commons in February 1974, and became Lord Glenkinglas. Deputy Chairman was Dean Swift, Director-General of the Agricultural Engineers Association, and a descendant of a famous figure with the same name. Glenkinglas, with his intimate knowledge of Government Departments, was an invigorating breath of fresh air to the BAEC, but he was on a sticky wicket. A new position of Director-General was created in January 1976, and an ex Under-Secretary in the Ministry of Agriculture, John Perrin, was appointed. Perrin had been Principal Private Secretary in the time of Heathcoat-Amory, had been the Ministry's Regional Controller for the Eastern Region, and had returned into the Whitehall orbit in 1967 to assist with the foot-and-mouth epidemic. When the crunch came Glenkinglas, Swift and Perrin all dramatically resigned at once.

After the publication of the Advisory Report which highlighted the necessity for greater funds a ham-fisted and at times acrimonious debate ensued. Into the picture now came the British Agricultural Council, a body which had been set up in April 1975, largely at the instigation of the NFU, to be an all-embracing and single voice representing seventeen organizations from the Marketing Boards, Co-Operative Organizations, Landowners Associations and the British Farm Produce Council. The BAC has a single role, to represent the voice of agriculture, but it has never become the authoritative body for which one might have hoped. Rival jealousies among all its sectionalized organizations ensure that any enhancement of its role will jeopardize the influence of its individual members; but in the matter of exports the NFU was cooling down, and kept a low profile. The office which had been in Agriculture House moved to 35 Belgrave Square, the London home of the RASE, in December 1976, and the RASE was beginning to come into the picture.

The question revolved around the financing of BAEC, and whilst the BAC promised £35,000 if the remaining money could be raised elsewhere, there was extreme reluctance among trade organizations to increase their subscriptions, even if the survival of BAEC were at stake. In the end the BAC withdrew its support, and Lord Glenkinglas (as he had now become), accused the NFU of sabotaging the whole organization. He and his colleagues resigned, and the RASE stepped into the breach to create a revamped council that could continue the promotion of British agricultural exports.

It is a moot point whether the BAEC could have continued in its low key co-ordinating role and occupied a useful, if minor, niche in the promotion of British exports, but the Advisory Council, under Sir Nigel Strutt, had advocated a massive enlargement of its role, and its Chairman, Glenkinglas, was set on this course. Richard Butler, Deputy President of the NFU, and Chairman of the Continuity Group of the British Agricultural Council, had said that the BAC made it clear that in its opinion there was no need for a greatly enlarged BAEC; it felt that a small co-ordinating body could carry out the necessary promotional and advisory work, while allowing the exporters to get on with the real work of selling their products overseas. Butler was a member of the RASE Committee set up with Frank Sykes as its Chairman, to pick up the pieces and to reconstruct the edifice. It issued a Confidential Prospectus in June 1977, yet the objectives of this new BAEC were little different from those of its defunct predecessor.

The major problem facing any organization designed to stimulate agricultural exports is that it strives to fulfil a role that is already largely conducted by other trade bodies, and entrepreneurial businessmen. As a co-ordinator, financial consultant, information desk or product research body, it cannot hope to compete with the existing enthusiasm of an energetic sales force, stimulated by a commercial company with its eye on expanding markets, and an overseas order book to prove its own success. With or without a BAEC, farm exports will continue, and market forces will prevail. It will have little impact upon farmers' pockets, and on the UK farming scene.

19 The Financial Structure

'Bankers are just like anybody else, except richer.'
Ogden Nash

The farming units of the big banks

The relative rating of the four major clearing banks in the UK is:

	Total Deposits	Advances
	(£m)	(£m)
National Westminster	13,395	7,125
Barclays	12,226	7,038
Lloyds	8,982	5,122
Midland	8,922	3,675

Source: Bank Returns 1977.[1]

They all claim to be the farmers' bank, and have the avowed intention of assisting him by overdrafts and advances; whatever the prosperity of farming may be, it certainly represents a good solid investment which won't run away. Farmers may be slow payers, but they always pay in the end, and the bankruptcy level is very low. Barclays and the Midland are jointly responsible for over 70 per cent of the total advances to farming, Lloyds has around 20 per cent and the National Westminster, the largest UK bank, has the smallest amount. Other banks such as Williams & Glyns now think it worth while to mount an exhibit at the Royal Show, and in 1972 the first merchant bank for agriculture was created in Scotland under the title 'Capital for Agriculture Ltd', although its headquarters were at Pocklington in Yorkshire. The Agricultural Mortgage Corporation supplies money for farm-purchase, and a small amount for improvement loans, the NFU-sponsored Agricultural Credit Corporation provides cash with a guarantee when all else has failed. United Dominions Trust is anxious to expand its loans to farmers for buying livestock, machinery and for modern buildings, while the pension funds have become large investors in land as well as farming on their own account. It all adds up to a massive effort to give farmers money: how lucky are the farmers?

This diversity of financial help is in contrast with the solitary but immense sources of aid which many other countries offer to their farmers, countries where agriculture is of greater relevance in the total economy. The Agricultural Bank of

[1] Barclays Bank Ltd comes out as the largest bank when combined with Barclays International. The above reading is the UK Internal League Table.

Greece or Crédit Agricole in France have no real counterparts in the UK.

Despite this pressure on them, farmers are in fact reluctant borrowers, and the old traditional method of financing a harvest was by way of credit from the merchants who supplied the seed and other ingredients throughout the year, then deducted these items from his cheque for the grain a year later. Merchants' credit terms have become expensive, and this method has largely died out, while it is estimated today that the total indebtedness of British agriculture is only between 5 and 7 per cent of its total equity. Against this, it would seem that British farmers and landowners own, without mortgage, nearly 95 per cent of the total industry, which puts it in an impregnable position but makes it a target for taxation. The massive security of farmers has sprung from the relative lack of extreme farming disasters, and from the business acumen of the agrobusinessmen. In Denmark, for example, 50 per cent of the equity of the industry is borrowed money.

With the ravages of inflation farmers' overdrafts have naturally risen. In 1945 they were only £74 million in debt to the major clearing banks, but this figure doubled in five years, doubled again in nine years, and doubled again in thirteen years. By 1971 it had reached a figure of £553 million, but by 1978 that figure had doubled again. Nevertheless, these increases have been remarkably small in relation to the massive shift in the development of farming techniques from men to machinery, which has been only achieved with a substitution of labour for capital investment. Farmers are small businessmen, and have largely financed their own expansion from their own retained profits. It is a situation which British industry cannot emulate, since its profits are largely distributed to expensive Boards of Directors, and its dividends to shareholders. The farmer takes no salary beyond his living expenses, and has no shareholders to pay.

During the past three decades when farming overdrafts have risen there has been a remarkable drop in the percentage of the total clearing banks advances to farming and its associated fishing industry. In 1956 farming took 11 per cent of total bank advances; ten years later, in 1966, it had dropped to only 9 per cent, and it then dropped dramatically in 1970 to only 4 per cent, where it has roughly remained ever since, with only minor fluctuations. At face value this situation would appear as a withdrawal by the major banks of their farming connections, but Peter Clery, Head of the National Westminster Farming Unit, put it in another light:[2]

> Bankers like farmers as borrowers. This relative decline does not, therefore, suggest a shortage of capital as it can be asserted with confidence that no sound viable proposition for a short term loan to a credit-worthy farmer or group is likely to be turned down by any of the clearing banks, except through some misunderstanding.

Banking is essentially short-term lending, but the needs of farming are long-term, and there has been some education of bank managers over the definition 'short-term'. This to the farmer may mean five years, whereas to a bank short-term is five months. The banks, moreover, have sought not to inject their funds

[2] *RASE Journal*, 1967, page 97.

into the very long-term purpose of financing additional land acquisitions; this at least was their declared policy, but under the guise of increasing overdraft limits, ostensibly to finance additional equipment to farm any expanded area, the banks have in fact financed land acquisition in a big way. Their vaults are today stuffed with the title deeds of more English land than ever before.

Although the monthly milk cheques for dairy farmers have been hailed as their salvation, and established their creditworthiness, nevertheless the seasonal demands of arable farmers suit the banks better. This is because it is the function of a bank to lend money for short periods, and since arable farmers with their seasonal income can technically repay the loans once a year, they are more in keeping with the ethics of good banking practice, and money turnover.

Farmers' bank borrowings in relation to other industries

	(£m)
Construction Industry	1,527
Chemical Industry	1,484
Food, drink and tobacco	1,474
Agriculture, Forestry and Fishing	1,152
Metal Manufacturing	542
Vehicles	507
Shipbuilding	447
Mining and Quarrying	466
Personal Loans	4,247

There has only been one report on farming finance on record. This report was entitled *Availability of Capital and Credit to UK Agriculture*, and the body that produced it was chaired by Professor John Wilson, head of the Department of Economics and Commerce at the University of Hull, and commissioned by the Minister of Agriculture in September 1970. The result of their lucubrations was not completed and published until three years later, produced no new facts, cost £9.50 per soft-cover copy, and was promptly pigeon-holed and forgotten. Nevertheless, it did suggest that there was no obvious requirement for new credit sources for farmers, and considered the existing financial institutions to be sufficient for farmers' needs. Professor Wilson even took the view that farmers had too easy a time obtaining credit. 'In some cases, bankers have lent farmers into trouble, and bank managers have not exercised sufficient control over their farmer customers,' said Professor Wilson. He recommended that farming did not warrant any 'special terms' or cheaper overdrafts, and emphasized that farmers should stand on their own financial feet, providing their own capital, and paying the interest on their borrowings from earnings. Professor Wilson came and went, and no one noticed.

The Farming Departments

Both Barclays and the Midland maintain a high-powered team which constitutes an Agricultural Department within the bank; the National Westminster have a small band, and Lloyds do not offer such a service to farmers in the UK. While most banks have specialized departments set up for the assistance of importers and exporters, and can usually get specialist advice on investment possibilities for their customers, the Farming Departments remain a strange and unique feature of the British banking scene.

Their objective would seem to be for monitoring the progress of farming accounts, to make a reputation for themselves within the semi-closed world of agriculture, and to retain some measure of security in the event of customers getting into deep water. The pragmatic approach of the banks differs. The Midland team stand on the inside, looking outward. The National Westminster looks inward to safeguard the bank's interests, and Barclays endeavours to look both ways at once. The origins of the Banking Departments were in 1955 at the Midland, but today it is only Barclays who have really joined in a massive push to invest their funds in farming. The leaders of the two teams, Dr Robert Bruce of the Midland and Philip Bolam of Barclays, are well known in the farming industry, using their prestigious platforms, and their inside knowledge to pontificate on the industry. It is said that a good MP represents his constituents at Westminster, and not Westminster in his constituency, but the banking representatives often represent their employers in draughty village halls.

They vie with each other to sit on the most influential bodies within agriculture; Dr Bruce was Chairman of the Oxford Farming Conference in 1976 and persuaded his boss, Lord Armstrong,[3] to be the principal speaker at the Pre-Conference Dinner. That speech was most unfortunate: after a downturn in farming fortunes and a very dry season, it might be thought hardly diplomatic to tell the farmers how well off they were. These things can sometimes rebound! Bruce and Bolam both sit on the important Committee of the Farmers Club, and they both sponsor important competitions at the Dairy Farming Annual Show. In other diverse ways, they seek to promote their banks' image. In this race the National Westminster and Lloyds fall far behind, but in particular areas of the country either may still be the largest farmers' bank. For instance, Lloyds has the majority of its farming customers in the West Country, Barclays in the eastern counties, while the Midland, as befits its name, is strongest in the territory from Northampton northward. The influence of the National Westminster is more thinly spread over the country.

The origins of the 'Agricultural Units' were in 1955, when Adrian Collingwood was appointed as a liaison officer between the Midland Bank and the NFU, to investigate cases where farmer customers felt that they were not getting sufficient credit or attention. Collingwood's banking knowledge, plus his considerable sympathy with farming matters—he came from a country background—convinced him that bankers as a race were grossly ignorant of the financial requirements and problems of farming. He also discovered that farmers were

---

[3] Formerly Sir William Armstrong, Secretary to the Cabinet.

largely frightened of their bank manager, fearing to pay the cost of increased overdrafts, but were paying higher charges to merchants for the time-honoured system of seasonal merchant credit. A bank manager on the farm was seen as a figure of doom.

There was the inevitable credit squeeze in operation when Collingwood completed his inquiries, but he convinced the Midland Bank that when credit facilities were easier it would be sensible to make a major incursion into farming. It was some years later, when the Land Boom was in full force, and scapegoats were being sought, that Dunstan Court[4] accused Collingwood, and the original Barclays man, Alan Mitchell, of being the two men most responsible for the horrifying escalation in land values. They had gone through the 1960s proclaiming the virtues of land-ownership as an under-valued asset, with obvious expansionist certainty, and choosing any baseline, they proclaimed that farmland was the best investment that could be obtained. In this they were right, and their major drive to push money into the hands of sometimes reluctant farmers gave the banks a substantial stake in the industry.

Collingwood's inquiry came up with four conclusions:

1 No bank appeared to be anxious to let farmers know what their range of facilities was, or how they could help. They remained dark-suited and aloof.
2 Bankers were adopting a close policy with farmers, frightening them with the typical banker's philosophy: 'How soon can I have the money back?' Not, as Collingwood observed, 'What stage have you reached in your development plans, and what are your future plans?'
3 Bank managers had a horrifying image among farmers, and if one sought to learn some of the intricacies of the business by a personal visit the neighbours would draw the wrong conclusion.
4 Most farmers did not regard their bank managers as professional advisers in the same sense as their land agents, or even their accountants, but were frightened of them and tried to shun them.

Collingwood did not mention that many of these points were typical of the general approach of bankers to all their customers, but his inquiry bore fruit, and in 1958 the Midland appointed him its first farming representative in the UK. It was a breakthrough, and the farmers found him a subject of awe and considerable interest. He was projected into the front line, with a full diary of talks, broadcasts, TV appearances and speeches. The Midland had already decided upon a major drive into a sector in which it was traditionally weak, and this was a project which took off from the outset. Collingwood soon acquired an assistant, while the financial and business aspects of farming took a sudden leap forward as farmers listened with respect to this erudite man, then went home and worked out their own figures.

Collingwood came upon the scene at the right historic moment. He propounded the philosophy that the technological and mechanical revolution in

[4] *British Farmer and Stockbreeder*, 25 November 1972.

farming needed finance, but that it could not all be provided from retained profits. Such was the faith of the Midland (which was to be fully justified in time) that it invested 10 per cent of its own money in this new-found and profitable outlet. Rules were laid down, of course, and bankers suddenly realized that a farm required continual injections of capital until it reached a zenith of efficiency, but providing the profits were good, and the farmer was not spending them all in the exotic Caribbean, or his time on the golf course, then his banker would always be his friend. Money for fast-depreciating machinery should be repayable relative to the depreciation, and overdraft facilities would not normally exceed the farmer's stake. They wanted him to be the major investor, and to sustain his majority enthusiasm; they were prepared to break their own rules and extend credit of 100 per cent for a farm purchase that would enable the customer to increase the profitability of his business. Certain that farmland was still too cheap, they decided with commendable foresight to back the young man with little track record. Local bank managers were encouraged to participate in local farming affairs, to visit farms at least once a year, and to dispel farmers' fears. This policy of humanization was an important public relations exercise.

Collingwood was a banker, and his first assistant, Emrys Evans, was another banker with experience in farming circles in Wales and the West Midlands, being manager at Oswestry and Cardiff. However, ten years after establishing the 'Agricultural Unit' the Midland broke new ground by appointing a non-banker to this select circle: he was Dr Robert Bruce, son of an agricultural adviser at the West of Scotland College of Agriculture in Dumfries, with a Ph.D at Durham in Grassland Management, with experience in the NAAS and later in the Agricultural Credit Corporation. It was an imaginative appointment, and when Collingwood retired to take over the Chairmanship of the British Egg Marketing Board (later, in 1971, to be called the Eggs Authority) it was Bruce who took over the job. The Midland team expanded with the addition of technical experts from farming fields, rather than bankers. Norman Coward came from the Milk Marketing Board Costings Division, Douglas McFarlane came from the Agricultural Credit Corporation, which he had joined as Bruce left, his previous experience having been with the MMB and the Farm Buildings Centre. Richard Bevan was Farms Manager to Viscount Leverhulme from 1959 to 1964, established the Inglewood Development Farm of R. Silcock & Sons, and was appointed Farm Management Adviser to BOCM-Silcock on the merger in February 1971. Edward Belk was a bank manager from Boston, but with a farming background. Thus the original solid banking background of the farming team was strengthened beyond all recognition by orientation towards the technical side of farming.

Barclays

It was nine years after the appointment of Collingwood by the Midland Bank before Barclays decided to establish the post of Barclays Group Farming

Representative on 1 May 1967, although six months earlier it had appointed an Agricultural Adviser to Barclays DCO with the avowed intention of increasing the involvement of Barclays in Africa and the Caribbean. Alan Mitchell was the first Barclays Farming Representative, and although the bank was later than the Midland in the field, the fast-talking and forceful Scot Mitchell soon took farming by storm. His views were similar: that farming was largely under-valued. Although the traditional East Anglian background of Barclays had firmly established its position in the major arable areas, there was still tremendous scope for expansion into farming. Mitchell was a banker, but he held a joint interest in a farm with his brother; so he was in effect himself a farmer. But it was his authoritative manner which established his reputation and the position of Barclays in the eyes of farmers.

Barclays produced the first, and one of the best, publications about the coming Common Market, followed it with another, and diagnosed the whole farming industry in a way in which it had not been done before. A comprehensive guide to sources of finance has been an annual and expanding popular publication, even if the Forward Budgeting Plan is the least comprehensible of those emanating from the clearing banks. Their popular representative, Mitchell, stayed in the post for only four years, until November 1971, when he was succeeded by another banker, Norman Kew. Mitchell went back into the internal banking circuit as a Local Director at Nottingham, but he later moved onto the international scene, utilizing his vast experience of food and farming matters. Kew was a banker first and foremost, and during his tenure the stock of Barclays among farmers fell as the Midland forged ahead, while the new conglomerate National Westminster also began to make an impact. Less than two years later, Kew was moved to Birmingham, and Barclays appointed an ex-ADAS officer, with a flamboyant personality and the rugged exterior of a farmer, in his place.

Philip Bolam took over from Kew with the experience of practical farming in Norfolk and the South-West Region based on Bristol. His Newcastle accent and his dynamic approach to farming matters, coupled with an intense energy, re-created for Barclays the prestige it had lost. Its team expanded, and diversified itself into Regional Representatives as the Midland had done in 1972. It launched new courses on farm management finance for its own branch managers, with visits to the National Agricultural Centre; it produced a film *Jack's All Right*, which took a Film Award, and it started sending its Assistants to the Royal Agricultural College, Cirencester, for a two-year secondment. Barclays has since appointed new Representatives with a farming background, but still concentrates more on banking experience than the Midland, which has gone wholeheartedly towards the practical side. Mitchell had seen his job as liaison between the bank and its customers, incorporating the trends, needs and problems with practice; it was a public relations job, but does not carry the authority to grant overdrafts *per se*, although local managers will act upon the agriculturalists' advice. He also conceived his task as a study of the agricultural industry, to detect movements in the Government support system, and to measure the impact of the EEC, which could affect farming fortunes. In short, the Barclays terms of reference are providing some service for their farmer customers, but also preserving a wary eye on the bank's interests. Thus Barclays did not, and does not, seek to emulate the open-handed dispensation of money which was a symbol of the Midland's approach.

The Farming Department does not see all the farming accounts of their customers, only those who are in trouble, but it knows the national trends, and can give practical advice on the farming system while standing in a draughty cowshed, or confidence to a hesitant bank manager who does not understand the seasonal vagaries of farming. Barclays has also, with heart-searching, readjusted its own ideas of the definition of these terms in farming circles.

National Westminster

The National Provincial and the Westminster Bank merged in September 1969, this proving one of the largest mergers ever to take place in British financial history. Barclays had taken over the North Country orientated Martins Bank in 1960 but the resulting new 'National Westminster' was a major feature of the UK banking scene, reducing the original 'Big Five' to the 'Big Four'. The Westminster had an agriculturalist amongst its staff who could deal with intricate farming matters, but the National Provincial, being more urban-orientated, had no such post. After the merger the Agricultural Unit was created, and Peter Clery was appointed its manager, a position he held until 1978.

Clery contrasted starkly with Bruce and Bolam, and played his role in a lower key. His Department consisted of himself and the objective was to advise the bank upon agricultural matters, both major and minor; thus overall policy matters regarding the future prosperity of the farming industry was an important aspect of his work. Another was the farming implications and likely financial involvement of proposals which came up from the bottom. It is a role which kept him ensconced largely in the city magnificence of the National Westminster Head Office in aptly named Poultry.

Nat-West do, however, produce an annual booklet on farm finance, and forward budgeting forms. Peter Clery, lithe and articulate, has an agricultural degree, owns his own small stock farm in Sussex, and was once a journalist. He has pipped the other banking representatives with an authoritative book entitled *Farming Finance*, and in more subtle ways represents the interests of his bank. But the whole policy is much quieter than that of the two major banks in the farming world.

Lloyds

Lloyds maintains that its interest in farming matters is as dedicated as its rivals, and its inbuilt strength in the West Country seems impregnable, but it has no Farming Unit as such and relies upon sending one manager each year for a course at Wye College, after which managers act as instructors to their colleagues, later returning to the normal management stream. Lloyds started this procedure in 1968 to ensure that its managers could have, within the organization, an expert opinion. It has no intention of setting up an Agricultural Department, and specific inquiries are resolved at one of the sixteen Regional Offices which its diversified organization sustains.

Lloyds sponsors cups and trophies on a smaller scale than do the other major banks, but it lacks a figurehead or a presence at the major farming events. However, the connection with farming remains, and the story is quoted[5] of a former bank manager cum farmer. 'In the 1870s the Gloucestershire Banking Company's Manager at Stow-in-the-Wold had a farm about six miles away, and spent much of his time running it, while the cashier kept an eye on his own farm next door to the bank'. When Birmingham was a market centre for farmers, and not the industrial centre it is today, Lloyds was there, and Howard Lloyd, writing of the 1860s, said, 'I recall the farmers and other country people who gravitated to the end of the counter where Mr Tatnall could talk of pigs, potatoes and turnips.' It would seem that Mr Tatnall was a clerk or cashier well acquainted with farming.

Bankers Avenue

The lavish permanent pavilions of the major banks at the Royal Showground have resulted in 'Bankers Avenue' adjacent to the Royal Pavilion, and forming a central meeting-place which emphasizes the deep involvement of the banks with the agricultural industry.

Barclays had a commanding position, with a massive pavilion built at a cost of £50,000, and an architectural award to boot, but the Agricultural Mortgage Corporation built another pavilion which spoilt its view in 1976.

Barclays is the largest pavilion, Lloyds the most solid, National Westminster architecturally the most avant garde, and the Midland, tucked at the back and almost hidden by trees, resembles a busy airport lounge. It was opened by Sir Henry Plumb in 1971.

Crédit Agricole

Crédit Agricole is certainly a farmer's bank in the truest sense, and acts as a catalyst for French farming finance in a way that is more comprehensive than anywhere else in the world. It is not simply just another rural-orientated co-operative bank, but is itself the world's third largest bank. Neither is it restricted nowadays to purely farming customers: its diversity into other business, and as a substantial force in the money markets of the world, belies its humble origin and its rural background.

[5] *History of Lloyds Bank* (R. S. Sayers, 1957).

France is more essentially than Britain a nation of small farmers, and the problems of dragging a peasant-type subsistence-level farming community into the highly pressurized farming world of today has been a slower process. It has, however, promoted the role of Crédit Agricole in the transformation process.

Crédit Agricole was founded in 1894 to meet the growing needs of the French farming community through a decentralized co-operative banking structure. Today it has over ten thousand branches, and its name is to be found all over France where the needs of farmers can be met. It is a measure of its diversification and its expansionist policy that only 53 per cent of its advances today are in agriculture, but even this contrasts starkly with the 4 per cent of the British clearing banks. In other more rural nations, there are facilities for farmers' banking, but in the UK the needs of farmers are met through the normal channels.

Agricultural Mortgage Corporation

'Worm or beetle—drought or tempest—on a farmer's land may fall
Each is loaded full of ruin—but a mortgage beats 'em all.'
'The Tramp's Story' (Will Carleton)

'One description of a farm is: a piece of land covered by a mortgage.'

In the first fifty years of its existence (1928–1978) the AMC assisted in the purchase of over 2 million hectares of farms in England and Wales at a cost of £461 million, but the farmers took up £351 million of this between 1964 and 1977, and since the corporation's inception they have repaid £150 million of the original loans. This represents more than the total lendings of the AMC from its year of origin to 1967. It is not a sinecure for cash unlimited.

The AMC is tough on its customers (as befits sound financial practice), and never grants 100 per cent loans to finance the purchase of a farm or farmland. It bases its loans upon a two-thirds/three-quarters advance of its own valuation of the property, which inevitably falls below the actual purchase price; thus the generosity of the AMC can often result in an advance to an applicant that is no more than 50 per cent of the proposed purchase price. However, since only 2 per cent of its advances are to newcomers into the farming scene, there is normally another farm which can be mortgaged to fulfil the security requirements. Certainly the prudence of the AMC is affected by its links with Government, even if these are tenuous, and contrasts sharply with the panache of the banks.

There is a difference—the AMC is lending money on the farm, and normally likes to have a complete one, with its farmhouse, farm buildings and surrounding land. The harshness of this policy has lessened in recent years as it realized that there was an open channel for a cash injection to finance existing farmers who wished to buy neighbouring land, and would not wish to retain the farmhouse, or even an indifferent set of buildings redundant to modern farming needs. But the

AMC loan is strictly on the property itself, while the banks are backing the individual. Farms can be sold with an existing AMC mortgage—some are still around which were taken out at very advantageous interest rates, and these continue with the farm—whereas a bank advance or overdraft cannot be transferred, and dies with its owner. The AMC keeps a watching brief upon farming trends, but is more interested in land values, while the banks take a pedantic interest in the farmer's annual turnover, cash flows and of course his profitability. Therein lies the difference.

The total stake of the AMC in agriculture represents only a quarter of that of the clearing banks, and is only 10 per cent of the total indebtedness of the farming industry. As such it fulfils a vital role but demonstrates that the AMC is in no way a counterpart of Crédit Agricole. Its origins were at a time of acute agricultural depression, to finance the purchase of land, when many landowners would willingly give farms to prospective tenants rent-free initially, simply to keep the weeds down—a strange way of providing assistance. Nevertheless, despite any original misconceptions, the AMC has adopted a more flexible role in recent years, and with the changing emphasis upon owner occupation the pre-existing AMC was an existing autonomous body that has come to fulfil a useful role.

A feature of the range of loans which the AMC grants is the amount which sitting tenants have borrowed to purchase their farms, a substantial amount which farmers have taken in lieu of the repayment of other loans (which may include taxes), and the considerable amount which is annually borrowed from the AMC for the purchase of additional land and farms by existing farmers.

A fluctuating variable interest rate loan was introduced in 1972, and five years later it had been taken up for about 25 per cent of the total amount lent, with about 50 per cent of the new loans being on a variable rate. The high interest rates of the mid-1970s deterred many farmers from embarking upon an indeterminate period of borrowing at a fixed high rate. It can be assumed that if rates are ever down to 4 per cent, then long-term borrowers will opt for the security which it can offer. The majority of farmers opt for the forty-year repayment basis, and only about 13 per cent for anything in the 8–10 year bracket. These are normally smaller loans which the farmer optimistically promises to wipe out in a short period. About 4 per cent of the AMC loans are for working capital, and about 5 per cent for capital improvements; the remainder goes solidly into the purchase of farms, which was the original intention. Two surveys, conducted by the AMC in 1970 and again in 1973, revealed that in the former year 25 per cent of its loan applications arrived via local bank managers, while in 1973 only 13 per cent came in this fashion. The obvious lesson to be drawn was that the banks were themselves accommodating those farmers who needed cash. The same surveys also recorded that in 1970 23 per cent of the applicants applied themselves, but three years later this had shot up to 32 per cent. This was a boost to the AMC, and the effectiveness of its public relations department. The banks had realized the potential in farming; the AMC just took a little longer.

Undoubtedly, AMC owed much to its managing director, Clive de Paula, a short, dapper man with a black military moustache. His distinguished wartime career had included liaison with the Free French Forces, service in the Middle East, East Africa, Ceylon and Burma, and he had finished up in charge of the Finance Division of the Control Commission in Germany. After a peacetime career in management, and a spell as industrial adviser to the Government, he came to the AMC in 1971 as a breath of fiery air. He enlivened proceedings with his peppery vitality; Collingwood and Mitchell had destroyed the dusty myths about bankers, and de Paula did the same for the AMC. His 'de Paula Plan'[6] was not adopted by the Government, but he focused attention upon the problems of land-ownership.

A company director, John Glyn, has been Chairman of AMC since 1964, but de Paula remains its flamboyant figurehead.

The early days

During the depressed 1920s it had become apparent that UK agriculture needed a source of uncallable long-term capital to finance the purchase and development of farmland. Industry had been able to exploit the joint stock company as a means for raising capital, but due to its fragmented structure farming was unable to employ this method. With these considerations in mind, the Agricultural Credits Act 1928 was passed, and AMC was set up as a lending agency, raising its funds on the London money market, and channelling them into agriculture. One of its early maxims was 'to lend on most favourable terms', a philosophy with which modern borrowers might not whole-heartedly agree. It is not a Government subsidiary, and the share capital is subscribed by the Bank of England and the London clearing banks, although the original Act empowered the Minister of Agriculture to advance money free of interest for sixty years. These advances were to be invested in gilt-edged securities to form a guarantee fund as backing for issues of AMC's debentures. The existence of this fund enabled the AMC to compete in the gilt-edged market on terms more favourable than those available to ordinary commercial or industrial companies. The AMC had a chequered history in the pre-War years; in its first year of operation, 1930, it lent no less than £4·1 million, illustrating the backlog of a depressed industry, but the following year, with the pressure reduced, it lent only half that amount, and a quarter in the following year. Until 1945 the amounts loaned annually to the industry were pathetically small, averaging about one-third of a million pounds. It was not until 1946 that the annual figure went over £1 million a year, and it was eighteen years later before it reached £10 million. In the year ending March 1977 that figure more than quadrupled.

The story of AMC was summed up by the Chairman, Glyn, in his Statement at the AGM in 1977, when he recorded:

[6]See page 149.

Soon after AMC's foundation in 1928, a sharp drop in interest rates caught it wrong footed, and it was necessary for the Government to make annual grants to balance our profit and loss account. In those circumstances from 1936–1963, we paid no dividend at all, but, nevertheless, in 1964, in consideration of further Government help, the maximum dividend payable to our shareholders was reduced from 5% to 3½% per annum. Now I am pleased to report that the whole sum of £1.5 million, which had been received in grants from the Government, has been repaid.

AMC's success has been helping in the purchase of farmland where the banks will not. It would seem that the Devonshire farmers, with their small-farm structure, have vied with the Norfolk farmers, with their traditionally larger farms, to compete in the League Table of County Uptake.

AMC loans from inception (without repayment)

County	(ha)	Number of Transactions	Amount
Devonshire	63,109	1,596	£22·1 m
Norfolk	57,075	797	£14·7 m
Shropshire	42,813	847	£15·14 m
Lincolnshire & Humberside	39,057	574	£15·1 m

It is not known how many approaches to bank managers are met with rebuttal, but the AMC shows that the number of applications which end in solid loans is only half the number of original applications. In 1948 only one in four applications were granted, but since 1967 this has averaged one in every two.

The AMC resides on one of the upper floors of Bucklersbury House in the City of London, hard by the Old Lady of Threadneedle Street herself. It looks down on the ancient foundations of the Temple of Mithras which was unearthed when Bucklersbury House was built. It would seem that the foundations of the AMC are solid and secure.

The Scottish Agricultural Securities Corporation Ltd

The SAS was founded in 1933, and is four years younger than its English counterpart, the AMC. By 1977 the total outstanding loans to Scottish farmers had amounted to £13·8 million, compared to the £311 million advanced and outstanding by the AMC. Though Scotland is a smaller country, the canny Scots farmers seem less in need of additional capital than do their English counterparts.

The 40th Annual Report of SAS in 1973 stated, with some alarm, that there was a rapidly reducing demand for loans, and cited two basic reasons: firstly, that there was a decrease in the number of farms on the market for sale; and secondly, that many farms were being purchased outright. Said the Annual Report: 'It is a matter of concern that enquiries and applications are received quite frequently from working farmers who find, when the price of a farm is advertised, that it is quite beyond their ability to meet the cash requirement towards the purchase price.'

The SAS altered its methods of valuation—1973 was a time of rapidly escalating land values—and opted for a new policy of providing a valuation for the money to be advanced on a basis of what could reasonably be paid in mortgage interest, expressed in terms of the earning capacity of the farm. Although this open-handed policy seemed contrary to the normal Scots character, there was a sting in the tail. SAS asked its valuers to fix a rental, and to calculate the leading valuation figure on a 4 per cent return. In other words, the amount to be lent would be twenty-five times what would be considered a normal rent. This hardly met a situation of rising prices, and although new lendings reached a peak of £1·5 million in 1973, they were not much over £2 million by 1978. Scottish land values in many areas are lower than those in England and Wales, although in favoured areas they can be substantially higher than in England. However, SAS has discovered a growing trend of applications from Englishmen and Irishmen who have sought to expand their farming enterprises in Scotland, while retaining their other farms.

Farmers in Northern Ireland do not have the advantages of either an AMC or an SAS, and loans (which are much smaller) are made through the Ministry of Agriculture, and called MANI loans. These may be for the purchase of new machinery or livestock or for the erection and improvement of farm buildings. These loans are not restricted to farmers, and agricultural contractors are also within the orbit for application. Farm amalgamation loans are available for periods up to forty years, and a MANI loan may be for as little as £100. The Wilson Enquiry[7] suggested that it might be advantageous to alter the constitution of the AMC and allow it to set up a branch in Northern Ireland, although it admitted that the needs were small.

The farmer and his taxes

'All taxes must, at last, fall upon agriculture.'
'Decline and Fall of the Roman Empire' (Edward Gibbon)

'The tax burden for some farmers may also have the effect of undermining any ambition to expand.'
'Agriculture into the 1980s: The Impact of Taxation',
NEDO, June 1977.

Farmers, like all other individuals, are subjected to the rigours of taxation, yet in some ways the burden is relieved and they are accorded special treatment, whereas in other directions it would seem that farming is a direct target of the Inland Revenue. Farm buildings are largely exempt from paying the sort of rates which industrial premises attract; the industrial user pays more towards local

---

[7] Availability of Capital and Credit to UK Agriculture. Professor J. S. G. Wilson (HMSO, 1973).

authority rates than do householders; although the clamour from householders is the greater. But although the advent of capital taxation hit hardest at farmers who own their land, a low-yielding asset such as farmland still enjoys a measure of protection, without being in any way a tax-saving dodge.

In terms of income tax, farmers have complained that the swings and roundabouts of their fortunes are the results of climatic and seasonal swings over which they have no control; thus 'averaging' farmers' income tax over three years would solve the problem of paying it all away in the good years, and having nothing left for investment in the bad ones. In the UK authors, sportsmen and pop stars are accorded an 'averaging' treatment, but there has been a reluctance on the part of successive Governments to press the case for agriculture with the Treasury again because of any possible 'bandwagon' effect which other sections might try to emulate. Certainly the shipping industry is one with enormous ups and downs, and which could well fall into the same category as farming, while many other small businessmen might feel that they also had a case for ironing out the fluctuations in their income. John Silkin in 1976, within weeks of coming to the Ministry of Agriculture, floated this idea to placate farmers for his refusal to devalue the green pound, which was having a harmful effect upon farm prices. While the farming organizations broadly supported him, they had in the past given only muted approval to this system, in all fairness leaning over backwards to maintain the farming dictum: 'that farmers accept the weather as part of the normal risks of the job'. When it was introduced in 1978 it was said that the NFU had campaigned for thirty years for this alleviation but many farmers believed it would be of little benefit, although in fact it would have made a considerable tax saving for the sky-high profits made from potatoes in 1976.

There are, however, certain aspects of income tax laws which favour farmers like no others. The farmhouse, as the farmer's residence, is not only assessed at a lower value for local authority rates but it is also considered the farm office, so that a proportion of its upkeep, its heating and lighting and its repairs, is eligible for income tax relief; similarly, the farmer's telephone and his motor-car are considered part of the business. In contrast, the commuter or other worker is never allowed relief on his expenses for travelling to his workplace, on the assumption that he lives near or far away from it by his own free choice. Since farmers are forced to live on the premises, it would seem that they can claim the expenses of travelling away from their work for income tax relief. Since they live in the country, moreover, they must have cars to conduct their business.

It is also assumed that farmhouses are large houses, and that the farmer chose his farm first and was saddled with whatever house was upon the land, so that lower rating assessments than would be normal for the same size hereditament are allowable. Farm buildings (much to the chagrin of industrialists) have not been subjected to normal rates since 1929, when de-rating was given as a measure to assist farming at a time of acute depression. It is fair to say that if all farm buildings were suddenly rated again, many which are picturesque buildings would be demolished, since they are unsuitable for the demands of modern farming. There have been demands for the reintroduction of rates on farm buildings several times in the period since 1945. There were proposals in the 1950s and 1960s, and again in the 1970s. In 1971 a Tory Government turned down proposals to re-rate agricultural land (which similarly bears no rates), but the Layfield Committee in 1975 produced its report on local government finance, which was under considerable pressure at the time, and incorporated into its recommendations a suggestion that farmland and buildings should once again be rated. The obvious problems of valuation and assessment on such a wide scale would keep an army of valuers busy for many years; in fact, the Inland Revenue itself suggested it would take five years to implement a Parliamentary Bill to re-rate agriculture. But the NFU quickly pointed out that, unlike most other industries, farmers, being subjected to price-fixing by the Government, could not pass on their costs to the consumer. Any remuneration that would accrue to them from rating farmland, while it would hurt the farming industry, would amount only to a mere 2·7 per cent of total rate income, while the cost of raising it would be exceptionally high.

In the early 1960s local authorities had woken up to the revolution that was taking place in the new broiler industry, the vertical integration that was producing 'factory farms'. Here, although the birds being kept were farm animals under the protection of the 1947 Agriculture Act, nevertheless, since many of these birds never saw daylight, and were not being kept in conjunction with the neighbouring farmland, while slaughtering facilities at the other end were preparing the birds for market, it all added up to a factory operation and not a farming one. The conditions for alleviation of rates were contained in the phrase 'used solely in connection with agricultural land in the same occupation, and any ancillary land or buildings'. These new broiler factories were against the spirit of that definition, and local authorities started a system of rating. Farmers could apply for exemption by proving that birds being kept in such buildings were eating the produce of the adjoining land, and it was an integrated part of a mixed farming system. Many could not prove this, the newly growing empires of the broiler kings were extending by the erection of highly concentrated chicken-rearing buildings sensibly placed in isolated plots of land, to remove the possibilities of contagious disease running rampant through a closely knit and larger single site.

In 1968 a Court of Appeal Case was heard called *W. & J. B. Eastwood Ltd* v. *Herrod* (Valuation Officer), overruling a decision of the Land Tribunal that a hundred buildings being used in conjunction with 460 hectares of land were not exempt because the hens stayed in the layer houses all their lives, the cockerels were only on free range for 12 weeks out of a 64-week life, and only 4 per cent of the feeding requirements of the birds came from the farm which surrounded the buildings. This decision placed broiler houses firmly within the category of normal rates, and went to the House of Lords for final judgment in March 1970.

The Lords endorsed the verdict of the Court of Appeal, and Eastwoods discovered that their broiler houses were to be rated. But the case had drawn attention to the thin dividing line between agricultural and ancillary usage and the Government was not happy that the law was as sensible as it should be. Following the House of Lords decision, the Department of the Environment in November 1970 circulated proposals for the de-rating of all buildings in which livestock were being intensively reared. These included egg-packing stations, slaughter-houses, stud farms, kennels and buildings used for bee-keeping, and it sought to widen the existing scope of rate alleviation. In 1971 all intensive livestock buildings were freed from rate-payment.

The Labour Party has advocated the rating of agricultural land, and in evidence to the Layfield Committee said, 'Whatever may have been the justification for the de-rating of agricultural land, the ending of it is now long overdue', while the Tory Party has generally defended the farmers' position. Certainly rural re-rating would be anomalous: the Government is responsible for regulating food prices, any additional costs for the farmer would rebound upon the cost of food, and consequently upon the popularity of any Government.

Capital taxation

Until 1965 farmers suffered very little from the ravages of penal taxation; the old death duties and the subsequent estate duty had embodied a 45 per cent relief on agricultural land. This had assisted in holding together the larger farms, although death duties had broken up many of the larger estates. The 45 per cent relief applied to agricultural land, and gave rise to the phenomenon known as 'death-bed purchasers', by which a wealthy man could buy a farm while virtually on his death-bed, saving 45 per cent of the tax bill after his demise. The property could be resold at a later date, and a large lump of the estate would have passed from one generation to another, and escaped the most penal of the tax bills. Some farms were the subject of a continual change of ownership, and the tenant farmer often had little knowledge of the identity of his current landlord. In total, the relief on agricultural property was £100 million per annum out of a total collection annually of £4,000 million. This was only a quarter of 1 per cent, but the outcry against such a blatant flouting of the tax laws was emotional rather than economic: politicians are swayed more often by emotive issues than by economic ones. This loophole was closed when capital transfer tax was introduced in 1975.

In 1965 capital gains tax was introduced, which aimed at taxing any increase in the valuation at death, or even on re-sale, from the assessed value as at 31 March 1965. In its initial years it gathered little for the tax man, and hurt the donors very little as well, but as inflation gathered pace and the 1965 value began to look historic, the knife began to bite deeper. Farmland was also escalating violently in price when planning permission was granted for development, and prior to 1965 there was little tax on this cash inflow into the industry, although the argument ran that the planners' seal should not be a licence to print money.

As the price of land rose farmers bitterly looked around for a scapegoat, and in desperation themselves opted to remove the 45 per cent death-duty relief and other benefits which were attracting financiers into farms as a tax haven. Since the vulnerability of farmers is allied to the price of land, then any reduction of this price would have beneficial effects in the process of handing over to one's son. Farmers and landowners may be considered in the category of 'small businessmen', but in practice many are millionaires when their land is assessed. Like an oil painting which is pleasant to look at, but yields little dividend, farmland is a highly priced object with a low return. If the objective of Governments is to retain the structure of a healthy industry, then its fragmentation through slashing taxation is contrary to this objective. Conversely, farmers and landowners must represent the largest remaining class of 'wealthy' people with assets which would make them appear very rich indeed if and when they were sold. The farmers' reply that they have no intention of selling carries little weight in a society which has been moving for a long time, and with the general acquiescence of both the major political parties, towards a greater sharing of wealth.

Estate duty was on the way out even under the Tory Government of Heath. In March 1972 it issued a Green Paper setting out a possible inheritance tax to replace estate duty, and the writing was on the wall for massive taxation changes. When Dennis Healey became Chancellor of the Exchequer after Wilson won the March 1974 Election he was pledged to a policy of soaking the rich. Even with a minuscule majority in the House, and the knowledge that another general election could not be long delayed, he published new proposals for wealth and capital transfer taxes in August 1974.

Wilson won the October election, and the real battle over the new taxes began. In the event, proposals for a wealth tax were discarded as being too difficult to implement, but the capital transfer tax set out to tax capital whenever it was transferred, and not just upon death. Prior to this large chunks of capital, or even farms, could be handed over to the next generation, and providing the donor lived long enough afterwards all taxes were evaded. Now the rule was to hit hard at any transfer from one person to another, with the exception that spouses could interchange property free of tax, and there was some reduction in the rates at the lower levels, with the first £15,000 duty-free (increased to £25,000 in October 1977). Farmers fought bitterly against the imposition of this tax, which created a double tax situation for lifetime gifts, whereby even if the capital transfer tax was paid, the donor was also responsible for any capital gains tax resulting from its enhanced value since 1965.

The CLA, in whose province taxation was, pointed out that the capital taxation per head of population in the UK now amounted to £10 per annum, but even in socialist Sweden it was only £8, in West Germany £6, and in Italy and France only £2. It also emphasized that income tax was higher in the UK than in the remainder of Europe, and that CTT, introduced in the Finance Bill in March 1975, would cost Britain's landowners and farmers at least £124 million every year, compared with only £37 million under the previous estate duty laws. (With the 45 per cent abatement, the Treasury in fact collected only £20 million.) It emphasized that there would be a sixfold increase in the impact of capital taxation.

In an unprecedented appeal to all parliamentary candidates in the 1974 Election, the CLA President, Tim Heywood, had pointed out that owners of farms would no longer be able to invest in the development and expansion of those farms; they would not be able to retire and hand over to their sons, but would have to hang on grimly until death. Farms were facing a run-down and fragmentation. The output of food in Britain would fall, scarcities would occur, consumer prices would soar, and the nation would suffer. Only those farms under 14 hectares would be better off under capital transfer tax than under estate duty. Moreover, that UK heritage of woodland which is a feature of the countryside would deteriorate, and planting would cease.

However, Hampshire farmer John Cherrington, in the *Financial Times*, thought that the new tax could assist farming by pushing land prices back down to sensible levels, and that there was no reason why farmers should be singled out for preferential treatment. His was a lone voice.

From the outset Healey had recognized that farmers were a special category—not that they were to be relieved of any of the burdens, but that assessment of a farmer's wealth was more difficult. He produced a formula for valuing farmland at twenty times its current rent value, a proposal which the CLA tried to amend unsuccessfully to fifteen times. This was plainly unsatisfactory, and in the April Budget of 1976 a new definition was announced which reduced the value of farmland to only 50 per cent of its true valuation. In effect, the 45 per cent Estate Duty abatement had become a 50 per cent abatement, but the concession was limited to 400 hectares, or £250,000 worth of farmland; thus the brakes were on for the expansion of UK farming into units of over this amount. Later, in October 1977, the 30 per cent relief accorded for business assets was extended to 50 per cent. By this time the Chancellor was recognizing that the severe tax burden on small, privately owned businesses (of which farming was only one) needed some relief. In April 1978 Healey, the man who had promulgated the severe CTT laws originally, started to make concessions—was he finally realizing the harm he had caused, or was it an election year that educated him?

Earlier, the qualifications for 'full-time working farmers' had been defined by the Inland Revenue as 'farmers who had occupied their land for the preceding two years before death, and who occupied it themselves at the time of death', so that handing over of the business of farming to a son was still an adverse qualification. The second criterion was that the farmer must have been engaged in full-time farming for at least five of the seven years preceding the transfer; 'full-time' farmers being defined as people who derived 75 per cent of their earned income from farming (thus negating this relief for the businessman, with his country estate and hobby farming).

The Irish problem

William Pitt first introduced income tax in Britain in 1799 as a temporary measure. Farmers came into the orbit of the tax-collector just prior to the 1939 outbreak of war, and under the old Schedule D arrangements for the first time they had to employ accountants and provide an annual balance sheet. Before this time there was so little profit in farming—and, indeed, considerable losses—that no income tax would have been levied anyway. Farm workers came into the orbit of PAYE in 1941, and their wages thereafter had to be recorded. Irish farmers were not subjected to Income Tax until 1974, and the total yield up to January 1977 was a miserable £6 million! Only one in twenty of the 180,000 Irish farmers paid any tax even in that period, and it was a matter of consternation to Irish farmers that they should be taxed at all. A strange situation in a nation geographically part of the British Isles, when compared with Britain's tax burden.

Irish farmers reacted angrily, and the blow was softened by a 7p increase on a gallon of milk. At this time Irish farmers were benefiting from the effects of joining the EEC, and land prices had risen to levels above those on the mainland of Britain. Speculators and large-scale ranchers had seized the opportunity of this tax-free haven, with its peasant structure, to institute modern business methods and mechanization, making Eire a target for outsiders. They were given the option of being taxed on the basis of farm accounts or on a notional income figure, but since the total income of Irish farmers was estimated at £70 million, the impact of the tax upon withdrawing capital needed for expansion would appear to be pretty minimal, nevertheless, Irish farmers reacted angrily to these new proposals as a fresh imposition

20 The Farmers

'The farmer will never be happy again
He carries his heart in his boots
For either the rain is destroying his grain
Or the drought is destroying his roots'
A. P. Herbert

There may be no real resemblance, but farmers, as businessmen employing a small labour force and achieving their success by the force of their own personalities, may be likened to small shopkeepers, jobbing builders or publicans. Each of these employs an outside staff of one or two people, is personally responsible for the business, gets his wife to help out in busy times, and probably does his own office work in his spare time in a more or less haphazard and disorganized fashion.

The comparison extends to the wide disparity between the highest and the lowest: you can go from a small country pub to the Savoy Hotel, from a one man village builder to the multinational civil engineering contractors, and from the village stores to Marks and Spencer, while in farming terms the largest enterprise in the UK is that of the CWS, with 14,000 hectares spread over many counties, contrasting starkly with the 8-hectare chap 'down the lane'. Yet they are both in the same business. The wide range of scales of business is one thing, but its success is another; put two farmers in hypothetical, adjacent, similar farms and ask them to provide an exact copy of livestock numbers and cropping rotations, give them the same staff and the same amount of capital, provide an almost identical situation, and yet their financial results will vary from poverty to riches.

Probably 99 per cent of farmers participate on equal terms with their employees in the day to day work of the farm. Maybe 1 per cent are tycoons or elderly farmers who exercise a supervisory role only, yet the absentee farmer is a sure condition for failure; in this respect the new institutional farmers, with large farms spread over several counties and run by managers, goes against the traditional outlook that 'the farmer's foot is the best muck'. The personal participation of the farmer has grown vastly as the number of workers has gone down, as the average size of farm has increased, and as mechanization has revolutionized farming. Twenty-five years ago many farmers spent their daily hours supervising their gangs of men or attending markets, and even this last occupation has been reduced.

Perhaps buying cattle and livestock still demands the personal appraisal of the farmer before he buys, but selling no longer commands the same personal attention that it once did. Local markets have honest auctioneers, and the 'rings' which would beat down the market prices by withholding bids, while not vanished, are less conspicuous. The farmer selling his cattle through an auctioneer is less likely to be robbed than twenty-five years ago, for the auctioneer realizes that his own reputation rests upon getting better prices and he relies upon a supply of stock to sell, more than he does upon itinerant dealers.

The old Corn Exchange was a meeting-place and social gathering for farmers, but laboratory tests for the nitrogen content of malting barley or the protein of milling wheat have superseded the expert eye and fingers of the frock-coated, wing-collared, stately corn merchants of yesteryear. The telephone has now taken the place of the glass roofed Corn Exchanges which were to be found in every market town, although some do still remain. The farmer has thus become a stay-at-home man.

The analogy with publicans is particularly apposite. Some 75 per cent of the brewery-owned pubs are in the hands of tenants, 25 per cent are managed direct, but the tenant is, like the farm tenant, not the owner of the property which provides his living. They are not alone in this, for the major oil companies also own an undisclosed number of garages. These are completely 'tied' tenancies which are bound to sell the brand of petrol supplied by the landlord, as the beer is also supplied by the owner of the pub. In farming 38 per cent of the farms are tenanted, although they do occupy 43 per cent of the land.

A farmer is by definition a man or woman who cultivates land as a business, so that a man who owns a farm, even if he leaves the day-to-day operation to his manager or foreman, is a farmer. The manager is not truly the farmer, but at the other end of the scale a man who owns farms as a territorial landowner, but with tenants cultivating the soil, is patently not a farmer either. The definition is thus a very wide one.

The most impressive country address today is probably 'The Old Rectory' or with a farm suffix. The Napoleonic prosperity has left a legacy of pseudo-Georgian Victoriana hiding an Elizabethan dwelling, and in many southern counties these today are the farmhouses, although even in northern climes the farmhouses are large and substantial. By the 'house definition' even the modest farmer gains several points over the other classes for the nature of his abode. It is not easy, though, to place farmers within any inflexible three-tier class structure.

Farmers are popularly thought to 'get up early in the morning, and work very hard'. Farmers are not alone in their early rising; farm workers' hours are now broadly equivalent to the hours of work of many industrial workers, and the farmer's hours are often tied to those of his men. The early-morning farming programme on BBC, *Farming Today*, is finished and over by 6.35 a.m.; the early-morning market reports are designed for the crack of dawn because that is the only time farmers can listen; but in actual fact around one million people in the UK listen to that particular programme. Since the listenership ratings far exceed the total number of farmers, and many farmers are not up in time to hear these reports, then it follows that there may be more early-morning risers among other workers and commuters than among farmers. The vast army of commuters (and with every village a dormitory who is not a commuter these days?) have probably risen as early as the farmer, have breakfasted before him because they will not be coming back again after they leave their homes. They leave home earlier and arrive home later. The benefits of farming are that the farmhouse is the farmer's home. Farm workers have the benefits of walking out of their back door and are straight on the job, without the time and expense of travelling.

This is not to deny that cowmen invariably start earlier, stockmen of all sorts may get up in the middle of the night to assist their animals and shepherds may sleep in a hillside hut at lambing time, pigmen may have an awkward sow who insists upon murdering her young as they are born. It is not to deny either that arable farmers have protracted and frustrating harvests which require all-night work in the barns, running a shift system drying grain or operating machinery. It is not to deny that sugar-beet growers get stuck in an intractable sea of mud in late December. But exceptional conditions occur in all occupations.

'Farmers work hard' conjures up the sweat and toil of forking muck or pitching sheaves in a sweltering summer—these images are far from the modern truth in mechanized Britain. Mechanization has taken the heavy physical labour out of farm work.

A growing number of farmers have outside interests and businesses beyond their actual farming, although often allied to it, and a growing number can be described as 'part-time' as college education and the use of the computer in the large farming operation becomes more frequent.

Although the farming industry has shown increases in its productivity nearly double those of the rest of industry, several reports have emphasized that farmers have little formal training, and even a bad education. A Survey[1] revealed that 33 per cent of farmers interviewed seemed mentally incapable of applying new techniques and advisory aids. This survey, which was carried out by a British and an American economist on twenty-nine farms of between 60 and 120 hectares in Nottinghamshire, revealed that only a third of the farmers were achieving 85 per cent or more of their potential maximum income, although they were generally progressive and mentally capable of adopting information and advice. Another third were only earning between 50 and 85 per cent and these included several of high mental ability who for reasons known to themselves did not achieve better results.

A report from agriculture's 'Little Neddy'[2] again emphasized the lack of formal education among farmers. It stated that the average age of all farmers was 46·3 years, but that 53 per cent were over forty-five and nearly 9 per cent were over sixty-five. This emphasizes that farmers never retire but hang on grimly to the

[1] 'The Human Side of Farm Management', be Gwyn Jones and Michael E. Daw (University of Nottingham, Department of Agricultural Economics).
[2] *Agricultural Manpower in England and Wales* 1972.

end, warping the statistics to the extent of giving farmers a higher average age than many other classes of businessmen. 21 per cent were under thirty-five but the revealing result of this particular survey was that the average school-leaving age was fifteen, although the most common school-leaving age was fourteen because of the preponderance of older farmers. The younger farmers have a higher average school-leaving age. However, 70 per cent of all farmers had left school by the time they were fifteen. In fact 85 per cent had left school by the age of sixteen. The scholastic qualifications of farmers in this survey showed that nearly 82 per cent had neither CSE, 'O' Level or 'A' Level. Yet many farmers have been to public or private schools. Another survey by Howard Newby[3] suggested 55 per cent of the farmers interviewed had attended a private or public school, 21 per cent went to grammar schools and only 20 per cent had an 'elementary education'. Among the larger farmers, those with over 400 hectares, 65 per cent were in fact the product of a private or public school.

This survey took place in East Anglia, where the proportion of more prosperous farmers would probably be higher than in any other part of the UK; nevertheless, the figures revealed follow a general pattern. Only 27 per cent went to an agricultural college and 17 per cent to a university; again, among the larger farmers 41 per cent went to an agricultural college. These figures show that a vast number of farmers have no agricultural qualifications, have not been to an agricultural college or even had the benefit of the public-school system.

The situation is still evolving, and with stable prosperity not only have the younger farmers been better educated but they are sending their children to public schools in greater numbers than any other class or profession. The top flight of public schools such as Eton, Harrow and Winchester have always contained an agricultural element from the families of the aristocratic landowners, or 'landed gentry'; in more recent years there has been a movement to the minor public schools by the middle range of larger farmers.

Seventy per cent of current UK farmers are the sons of farmers, and Newby records that a further 12 per cent were born in a rural area. The importance of these figures is that 30 per cent of all farmers are first-generation newcomers into an occupation that is traditionally handed down from father to son. The influx is further proof that within the social strata of modern UK society it is certainly no disgrace to go into farming. Moreover, 18 per cent of the total were not even born in the countryside.

However, farming has now become very obviously a closed shop, with only the very remotest possibility of a newcomer gaining a farm. Purchase at current price-levels is clearly impossible, and there are restrictions upon tenancies, since it would take at least two generations to get the farm back again under the Inheritance of Tenancies Act 1976.

The alternative is entry into the growing band of farm managers, and this has become a profession within a profession. When existing farmers seek to increase

[3] Sociologist at the University of Essex and author of *The Deferential Worker (Allen Lane, 1977); Survey of East Anglian Farmers*, 1975.

the scale of their farming enterprise this is often only possible by the acquisition of more land which may be kilometres away from the main homestead. If the holding is large enough, or the livestock and cropping sufficiently complex, it can warrant a manager. This would appear to be the only way in which the town-bred young man can force his way into the industry.

The closed shop image of farming is to some extent a false one, though, even if the future lies in that direction. Within the UK one in four farmers is listed, by his own admission in the Ministry returns, as part-time. Businessmen may buy a 'hobby-farm' whereby they can at once indulge in the spaciousness of a country house, enjoy the free shooting, and lord it over their land, while until changes under a past Chancellor of the Exchequer (Callaghan) these 'hobby-farmers' were entitled to offset the losses they invariably made on their farms against the profits they made in their factories. This type of farmer still exists, although to a less extent. Newby found that 46 per cent of the larger farmers had business interests outside their farms. The most common was a directorship of an agricultural-related company which could be involved in the seed-merchanting trade or farm machinery. However, 58 per cent among the larger farmers said that these interests were financially insignificant in relation to their farming. The membership of Lloyds of London is restricted to those who can show £75,000 worth of wealth. A farm, with its high capital value but low return, offers an excellent security for the insurance stability and backing for which Lloyds is world-renowned. Many farmers thus have a passive interest as membership of Lloyds, although the time commitment is practically non-existent.

If a quarter of UK farmers care to call themselves 'part-time', in Germany 55 per cent of all farmers are part-time, but produce only about one-third of the total farm output. In Japan over 87 per cent of farm households have another source of income or employment. In Norway 33 per cent of the farmers had only the farm to support them, while 67 went out to work in other areas.

If this seems surprising, the reason in other nations has been that farming deprivation with its seasonal peaks has prompted Governments to create rural industries, or even seasonal industries, to take up the spare time. In the Low Countries farmers work on the land in the summer, and in the local factory in the winter, with either their wives or themselves attending to the routine livestock-feeding activities during the winter months. This has been a deliberate policy. In the UK, however, planning restrictions have been severely designed to prevent any form of light industry in country villages, and this despite the payment of lip service to the problems of village depopulation, or its new status as a dormitory.

In an earlier chapter it was stated that Lord Netherthorpe's ancestor had considered he was being overcharged for fodder for his horse transport in carrying stone from Warwickshire to the Palace of Westminster. He bought a farm, and proceeded to produce his own forage and fodder. This type of example has been copied by many farmers, who have weighed up the volume of goods which arrives on the farm in a year in the form of animal feeding-stuffs, fertilizer and machinery; and have bought their own lorry.

The production of the farm, particularly sugar beet but including grain and other products, can be transported by the farmer's own lorry, and some have developed this into a Transport Company of their own. The expense of farm machinery and its rapid depreciation has encouraged farmers to invest in some of these larger machines with the objective of making the proposition viable by contracting. Many farmers are also agricultural contractors. Thus within the farming field the diversity of occupations can justify the designation 'part-time'.

Another job can be taken on for filling in time available on a small farm, and for supplementing the family income. Even taking in tourists in the summer months, or running a caravan park in sheltered meadows, constitutes the most humble form of diversified part-time farming. The same situation occurs at the larger end of the spectrum, when a larger farmer with time on his hands and an agile mind diversifies into forming other companies, and other operations. Many of the innovators of farm machinery have been men who built their own machines to fulfil the practical conditions which they were meeting, but which the established market was not satisfying. Some of the larger machinery companies in the UK today started life as an offshoot to a farming enterprise.

In the United States many part-time farmers use the additional income as a stepping-stone on the way out of farming. In the UK this is indeed a rarity. More people are trying to get into the job than those who want to get out. A report[4] on the subject of part-time farming set out the entire problem and variations. Its authors said:

> Part-time farming is often regarded as an agricultural problem. Those concerned with agricultural policy may tend to think in terms of a sector of agriculture which is losing part of its labour supply. By definition, however, part-time farming families are also contributing labour to other sectors. Policy issues may arise about the industries which draw labour from agriculture, from part-time farming families.
>
> Where part-time farming is perpetuated as part of a deliberate policy, as for example in the Netherlands, Bavaria or part of Western Ireland Governments have introduced industry to rural areas in order to maintain a rural farm population.

This report stressed that supplementing the farm income is vital in depressed regions, but that there is another sector of part-time farmers in a category that is often forgotten. They are the magistrates, county councillors, committee members and even full-time NFU committee chairmen who have dedicated their lives to public service in many fields, some of which are not agriculturally orientated. With farming only representing in its actual working numbers about 2½ per cent of the voting public, the numbers of councillors at the various levels of local government who are genuine if not full-time farmers is quadrupled in relation to their proportional representation. While this does not apply to the major conurbations, the average county council has about 10 per cent of its members farmers and perhaps others who are farmer's wives, so that the voice of the countryside can be heard effectively.

[4] *Part-time Farming: Its Nature and Implications* (Wye College, 1977).

But perhaps more emphasis should be placed upon the 76 per cent of UK farmers—by far the largest majority—who are dedicated and wedded to their farms, who seldom leave them, and who have no other interest in life.

These are the men of whom Newby reported that 19 per cent worked 40-49 hours each week, 19 per cent worked up to 59 hours, a further 25 per cent worked up to 69 hours and 18 per cent worked 70 hours and more. This was not restricted either to the one-man farmer, even though this man must of necessity work long hours, yet many of the larger farmers found themselves doing office work and running their farms, this taking all their daylight hours to perform. Why do farmers follow this rigorous life?

What East Anglian farmers like about their job

	Under-600[5] smd farmers	600 smd and over
Independence	42·8	13·5
Way of life, open-air, country life	27·0	32·2
Aspects of work	14·8	8·5
Challenge, risk, gamble	5·0	1·7
Achievement, creativity	2·7	11·8
Pride of ownership	—	3·4
Self-respect	—	1·7
Income, cheaper living	3·2	6·8
Chance of capital gain	2·3	5·1
Family tradition	—	8·5
Interaction with other farmers	1·3	6·8

Ruth Gasson, of Cambridge University's Department of Land Economy, produced this survey of East Anglian farmers in 1973. It showed that among the smaller farmers independence was valued most. Surprisingly this was not in the attitude of the larger farmers; they regarded farming as fresh air and a way of life, but perhaps they could afford to. The freedom and fresh-air aspect of the job accounted for 70 per cent of the rating among the small farmers, but only 46 per cent among the larger ones. This freedom of action was reflected in further questions about the attraction of a job for a young man.

Enjoyment of occupation came top, and the chance of making his own decisions came second. The variety of farm-work, which changes throughout the seasons, a healthy life and good prospects for advancement, with the security of knowing that the job goes on for ever, with little risk of unemployment, were all given a high rating. The fresh-air aspect of farm life is a rapidly diminishing bonus; the modern pig palace has a controlled environment for the animals but can be stifling for the attendant; and the advances in driver comfort have put the modern tractor-driver into a 'module' superimposed on to a tractor frame which reduces the noise-level to an acceptable number of decibels. The modern combine cab is a sophisticated box of dials and flashing lights with the driver controlling his personal comfort through the air conditioning.

[5] 600 standard man-days work per annum.

It is surprising to find from the above table that so few farmers saw the job as a 'challenge, risk or gamble'. Certainly among the larger farmers this hardly rated at all. The continuity of the family tradition of farming was non-existent in the smaller farmers' minds and rated only 8·5 per cent for the larger farmer. This disproves the alleged extra motivation of farmers' sons, while the accepted gregariousness of farmers is also a false impression. 'Interaction with other farmers'—which means being part of the large family which the farming community creates within itself—does not rate very highly; the smaller farmers probably have their noses to the plough too much for social gallivanting.

Perhaps the dictatorial role and independence of the farmer makes him king of his own castle and removes the need for a community feeling. Income also rated much lower than might have been imagined.

Despite the so-called healthiness of a fresh-air life, a respiratory disease known as 'farmer's lung' is prevalent. The disease is contracted from the dusty conditions which often exist on farms; handling large amounts of dusty hay on a dairy farm has been known to create it, and mouldy hay or straw is the cause of 54 per cent of cases. 27 per cent is caused by grain, and in modern dusty silos a bin of grain which goes mouldy sets up an atmosphere that is totally unhealthy. Barley when heating can resemble a brewery, and working in this atmosphere can have unfortunate repercussions. The incidence of 86 per 1,000 people who reported symptoms of 'farmer's lung' dropped to 23 per 1,000 on arable farms.

Holidays

With professional men entitled to six weeks holiday per year, many workers in industry having a month, and farm-workers having three weeks (with qualifications), it is left to the small one-man business to achieve the least time off. Obviously such men have difficulties in continuing their businesses in their absence, but farmers probably take less holidays than almost any other class. A survey by the Ford Motor Company Limited[6] gave a unique picture of the holiday-habit of that nesting bird the farmer.

In the year of this report 37 per cent of all farmers had no holiday at all and 20 per cent had not been on holiday for the last five years. Understandably, smaller farmers had less holidays, and 66 per cent had no holiday in 1970, while 40 per cent had not taken time off for five years. Even in the 100 hectare-plus bracket 20 per cent had not had a holiday for five years.

Farmers tend to take their work with them wherever they go and 58 per cent of those who went to foreign parts visited agricultural establishments or farms as part of their holiday. The *Farmers Weekly* advertises various holiday trips and 'study-tours' to faraway places such as New Zealand and the United States. These trips are high-pressure, very serious studies of farms, farming methods, experimental and research stations in other countries where farmers can hope to

[6] Published in the Ford magazine *Farm*, December 1971.

increase their knowledge. The CLA also organizes occasional trips to study aspects of forestry or land ownership abroad, but the enthusiasm for these excursions is not widespread, despite the fact that they would rate as expenses of the farm for income-tax purposes.

Love of the countryside is emphasized by the fact that only 6 per cent of farmers went to London for their holiday, or part of it. London turned out to be an unpopular venue, although the Scots descend upon London hotels in force for Smithfield week in early December, when the men can visit the Show at Earl's Court, while their wives do the Christmas shopping; but perhaps this is not regarded as a holiday.

Hunting, shooting, and fishing is practised by fewer farmers than may be imagined. Hunting as a traditional part of the British countryside was only enjoyed by 2 per cent of farmers with under 40 hectares, 7 per cent of farmers owning 40 to 100 hectares and 14 per cent with over 100 hectares, but those farmers who loyally supported the hunt did so very enthusiastically. It is always assumed that every farmer has a gun, and that he shoots regularly, but while many keep one for pests 47 per cent never go shooting, in the accepted sense of a day's shooting in an organized fashion. Perhaps the hand-rearing of pheasants, the organization of 'beaters' to flush out the birds and an array of guns to shoot them down is only for the wealthy business-man seeking a day in that fresh air which the farmer is said to have all the year around. Fishing is a sport which nearly half all farmers had embarked upon at one stage or another, but few seemed to be regular followers of Izaak Walton. Sea fishing turned out to be the most popular form of the sport, with fly and coarse fishing equally popular in the league table, though slightly less popular than sea fishing.

The other aspect revealed by the Ford survey was that TV was decreasing but radio was holding its own among farmers, or even increasing its popularity. The sheer weight of broadcasting time devoted to an industry which in numerical terms is such a small part of the audience, and which is the only topic on both radio and TV seven days a week, remains a paradox of the media.

Self-imposed constraints

Although farming productivity has streaked ahead of the remainder of UK industry, a business-man's heart quails at the wastage and vulnerability of farming as a business. Thousands of pounds are at risk in the harvest: freak hailstorms strip the corn naked, and summer thunderstorms wash away the crops, or an inclement autumn necessitates leaving potatoes unharvested until the following spring, when many of them will be rotten. All this is allied to the heavy capital involvement in farm machinery which will have a very limited seasonal use throughout the year. In business terms, the justification of an expensive item of machinery is in its capacity to earn its keep, and tractors apart, few items of farm machinery do this. The whole business of farming is on an escalating cost graph, spread over twelve months, and growing crops for an unknown terminal price.

There is a general impression that farms are untidy places, where wastage occurs. This is patently not true in the daily work output of the farmer and his employees, with every hour productively occupied and no evidence of over-manning. There is a wastage, though, partly from losses in the field or farmyard from the weather, and partly from a lack of appreciation by the farmer; unhappily, grain is cosseted from sowing to harvesting, but thereafter the farmer's interest wanes, and it is often put into leaky sheds, or eaten by rats.

The constraints upon farm productivity may be self-imposed, or constraints by the nature of the industry's subjugation to Government and legal interference. But a report[7] revealed that farmers put social responsibility before profit, and that there were constraints of a self-imposed nature that were greater than were envisaged. Since more than 90 per cent of the total equity of the land and the farming business is wholly owned by farmers, and only 10 per cent is borrowed money, it would appear that the massive security which the land of Britain represents, plus a healthy viability of the industry, places it in a good position to borrow more capital for expansion. Farmers, though, are generally reluctant borrowers; difficulties from lack of capital would appear to be rare, and if they occur, to be self-imposed. The report discovered that there were many reasons why a farmer did not maximize his profits, but that the industry as a whole did not always recognize the full extent of these factors. It said, 'The balance between these considerations and the profit motive may be influenced by age, education, income, assets, background and personality.'

But it went on that while standards of management had improved immeasurably, a wide spread of performance still exists, and that improved education could help to raise standards generally. The outstanding conclusion of this survey was that social responsibility and dedication towards the traditions of the countryside were often more noticeable than any aspiration towards profit. It stated:

> There are however obstacles to progress in achieving or improving efficiency. Some of these reflect a sense of tradition and responsibility in land owners and farmers which prevents them putting the pursuit of profit or capital gain before all other considerations.

Farmers are accused of making too much money, and in the next breath given sympathy for a hard life with a low return. The truth as usual is halfway between the two. Some years the profit levels are good, but in others they are not, and it is the long-term annual turnover which creates its problems; a bad harvest has to be lived with, perhaps entails stringencies in the household budget for a full year until the next harvest arrives.

Farmers, like everybody else, are required to submit their accounts annually to

[7]*Constraints on Business Organisation in Agriculture.* CLA Report, February 1974, by Chairman of Working Party, Lord Davidson.

the Inspector of Taxes. The majority employ an accountant to do this work. One could not discover the true profitability of farming from these figures, which in any case are not published. The profit from a farm disguises the fact that the farm may be owned by the farmer, purchased many years ago and have no outstanding mortgage or annual debts, whereas a farm more recently purchased will bear a heavier burden. Also, since the farmer's own work and that of his wife is not included, the real farm profit after the deductions of managerial effort, additional free labour and rent free farms, is far removed from the actual profit.

Relatively speaking, farmers in the UK have done better in the 1970s than in the 1960s, but within this decade there have been periods of acute loss-making depression in the pig industry, in beef and eggs and to a lesser extent in milk.

If one looks in general at the historical pattern of farm incomes, the industry has seen a period of stable prosperity since 1939 which has enabled it to drag itself into the capital-intensive mechanical era, to modernize its farm buildings, drain its land, and continue the march of technological progress unabated. Most of northern Europe has seen this same period, when the insolvency of farmers has been minimal.

Bankruptcies (England and Wales)

	Total Bankruptcies	Farmers
1969	4,347	225
1970	4,622	214
1971	4,353	193
1972	3,860	108
1973	3,363	69
1976	6,700	133

It will be seen from the table that farming bankruptcies represented 5 per cent of the total in 1969 but only 2 per cent five years later. Throughout the 1960s there were an average 170 farming bankruptcies per annum. In the 1970s there would appear to be fewer and from this it can be surmised that the inefficient farmer may have been weeded out. Bankruptcies in general rose to levels of 7,000 per annum in the years 1976–7, and self-employed categories head the list. Small builders have always been the most risky proposition for solvency, and they now account for nearly 25 per cent of all bankruptcies; non-food retailers—i.e. small shopkeepers—account for 10 per cent; and food stores for another 6 per cent. Road hauliers—which include one-man businesses with one lorry—are a more risky proposition than farmers. The only other significant category annually are hoteliers and restaurateurs. This of course ignores the very large liquidation problems which have hit some of our major companies from time to time. Overall within the context of British industry farming bankruptcies are commendably small.

In the United States one opens conversation by asking how much money your friend earns. The Americans are uninhibited about this, while the British are more reticent, and prefer to talk about the weather. Yet even in Britain farm incomes and farming profitability suffer from over-exposure. There is a spate of annual studies of farm incomes published in a blaze of glory; individual farmers contribute their private figures to statisticians; and many voluntarily contribute to studies concerned with assessing the swings and roundabouts of farming incomes. This is in complete isolation to any other UK industry, trade or profession. The answer may lie partly in the quasi-nationalized position of the industry, whereby the Government must be satisfied that any financial support is going to a truly deserving cause, not propping up an ailing business or making the rich richer. It is also useful to the farmers as a yardstick of their neighbour's performance, or for 'averages' within their part of the country. Its usefulness is to guide those below average into a higher bracket, although it is highly doubtful if it works. One is forced to conclude that neither the Government nor the farming industry would be any worse off if the statisticians and economists ceased their work in collating and publishing the results of farm incomes.

The Ministry of Agriculture produces an annual balance sheet for the national farm, with a figure which shows the total net income. This in no way portrays individual trends, and cannot be used as anything more than a rough guide. Various universities such as Cambridge, Reading, Newcastle and Oxford produce 'farm management surveys' giving the results of farming profitability from selected farmers within their own area.

The *Farmers Weekly* runs its own farms and publishes the detailed financial results with an analysis of the reasons, but the most headline-hitting farming income to be published comes from ICI.

Net farming income according to the Ministry of Agriculture

Year	Actual Income
1967	£546 m
1968	£504 m
1969	£566 m
1970	£539 m
1971	£686 m
1972	£706 m
1973	£1,198 m
1974	£1,340 m
1975	£1,435 m
1976	£1,835 m
1977	(estimated £1,796 m)

Source: Annual Review of Agriculture, 1978.

While the figures quoted are from the above impeccable source they must not be taken as final or precise, for the economists at the Ministry would seem to revise their own figures in retrospect. However, taken as a whole they do illustrate the pattern of the changes and show that in 1968–9 there was in fact a decrease in income level.

The above figures show an increase of almost 300 per cent from 1970 to 1976. This looks formidable, but these were years when inflation was at its highest, and pegged salaries did not reflect such increases; however, many manual workers belonging to the more militant trade unions had disparate rises. The real question remains; are farmers underpaid or overpaid? Certainly they do not appear to be underpaid, but neither do they appear to be overpaid: the basis for calculation must be a proper remuneration for personal efforts during the year and a proper return on their capital—and such return itself varies from one industry to another.

Since the land is the basic workshop of the farming industry, and yet it is patently obvious that it does not require the freehold ownership of land to operate a farming business, the return on capital is patently greater for a tenant. The vast majority of farmers are now owner-occupiers and in this region there is patently a remarkably low return on capital. If one takes the full face value of the farm itself, if sold at current values, then the return probably looks rather silly at about 2 per cent, but since the investment in the farm itself has shown a continuous growth, there must be a hidden element of return from possession of such an asset. The modern price of land is often quoted in an effort to proclaim the low return from farming, but even when land was £250 a hectare it would have paid the farmer handsomely to sell up and live in a tax-free haven somewhere in the world.

Do farmers in the UK fare better or worse than their counterparts in other countries? The answer must be that they do better than some, and worse than others. How many are at a subsistence level? Certainly small uneconomic units anywhere in the country are on a low income level, and in the Celtic fringe or other poor areas they are no more average than are the barley barons of East Anglia. Are farmers as hard up as the NFU continually complains? Certainly crises occur in sectors of the industry from time to time, and the NFU (although accused of crying wolf too often), is right to use its considerable lobbying power to bring pressure upon the Minister. Have farmers kept pace with inflation? Has anyone? British agriculture is fully and efficiently mechanized; some say that individual farms are over-mechanized. Does this represent a massive capital investment from a thriving industry, perpetually seeking to increase its efficiency and remain competitive? Or is it one way of saving tax? These questions come near to providing a picture of farm-income levels, which must always be taken in relation to the cost of living, and must be allied to a proper return for effort in relation to the national level of prosperity. Within this context it is difficult to find evidence that farmers' standards of living have not improved in common with those of all other sectors of the community.

One body which thought the farmers were doing too well was the Trade Union Research Unit at Ruskin College, Oxford, which in 1974 published a paper on the subject of farmers' incomes entitled 'The Separation of Reality from Illusion'. This paper set out to examine farmers' prosperity, and suggested that they had enjoyed a period of 'unprecedented prosperity' but qualified this by saying, 'Many of the holdings included in aggregate farm income are small farms which make little or no profit. The main reason for the survival of small farms is that they provide returns which are not quantifiable in monetary terms.' Nevertheless the Ruskin College paper did look at the increases in farm income, and its most revealing conclusion was:

> Clearly, the dire warnings of approaching disaster in various sectors of the agricultural industry, which are constantly propounded by the NFU, need to be viewed with a liberal sprinkling of cynicism. Farmers have done extremely well in recent years; . . . the NFU constantly create the illusion that farmers are on the verge of bankruptcy; in reality they are enjoying a period of unprecedented prosperity.

The Unit examined the fortunes of farming, and although it admitted that the aggregate net farm income grew at only a steady rate for twenty years up to 1968–9 it noted that it had rocketed after that period. It also examined the differential between farmers in England and Wales, and in Scotland. Over the period 1968–9 to 1972–3 the English and Welsh farmers' incomes had risen by 176 per cent, but the Scots had done better with 226 per cent. Part of the explanation of rising farm incomes was the reduction of the number of farmers with the amalgamation of farms, creating larger business units.

The Ruskin College paper also characterized as melodramatic the NFU line, with its perpetual quest to emphasize falling farm profits, in terms like these:

> We are on the brink of the most desperate financial crisis to face British agriculture since the end of World War II. The plain fact is that agriculture and horticulture simply have not had the cash needed to meet continuously rising costs.
>
> (*NFU News*, 26 January 1970)

> The raging inflation which is sending farmers' costs soaring to record levels is posing the most serious threat to food production in this country since the War.
>
> (*NFU News*, 25 February 1971)

> The Unions emphasised to the Minister the need for an immediate cash injection to save the pig industry from disaster.
>
> (*NFU News*, 7 March 1974)

The NFU replied angrily to the Ruskin College paper and vigorously defended its role as guardian of the hard-pressed farmers:

> The TURU paper has presented a distorted picture of the improvement in agricultural incomes in recent years.

> The element of deliberate distortion in the research unit's figures for farm income growth has been introduced by taking as a base year 1968/1969. This was the year in which very abnormal weather conditions combined with outbreaks of disease to make farm income the lowest in real terms throughout the 1960's.

> Meanwhile in the economy as a whole, personal income per head rose by 20% in real terms. This is scarcely a picture of farmers growing rich and fat whilst the rest of the national becomes poorer.

The Ruskin College paper also made another curious statement which was not commented upon by the NFU. It said, 'During periods when the Labour Party was in office, farm income was usually above the trend line, the opposite being the case while the Conservative Party was in office.' No one set out to dispute this and the non-partisan NFU could hardly pass judgment.

ICI Recorded Farms Scheme

Since 1967 the Economics Division of the Farm Advisory Service instituted by ICI has collated and produced a series of annual investigations into farm income, although it stresses that the end figures are 'management and investment income' and not profit. Initially over three hundred farmers co-operated voluntarily to produce confidential figures; in more recent years the number of participating farmers has dropped to just over two hundred, and these are divided into eight farming types, so that the comprehensiveness of the results leaves much to be desired. Also it is unquestionable that only those most cost-conscious farmers are likely to consider contributing to this survey. The survey does, however, select the top 25 per cent and sets these figures against the average, and in this way the disparity in the range is still pretty glaring. But if the NFU are accused of overstating the plight of farming, the ICI annual comments make interesting reading too.

> In spite of a rise of 7% in the level of fixed costs, and big increases in compound feed prices, management and investment income rose on each farming type.
>
> (ICI *Recorded Farms*, 1972)

> Since the previous report livestock farms have been adversely affected while many arable farms appear to have improved their relative position.
>
> (ICI *Recorded Farms*, 1973)

> A comparison of the 1974 results with those of 1972 highlights the reversal which has occurred in the relative profitability of livestock and arable production.
>
> (ICI *Recorded Farms*, 1974)

> Except for cereal cropping farms each farm type showed an improvement in the overall farm gross margin during the year.
>
> (ICI *Recorded Farms*, 1975)

The comments of the NFU upon these statements vary in accordance with the degree to which the ICI economists support the NFU 'poverty line' contentions. Thus after the 1974 results the NFU commented, 'The latest survey of economic results from ICI's 235 recorded farms provides firm evidence of the critical situation which the industry now faces', but after the 1975 results the NFU was quick to point out that 'those taking part in the survey are, in the main, "selected farmers" and these figures should not therefore be considered as representative of the industry as a whole', and it suggested that when the following year's drought was taken into consideration the industry would be seen to have suffered immeasurably, adding:

> The general lesson to be drawn from this survey is that the returns from agriculture are not yet adequate to provide the profits from which investment funds can be drawn to

ensure the expansion of domestic food production which both the Unions and the Government recognise as being vital to the national interest.

The interest of ICI in producing such annual reports is explained by its vested interest in selling fertilizers to farmers. It has proclaimed constantly, and quite correctly, that Britain's greatest wasted asset is its grassland, and that more nitrogen should be applied. Said the 1975 report:

> Grass is a resource of similar importance to North Sea oil and coal to the UK. By 1975 the total food import bill to the UK amounted to £3,900 million and was only 7% less than the bill for petroleum products. The UK will always have to import non-temperate foods but these account for only 25% of the total bill.

The University economists have devised a financial accounting system for farming which is labelled the 'Gross-Margin System'. This system disguises farm profit and subdivides the annual costs into the variables, such as seeds, fertilizers and animal feeding stuffs, that will alter directly with the area of crops or the number of livestock, the 'fixed' costs being the regular labour force, the machinery, rent and other overheads. These are sometimes called 'common costs' because many of them are entwined into both the arable and livestock sectors of the farming enterprise. Farm profit is still heavily disguised by the 25 per cent of farmers who are 'part-time' and may have additional income as well, as by those who are full-time but may still have investments or other income. While financial results are important, the main conclusion is that farmers are not really in it for the money.

21 Farming Demonstrations

'We do not want hare-brained cranks and idiots with more time for marching than farming.'

George Cattell, Director-General NFU,
Speech at York NFU, December 1974.

'A little rebellion now and then is a good thing.'

Thomas Jefferson

There have been three major disturbances in the agricultural scene since the War—in 1965, 1970 and most disruptive of all in 1974. UK farmers' militant action in taking to the streets, blocking roads with tractors, marching upon Westminster, smothering towns with leaflets, or even blocking roads with loads of artichokes as the French farmers have done are all muted actions when compared to the more blatant militancy of Continental farmers throughout the last twenty years. From which it may be concluded that when the farmers take to the streets they have very good reason to do so.

There were two marches through the streets of London in pre-War days; in 1936 a mass demonstration blocked the streets of London and lobbied MPs on the iniquitous tithes which were being levied, and which were finally abolished only in 1977. The 'tithe' was originally one-tenth of all the produce, which was paid to the Church.

While other sectors were absolved of their tithes, the charge on land remained. Throughout a long period the battle raged, and farmers were always incensed at this payment, which they considered was quite without foundation. The Government paid the Church of England a massive sum in commutation of the tithe income and took over its collection themselves, setting up a Tithe Redemption Commission at Worthing; they continued to levy the tithes upon land annually, but when smaller parcels of land changed hands it was automatic that the tithe should be redeemed by paying twenty times the annual charge. At any stage a landowner was free to commute his tithe payments by paying this sum. It was all scheduled to end in 1992. Finally, without any agitation from farmers at all, the Government decided in 1976 that the cost of collection had outgrown the income, and the 'battle' concluded quietly with the last payments in 1977.

The other pre-War mass demonstration by farmers was in 1939, when they marched through London to call attention to the serious state of the industry.

With a war around the corner and the need for home food-production the situation changed over-night. Thus the farmers' action was answered by Adolf Hitler. From then until 1965 there was little serious unrest among UK farmers. The story of the 1965 troubles is already recorded.[1]

In 1970 the troubles emanated from a shortfall in the Price Review Award of £85 million by Cledwyn Hughes (who thought he had been generous). Farming in the late 1960s had been gradually falling behind, and an epidemic of foot-and-mouth disease, coupled with a poor harvest in 1969, culminated in a lower level of income than farmers were requesting. Back in 1965 they had said:

> The net profit from arable land is £10 per acre. In addition production costs have increased by 7½% (this is agreed by the Government) so the farmer with 100 acres has taken a cut of 30/- a week and under this price review from his wheat and barley he will be losing £2 per acre. A total of £5 10s. 0d. per week loss of income. What would happen if the industrial unions had their wages slashed from £20 to £14 10s. 0d. per week?

The position had got steadily worse, and in 1970 it spilled out into extreme dissatisfaction. Even before the review was announced on 18 March 1970 farmers had been discussing what sort of militant action they could embark upon. The workers, as recorded,[2] had always found difficulty in organizing a strike with such a fragmented body of members spread thinly over the entire country, but farmers also had problems in deciding the most effective way to make their case, and bring the Government to heel. In January a National Farmers Action Committee was formed, and this threatened to withhold all payments to the Government, such as PAYE and SET (Selective Employment Tax), income tax and rates. Farmers threatened to withhold these payments if the Price Review was unfavourable, but they got no support from NFU President Williams, who was ousted at the January AGM and replaced by Henry Plumb. To withhold taxes would be disruptive, but nevertheless illegal; to pour milk down the drain was only throwing away the farmers' own money, to withhold supplies of fresh vegetables was only to let them rot in the fields; to plan a market boycott would mean that the public would go on short rations for a while, but the beasts would over-fatten and incur heavy feeding costs. In any case, they would create a glut in the markets when they were eventually sold. Arable farmers could not sensibly contribute to any of this disruption, and so the burden of any militancy would fall unequally, while its effectiveness could not be estimated.

Certainly the farmers can create massive disruption throughout the UK. In April 1970 the NFU proposed a six-point plan of (mostly legal) disruption:

1 There should be a ban on sending cattle, sheep and pigs to local markets for one week.
2 Farmers should no longer allow access to their land for new projects such as gas, electricity and oil pipelines.

[1] See p. 336. *The 1965 Price Review* (Lord Peart).
[2] See p. 291. (NUAAW).

3   Farmers should buy no new tractors or farm machinery except from companies charging prices which had not gone up since the recent Price Review, and which would give a pledge not to put prices up in the ensuing year.
4   The protests of NFU members should be registered at divisional offices of the Ministry of Agriculture.
5   A survey should be undertaken with individual farmers to see how the Price Review was affecting farm incomes.
6   There should be study of supply management schemes to limit production of farm products to demand.

President Plumb called it 'a token or gesture of our annoyance' and a 'muscle-flexing exercise'. In the event a week of market boycott was arranged for the following month, but some farmers broke the boycott. Machinery sales were already declining in respect of the lower farm incomes: any ban would plainly hurt the farmers more than the machinery-dealers, who might in fact get more work repairing the older tractors still in service. The NFU was also warned that it would be illegal to sponsor a programme of disruption of this nature. Anyway, a General Election was in the offing, and Wilson lost office to Edward Heath in June. On 19 June 1970 Jim Prior became the new Minister, and the agitation among farmers subsided.

1974—a year of unrest

1974, and spilling over into 1975, proved a year of militant demonstrations by UK farmers, as well as being a traumatic year for the nation as a whole, with two General Elections, a miners' strike, a three-day week and all that went with it. Trouble was not confined to Britain, while in Europe farmers were seething with unrest throughout the whole year.

In March Spanish farmers were upset over potato prices and parked their tractors on main roads, severely disrupting the traffic. They also were agitating over low farm prices, high wages and fuel bills, inequalities in the taxation system and social security payments, which some landowners bitterly proclaimed had turned the peasants into princes. The Spanish demonstrations started in the northern province of Logroño when four thousand farmers took to the roads on their tractors over the low potato prices and quickly spread, with tractors being paraded on the tourist highways. In March demonstrations by rice-growers around Valencia showed a remarkable solidarity among farmers which produced an estimated thirty thousand tractors formed up in parked lines several kilometres long on the main motorways. The demonstrations erupted into violence when tractors were overturned near Valladolid and riot police used rubber bullets and smoke canisters. Roads were blocked for several hours, but country traffic was not affected.

In May farmers in Norway held back their produce of milk, dairy products, meat, poultry, eggs and vegetables for a weekend in an effort to persuade their

Government that the offers of price increases should be doubled. In August Dutch farmers took to the roads, and 950 of them closed a key road from 5.30 a.m., blocking lorries coming from Paris with fresh vegetables, fruit and fish. Clashes between angry lorry-drivers and the farmers finished up with physical violence; the farmers cleared the road, but others leading to Rotterdam and Amsterdam were closed for a longer period. Also in August French farmers displayed their own dissatisfaction at their problems. An ex-Government Minister had the misfortune to run foul of a contingent of militant farmers on their way to take part in a 20,000 mass demonstration in support of their claims. The poor man's tyres were slashed, his car immobilized and he himself forced to take part in an hour-long heated debate on the farm prices. The French farmers blocked their main roads, busy with tourists, and hit the headlines in a manner that appeared more effective than previous demonstrations. There were some instances of tragic injuries to passers-by and they dressed up their cows with placards which were paraded along crowded holiday beaches, among the bikinis and the bathers.

Later that year, in September, Belgian farmers drove their tractors into the centre of Brussels to protest outside the German Embassy against the German veto of the EEC Farm Price Package. As the column of forty-three tractors reached the Embassy a massive display of thirty eight police cars and riot trucks quickly surrounded the demonstrating farmers, and a deputation of only seven was allowed into the Embassy. There they expressed their amazement at the German veto on the 5 per cent across-the-board rise in prices that had been agreed at the EEC talks earlier that month.

Earlier in September a unanimous and well-supported demonstration of farmers throughout the whole of Europe co-operated in a massive revolt. British farmers joined in, for they had their own particular deep-seated problems as well. It was an unprecedented expression of militancy, and the most widespread ever to be organized. Whether it was effective or not, it certainly brought home to the non-farming food-eating public that farmers were in deep trouble.

The disturbances to UK farming in 1974 took the form of a dramatic debate in the House of Commons, mass lobbying of MPs by farmers, a parade through the streets of London and a presentation of some pork to Prime Minister Wilson. There was a nation-wide tractor demonstration through the streets of every town in the country in September, and an angry blockade along the north-west coast ports, with violence and clashes with the police, and farmers forming picket lines. In the end an appeal by NFU President Plumb restored order. The following year, 1975, there were still more problems, but the 1974 disruption was not all the fault of the Government. The proverbial anchovies swam away from their traditional habitats and created a world protein shortage, the Russians bought up all the spare grain in the world and forced up prices, the Government promised a buoyant market for beef, and then as prices tumbled withdrew their support, there was a wet summer which ruined the hay crop and created a dire shortage of winter fodder, and the new Labour Government hit savagely at farmers with the introduction of a new and penal tax. These factors culminated in the demonstrations, and were complex and often unrelated, yet they built up a picture of acute dissatisfaction, despair and near-bankruptcy for many farmers.

The problems were with pigs, milk and beef, yet the cereal harvest was a record 16 million tonnes and corn-growers went laughing to the bank. Although the dramatic rise had not been the result of Government levels, or of farming pressure, it resulted in half the country's farmers hitting the jackpot, while the other half suffered severely from a sudden escalation in their feed prices. But the Government were responsible for the beef crisis, and it was this which led to the ugly scenes of violence which filled the autumn months.

The General Election had taken place on 28 February 1974, and Godber had been replaced as Peart came back for this second spell at the Ministry. Godber had abolished the deficiency payments system and replaced it with what in EEC jargon was known as 'intervention buying', which was destined to provide a bottom to the market. The Labour Government was pledged to renegotiate the CAP, while the nightmare of a beef 'mountain' appeared as Europe suddenly discovered a vast build-up of beef supplies. Peart opted out of the Conservative intervention buying level and left beef-producers hanging on a limb with no bottom to their market. This might not have been a cause for excessive complaint if market prices had remained at an acceptable level, but they plummeted disastrously. Live cattle prices per hundredweight (50 kilos) had been at £13 in 1971, had rocketed to over £20, with some at £24 in early 1973, had remained above the £18 mark until mid-1974, and then dramatically and disastrously dropped to £13. Farmers had purchased calves up to £75 for a seven-day-old animal, and it was these expensively bought and expensively reared animals which were coming to market when the disastrously low prices resulting from the beef mountain appeared. Seven-day-old calves dropped to only 50p each, and many were slaughtered because the cost of transport to the market would be more than the return from the beast. For the first time in twenty-five years there was no bottom support for the market. In theory beef prices could drop to a give-away level, and there was nothing to stop them.

Soon after Peart came back into office pig farmers were bitterly complaining that the country could be three million pigs short due to the reduction in the breeding herd. Despite the sophistication of the Ministry returns which farmers are statutorily obliged to deliver, the NFU conducted its own survey of breeding-pig numbers in the country, and Sir Henry Plumb commented:

> Results of a sample survey of breeding-pig numbers in England and Wales carried out by the NFU in the last three weeks indicate that the fall in the breeding herd is far more severe than had been previously thought.

It was estimated that the oncoming pig-meat shortage would add £110 million to the UK food-import bill.

Dairy farmers too were in trouble: with costs at 1·3p per litre more than the previous year (largely due to increased feeding costs) the price review had only added the equivalent of 1·1p. This was an equation that was tantamount to a loss-making situation with the inevitable decline in production as farmers slaughtered their cows in an effort to mitigate their losses. At the end of March five farmers in Sussex, members of Horsham NFU, paid for a half-page advertisement to illustrate that food prices were too cheap. They claimed they were losing £10 per head on barley beef, 1p per kilo on poultry meat, 0·6p a dozen on eggs, £3 per pig on porkers and £5 per pig on baconers. Obviously with the whole livestock industry losing money rapidly, the farmers were getting worried. Next month Fred Peart introduced a 50p per score subsidy on pigs[3]. This subsidy was casting a boy to do a man's job, and while it helped did not sufficiently reverse the situation. In April subsidized German and Danish beef was arriving in the British butcher's shops as low as 3p per kilo; this further hit at the price of British supplies in the markets, and farmers started to make plans for a cutback in production. In Wales the Chairman of the Royal Agricultural Society of Wales, Colonel John Williams-Wynne, declared:

> Let Britons see how they get along when those same foreigners discover, as they soon will, that they have us over a barrel like the oil sheikhs and the phosphate kings of Morocco.

Farmers were getting very angry, but as the *Farmers Weekly*[4] commented:

> Our precarious vote catching Government is clearly prepared to exploit any weak minority to win safety for itself after the next Election. Farmers who do not intend to remain weak and be exploited must be prepared to stand up, be counted, and work out new ways of putting pressure on Whitehall now that the old, gentlemanly discussion days are over.

Farmers planned a mass lobby of their MPs at Westminster, timed for a major debate in the House on 5 May. Farmers from Scotland flew down to join the NFU Council delegates and other farmers from the main livestock areas of England, and while Plumb continued his pressure upon the Minister in Luxemburg the EEC Council of Ministers announced a plan to sell surplus beef-supplies to hospitals and schools at cut prices. This added strength to the Government's case that the CAP was in ruins, and that renegotiation of Britain's membership of the EEC was a priority, in view of the foolish food mountains.

In the middle of this, on 3 May, just before the debate in the House of Commons, the NFU rather tactlessly published the results of its survey of 2,400 farm businesses for the 1972–3 farming year. It showed that average profits had risen by just over £400, to £3,117. There were mathematical manipulations to prove that inflation had eroded this increase, but the publicity of these profits was ill-timed and unwelcome.

The following day poultry-producers announced that they were losing £½ million each week from eggs, and £¾ million each week from poultry-meat production.

[3] Silkin did exactly the same in 1976, but the subsidy was later declared illegal by the EEC.
[4] 26 April 1974.

This, in fact, was the worst crisis ever facing the poultry industry, and more than 100,000 tonnes of surplus poultry meat was stockpiled in refrigerated stores in Europe. Even in the UK stockpiles were twice as large as a year previously, and consumption was dropping. The debate in the Commons took place, and ended with the Liberals and Scottish Nationalists joining the Conservatives against the Socialists, and ended up with an unexplained Government majority of eleven. Conservatives were accused of missing the vote deliberately because they did not wish to defeat the Government so quickly after a General Election. In the debate Peart had said that he was not neglecting farmers' interests, but had added, 'Beef is produced for people to eat, and it must be sold at prices they can afford.' For the Opposition Francis Pym criticized the Government for the confidence trick it was playing on the public and added, 'They pretend to be the friend and guardian of the consumer, while really they are only interested in the short-term effect.'

Poultry, pig and beef farmers were losing money, and they began to complain of the encouragement which they had been given by both Prior and Godber to expand production 'across the board', as Prior had said. Between 1969 and 1973 the number of cattle in the UK went up by no less than two million head, and in May angry farmers were back in London, bringing live calves into Whitehall and planning another mass meeting. One angry farmer wrote to the *Farmers Weekly*, 'After 12 years of hard slog with no holiday I say damn to farming. Let England starve.' On the day of the London invasion one Devon beef farmer said, 'It shows how desperate we small livestock farmers are when we neglect our stock to spend a day in London.'

The next week pig farmers came to town again and released a 113-kilo sow from a van in Whitehall, while a group of 150 farmers and supporters of the National Pig Action Group were waiting outside 10 Downing Street to hand a 1 kilo leg of pork through the door for Harold Wilson, with a letter pointing out that the average housewife would be unable to buy such a piece of meat in future if immediate aid was not forthcoming. The farmers marched around Trafalgar Square carrying a purple draped coffin with the inscription 'the funeral of British pigs', to the sound of Chopin's funeral march. By this time pig farmers were losing up to £6 per head. The farmers were not allowed to carry their coffin into Downing Street because the police pointed out it was illegal to hold a demonstration within two kilometres of Parliament while it was in session. This was the second London demonstration by irate and disappointed farmers within five days.

Two weeks later militant, banner-carrying pig farmers halted traffic in Cardigan with their placards 'It's cheaper to let them die', hung with two dead piglets. By this time the weather (which was to play an important part in the beef demonstrations against imported Irish beef later in the year) was beginning to show that it was not on the farmers' side. The driest April and May for almost eighty years had ruined any hope of grass-growth, and severely damaged hay and silage prospects for winter keep. This was to be followed by rain, which came too late, and which ruined what little crops the Welsh and western farmers had cut. In early June feeding-stuff manufacturers estimated that they would sell one million tonnes less feed in the year because of a massive reduction in livestock, while the Moroccan phosphate-producers suddenly slammed an increase of 50 per cent on their product, following the example of the Middle East oil sheikhs earlier. Nitrogen-supplies in the UK were already hit when an explosion at Flixborough, Fisons plant, stopped production.

NFU President Plumb and the Director-General Cattell made an emergency helicopter dash to Wales to calm down the militants, who were getting angrier, threatening break-away groups, withholding of NFU subscriptions and unilateral unlawful action, and were bombarding NFU headquarters in London with telegrams. This dash defused the situation for the time being and farmers began to get busy on their farms, with the frustrating hay season and harvest.

Peart opened the Royal Show at Stoneleigh on 1 July, and in torrential rain almost 200,000 people turned up. His speech in opening the Show from a rostrum in the Grand Ring was received with perfunctory applause, and he remained adamant that the short period of difficulty would soon be forgotten as his policies for pigs and beef came into effect. He was not to be drawn into details, and the farmers remained unconvinced of his sincerity.

A mark of the instability of the industry, and of its credit rating in the outside world, was the rapid decline in land prices, which had been falling from January. Further fuel was added to the drop when property speculator Ronald Lyon went spectacularly bankrupt and put his 5,200-hectare farming empire on the market to realize cash for his creditors. Farmers heard of the collapse with some glee, emphasizing that outsiders into the industry were not welcome. 'Just what we predicted!' they said in unison. Beef prices went down to £16 for 50 kilos, and Peart was now paying a headage of £9 for a subsidy, but angry pig farmers were at the Ministry in Whitehall again in August. On 14 September 1974 a massive display of farming strength took place, when processions of tractors and muck-spreaders paraded through two hundred towns in England and Wales. Plumb led a tractorcade into the centre of Birmingham and then made a whistle-stop tour of other parades in the Midlands, while a hundred farm vehicles made a major procession around Birmingham's famous Bull Ring. From Lancashire down to Somerset and Gloucester, in Wales and East Anglia, vehicles formed processions to bring home the message to the urban public, and 20,000 copies of a twenty page glossy election booklet produced by the NFU and entitled *Vote for Food* were distributed. Newspapers, radio, television, industrial and trade union leaders, local authorities and MPs were bombarded with the farmers' case. At Portadown in Northern Ireland a coffin was carried by local farmers wearing black suits and bowler hats. Another petition was handed in at 10 Downing Street and at the headquarters of the main political parties. The pedestrians' reaction to the farmers' demonstrations was sympathetic—especially on the forecourt of Sheffield Cathedral, where farmers gave away nearly 570 litres of free milk, 400 dozen eggs, home-cured bacon, chickens, cabbages, cauliflowers and other vegetables.

A fighting fund for the poultry industry topped £5,000 when the industry endured new frustration. This was in the nature of some small print from the CAP, proposing to abolish New York Dressed poultry[5]. As the autumn days arrived Wilson set out to consolidate his majority in Parliament through another General Election timed for 31 October. The furore over farm prices was unabated and a new dimension had arrived. In early October angry Anglesey farmers had discovered that Irish beef cattle were coming in through their port at Holyhead and further exacerbating the crisis in the beef industry by contributing to the over-production.

The Irish Minister of Agriculture, Mark Clinton, denied that Irish beasts were being 'dumped' on to the UK market; under the Anglo-Irish Free Trade Agreement there was an undertaking by the Irish to supply store cattle every year, but the farmers saw these as cattle for immediate slaughter and not for fattening, and were incensed once again. The MMB estimated that September milk-production was 27 million litres lower than the previous year, and 345 million litres down on the twelve month figure. Again Wales was suffering the most.

Anglesey farmers took the law into their own hands, and three hundred of them set out to stop the unloading of 570 'forward stores' (i.e. almost fat cattle ready for slaughter) from a ship which had arrived from Dublin. The cattle disembarked, but their transfer to railway wagons was delayed, as was the ship's departure for its next load. Farmers from western and south-western counties of England saw the Anglesey farmers' demonstration of solidarity as an effective move, and they rallied to their support. Meanwhile sugar and its world-supply situation was creating another diversion, and Peart plucked another cheap-food rabbit from the EEC hat by bringing back from Brussels an assurance that British sugar beet growers would have the opportunity to expand their production. But the autumn had turned wet, and farmers in the arable counties were finding difficulty in getting on to the fields to lift their sugar beet, or to complete their autumn drilling programme.

The Holyhead action prompted British Rail to agree to the suspension of shipments of Irish cattle into the port for two days, and the MP for Anglesey, former Minister of Agriculture Cledwyn Hughes, was brought into the picture. The NFU was hampered in encouraging its members by the Restrictive Trade Practices Act, but farmers were acting on their own.

The week after the initial success at Holyhead another demonstration took place, when eight hundred farmers broke through a cordon of police on 29 October to reach a part of the dock and prevent an Irish boat with five hundred cattle on board being unloaded. They delayed the boat for twelve hours, and the police radioed a warning to another cattle ship from Dublin not to enter port. She waited in a Force 9 gale some thirty kilometres off the coast until the farmers had gone home. Two days later Plumb called an emergency meeting of livestock-producers at Central Hall Library, Westminster. He castigated Minister Peart

---

[5] New York Dressed is the traditional fresh-plucked poultry. The British public buys 25 per cent of its chicken meat in this manner.

for his ineffective action, and roundly accused the Government of walking away from a serious position. Said Plumb:

'Let me remind you of Mr Peart's past pledges.

He gave us a firm promise in the House of Commons on 11 April that he would not allow market prices to fall to 'unrealistic levels'. At that time the average market price was over £18.50 per live hundredweight. Today the market average is £12.50. Despite all the palliatives, the Minister's promise to the House of Commons and to the industry has not been kept.

On 26 June the Minister made a statement which was widely taken to be a promise of a £18 minimum price guarantee over a period.

On 17 July Mr Peart said, when introducing his beef headage payment schemes, 'They amply fulfil the intention I announced in the House of Commons on 26 June of giving our beef-producers an assurance that over a period their returns would not fall below £18 per live hundredweight for clean cattle.'

With these pledges on record I must say bluntly that further promises of action next March will simply not be believed by farmers unless action is taken now to honour, effectively and fully, the previous promises to the industry. Only this can restore any semblance of confidence.

Action must now be taken. What the previous Government did is irrelevant—Mr Peart has been Minister for eight months during which the beef industry has plunged deeper into disaster week by week.

After the meeting the farmers went to the House of Commons, where 30 MPs attended in the Grand Committee Room of the House. Plumb sent a telegram to the Prime Minister and urged that the then Irish Prime Minister, Mr Cosgrave, should cut down in the export of Irish cattle to an already glutted UK market.

The next day, 1 November, violence flared again between police and Welsh farmers picketing Irish meat imports, 150 police grappled with more than a thousand farmers at Fishguard in Pembrokeshire. Three farmers drove tractor ploughs at the police line, two farmers were arrested and two policemen were injured, a farmer was run over by a lorry and his leg broken. But fifty refrigerated twenty-tonne lorries stood marooned in the dock area, unable to move. A telegram was sent to Wilson demanding the immediate dismissal of Peart, and an instant ban on the import of Irish cattle was requested. There had been three days of peaceful picketing, but the angry battles now brought the headlines, and the *Daily Mail* blazoned its front page with 'Charge of the Farm Brigade'.

The following week farmers blocked the main Holyhead-London railway line to prevent trains carrying the cattle from the boats, and on 5 November trains were prevented from crossing Anglesey. In Barry, South Wales, farmers' pickets persuaded the drivers of two refrigerated meat lorries not to leave the docks, and in Glasgow a huge cattle-transporter burst through the picket lines across the dock. Flying squads of militant farmers stood by to descend upon any port where Irish meat was being unloaded, and while farmers lifted their blockade of Fishguard other farmers in Shropshire organized the mass slaughter of over ninety worthless calves.

In Anglesey a policeman was hurt, a farmer arrested, pig and poultry farmers issued a warning that they were considering militant action and Scottish farmers picketed the Glasgow docks. A peaceful demonstration of a thousand farmers from seven counties descended upon the docks at Birkenhead, and the ferment continued. Fred Peart in the House of Commons remained adamant that he was doing his best, but the weather was still deteriorating.

NFU officials predicted that 40 per cent of the Welsh cattle herd would die from starvation before the spring, and in Carmarthenshire auctioneers had to beg for bids when farmers refused to take home animals which they could no longer afford to feed. The NFU found the farmers' militancy and their rail blockades embarrassing, even though it did temporarily suppress the differences between the NFU and the rebel breakaway Farmers Union of Wales. Said an NFU official, 'Farmers just do not do this sort of thing, but if the Government does not like it, let them tell it to those who taught us how to do it, like the dockers.' Finally, on the 9 November, pickets of militant farmers began to go home, and plans for further demonstrations were shelved as Plumb appealed to farmers throughout the country to hold their fire while the NFU and the Ministry of Agriculture held urgent talks to find a solution. At Barry Docks the workers agreed not to handle vessels carrying Irish cattle or meat imports diverted from other docks, and at Birkenhead dockers took a similar decision. The demonstrations ceased fairly quickly, Peart arranged a bottom to the market and the Holyhead police chief said that the cost of the farmer demonstrations had been £150,000. It had cost the farmers themselves more than that.

The farmers certainly believed that the dock-picketing operations had speeded up the lamentably slow process of decision-making, both in the UK and in Brussels, but there were misgivings that it had shown the NFU, and farmers in general, in an uncharacteristic role. Said Monty Keen[6], 'Even if militancy were acceptable as a permanent instrument of NFU policy, it would not work. We are self-employed entrepreneurs, the potential victims, not the perpetrators, of "industrial" action.' And NFU Director-General Cattell warned farmers that if they stopped lorries again they would be 'in dead trouble'. The NFU saw the spontaneous farmers' action as detracting from its own carefully nurtured influence, and it could not admit officially that it had inspired the demonstrations, or even encouraged them. The following year, 1975, there were two more examples of UK farmers' militancy; the first took place in the spring, and the problem was eggs, the second was an autumn demonstration and a mass rally, when the problem was milk.

In January 1975 egg prices had dropped by 10p a dozen, and the foundation of a crisis was well and truly laid. Egg-producers had been seething and suffering under the EEC, which permitted imports of cheap Continental eggs onto the UK market, but which paradoxically hampered the export of British eggs to other EEC nations. In February, angered by the situation, three hundred egg farmers gathered in London to demonstrate and lobby their MPs.

[6] *British Farmer and Stockbreeder*, 4 January 1975.

It was a decorous meeting, and they went home again afterwards. The next month, however, they were back in London, when a thousand egg farmers joined in a larger meeting aimed at banning the import of French eggs. At a meeting at Central Hall, Westminster, Tom Torney, the Chairman of the Labour Party Agricultural Committee, was uncharacteristically not given a fair hearing when he attempted to address the meeting. A meeting was one thing, but it did not resolve the crisis, and later in March egg farmers threatened direct action at the ports to prevent the unloading of allegedly subsidized French eggs. They were emulating the dock picketing at Holyhead and Fishguard which had produced a more urgent response to their demands, and on 8 April they turned back a consignment of 800 cases of French eggs from Poole harbour, Dorset. Seventy farmers' cars blocked the exit to the ferry terminal for about five hours until they had received a written assurance that no more French eggs would be imported during the day.

The autumn demonstration started in August, when five farmer's wives from south-west Sussex delivered a petition to 10 Downing Street demanding better milk prices for dairy farmers. This was signed by sixty farmers, and threatened 'We shall have no alternative but to take extreme measures by withholding supplies.' This time the NFU saw the light and organized a mass rally in London for 25 September. Although the dairy sector was in trouble, other parts of British farming were also being affected and it looked like a repetition of 1974 all over again.

This time, however, on the platform with NFU President Plumb were representatives of the CBI, the TUC, the major banks, food-manufacturing companies, members of associated farming bodies, and members of consumers' and women's organizations. It was a representative galaxy of talent to embrace the whole of the food-production chain, and it sought to widen agitation beyond farmers alone.

The CBI man pledged the support of UK industry for agriculture, which he said was a world leader and an industry of potential: 'Britain must learn to back success for the future and not for the sake of Auld Lang Syne.' The man from the Transport and General Workers Union backed the farmers' calls for assistance in the dairy industry, which he said was 'tottering on the brink of disaster'. There were 2,500 farmers at this mass meeting. It did not erupt into violence, and perhaps both the Ministry and the NFU were learning that the hard, patient road of negotiation and talking would produce results. In the event prices gradually improved, supplies were not withheld, production rose and the threatened rationing did not materialize. But at the time the farmers' worries had been real enough.

The record of farmers' militancy in the UK has not been as tumultuous as in many other countries, the machinery for talking has become sophisticated, if hamstrung by its own traditions, and the Brussels veto creates a delay before announced decisions become a pay cheque. Farmers, like their workers, are acting out of character when they take to the streets, or form picket lines.

22 The Effects of Modern Farming

'For the factory farmer and the agri-industrial world behind him, cruelty is acknowledged only where profitability ceases.'

Animal Machines (Harrison, 1964)

'Progress, therefore is not an accident, but a necessity. It is part of nature.'

Herbert Spencer

In the 40's; food was rationed.
In the 50's; food was plentiful.
In the 60's; food was both plentiful and cheap.
In the 70's; food became more expensive and less plentiful.

Farming is about food, and food-production within the inelastic area of the British Isles where it is naturally in deficit, yet even exported. It was the 1960s which brought all this to the fore. Much emotion is generated by alleged tampering with the balance of nature, or doubts cast on the purity of the food we eat. Both these accusations were levelled at modern farming methods. Farmers were poisoning the land with their chemicals, and poisoning the public with the food it produced, went up the cry.

Battery hens were being kept in claustrophobic cages with considerable cruelty, pigs in pens, and beef had been reared in cubicles instead of grazing lush pastures. Animal husbandry had gone to the dogs, and toxic chemicals and 'artificial' fertilizer were sterilizing the soil of Britain. As for the incomparable beauty of the English landscape, farmers were crashing bulldozers into the hedgerows, cutting down the woods, removing the trees and creating vast prairies, which would be another 'dust-bowl' given time.

All this was reinforced by a book published originally in America, a book by Rachel Carson called *Silent Spring*, which drew a picture of a springtime where no birds sang, where no lambs frolicked in the fields, and where the silence was a silence from the poisoning of the whole world population. It caused some deep thinking, and was followed in the UK by Ruth Harrison's *Animal Machines*, which brought forceably to the public notice the new farming method of keeping hens in cages. The Brambell Committee reported in 1965, and although it discovered that there were obnoxious practices being carried out by farmers in the matter of modern livestock-keeping, the recommendations were in the end too complex to be satisfactorily administered. The Government adopted enabling powers by which enforceable regulations could be issued about such matters as dimensions and layout of livestock accommodation; these were issued in the form of codes of practice, but nevertheless unilaterally adopted by livestock farmers.

There had been a bewildering assortment of contradictory advice and information upon almost every aspect of animal husbandry and modern farming methods. The net result was that the Ministry created a Farm Animal Welfare Advisory Committee which exists to this day.

If the keeping of animals in cramped conditions and an unsavoury environment was enough to make the soft-hearted British public see red, then the other fundamental question-mark was set against the effects which modern farming might be having upon that fundamental and self-replenishing natural asset of Britain—the soil itself. There was a rising tide of public indignation, but the Committee to study the soil was created by Minister Hughes after the bad autumn and winter of 1968-9, which had worried many farmers also.

The Committee was chaired by the then Mr (now Sir) Nigel Strutt, and became known as the 'Strutt Report'. Like the Brambell Report, it became a best-seller, and 6,000 copies were printed and sold. One suspects that they went in wholesale batches to farmers themselves.

In the introduction the Committee stated:

> Much is said and written nowadays in rather vague and sweeping terms about the way we farm our land. An underlying fear in all these statements is that the inherent fertility of the soil is being eroded and the fundamental structure of the soil damaged beyond repair.

The Strutt Report was published in 1970, and while it played down any ideas of a wholesale erosion of the fertility of British soil, and was not in any way an alarmist report, nevertheless it did state that it 'could not find the national farm in a state of perfect health'. The inherent problem lay in the greater mechanization of British farms, and the sheer weight of tractors traversing the soil and compacting it, but there was also a problem which has since been rectified. Farm labour had been disappearing from the farms, farmers had been replacing the labourers with bigger machines, but they were falling behind by stretching their resources beyond mere substitution, and thus cultivations were being carried out later in the season than was good husbandry practice. The potato bonanza in the mid-1970s, and an escalation of grain prices after 1973, put more money into arable farmers' pockets and enabled them to invest in even larger and more powerful tractors—it gave them a greater mastery over the weather.

Sir Nigel Strutt[1] said:

> All these things are happening, and they are largely happening because of lack of precise knowledge of the subsoil, of what it is composed, its porosity, its structure and the details of its layers. This knowledge is now much more necessary than ever before. ... No farmer need be ashamed of not having this knowledge, and agricultural education has been pretty feeble, to say the least of it, in this sphere.

[1] Speaking at The Farmers Club, January 1972, under the title 'Good Farming and the Soil'.

Later, opening the discussion at the same meeting, Professor E. W. Russell said:

> The Report might have been more explicit in saying that compaction is due to the farmer using machinery at the wrong time. No farmer in this country, of course, uses the machine at the wrong time unless he has to. It is not due to the incompetence or carelessness or foolishness or ignorance of the farmer, but to the fact that he is trying to do something which in a sense he should not be doing.

The 'Strutt Report' became a Bible for arable farmers, and it emphasized the importance of drainage as an essential ingredient of soil husbandry, but despite heavy Government grants and even a protracted programme of land drainage which had been carried out on British farms since 1940, the Committee nevertheless reported that if all the essential schemes were started in 1970 it would take well into the twenty-first century before they were all finished at the present rate of work. There was another problem even beyond this, that if all the fields were artificially drained there would be nowhere for the water to go, as there was insufficient arterial drainage work completed to carry the excess to the coastline.

The pace of technological discovery has accelerated rapidly. It is inevitable that with so many new methods, there should be some mistakes. Perhaps historians of the future will comment upon their small number! Farming has not been without mistakes, and the powerful chemicals utilized in crop husbandry have in some instances themselves proved a toxic mixture, stagnating the soil itself; but in the UK at least the examples have been on a minimal scale. DDT, the wonder compound which contributed to the reduction of malaria in tropical countries, and had positive advantages to mankind, was banned in the United States when traces were discovered in food. Even the fall-out from nuclear explosions has led to radioactive milk from the Welsh hills, while in the UK aldrin and dieldrin—used for cereal seed dressing against wheat bulb fly—were banned after December 1973. But by this time more effective additives had already been discovered.

In May 1973 tomato crops at thirty Essex nurseries died dramatically; the contamination was introduced through the water-supply, and was later identified as a chemical known as TBA. This had arrived on the farms through the river sources, but had emanated from Fisons Chemical Works far away near Cambridge.

Two years later compensation was agreed, and the affair largely forgotten, but farmers themselves have introduced powerful animal effluent in the form of slurry into watercourses, and regulations were introduced which forced farmers producing slurry to ensure that it did not leak off their farms and create pollution.

In 1973 a chemical company in Michigan made a tragic blunder when they sent out a poisonous substance, PBB, in place of animal feed. Farmers' stock died or was deformed, and massive slaughter took place to isolate the contamination. It also had effects upon humans, with damage to the brain, liver and the nervous system, and the company paid out 100 million dollars in compensation, although the case was not finalized by 1978. In Italy in 1976 an explosion at a pharmaceutical factory distributed a thick white cloud of big snowflakes over a wide area. For ten days after this freak occurrence life went on as usual, but soon the children became affected with a severe skin disease. Thirty-four women rushed to have abortions because they feared their children could be deformed. Sixty thousand animals were killed and the carcasses collected in plastic bags; all the trees over a wide area were cut down, and vegetation left to rot behind barbed wire. The poison spread over the landscape and seeped into the soil.

These are perhaps the extreme examples of playing with fire, and there have been international agreements on the safe regulation of chemicals. This has meant considerable additional expenditure for the chemical industry, to the extent that this will probably mean that few new basic chemicals will be introduced. Nevertheless, with the wide range of formulations available, there is considerable armoury for the eradication of crop pests and diseases.

In the 1970s, with the arrival of the 'age of leisure', the countryside came to be regarded as the working-man's playground. To the surprise of the countrymen the newcomers complained about the lack of street lights, laundrettes in the village street or fish and chip shop, while the new country-dwellers found that rural life differed greatly from its romantic image.

The buttercups and daisies had been removed from the meadows by selective chemicals, which had also eradicated the poppies and thistles from the corn. Farmers, it was truthfully rumoured, were applying nitrogen to stimulate the growth of their crops, and then applying a growth regulator to curtail the very growth they had sought to stimulate! It was all very confusing, and they didn't like it.

Farming had moved from its centuries-old methods into the new techno-logical, mechanical and revolutionary age; it had changed the countryside and the townsmen's nostalgic image of it. However, the world, and Britain, had moved into another age, and farming had moved with it.

Pleasant market towns became a nightmare of 'one-way systems', self-service replaced personal homage, the wire basket replaced the porter. Motorways carved great scars across the face of the countryside, and Government money changed the face of Britain—until it all ran out about 1976. If the towns and cities had changed their faces, then the farms had also changed. The pressures of economic survival would not allow farming and farmers to continue in the old ways, just as the ever-encroaching sea of cars would not allow the ancient streets to continue as in the days of horses and carriages.

The revolution in farming methods was engendered by the pressure of a cost squeeze accompanying stable prices, as successive Governments fought a rearguard action to perpetuate the myth of cheap food. A complete farming revolution in such a short period was bound to bring mistakes in its wake. It has been those mistakes which the emotional eye of the public has highlighted. However, farming has not been alone in its mistakes, and the thalidomide babies disaster is only the most dramatic of a series of unfortunate by-products of a rush to change everything. The mistakes in farming have on balance been less lethal.

The pressures which stimulated the farming revolution stemmed largely from the reduction in the labour force (which has gone down to only one-third of its 1945 size in thirty years) and without strikes and disruption. The movement away from manual work, and the redesignation of farm workers (from labourers to farm employees) illustrates the changing status.

The economic squeeze too had its effects in speeding up the revolution in methods, and where a farmer milking say forty cows with one cowman found that milk prices were not consistent with rising costs he naturally sought to rectify the position by making one cowman milk forty-five cows. This exacerbated the over-production of milk for a few years, but even without the aid of Government cash incentives farming has become streamlined.

Although a balanced and mixed form of farming helps to equalize the workload throughout the year from what is a very seasonal occupation, farmers have reduced the diversity of their stock-keeping and their cropping, following the dictum that to specialize is to economize; the larger and more expensive machines also meant that they would be viable only if there was sufficient area to be covered. In the 1970s a further extension of this specialization took place, when many farmers who had traditionally grown both potatoes and sugar beet as profitable root crops found that they had to make a choice between one or the other. The advent of all-cereal farms is nothing new, and although lip-service has been paid to the search for an eternal 'break' crop to put between cereal crops and provide a rotation, nevertheless many cereal farmers have continued to grow continuous corn year after year, even improving their yields. Rotations have in many senses gone out of the window.

The changeover to a greater emphasis upon 'bag-muck' or artificial fertilizer has been singled out as a movement away from the 'natural' method of crop-growing, yet the application of quantifiable measurements of phosphate, potash and nitrogen to the soil has been a part of British farming methods for over one hundred years, even though the extent or sophistication of the material applied has grown immeasurably in more recent years. To contrast this with the natural dung of cattle mixed with straw is to miss the point that the farmyard manure is very much less concentrated, while there has not only been a reduction in the output of farmyard manure with the advent of covered yards producing less wet straw, but the mechanical methods of handling have reduced this as well. The advent of 'bag-muck' has given the farmer the opportunity to apply proper amounts of the relevant substances to his soil. Although there is still a ham-fisted approach by many farmers towards fertilizer application, there is little doubt that without this aid to crop growing UK agriculture could not produce the quantities of food it has during the last three decades. About one-third of the total UK harvest of wheat, barley and oats, it is estimated, is produced from the application of nitrogen alone. In total this adds up to five million tonnes of grain out of a UK production that varies between 13 million and 16 million tonnes.

With sugar beet the combined phosphate and potash adds 75 kilos per hectare, and with potatoes 1,017 per hectare. These figures illustrate that without the aid of modern fertilizers farming production would plummet, and no amount of farmyard manure could make up the deficit. Does food produced with the aid of science become less nutritious?

Certainly the scientists would adamantly proclaim that in terms of nutritional analysis there is no difference, yet the discerning public would emphasize that there is a lack of taste, and this is true. Against this must be set the modern trend towards relative tastelessness, but nevertheless one is forced to admit that the modern broiler chicken tastes more like blotting paper than anything else.

Destroying the wild life

'In the past 35 years we have destroyed more of Britain's wild life than in the whole of history.'

Jane McLoughlin, 'Daily Mail', 18 April 1977

It is unquestionable that the wild life of Britain has been radically changed by modern farming methods, but then many of nature's charming creatures (like pigeons!) are the farmer's enemy. The naturalists may well condemn farmers for disturbing the balance of nature, and for the suppression or even extinction of some species, but farmers on the whole would reply that these species were pests that should best be destroyed.

It is easy to suggest that nature should be left to create its own balance, and that the predatory and the non-predatory species will provide balance, but man has carved out the landscape and the farms from the jungle and woodland. He has harnessed the fertile soil for food and farming, and as such many of the birds and animals are his natural enemies. It is very difficult to be selective in the extermination process (poisonous bait which could be eaten by domestic pets as well as pests is outlawed anyway), but if man is to harness the countryside for food-production purposes it is inevitable that he must be responsible for the entire balance of nature. You cannot control one species and allow another to thrive. That in itself would not be the so-called 'balance of nature'.

Of course farmers and countrymen do exercise some selectivity in their attempts to harness nature. You do not shoot hen pheasants in the closing weeks of the season, and the law protects them during their breeding period, while since the more destructive grey squirrels are themselves exterminating the red ones it makes more sense to shoot the grey ones, and protect the red. A chemical environment may not sound the ideally attractive atmosphere in which we would wish to rear our children, but the balance of nature is now being strongly controlled by chemicals, whether we like it or not. In 1976 a plague of grain-sucking aphides descended upon the corn fields in southern England, but voracious ladybirds appeared and multiplied miraculously, with their insatiable appetite for aphides. Nevertheless, farmers could not sit back and see the crops ravaged, so helicopters appeared and sprayed off the aphides. The workings of mother nature, left to her own devices, would have provided a solution that was too slow.

As long ago as 1952 the public was outraged when large numbers of corpses of birds and mammals were discovered in fields which had been sprayed with organo-phosphorus insecticides. Three years later the Zuckerman Committee[2] was set up to inquire into the effects of chemicals upon wild life. It admitted that dangers existed, but declined to define them precisely, although it emphasized that steps should be taken to minimize dangers.

In 1957 James Wentworth-Day wrote[3], 'The average person, I think, will agree that the laws governing farm chemicals, their manufacture and use, must be tightened up.' He drew attention in his timely book to the dangers and problems of modern farming, and continued:

> Chemical crop sprays, some so deadly that they will slay a man, let alone a bird or an animal, do the work of the hoer with his hoe. Artificial fertilizers too often take the place of the rich manure which was the medicine and food of the soil, the breeding place of worms, the food store of birds.

Twenty years later the EEC was warning, 'Some 400 species of birds observed regularly within the Community Territory are threatened. About 60 species could soon be extinct, whilst in most others ornithologists have found evidence of population decline.'

Few if any of nature's wild animals are the friends of man, and they are certainly all the enemy of farmers, but passions are raised and brother set against brother when the thorny subject of fox-hunting is raised. Anyone who has seen the carnage among a flock of chickens will have no sympathy with the fox, however he is hunted, trapped, shot or otherwise exterminated, yet the Anti-Hunting League placards its case vehemently and annually. It is doubtful whether many of them have ever even seen a fox at close quarters. No one complains of the annihilation of rats, but the fox and the rabbit of the children's nursery stories are a different matter. Rabbits are not indigenous to Australia, yet a handful imported in the nineteenth century multiplied into millions, and ravaged the whole continent. They cost the whole world millions of tonnes of food.

Myxomatosis arrived in Britain in 1953: it had already swept across France, and had created vast new areas where farming was possible. It first appeared in Britain in Kent, Sussex and Essex. It may have crossed the Channel by accident, but it was certainly carried from farm to farm by farmers, who eagerly introduced an infected rabbit on to their farms. The results were dramatic. Millions of rabbits died, and vast areas of Britain which had never grown a blade of grass suddenly blossomed forth; fields adjacent to woods which had never grown corn were now lush, and the scourge of the rabbit was over. It has been said that ten

[2] Lord Zuckerman was Chief Scientific Adviser to HM Government.
[3] In *Poison on the Land,* 1957.

rabbits ate as much grass as one cow, yet the outcry in protection of this little furry creature reached high proportions. Eventually in 1954 it was made illegal to spread myxomatosis deliberately, and this continues to be a criminal offence, yet today land-occupiers have a statutory obligation to keep their land free from rabbits. When the rabbit population had reached bare survival numbers the Ministry of Agriculture grant-aided and formed Rabbit Clearance Societies, which in 1970–71 were costing £73,016. These societies became defunct, losing Ministry support; by 1975–6 the financial contribution from the MoA had dropped to £634. The farmers' attitude to these pests cannot but be markedly in opposition to the townsmen's emotional and romantic viewpoint.

Farmers have cut down and bulldozed hedges, and this has opened up the countryside, but again it has been viewed as a retrograde step by the urbanized, so-called country-lovers. (Paradoxically, farmers in East Sussex were asked to cut their overgrown hedges by the county council because of the obstruction to the vision of road-users.) The East Sussex county council, along with others, even has powers to make landowners cut back offending hedgerows, and although townsmen do not object to farm-workers cutting hedges by hand in the winter months, there has been an outcry when the same job is done with machines.

The advent of the mechanical hedgecutter has had a curious side effect inasmuch as many southern counties where arable farming is practised were for many years hedgeless. This was the case even though in the light, sandy fenland soils hedges protect the soil from wind erosion, but with mechanical hedgecutters many farmers are now finding that hedge maintenance has once again become a viable proposition, and some nice thick hedgerows are reappearing—well trimmed and neat. Nevertheless, modern farm machinery requires larger fields than was the norm in the arable areas before the days of bulldozers.

Farmers are not entirely Philistines who regard their land as an exploitable asset, but they do regard it as their workshop. They are also neither conservationists, naturalists or sportsmen and since most of them are not in it for the money the motivation for the removal of hedgerows and woodland habitats is the more efficient management of the land.

A survey[4] set out to investigate farmers' attitudes and intentions towards semi-natural habitats on farms, and came out with the startling fact that despite the thirty year programme of field restructuring 13 per cent of farmers still intend to remove an appreciable amount of their remaining habitat over the next ten years. The survey added, 'but the incidence of which is more likely to be dependent on agricultural factors than on farmers' desires to conserve wild life'. Another 13 per cent of farmers, however, had decided that the reduction of their habitat area had gone too far, and were intending to improve it, or even to create new habitats.

Some farmers have a wide interest in wild life, and some have an interest in the sporting aspects. The larger farmers, it was revealed, are more likely to be

[4] *Wild Life Conservation in Semi-Natural Habitats on Farms.* ADAS November 1975.

conscious of the need to improve or create wildlife habitats on their farms. It is arguable whether this comes from the urgings of the press and the conservation societies, or from their natural desire. The survey added that farmers' primary reasons for allowing wild life to exist at all on their farms was personal pleasure (50 per cent of all farmers), while lip-service to the 'balance of nature' was foremost in the minds of nearly 43 per cent, and just under 7 per cent felt that additional wild life would increase the sporting benefits.

With regard to knowledge of wild life, nearly 32 per cent admitted that they knew virtually nothing about it, and just under 5 per cent said they knew 'a great deal'. This may appear surprising to those who would imagine that farmers, living in the countryside and gleaning their living from it, would be in the forefront of those with an intimate knowledge of the wild life that still abounds in the UK.

Since conservation is at variance with farming the farmer's attitude has been that if the nation wishes to create a museum in the countryside it should foot the bill. This survey showed that expenditure on conservation (not surprisingly) increased with farm size, and there were indications that more money will be spent in the future. Ten per cent of those who had spent nothing in the past intended to do so in the future, but 33 per cent said that they would contribute if proper financial encouragement was given.

This theme was continued in another survey:[5] that farmers needed financial support if they were to create habitats. The NCC said that fiscal measures such as an alleviation of capital transfer tax should take nature-conservation requirements into account, and Essex farmer and member of the Nature Conservancy Council Hew Watt said:

> as a nation we have got to accept the need to pay if we want to keep all our wild plants and animals. We have had them free for so long that we find this hard to accept, but the farmer cannot be expected to foot the bill alone.

The Council discovered that although there was rapidly declining wild life in agricultural areas of England and Wales, this was also affecting the lowlands, and the more fertile uplands in Scotland:

> While a small proportion of the total wild life in Scotland is dependent on farm land habitats than in England and Wales, wild life in the Scottish lowlands may be under greater threat than in England and Wales because it is supported by smaller areas of these habitats, and for that reason is more vulnerable.

There can surely be no other industry or sector of British life which is subjected to such an everlasting series of reports, surveys and glossy publications, or on which major conclusions appear at the rate of about twenty per year. These may be official, semi-official, unofficial or commercially inspired. It took three years to produce *New Agricultural Landscapes*,[6] by Richard Westmacott and Tom

[5] *Nature Conservation and Agriculture*, Nature Conservancy Council, 1977.
[6] Countryside Commission, November 1974.

Worthington, who produced a 98-page study based on seven areas broadly representing different types of lowland farming: Prick Willow (Cambridgeshire); Leighton-Bromswold (Huntingdonshire); Piddlehinton (Dorset); Crewkerne (Somerset); Preston-on-Wye (Herefordshire); Myton-upon-Swale (Yorkshire); and Grandborough (Warwickshire).

Their survey showed a rapidly changing countryside, and among their most revealing discoveries was a 106-hectare grass farm which before the reorganization of field boundaries had fields with an average size of $3\frac{1}{2}$ hectares. When this survey was conducted the field size had grown to 17 hectares, and even some of these fields were subdivided by wire fences. Four kilometres of hedges had been removed; and this was on a grass farm in a livestock farming area.

In the introduction the Countryside Commission Chairman, John Cripps, said that farmers preferred an efficient, tidy scene and once features such as ponds and hedges lost their agricultural significance they were vulnerable to removal. It was also emphasized that financial incentives would help farmers to co-operate in positive landscape planning. He emphasized that within the next twenty-five years almost all hedgerow trees would disappear, and this without the disastrous effects of Dutch Elm Disease, which has ravaged many counties of England, decimating the elms.

The dictates of modern farming have brought about a revolutionary change in the landscape of Britain, yet we are not a treeless, hedgeless, barren lunar landscape. Some people criticize the lack of woodland in Britain when compared with Scandinavian countries which have over 50 per cent of their land mass covered with trees—in Britain it is only 8 per cent—but the climate and the soil texture is more conducive in the UK to intensive farming.

The British countryside can still be called one of the most beautiful on earth. Farming and beauty can exist side by side, but with due emphasis on the priority.

23 The Honours Game

'The Knighthood game seems more like a game of snakes and ladders, with a good many snakes and only one ladder.'

My Queen and I (Willie Hamilton, 1975)

'Even now, the number of those who are not knighted exceeds the number of those who are. Time, doubtless, will reverse these figures.'

Sir Max Beerbohm

Politicians have always been inclined to reward themselves and their civil servants with a galaxy of medals and titles, but in more recent years it has been a feature of the New Year and Birthday Honours Lists to emphasize the importance of trade by including 'services to exports', and the importance of devaluing the honours system by democratizing it has necessitated the inclusion of pop stars and successful sportsmen. In the farming and agricultural sphere there would appear to have been a dearth of recognition. It is true that civil servants can gain their honours in a routine manner, while since the politicians reward themselves, past Ministers of Agriculture have almost to a man received a peerage; but on the lower levels farming seems to be largely ignored.

Another accolade of achievement, instituted in more recent years, is the 'Queen's Award to Industry', where the technological advances in the agricultural world have been more equitably recognized. Beyond those honours distributed in the official manner by the establishment, moreover, there is a multitude of ways in which achievement has been recognized. The farming world has its own particular set of honours, which, being internal to farming, carry more weight there.

The farming knights

There are knights who have been so honoured in reward for their services to agriculture, and óthers who earned the honour elsewhere but became prominent in agriculture afterwards. It would appear that a knighthood for services to the farming industry is a very rare honour indeed; by comparison, show business collects them in profusion, and this bears out the general paradox that however the share-out of honours is calculated, farming does not have its just rewards.

The New Year Honours List in 1976 was a typical example; in total, 744 honours were dished out, including five life peerages, 34 knighthoods, 105 CBEs, 199 OBEs, and 339 MBEs. This quota included only three farmers, and two of these were for their work with farming organizations. It was only Alex Haggart, a 36-hectare mixed farmer from Perthshire, with a further 260 hectares of rented potato land, who received an OBE for his pioneering work on the box storage of potatoes. Agriculture mustered only 14 awards out of the total of 744.

Honours are distributed as a mark of recognition on a fairly rigid rotational basis; thus the police force, as an example, are entitled to their annual ration of knighthoods and lesser honours. When the rota comes up for, shall we say, road-traffic engineers, the backroom boys get to work and find the most suitable road-traffic engineer with a clean face and long service. In the end, the award is merely a recognition of all road-traffic engineers. Life peerages and knighthoods are more important, although many knighthoods are 'automatic' by virtue of an acquired position, such as the Chairmen of many of Britain's largest companies or a high enough grading in the Civil Service. A KCB can come automatically for the higher ranks of the armed forces. Some recipients are actually awarded for merit, and a few for philanthropy, although heavy financial contributions to a political party can also be helpful.

The Presidency of the NFU rates as an 'automatic' knighthood grading. Leadership of the industry warrants a title; it gives authority to the President with his own members, and is an accolade for the whole industry. It also carries more weight in Whitehall, where these things matter. How much it adds to the stature of the recipient throughout the country is debatable. Promotion to the peerage is a passport to a very exclusive club with around 1,500 members, but it is more importantly a platform on the stage of the House of Lords itself. It is a sign of the embarrassment which many new peers feel that they prefer to retain their more familiar names; thus Lord Clark is better known as Kenneth Clark, and Lord Willis as 'Ted Willis', whilst Lord Beaumont goes on a TV Mastermind Programme as plain 'Tim Beaumont'.

Certainly, Sir Henry Plumb gains stature in most people's eyes above that which he would acquire as plain 'Mr Plumb'. He, like his predecessors, Sir Gwilym Williams, Sir Harold Woolley and Sir James Turner (Lord Nether-thorpe) have been knighted whilst they held the office of President. Turner, with fourteen years in the hot seat, and Woolley, with six years, both became peers upon retirement. It looked as if a ladder had been prepared, but Williams, incontinently sacked after four years as President of the NFU, was not considered a suitable candidate.

The only other two peerages granted to agriculture, apart from the ex-Ministers of Agriculture, have been to my lords Collison and Hilton, both from the NUAAW. These were given by Harold Wilson, to strengthen the Socialist representation in the Lords. Hilton died in 1977.

It is automatic and non-political for the Permanent Secretary to the Ministry of Agriculture to be knighted, but Sir Alan Neale received his KCB while he was Second Permanent Secretary to the Treasury, a year before he went to agriculture. His predecessor, Sir Basil Engholm, came up through the ranks at Agriculture, and received his title when he succeeded Sir John Winnifrith in 1968. A second knight has appeared within the Ministry in more recent years. This is not only a mark of upgrading agriculture's importance in the national context; within the wider field of the EEC the post of Second Permanent Secretary was graded, and in 1975 Freddie Kearns was appointed. It was felt appropriate that he should become 'Sir Frederick', with the prospect of hobnobbing with the Commissariat in Brussels, and as a mark of his importance within the Ministry at home. But earlier than this, in 1971, the Director-General of the newly created ADAS became 'Sir' Emrys Jones, which added lustre to the service he headed, although in the same breath Jim Prior announced a slashing of that service. Also within the Ministry in 1977 the Chief Scientist became Sir Charles Pereira, like Sir Harold Sanders (knighted 1963), and Chief Scientific Adviser 1955–64, although Pereira's post had wider implications.

Sir Roger Falk (knighted 1969) acquired his preferment while he was Chairman of the Central Council for Agricultural and Horticultural Co-operation, one of the more prominent of the bodies supporting farming progress. But Sir Roger was also a member of the Monopolies Commission at the time, and had an energetic and striking record of public service—but in non-agricultural fields. His successor, Sir James Barker, had a background in the food-manufacturing industry, finishing up as Chairman of Unigate.

Sir Gerald Thorley was knighted as Chairman of Allied Breweries Ltd in 1973, but was also Chairman of the British Sugar Corporation, the monopoly buyer of farmers' sugar beet, and controller of the seventeen factories which form the sugar beet industry in the UK. Sir Henry Hardman acquired his title from a succession of Whitehall postings, as he rose through the ranks of the Civil Service; at Agriculture, Aviation and Defence. He chaired the Covent Garden Market Authority during its transition from the Strand to Nine Elms, and was Chairman of the Home Grown Cereals Authority from 1968 to 1977.

A Dorset dairy farmer, Dick Trehane, became Chairman of the Milk Marketing Board in 1958, and nine years later became Sir Richard, while Bill Young from Kilmarnock became Chairman of the Scottish Milk Marketing Board in 1962, but had to wait thirteen years before becoming Sir William. A Cambridgeshire Land Agent, Francis Pemberton, was knighted in the Birthday Honours List in 1976 for his work and devotion to the cause of the Royal Agricultural Society of England, of which he was Deputy President at the time.

Sir Nigel Strutt, heading one of the largest farming companies in the UK, and Chairman of the influential Ministerial Advisory Committee for Agriculture, received his knighthood in recognition of his masterpiece, the survey of modern farming methods, entitled 'Modern Farming and the Soil'. The entrepreneurial head of the chicken empire bearing his name became Sir John Eastwood in the New Year Honours List in 1975, and George Huckle exchanged his plain 'Mr' similarly in 1977. A former executive with Shell, he was Chairman of the Agricultural Training Board when he was knighted, and just before he succeeded Sir Henry Hardman as Chairman of the HGCA.

Although Sir Emrys Jones exchanged his Ministerial role for an academic hat after he was knighted, it was Sir Kenneth Blaxter, one of Britain's leading animal nutritionists, and Director of the Rowett Research Institute, near

Aberdeen, who became the first 'academic' knight when the Jubilee Honours List was announced in 1977.

There only remains the knighthoods given to ex-CLA Presidents Lord De Ramsey and Sir Ralph Verney (both already titled in their own right). It is still considered appropriate to grant a second title to an existing holder, even if the honour rates a lower precedence than the one they already possess. In both these two honours the awards were for services they had rendered after their CLA role, and not because of it.

Below the knighthood level, a bevy of officials in the Ministry, and in the ancillary industries to farming, figure in the annual New Year and Birthday Lists, but it would seem that there has been a remarkable dearth of official recognition for an industry which has thrown up so many pioneers and leaders. Farmers, of course, do get a modicum of the honours distributed, but few are for their farming achievements; thus in 1972 a farmer, Dennis Hutchinson, was awarded a CBE, but it was as an Alderman on Northants County Council, while Suffolk farmer Roger Paul was awarded an OBE which disguised the fact that he was a local bigwig in the Eye Constituency Conservative Association. There are others who may be farmers as well who have been rewarded for other services.

In 1973 Frank Arden, described as one of Britain's largest farming operators, got a CBE for 'services to agriculture', and the previous year Denis Cadzow's work in the development of the Scottish Luing Cattle Breed was recognized by an OBE; but in the main the honours bestowed upon agriculture are few.

The Queen's Award for Agriculture

The Queen's Award to Industry was instituted in 1966; it annually attracts about 1,200 applications, and grants about one in every ten of these. The Awards numbered 115 in the initial year, dropped to only 78 in 1974, and peaked in Jubilee Year at 125. It is a coveted award, which carries a handsome blue flag, a presentation replica, besides prestige which can be exploited commercially in a blaze of publicity. It is a type of Royal bestowal beyond the honours system itself, and is awarded to companies and not individuals. An honour and title, though, is bestowed for life, and only in rare and extreme circumstances does the Palace politely ask for it to be returned; but the Queen's Award to Industry is bestowed only for the limited period of five years.

It is announced on the 21st April annually, the Queen's real Birthday (as opposed to the Birthday Honours announced on the Queen's 'Official' Birthday, 6 June). It is divided into two classes: export achievements and technological innovation. The former is not the prerogative of the larger companies solely, being adjudged on increases in export sales; thus small companies with up to twenty employees figure in the list. The Award to the Mermaid Hotel (1973), one of the prettiest inns of Southern England, tucked away in the narrow streets of the Sussex town of Rye, was an Award which strikes the imagination. The Mermaid had attracted more than three thousand foreign visitors through its doors in the previous year. Britain's car-manufacturers, with an enormous export market, do not appear in the annual lists.

Agricultural establishments, in the widest sense of the word, gain on average 4 per cent of those awards in the export section annually, but 17 per cent in the section for technological innovation. Thus it is recognized that agriculture's contribution to scientific and technical breakthrough is way ahead of the remainder of British industry, for its size. The lack of Awards in the exports category emphasizes that as a nation we import more agricultural produce and knowhow than we export.

The Export Awards seem to be divided between farm machinery and agrochemicals, with livestock rarely mentioned. This is surprising in view of the premier position of British bloodstock, and British pedigree animals. The technical class is dominated by advances in agrochemicals particularly by plant-breeders, with machinery development getting only an occasional mention. The repetition Awards to the same company emphasizes that those who are good are very good; International Harvester, Massey-Ferguson, the Howard Machinery Company—all as farm-machinery manufacturers—have each won three Awards through the years. Another machinery company, David Brown, has won three Awards for exports and one for technical advances. The Plant Protection Division of ICI has a record of three in the export section and three technical Awards (with a total of thirty to the credit of all the divisions of ICI Ltd).

The Awards to Agricultural Companies

Year	Technological Innovation	Awards for Exports

1973 Plant Breeding Institute
The breeding programme which produced a new generation of highly productive varieties with increases in yield of up to 15 per cent for winter wheat varieties. Eight Maris varieties (Widgeon, Ranger, Settler, Beacon, Nimrod, Huntsman, Templer and Freeman). The citation called this 'unprecedented'.

Ross Poultry
A Division of Imperial Foods Group, for the development of a highly specialized broiler breeding-stock which largely displaced US stocks from the UK and other countries. An achievement of genetic engineering that tripled sales in the four years ending 1972.

Plant Protection Ltd
Awarded for the development of 'Milstem', a fungicide for the control of powdery mildew in barley and developed for cereal crops. It represented an important advance in agricultural chemical science. It also had good export sales, which in two years increased six times.

British United Turkeys
BUT strains comprise 50 per cent of all the turkeys eaten in the UK, and 30 per cent of those eaten in Western Europe. BUT had taken over from the Americans the leadership in the development of poultry breeding-stock.

International Harvester Company of Great Britain
For the export of agricultural tractors and construction equipment.

Year	Technological Innovation	Awards for Exports

1974 Plant Protection Ltd
For the development of Gramoxone, new designs of drills and the innovation of the method of 'direct-drilling'. 67 per cent of Gramoxone sales were exported.

May & Baker Ltd
For the development of 'Asulox', a slow-acting weed-killer, non-toxic to wild life and selective in its action, to be used post-emergence; this last feature enabled it to be used against weeds in sugar-cane and bracken. Sales of £1·6 million in 1972–3 of which #1·5 million were exported.

David Brown Tractors
An Award for a unique transmission system comprising 4-speed semi- automatic shift gearing followed by orthodox 3-speed and reverse range gearing. With a hydra-Shift tractor-driving is much easier. Export sales represented just under 50 per cent of £1·9 million sales in 1973.

1975 Plant Breeding Institute
For the development of marrow-stem kale 'Maris Kestrel' by a new breeding method.

Micron Sprayers
A small company with only thirteen employees for the development of ultra-low-volume farm-spraying equipment, using natural forces for its power of distribution and atomizing into fine even-sized droplets. Mainly designed for peasant farmers in development countries, in Tanzania 50,000 had been sold for the protection of the cotton crop.

Albright and Wilson
Although the company manufactured agrochemicals, this Award was for general exports including detergent and toilet-article manufacture.

International Harvester Co. of GB.
Exporting 70 per cent of the output of wheel tractors, also exporting industrial tractors, farm machinery and construction equipment.

Massey-Ferguson Holdings Ltd
The British parent of the M-F Organisation, with 70 per cent of its sales being exported, in particular a £150 million programme extending over the next fifteen years to modernize farm mechanization in Poland.

Stanhay (Ashford) Ltd
The Stanhay precision seed-drill being used in more than fifty countries, and for sowing vegetables within the Arctic Circle and peanuts on the Equator. A precision machine, handling seed gently and positioning it in the soil with accuracy. Company employing 175 people.

Pig Improvement Company
A rare Award for livestock, this one was in the field of pig-breeding and exporting.

Year	Technological Innovation	Awards for Exports

1976 Rothamsted Experimental Station
Awarded for the development of ultra-safe insecticides which are valued for their rapid action and lack of toxicity to mammals. Also for the clearance of any residues which could be harmful to the environment.

Welsh Plant Breeding Station
For the development of new and improved varieties of hybrid ryegrasses. From the two ryegrasses, perennial and Italian, which are the most important species involved in Britain's grassland-based livestock industry. From this new stable hybrids of high agronomic value were developed.

Caterpillar Tractor Company
For the export of earth-moving equipment.

Fisons Ltd
To the Fertiliser Division for the export of inorganic fertilizers.

Howard Rotavator Company
Also given an Award in 1966 and 1971 for the export of farm machinery.

Plant Protection Ltd
Division of ICI for the export of crop-protection products and agrochemicals; Awards also in 1967 and 1970.

1977 Fisons Ltd
For the development of 'Norton', a selective herbicide for the control of weeds in sugar-beet, and the first of its kind to have a world market. With a wide range of both pre- and post-emergence applications.
Also for its development and use on grass crops, being uniquely selective in rygrass, eradicating other grass weeds.

National Vegetable Research Station
For the development work on onions under two research projects which made it possible by 1977 to produce 50 per cent of UK requirements against only 10 per cent being locally grown in 1960. The elimination of the major storage disease of bulb onions, neck rot, by a simple seed dressing.

Plant Protection Ltd
An Award for the development of Pirimi-carb, a new specific aphicide, with a high toxicity to all aphides, combined with a low toxicity to bees and ladybirds. This product is used by both farmers and gardeners.

1978 East Malling Research Station
An award in collaboration with Wye College for the development of hop plants with greatly improved performance, due to freedom from virus-infection. The project also identified wilt-resistant varieties and devised a a new cultural system which increased the productivity and profitability of hops in the UK, but mainly in Kent and Sussex.

Booker Agriculture International
Over a three-year period overseas earnings had more than doubled for this consultancy division of Booker Mc-Connell, giving management consultancy, techanical training for agricultural and agro-industrial projects in tropical, sub-tropical and arid areas.

Year	Technological Innovation	Awards for Exports

1978 Wye College (Department of Hop Research)
An adjacent award to the one above, which resulted in new varieties of hop plants with increased brewing value, and disease resistance, giving higher yields and improved profitability.

Boythorpe Cropstores
For the export of agricultural storage equipment.

Plant Protection Ltd
Another award for this Division of ICI for the development of Pirimiphos-methyl, an insecticide marketed under the trade name 'Actellic', 'Silosan' and 'Blex', used for a wide variety of pests, and with particular application to public health and domestic situations, as well as for agriculture and horticulture.

David Brown Tractors
Tractor exports.

Farrow Irrigation
Advanced irrigation equipment perfected in the UK but exported to many overseas countries.

Queen's Awards to Industry

Year	Total Awards	Technical Innovations	(Agri)	Export Achievements	(Agri)
1973	83	17	(3)	66	(2)
1974	78	19	(3)	59	(0)
1975	93	17	(2)	76	(5)
1976	115	20	(2)	95	(4)
1977	125	19	(3)	106	(0)
1978	124	17	(3)	107	(4)

In assessing the Awards that are applicable to agriculture or agricultural companies there is always a dividing line; the Award for the export of malt extract, because it is made from farmers' barley, hardly warrants an agricultural inclusion, as does the export of whisky, again made largely from malting barley. The Awards for food products exported again bear little connection to the product which leaves the farm, and many of the companies involved in agrochemicals, and heavy construction equipment, both have agricultural divisions, but the exports may be for products which are of industrial usage. Thus the list above highlights those Awards which can be more directly attributed to a positive agricultural connection.

The Massey-Ferguson Award

Lord Lucky (who you will recall),
'By a curious flook became a most important Duke.
From living in a vile hotel a long way east of Camberwell—
He rose in less than half an hour to riches, dignity and power'.
Duke of Northumberland, on his receipt of the Massey-Ferguson National
Award for 1974.

Top among the annual farming honours must be the Massey-Ferguson Annual

Award; it singles out one outstanding individual and places him on a pedestal, with a cheque for £1,000 to boot. The roll of honour since the inception in 1964 is interesting, if only for the diversity of the recipients' contributions. The sponsors, as farm-machinery manufacturers, have not influenced the selection; if anything, there has been a bias against pioneers in the machinery field.

No Award was made in 1968, as no outstanding candidate could be found, but prior to that date the first four Awards went to practical farmers who had been pioneers 'down on the farm'. It may be significant that there has only been one Award since that time for pure farming innovation. The Awards have instead put the spotlight upon the policy-makers, and the technical academicians. The Cadzow brothers were in 1972 honoured for developing the Luing cattle.

The Award is administered by a Committee under a Massey-Ferguson director and friend of the Queen, Lord Abergavenny, who holds a Marquessate dating from 1876, and a family Barony going back to 1450. The Committee set as their criteria 'Developments in annual crop husbandry or the design of buildings or machinery, the development of new systems of farm management or administration, or matters relating to the general welfare of the farming community'. This is a wide brief, but one which precludes those who are not engaged full-time in agriculture—those in commercial employment are in fact barred. The annual ceremony takes place in the opulence of Claridge's Hotel, which happens to be opposite the quite modest London home of Massey-Ferguson in near-by Davies Street, all in fashionable Mayfair. It is a glittering event, which is normally attended by the current Minister of Agriculture, with a galaxy of ex-Ministers, and even Shadow Ministers, also in attendance.

Massey-Ferguson National Award

1964   Howell Evans, MBE
       Cow Cubicles
1965   Rex Paterson, OBE
       Milk from Grass
1966   Leslie Aylward, OBE
       Farm Machinery Syndicates
1967   Trevor Ensor
       Floor Drying of Cereals
1969   Lord Netherthorpe
       Shaping Agricultural Policy while President of the NFU
1970   Professor M. McG. Cooper, CBE
       Advancing knowledge of Grassland and Grazing Animals
1971   Sir Richard Trehane
       Services to the Dairy Industry
1972   Cadzow Brothers
       Development of the Luing Breed
1973   Dr G. D. H. Bell, CBE, FRSE
       Service to Plant Breeding
1974   The Duke of Northumberland, KG, PC, TD
       National Service to Agriculture

1975 W. H. Cashmore, CBE, BA, NDA
      Services to Farm Mechanization
1976 Sir Nigel Strutt, TD, DL, FRAgS
      Service to Agriculture at Government and non-Government level.
1977 Sir Kenneth Blaxter
      Service to Agriculture in the field of animal nutrition.

Bell had retired two years before he was recognized in 1973, and twenty years after his outstanding achievement, the introduction of Proctor barley, had been placed on the NIAB Recommended List. Cashmore had left Silsoe ten years before his Award, and Netherthorpe had departed from the NFU scene nine years before he too was awarded this honour.

The Cadzow Brothers, James Denis and Ralph, farmed a 1,600-hectare holding on the island of Luing in the Inner Hebrides, which was the scene of the development programme which gave its name to a new breed of cattle. The Luing breed was developed from a beef shorthorn x Highland Cross, and produced an animal with top-quality meat under difficult hill and upland grazing conditions more quickly than had previously been possible. The Cadzow Brothers began their work in 1947, and the Luing was given official recognition as a breed in its own right by an Act of Parliament.

Dr Bell joined the Plant Breeding Institute at Cambridge in 1928, and was appointed Director in 1947 when the Institute became independent of the University. He was responsible for the programme and development of new cereal varieties, especially barleys, which produced Proctor, probably the most successful barley to have been grown by British farmers. His citation also recognized the reputation which the PBI had won for itself in British agriculture. The Duke of Northumberland chaired the Government Committee of Inquiry which followed the epidemic of foot-and-mouth disease in 1967. The 'Northumberland Committee', as it was called, has often been hailed as one of the most decisive reports ever drawn up by a Committee of Inquiry. Its recommendations came to form the British policy which evolved for the control and prevention of this disease, but on his own estate at Alnwick he had proved a model landowner, owning all the farmhouses and cottages in eleven villages. His modernization programme with houses and buildings in addition to the many thousands of hectares which were drained, reclaimed and made productive, is a story which has never been given its share of praise, but ranks with the achievements of the seventeenth-century landowners who were the real founding fathers of British agriculture. The Duke's knowledge and interest in forestry resulted in the planting or replanting of over 40 hectares of woodlands annually for nearly forty years.

The Award to W. H. Cashmore was for the development of mechanized farming in Britain, something that must be dear to the heart of Massey-Ferguson Ltd. His researches into the efficient application of mechanized systems of crop harvesting and conservation, including grass- and hay-drying, pneumatic grain conveyors and the integrated use of combine harvesters and grain-driers, with the design of pick-up balers, was a masterpiece of mechanical engineering. His Award also recognized his role as Director of the National Institute of Agricultural Engineering at Silsoe in Bedfordshire from 1947 to 1965. Like Dr Bell at the PBI, he enhanced the reputation of the NIAE by his personal aplomb. Sir Nigel Strutt's Award was for his long service in the unique position as a liaison between the corridors of Whitehall and the farmers' fields. His 'Strutt Report' was published in 1971, but his personal farming responsibilities over 9,200 hectares in Essex and West Suffolk combined with his close interests in the British Friesian Society, of which he was President in 1974. Two years before his M-F Award, Strutt was awarded the Johann Heinrich von Thunen Gold Medal of Kiel University.

Prizes galore

> *'There was a young man of Devizes*
> *Whose cows were of different sizes:*
> *The one that was small*
> *Was no use at all*
> *But the other won several prizes.'*

Traditional limerick (slightly altered)

The RASE has its own honours system, with a host of gold and silver medals, trophies, cups and accolades. There are the Burke Trophies for the best two champions in dairy and dual-purpose, and in the beef classes at the Annual Royal Show; and there is a Burke Trophy for new development in machinery. They are in memory of Old Etonian Sir Ronald Burke, sometime agent to the Duke of Devonshire and Honorary Director of the Royal Show for nineteen years until 1950, a record only beaten by the 31-year stint of Sir Brandreth Gibbs, from 1843 to 1874. Nowadays the Honorary Directors last about four years.

There is a gold medal donated by the first Viscount Bledisloe for landowners, and a Bledisloe Veterinary Silver Medal. There is a gold medal for distinguished services to agriculture awarded occasionally (seven times between 1950 and 1974), and the RASE grant the distinction of Honorary Fellowship to a select few who carry the letters FRAgS after their names. The Presidency of the Royal Show is normally occupied by Royalty, interspersed with the occasional commoner, such as Sir Christopher Soames (1973), Sir Francis Pemberton (1975), Sir Henry Plumb (1977). All in all, the RASE has its own complete honours system for the agricultural industry. But there are many more.

The man or woman (although no woman has yet won it), who makes the major contribution annually to the British pig industry gets the David Black Pig Award, bestowed since 1960 by the magazine *Pig Farming*, while IPC's *Poultry World* gives the annual George May Award for poultry journalism. May was the magazines editor for thirty years, and the award was instituted in 1974. Agricultural journalists also get awards in the form of travelling expenses from

Fisons and John Deere. The NIAB gives an Annual Cereal Cup for plant breeding, and instituted the Frank Horne Memorial Award in honour of its Director from 1945 to 1970. Travel grants to study potatoes are the reward which comes from the Potato Marketing Board with the James E. Rennie Annual Awards given in honour of its late Chairman, and instituted in the year of his death in a car accident, 1975. The PMB also grant Graduate Awards for research. The Milk Marketing Board, not to be outdone, instituted the Sir Richard Trehane Award on the retirement of Trehane from the Chairmanship in 1977.

The George Hedley Award is a silver medallion given by the National Sheep Association since 1961 for outstanding service to the sheep industry. Titles abound, too, although they may not conform to the traditional Establishment style. The title 'Dairy Herdsman of the Year' is awarded by BOCM-Silcock, and *Livestock Farming*, who also sponsor the award to the 'Shepherd of the Year', with the commercial support of pharmaceutical manufacturers Merck, Sharp and Dohme Ltd, who stepped into the breach in 1977 when Pfizers presumably decided that their financial support and commitment was not bearing sufficent fruit. They had been involved for the first four years in the Shepherd of the Year Award. Massey-Ferguson sponsor the title 'Top Technician' jointly with BP Farm Service, who themselves started a competition for Farm Machinery Ideas of the Year in 1971, and dropped it again after 1972.

The Eggs Authority award post-graduate scholarships in egg marketing, and the Nuffield UK Farming Scholarship Trust finances overseas study tours for UK farmers annually. Other Nuffield scholars come to study UK farming.

The prosperous agrochemical companies give very little in return for the riches they gain from British agriculture; although Ciba-Giegy channel considerable financial support to the Young Farmers movement, with cash prizes and sponsorship, several of the major national and multi-national tractor and farm machinery companies give nothing, as does the NFU or CLA. The Farmers Union of Wales, however, do give an 'occasional' award to the individual who in their opinion has made an outstanding contribution to British farming. In 1976 this was given to Travers Legge, Editor of the *Farmers Weekly*, which itself awards no cups, trophies, scholarships or titles, having just the occasional magazine-style competition. ICI instituted a national competition to judge the best crops of winter wheat by using the direct-drilling method, plugged by them in an effort to increase sales of their own Paraquat, which is an essential ingredient of this system. They gave away £16,000 worth of machinery and chemicals in this first national-style competition in 1978.

The Farm Colleges

'That part of the holding of a farmer or landowner that pays best for cultivation is the small estate within the ring fence of his skull.'

Charles Dickens

The academic approach to farming which was once disdained has undergone a radical change, and the ancient feeling that the best farming could only be learnt by muck-raking has given way to a greater appreciation that a course in an Agricultural College can perhaps yield some benefits.

There are forty-one Agricultural Colleges in England and Wales, and another two hundred educational establishments of further education, where agricultural and horticultural courses are given. Of the forty-one colleges proper, five are independent or voluntary. Three of these receive direct grants from the Department of Education and Science and two are independent—the Royal Agricultural College at Cirencester and Chadacre Agricultural Institute in Suffolk. Approximately 850 residential places are available at the independent and direct-grant colleges, and about 3,600 places at the maintained colleges. There was a movement in the 1960s to upgrade farm institutes to a minimum of 100 full-time places, but almost half the county farm institutes are below that figure. Of those that are larger, some have incorporated non-agricultural courses. Ryecotewood in Oxfordshire has an engineering course intended for tractor mechanics rather than farmers, and half the students are doing a woodworking and carpentry course designed for the building trade. Others have diversified their interests, and widened the scope of their curriculum to an extent to which any links with agriculture are indeed tenuous.

During a period when agriculture has been losing employees, the farm colleges have been continually expanding. This is a paradox, although it is in line with the total expansion of educational facilities at all levels.

Agricultural colleges do not exist only for the training of farmers' sons and daughters. With the greater appreciation of training since the ATB achieved its present respectability, there has been a movement to instruct farm-workers as well, and a secondary role for the county agricultural colleges has been the institution of part-time courses to cover the social scale. Sandwich courses at which the student occupies the middle of his three years on a farm, doing practical work, have become a feature, and most farm colleges require as a condition of entry that the student has worked on a farm for at least one year. Nevertheless, even with academic standards rising, the dim-wit who happens to be in line for his father's farm can be almost sure of a place. The colleges embrace the children of 'real farmers' with open arms. Nevertheless, the case for agricultural colleges expanding their role is a doubtful one, and there have been criticisms that they are already too large.

There is respect for the college-trained boy, even though the college will not teach him how to haggle in the market-place, or the more practical aspects of business dealings. Of necessity, the training provided is mainly on academic lines. Farm colleges are not a new phenomenon; it is only the appreciation of their role which has changed.

Before 1939 there were already eighteen farm institutes, and as a result of the Luxmoor Report in 1943, the post-War aftermath saw a galaxy of new farm colleges, which sprung up even faster than the redbrick universities. But even before 1939 agricultural education was not without its status.

In 1900 there were already five in existence, the oldest being the independent Royal Agricultural College at Circencester, which was founded in 1845. The others which existed pre-1900 were the County Farm Institutes in Essex, Cumberland, Lancashire and Hampshire, while in 1901, Harper Adams in Shropshire was founded. Madrym Castle Farm School, although now resited, was established in Wales in 1914, but after the First World War another fourteen counties in England and Wales established their own farm institutes. The next burst came after 1945, and the expansion pushed up the total college places to a figure of 12,000 full-time, part-time and evening class courses. This compares with the 1938–9 period, when there was a total of 1,559, of which 399 were for women.

It is significant that many of the students who go through an agricultural course at a farm college are not the children of farmers, have no family farm to inherit, and in many cases do not intend to make farming their livelihood. In 1972 Dr G. J. Dowrick, Principal of Seale-Hayne, conducted a survey of students leaving his college. From eighty-three interviews, it transpired that 47 students were destined to go into practical farming, 17 into ancillary work, 5 as agricultural teachers, 4 into research and advisory work. Ten went overseas, but this was to their countries of origin. Of those entering farming, only a third returned to the family farm. Thirty-five per cent became managers of farms, and twenty-nine per cent farm workers. From this break-down, it appears that only one in six actually finished up back on the family farm. Dowrick looked at the applications which came through his hands, and discovered that only 41 per cent were for vacancies in farming posts; 38 per cent were in the ancillary industries, 5 per cent for overseas postings and 16 per cent miscellaneous.

Above the level of farm institutes, ten English universities offer degree courses in various sectors of agriculture. Four have a school or faculty of veterinary science—the Universities of Bristol, Cambridge and Liverpool, and the Royal Veterinary College which is part of the University of London. Wye at Ashford is also part of London, and the Centre of European Agricultural Studies under Ian Reid is the latest innovation into the scene. Reading has become a centre for the computerization of farm management, and with its museum of English Rural Life, has become firmly established on the farming map.

Farm education has been subjected to a plethora of Official Reports: Luxmoor, 1943; Alness, 1945 (Scotland); Loveday, 1947; De La Warr, 1958; Lampard-Vachell, 1960; Pilkington, 1966; Hudson, 1973. This series attempts to diagnose the direction in which agricultural education should go, and after it several reversals of policy have taken place, reversals which educationalists have found perplexing and confusing.

Luxmoor had suggested there should be a Farm Institute in each county; when it was written in 1943 farming was on the crest of a wave, and there seemed great demand. In 1958 the De La Warr Report reversed that decision; enough was enough, they cried, and in 1959 administrative responsibility was transferred from the Ministry of Agriculture to the then Minister of Education. In Scotland there were three colleges before 1900 under the Scottish Education Department, but in 1912 they transferred to the new Board of Agriculture for Scotland, and are still financed by Grant-Aid from the Department of Agriculture and Fisheries for Scotland, while after 1959 farm education was transferred from the Agricultural Departments for England and Wales. The 1966 Pilkington Report altered the name from Farm Institute to Agricultural College, and it launched the OND (Ordinary National Diploma) and the HND. These replaced the old National Diplomas in Agriculture, and following Hudson 1973 the whole structure has been put in the melting-pot yet again!

Munificent benefactors

Chadacre, near Bury St Edmunds, was created in 1918 by a Trust Fund set up by the Suffolk landowner, and head of the Guinness Empire, Lord Iveagh. It opened in 1921, and offers a junior role for younger students. There are no specialist courses, and the students help to feed the sheep and to participate in the work of the annexed farm. Harper-Adams in Shropshire was founded in 1901 under the will of a local landowner, Thomas Harper-Adams. Its possession of the Harper-Adams Piggery, and its involvement with the National Institute of Poultry Husbandry, have been facets of its reputation. In Bedfordshire Shuttleworth College was founded to commemorate a young fighter pilot, Richard Shuttleworth, who was killed in 1940. His mother, Mrs Dorothy Shuttleworth, left her mansion and the adjoining estate as an Agricultural College in memory of Richard. The Trust was formed in 1944, and it opened its doors two years later.

Seale-Hayne stands on high ground in Devonshire, with the Atlantic on one side, and the Dartmoor National Park on the other. It specializes in farm management, and was founded and endowed under the will of Charles Seale-Hayne, who died in 1903. Among the colleges formed by the county councils, pride of place for longevity goes to the East Anglian School of Agriculture, established at Chelmsford in 1893. It has since changed its name twice, first becoming the Essex Institute of Agriculture, but today being known more simply as Writtle Agricultural College. It is the only one to embrace the HND course in commercial horticulture, and this type of specialization is a feature of the colleges, which initially sought to establish a high reputation in those branches of farming which were traditionally famous in their home counties. Now it has become a matter of survival to establish a nationwide reputation in one branch, and to attract students from throughout the UK. Bicton in Devon is famed for its grassland and market gardening, Hadlow in Kent for its fruit, the Hertfordshire College of Agriculture and Horticulture for its glasshouse production and horticultural management.

There are many farm colleges, and new ones continue to be opened, while county councils often expand the existing establishments. In the early 1970s a new college in Scotland and another in Wales were opened, but in 1969 the

Studley Agricultural College for Women in Warwickshire was summarily closed. It dated back to 1896, but a waning interest in single-sex educational establishments, and a period of Government retrenchment, forced its closure. Some grants and trusts that it owned were recreated into a new Trust Fund which annually administered grants to young people wishing to study agriculture, horticulture or forestry, but without the requisite finances.

The Royal Agricultural College

'*A college which can still run a pack of beagles, provide a rider in the Grand National, the winner of the Empire Trophy (1948), and beat L'Institut d'Agriculture de Paris at Rugby in Paris, shows that it has not allowed the technical burden of modern days to oust altogether the joys of life.*'

H. Bailey, Bursar RAC.

'*Gordon Dickson created four Departments — and completed the destruction of the playboy image the College once enjoyed.*'

'Modern Farmer' (Peter Bell, 1973)

Although the playboy image has partly been dispelled, the exuberance of youth manifests itself from time to time. However, while the aristocratic land-owning heirs still come to Cirencester, they now have to work hard at rural estate management, as a training for their future role as active participating farmers on their own estates. Eighty-six per cent of the students come from public schools, and there is a staffing ratio of twenty students to one staff member. In the county-council-operated farm colleges the ratio is seven students to every staff member.

Set amid tree-lined parkland, two kilometres from Cirencester, 136 metres above sea-level on the edge of the Cotswold Hills, and with distant views to the Wiltshire Downs, the RAC sits in pleasant Avon on a site where Earl Bathurst, its first President, donated a farm of 166 hectares to establish a unique college. This was in 1845, when the main Victorian college building was erected; the student common room, however, occupies a tithe barn that is four hundred years old. New buildings have been erected in the 1970s, and the RAC accommodates over six hundred students, of which nearly half embark upon the three-year Rural Estate Management Diploma. Membership entitles one to the letters MRAC.

A privately owned institution, with no Government Grants, the RAC relies upon the fees of its students to support it. However, there is a 562-hectare ring of college farms which has become an important source of revenue, while the problems of reorganizing the farming cannot but provide practical examples to the students. The fees are high, but there always seems to be a waiting list. The dedication of the British parent to paying for education which can be obtained for nothing through the State system is incomprehensible to other nations.

The RAC has not disdained commercial links; Boots contributed to Trent Lodge in 1947, while in 1958 BOCM paid 50 per cent of the cost of a new hall. Although the college is not supported by the Government, the Ministry of

Agriculture did assist in the acquisition of Bledisloe Lodge (formerly known as Coates Manor) in 1950.

The RAC was for many years Bobby Boutflour, who became its Principal in 1931, and stayed for twenty-seven years. There were only forty-eight students when he arrived, and farming was in an acute depression. During the War the RAC closed, and opened again in 1945. It has never looked back, but it was Robert Boutflour who built up its image. He was succeeded by Frank Garner, who had been manager of over 2,900 hectares of the Hiam Farms in the Fens. He retired to run his own dairy farm in Buckinghamshire, in which he held an interest during his period as Principal. Garner was succeeded by Gordon Dickson, who had been Farms Manager to the Duke of Norfolk. There were many red faces among the Governors when he resigned only two years later to take up the influential Chair of Agriculture at Newcastle—often quoted as the most prestigious academic job in UK agriculture. Before Dickson's time another Principal, Professor J. A. Hanley, had done the same—but he had stayed at the RAC for four years.

In a brilliant move, the RAC redressed its lost prestige by appointing the elegant Welshman who was then Director-General of ADAS—Sir Emrys Jones, who took a cut in salary to accept the post. Relieved from the shackles of the Official Secrets Act, Jones bounced to the fore, but he was soon faced with the problems of escalating fees and a reorganization of the farming management on the RAC Farms. Obviously, if it set out to be a paragon of sound management, it could not show a bad example—but money was a pressing matter, too. Jones retired after five years, and in 1978 Vic Hughes, the previous Farms Director, became the new Principal.

    1846 Rev. G. C. Hodgkinson
    1847 John Wilson
    1851 Rev. J. S. Haygarth
    1860 Rev. J. Constable
    1880 Rev. J. B. McClellan
    1908 J. R. Ainsworth Davis
    1921 Prof. M. J. R. Dunstan
    1927 Prof. J. A. Hanley
    1931 Prof. Robert Boutflour
    1958 Frank H. Garner
    1971 Prof. G. R. Dickson
    1973 Sir Emrys Jones
    1978 H. V. Hughes

Wye College

In a pleasant village in Kent, a hundred kilometres from London and its university, exists Wye College, the Agricultural Division of the University of London. Wye is unique as an off-campus part of a university geographically far removed. It occupies a special place in the structure of agricultural education, and is to the Royal Agricultural College at Cirencester what Winchester is to Eton. It is also the seat of the Centre of European Agricultural Studies, another unique body which Britain instituted.

Wye, though part of a university, is a college that fills its own educational niche. Although a College of St Gregory and St Martin was founded by Cardinal John Kempe, Archbishop of Canterbury in 1447[1], 'it achieved its present structure only in 1945, when it amalgamated with the Swanley Horticultural College for Women under the original title of Wye College. Three years later it was incorporated by Royal Charter, and when the Appeal for the European Centre was launched the Queen Mother (as Chancellor of the University of London) attended at the Mansion House to add royal lustre for this new project.

The original Grammar School at Wye survived for four hundred years, and in 1893 the buildings were transferred to the county councils of both Kent and Surrey jointly for the purpose of a newly formed South-Eastern Agricultural College. Seven years later, in 1900, the College became part of the University of London. Its B.Sc. in Agriculture dates from 1902, and the B.Sc. in Horticulture from 1916.

Politicians throughout the world are embroiled in their daily problems of governmental administration, and have little time for forward thinking or deep study. Thus they rely upon the services of impartial academic bodies to provide quantitative reports from which they can filch the best ideas and occasionally take legislative action. Within this context there is a dearth of academic study upon the world problems of farming and food-supplies. In the post-War period there has been considerable co-operation between nations, the richer supporting the poorer. (After all, rebellion and insurgence is fostered and stimulated by empty bellies.) The FAO in Rome is part of the United Nations, and keeps an eye on agricultural production throughout the world, but upon Britain's entry into the EEC it was apparent that there was little concrete knowledge about the existing six members. With the countries expanded to nine, the problem was even more apparent, but it took British initiative to establish a Centre for European Agricultural Studies at Wye College. The first moves were made in 1971, when the Worshipful Company of Farmers, with the Ernest Cook Trust, invited a selection of European farmers to Wye College as a preliminary to European co-operation. In 1972 Marks & Spencer financed a Research Fellowship in European Agricultural Economics, and in 1973 an Appeal was launched to build a complete Centre devoted to the study of European agricultural problems. Thus has the importance of Wye grown.

---

[1]According to the College he was Archbishop of Canterbury in 1447, but the *Dictionary of National Biography*, the *Encyclopaedia Britannica* and other authorities say he was not translated from York until 1452.

24 Bodies and Antibodies

'Within farming lies a multiplicity of overlapping bodies, and nowhere is this more apparent than in the hen and chicken world, where Federations, Authorities, Affiliations and Societies abound and multiply faster than chicks pop out of eggs.'

Peter Wormell

The UK agricultural industry has a haphazard collection of Councils, Boards, Associations, Federations, amalgamations, proliferations and even adulterations. It is a complex structure that is Government, quasi-Government, NFU-inspired, independent, quasi-independent, sectionalized and often overlapping. Since farmers are highly independent people, the number and complexity of these bodies may seem an anomaly, but farmers are also dependent one upon another, and the advances in knowledge which can be gained from talking in the market-place, or from pooling and sharing the knowledge of a farm application of the latest technological developments from the boffins, far outweigh any thoughts that in reality every farmer is his neighbour's rival. Certainly, farmers with humility do not think that way, and are prepared to share their business secrets.

This vast collection of organizations is also sustained by active farmer participation, stemming from their gregarious nature; indeed, it would be no exaggeration to call farmers 'professional committee men'. At its lowest this collection of bodies starts with the ring of local discussion societies, meeting in village halls during the winter months, and visiting local farms in the summer. Many of these discussion groups stem from the 1940–3 period, when the dissemination of farming knowledge became of paramount importance. Machinery clubs and stockmen's clubs largely came later, and are the province of tractor drivers and stockmen.

The larger and more ancient local Farmers Clubs hold their Annual Show, crop-judging competitions and ploughing matches. They are one step above that pleasant English pastime, the village fete. Commercial links have been forged at a local level in more recent years, with the rapid growth of 'quality pig-producers'; 'pea-growers'; 'grassland societies'; 'milk clubs', and the monthly farmhouse meeting of trading groups for bulk buying from Agricultural Central Trading. The '300 Cow Club' was formed in 1972; it has a maximum of 75 members, all with 300 cows or more, meets twice a year, and is serviced by BOCM-Silcock. The 'Grasshoppers' is based in Hampshire, and consists of leading farmers who can attract national speakers to its meetings. The 'Yorkshire Venturers' is restricted to enterprising farmers who have been, or are, pioneers in their own sphere of farming.

ICI formed a ring of 'Ten Tonne Clubs' in 1976 to promote the Laloux system of wheat-growing, and farmers meet regularly to exchange a progress report on their wheat crops throughout the growing season. Every aspect of farming is covered by a multitude of organizations where farmers can discuss the latest techniques, and although no central directory has ever been compiled of these, there must be around two thousand such bodies in England alone.

Superimposed upon this lower tier of farming bodies is another complex structure which embraces the Government-sponsored Marketing Boards, such odd organizations as the National Institute of Agricultural Botany, the Processers, Growers and Research Organisation, the Farm Management Association which exists for farm managers, the Worshipful Company of Farmers, London-based Farmers Club, and the National Federation of Young Farmers Clubs. In total, it amounts to a perplexing and conflicting structure.

The Young Farmers Clubs

'I pledge My Head to clearer thinking,
My heart to greater loyalty,
My Hands to larger service, and
My Health to better living.
For my Club, my Community and my Country
  Pledge of Service of the 4-H Movement in the USA.

The youth movement of the countryside is one description for almost nine hundred Young Farmers Clubs existing in England and Wales; Scotland, as in so many other ways, has its own organization. Another oft-used description is that of a Young Farmers Marriage Bureau, and it is unquestionably true that the mixture of farmers' sons and daughters does result in many farming marriages. The YFC protest that this is not the primary reason for their existence!

The Young Farmers Club movement in the UK has its counterparts in the Rural Youth Movement in many distant parts of the world, providing a basis for the valuable exchange visits. Its nearest counterpart in the UK is the Young Conservatives, who form a more social, club-like attitude, and discuss politics far less than the Young Farmers do farming. The Round Table movement is international, and disclaims any notion that it is a sort of Junior Rotary; its idealism is directed towards community help, and friendship among diverse professions and trades. It is an important stipulation that there should be no more than two of any profession in the same club. This is not to deny that in certain rural areas of Britain there may be Round Tables with a selection of farmers under different pseudonyms. A poultry farmer could genuinely claim to be a different breed of animal from an arable farmer, just as insurance men come as brokers, representatives, managers, with divisions between general and life assurance. Membership of the YFCs ceases at twenty-five years, of the Young Conservatives at thirty, and of the Round Table at forty.

Membership peaked in 1955 at over 70,000, and has steadily declined ever since, to a total of just over 50,000. It is divided into 'open' and 'school' clubs, of which there are six times as many 'open' or senior clubs. In these clubs there are three girls for every four boys, but in the school clubs there are only one and a half girls for every four boys. In the Young Conservatives the balance of the sexes is more equal, with an emphasis in some areas towards a majority of girls. Membership of the Young Farmers is not restricted to farmers' offspring, and many come from an urban background, but are attracted by their employment in the ancillary industries, such as tractor salesmen. The girls too may be attracted from the towns to join a youth club with a difference, though the dedication of the Young Farmers to solid talks upon aspects of dairy cows or pig housing soon dispels any beliefs that this is just another social club.

The YFCs have from early times placed an emphasis upon public speaking, and remarkably enough can usually turn out more proficient speakers than can the Young Conservatives. The inarticulateness of farmers was a weakness of the industry in the pre-War days, and the movement has sought to provide a sound training ground to rectify this omission. Another important aspect of the YFC work is the training for stock judging, and Young Farmers teams are at the Smithfield and Royal Shows, assessing the merits of prize-winning animals.

The YFC movement in England and Wales originated with formation of the first club in 1921 at Hemyock in Devon. It was encouraged by United Dairies Ltd, and their technical adviser, P. B. Tustin, and then in the following year Lord Northcliffe gave his blessing and the full support of the *Daily Mail.* At the 1922 Ideal Home Exhibition at Olympia there was a display of Young Farmers' activities. By 1928 there was forty clubs in the country, with a membership of five hundred. Just over ten years later, at the outbreak of war, the number of clubs had risen tenfold, to 412; it trebled by the end of 1945, peaked at over 1,500 clubs in 1955, and, like the membership, has steadily declined ever since.

The original office was an attic in Russell Square, but in 1932 the YFC moved to 55 Gower Street, later to be known as Morton Hiles House[1]. It was among the earliest national organizations to establish its permanent HQ at the National Agricultural Centre in 1969, when it built a pleasing building at a cost of £25,000, situated near the new Conference Hall. Here the General Secretary, F. E. (Tanner) Shields, resides with an energetic office staff. In each county federation there is a full-time employed organizer; thus the YFC movement operates the three tier system, as does the NFU. It was in 1945 that the National Federation threw back to the counties the problems of their own finances and operation.

[1] Major Morton Hiles was appointed first National Secretary and Treasurer in 1932, served the Federation until 1959, and died in 1962.

Each county is autonomous, being affiliated to the national body. There are financial problems like those of the NFU before its own massive shake-up.

In the early days support had come from the Carnegie United Kingdom Trust, and from the W. K. Kellogg Foundation in 1952. The King George VI National Memorial Fund has also assisted in the support of the YFC movement. As a support for the education of rural youth, many county councils grant aided the YF activities, but many did not, and this resulted in an uneven spread of the activities throughout the UK. Even in 1975 the grants from the Ministry of Agriculture only amounted to just over £5,000, when the National Federation was spending £62,000 to maintain its operations. The Department of Education and Science contributed another £17,000. This comparative lack of official financial support came to a head in 1969.

A shake-up ensued, with axing of HQ staff, the cessation of the *Young Farmer* magazine, and the movement of headquarters to the NAC. Although running at a modest deficit in many of the succeeding years, the Federation stoutly maintains its voluntary status within the social services designed for the youth movements. But the problems of finance are always with it. In the past it has leant more towards the educational services than the farming organizations, and in those counties where financial support is given it comes from the education budget. There is a tiered power-structure, a situation which keeps the top brass in order, and sustains the leadership from below. It could be considered to be top heavy in permanent staff, with fifty county organizers in England and Wales, of whom a majority are females. Many of the local offices are within the county NFU building, and county organizers often gain promotion to the Secretaryship of an NFU Branch. It remains a vital part of the formal training of those who will later go up to the multitude of jobs within the NFU.

The Cambridge influence

> *'Oxford is, on the whole, more attractive than Cambridge to the ordinary visitor, and the traveller is therefore recommended to visit Cambridge first, or to omit it altogether if he cannot visit both.'*
>
> Carl Baedeker

> *'England's the one land, I know,*
> *Where men with splendid hearts may go;*
> *And Cambridgeshire, of all England,*
> *The shire for men who understand.'*
> Rupert Brooke
> 'The Old Vicarage, Grantchester'.

Situated in and around the city of Cambridge is a multitude of influential establishments concerned with the scientific, commercial and practical aspects of farming. The link with the University is through the Department of Land

Economy: immortalized by its intimate studies of farm management and land problems, and characterized by Professor Denman, the Magnus Pyke of agriculture, it has become a well-known force beyond the campus. The Department of Biology also adds to its prestige. At Boxworth is the Ministry Experimental Husbandry Farm, specializing in aspects of heavy-land farming problems. At Babraham is the Institute of Animal Physiology, and in the commercial field the original Pest Control Ltd (now part of Fisons) was established at Harston. Today Fisons have their Research Laboratories and Station at Chesterford Park, just inside the Essex border, but within a stone's throw of Cambridge, while CIBA-Geigy Ltd have their Trial Grounds for new chemicals at Whittlesford. In addition, the triumvirate Plant Breeders Institute, National Institute of Agricultural Botany and the National Seed Development Organisation are all concentrated in and around the city of Cambridge. This is an agricultural think-tank in the strongest traditions of an ancient University city.

The PBI is in Maris Lane at Grantchester, which Rupert Brooke immortalized. The NIAB is off the busy Huntingdon Road on the other side of the city, and the NSDO is a mock Queen Anne mansion at Newton. The relative roles of the three bodies means that the PBI breeds new plant varieties, the NIAB approves them and the NSDO sells them. As three independent organizations, with vastly differing origins, they present a chronological path of progress in the field of upgrading plant varieties. With their differing backgrounds, and mutually independent status, this is a typically British situation, and in spite of the apparent lack of liaison between them, it seems to work. Both the PBI and NSDO are companies within the meaning of the Companies Act 1948, although resulting similarity between them is hard to find. The PBI comes under the wing of the Agricultural Research Council, and is funded through the Department of Education and Science, whose money comes in turn from the Exchequer. NSDO, on the other hand, is a profit-making company, whose shares are held by members of the Governing Body as nominees of the Minister of Agriculture. The dividends are paid to the Exchequer. Thus the products of research can be financially exploited in the national interest. The NIAB is a highly independent organization controlled under a Trust Deed, and only supported by the Ministry of Agriculture from agency fees as its Official Seed Testing Station, but it primarily belongs to its five thousand Fellows, of whom two thousand are fully paid up farmers. The PBI was created in 1912, the NIAB just after the Great War in 1919, the NSDO in 1967, as an agency for the products of Ministry research to be marketed. The NSDO was a direct result of the Plant Varieties and Seed Act 1964, which belatedly granted royalty dues for those who had carried out of the research and propagation of new varieties. The NSDO has been an unqualified success, shows a flair for marketing that is quite unparalleled for what is in effect an adjunct of a Government Department. The Ministry tried to take over the NIAB in 1968, but after a successful rearguard action by its Fellows a new trust was arranged. The NIAB remains highly independent, and proud of it.

The Plant Breeding Institute

'The beginning of agricultural plant breeding at Cambridge in the first decade of this century was due to the work and foresight of R. H. Biffen, MA, later Sir Roland Biffen, FRS.'

Dr G. D. H. Bell, Director

The PBI is situated down leafy Maris Lane at Trumpington, by Grantchester; it moved there in 1955. The builders had moved in five years earlier, and have been there ever since. They have been covering Anstey Hall Farm with a complex of experimental glasshouses, seed-cleaning sheds, and research buildings; only the cricket pitch between the administrative block and the sugar beet research building seems inviolate. A railway cutting once circumscribed the land, but infilling from the spoil of Victorian coprolite[2] diggings has removed an eyesore and levelled the cutting of pre-Beeching origin. Concrete roads now lead to the fields where hundreds of diligent fact-seeking visitors descend during the summer months to study at this world-renowned centre of plant-breeding techniques.

While the PBI grants access to its secrets, and co-operation with the many commercial plant-breeders, this open access to new developments is a one-way traffic. The vested commercial interests send their trained men to filch the latest developments, but carefully guard their own secrets, with shareholders' interests uppermost. There is a staff of 250, and one-third of these are graduates.

The Department of Agriculture in the University of Cambridge was established in 1899, and in the early years of its existence Sir Roland Biffen was its Professor. The introduction of a new winter wheat variety in 1910 called Little Joss, which was for forty-six years on the NIAB Recommended List, was a mark of the early pioneering work on plant-breeding by Biffen and his associates. It was in 1912 that the then Board of Agriculture gave further support to Biffen by establishing the 'Cambridge University Plant Breeding Institute'. It was the first State-aided plant-breeding centre in the country, and the work was carried out at Burgoynes Farm, the University Farm, and after 1910 at Gravel Hill Farm within the city boundaries, which the University authorities had purchased. Although the PBI was created as part of the University, this relationship ceased in 1947, now it comes under the wing of the Agricultural Research Council and the Ministry. It severed its connections, and needed a new site. Anstey Hall Farm was acquired in March 1950, but it was to be five years before the new premises were officially opened by the then Minister of Agriculture, Heathcoat-Amory.

But the joint control with the Ministry was short-lived, and as the Minister opened the new building his Ministry ceased to have any control over its affairs, then transferred entirely to the ARC.

The fame of the PBI has lain in the 'Maris' prefix to its never-ending introduction of new varieties of cereals, roots and vegetables. This prefix stems from Maris Lane, some say a corruption of the near-by church, St Mary's.

[2] Coprolite, which is chiefly calcium phosphate, is the fossilized excrement of extinct animals. It was early used as artificial fertilizer.

However, a family with the unusual name of Maris has since laid claim to being the descendants of some farmers who resided in the area many centuries ago. In any event, Maris has become a world-renowned prefix. Outstandingly, the PBI has upgraded cereal varieties, which the NSDO has successfully marketed and exploited. It has brought Britain to the forefront of plant-breeding, and although many commercial companies have established reputable plant-breeding stations, and have produced a succession of successful varieties, nevertheless the State-owned institute has for once beaten private enterprise at its own game. Dr Bell produced Proctor barley, and this gained him the Massey-Ferguson Award in 1973, but Maris Huntsman, the 'Wonder Wheat', took the country by storm in 1974, and ousted a popular French variety which had been the main-stay of British wheat farming for a quarter of a century. That illustrates its success.

National Institute of Agricultural Botany

'"Are you a botanist, Dr Johnson?"
"No, Sir. I am not a botanist; and should I wish to become a botanist, I must
first turn myself into a reptile."'

Samuel Johnson

'Cambridge June 28.
For the first time in nearly 50 years a storm developed at the Annual Meeting
of Fellows of the National Institute of Agricultural Botany here today.'
'The Times', 29 June, 1968.

The NIAB publishes annually its 'Recommended List', a sort of Birthday Honours List for plant varieties. In fact, the most diligent and extensive trials are conducted upon new plant varieties over a period of years before they can be given this mark of favour. Farmers too accept that varieties and strains which are on the Official Recommended List are bound to be good ones.

Occasionally up-and-coming varieties miss the list, much to the chagrin of their breeders. A spring barley variety named Sabarlis did not appear on the 1972 NIAB List; it was the product of the Welsh Plant Breeding Station, and was hailed as Britain's only eelworm-resistant spring barley. But a much more serious row erupted in 1975, when a variety which had been bred by the Plant Breeding Institute failed to make the grade. It was named Maris Hobbitt, and the NSDO had already invested a large sum of money in publicizing this variety with its shorter straw length, recalling Tolkien's little men in *The Hobbit*. Indeed, the NSDO had already taken delivery of a quantity of Tolkien's books, and had started to distribute these as part of its flair for gimmickry. But the NIAB stuck to its guns that to bless Maris Hobbitt in 1975 was not possible; it later acquired its status, and became a highly successful wheat variety on the UK market.

The original establishment of the NIAB in 1919 was a natural follow-on from the now expanding work of the PBI. Inferior seed was being used by many farmers, and the food shortages in the First World War had emphasized this. The

Wrest Park, Bedfordshire, the impressive home of the National Institute of Agricultural Engineering. It has the look of a French Château
Photo National Institute of Agricultural Engineering

The view in the other direction, showing the complex of architecturally designed research buildings where new improvements in farm machinery are evolved
Photo National Institute of Agricultural Engineering

Horstine Farmery's Microband Delta applicator designed for adding chemicals and seed to the soil together. The once simple farming of cereals is becoming technically advanced *Photo Horstine Farmery*

Ransome's Hunter, two-row self-propelled combine sugar-beet harvester, traversing the fields like a dinosaur *Photo Ransomes Sims and Jefferies*

Penn Place, Rickmansworth. The home of the British Friesian Breeders Society, criticized by some of the members as resembling a luxury Country Club, and too ostentatious *Photo British Friesian Herd Book Society*

Friesian cows now produce over 80 per cent of Britain's milk, yet the breed is of Dutch origin *Photo British Friesian Herd Book Society*

The Milk Marketing Board's multi-million-pound Creamery at Maelor, in North Wales. It is an example of the vast business of milk-producing, and of the extension of the MMB's empire *Photo The Milk Marketing Board*

Sir Richard Trehane, Chairman of the Milk Marketing Board 1958–77. A Dorset farmer who nearly became an academic *Photo The Milk Marketing Board*

Steve Roberts, who took over as Chairman of the Milk Marketing Board in October 1977 *Photo The Milk Marketing Board*

NIAB was created by private subscription from seed merchants and farmers, although there was an initial Government grant and loan. Thus in its origins it provided an independent foundation that was to be a crucial factor in the abortive Ministry take-over bid in 1968. Its first Director was W. H. Parker, a former Assistant of Biffen. He guided it through its first nineteen years, was followed for five years during the Second World War by Dr H. Hunter, who was also Director of the Cambridge University Plant Breeding Institute. It was after this that the two organizations went their own separate ways. Affable Frank Horne was appointed Director in 1945; tall and rugged, he was a tower of strength in the farming world for many years, until he was finally succeeded by a slight and elegant ex-RAF pilot, Dr Peter Wellington.

The Institute was established at 16-hectare Howe Farm on the Huntingdon Road, opposite the then University Farm, and in 1920 it purchased Dark Lane Farm, where testing of potato varieties was carried out until 1940. It acquired 208-hectare Hill Farm, Lolworth, in 1957, and sold this again in 1971, when 66-hectare Park Farm, Histon, was purchased. There are NIAB Trials Centres in many areas of the UK, but the central direction comes from this complex of proving grounds in and around Cambridge. From its earliest days, the Institute was also designated as the Ministry's 'Official Seed Testing Station'.

The 1968 democratic revolt

The passing of the Plant Varieties and Seed Act 1964 placed a new importance upon the commercial aspect of plant-breeding, and raised the possibility of lucrative returns. The Government wished to harness the new varieties being produced by its own Plant Breeding Institutes, and in 1967 NSDO Ltd was created. But as a result of this Act the Ministry men also started looking carefully at the NIAB. They concluded that it was incongruous to have an 'official' Seed Testing Station wielding so much power, yet not under their own control, though the Ministry provided the major share of finance through Grants-in-aid. The problem was how to prise away the independence of the NIAB, and to gain a majority control for the Ministry.

After a decade when the power of the trade unions had increased, Governments have learnt that careful, patient negotiation is more productive than confrontation, but by today's standards the prelude to the 1968 bombshell striking the Fellows gathered in solemn conclave at Cambridge on 28 June was a masterpiece of ineptitude. Talks had been conducted between Ministry men and three members of the NIAB Council. These secretly reported to the Minister, and the NIAB Council was informed in March 1968—but the members were sworn to secrecy about the report, and although many of them were representatives of participating organizations, they were barred from even confidentially reporting back. Thus on 28 June it was only rumours that circulated. In a lengthy speech the NIAB Council Chairman, Sir Harold Sanders—himself formerly Chief Scientific Adviser to the Ministry, and later a consultant to the Shell Organisation—

explained the new proposals. The Council would be reconstituted, with a vast majority of official members, and only two Fellows, instead of the four previously. More importantly, the institute would be financed directly under the Ministry, replacing the system of grants-in-aid. It was a scheme to bring the NIAB firmly under the Ministry wing. The fear was raised at the meeting that if the Ministry took over the staff would then become civil servants, and if they were civil servants they would have to sign the Official Secrets Act. How then could they disseminate the knowledge that was so vital to the advancement of plant-breeding? Many of the senior staff in fact wanted to become civil servants, possibly with the thought of advancement within the broader framework of the Ministry.

In December a Special Meeting was called, attended by upward of six hundred Fellows, which had before it details of the proposals, and it unanimously threw them out. The Ministry thought again, and a new Trust Deed came into operation in 1970, which consolidated the role and the independence of the NIAB, but in 1974 the Ministry decided to abandon the idea of finance by grant-in-aid, and substituted direct payments on a customer basis.

By this time, however, another body had been created. It was the United Kingdom Seeds Executive, which came into being on 23 March 1973. It is a Committee of the Intervention Board for Agricultural Produce, another ramification of the involved structure of agriculture that resulted from Britain joining the EEC. The UK Seeds Executive operates the statuory requirements of seed in its standard and varietal performance, and produces a 'National List' which is in no way to be confused with the NIAB 'Recommended List'. The National List has statutory force, in that only seed of varieties contained in it may be marketed in this country without specific permission for special purposes. It has no advisory function whatever. Certain criteria are needed for new varieties to gain entry on the List. These include distinctiveness, stability and one or two other factors. Tests of varieties for these are carried out under contract by the NIAB in conditions of strict confidentiality.

In addition to the Annual Recommended Lists, the NIAB were also responsible for the varietal purity of strains, and their general health, which they expressed by means of the labels 'Field Approved' (FA), or 'Field Inspected' (FI). These were standards laid down by the NIAB, who also organized courses to train local seed merchants personnel. The Annual Reports of NIAB during the many years this scheme operated always showed a not inconsiderable proportion of crops rejected on inspection. There was also a list of firms annually participating in the Scheme, and it was by no means unknown for firms to be refused permission to continue on the list. Anyway, FA and FI have been completely superseded under EEC rules by '1st Generation' and '2nd Generation' seed.

Meanwhile the breeder, with the vast cost of research and breeding programmes, played it cool, and although progress in plant varieties continued the pace was steady, rather than expansionist. The 1964 Act was to inject vast sums of money into the plant-breeders' pockets, and to unleash upon the farming world a multitude and complexity of new varieties sufficient to leave him reeling. Private plant-breeders beavered away, producing their own new strains, but lived by importing Swedish or French cereal varieties, and obtaining sole marketing rights. Proctor barley was the introduction of Bell at the PBI, but the dominant wheat variety, Cappelle Desprez, was French. The private breeders introduced dozens of new varieties during this time, but they faded from the scene quickly. It was the Paris Convention of 1959 which spotlighted the problem, and in the UK the 1964 Act was a result of this.

The British Seeds Council is another body operating in the same field, but with an emphasis upon quality seed. It is a joint Council between the corn merchants and the farmers, being partly a brain child of the NFU, and was launched on 13 January 1956, with the objectives of improving the quality and expansion of seed-production. Initially it emphasized the Aberystwyth herbage seeds, and dealt with vegetable seeds and others, but excluded cereal seed. It has since embraced cereals, and has launched quality seed campaigns to uplift the potential crops for farmers. Nevertheless, with half its support coming from the corn merchants, plant-breeders and seeds industry, it has a strong interest in promoting its own goods.

Other recommended lists

The NIAB looks at its plant varieties with an eye towards their application in the farmer's fields; it concerns itself with the disease-resistance and yield potential of a wide range of varieties. It is not a criterion for admittance that a variety is of high or low quality: both may be culturally sound, and the end product will have a different destination. Therefore the NIAB Recommended List is supplemented by other organizations, and the picture becomes more complex. The Flour Milling and Baking Research Association, at Chorleywood, near Rickmansworth in leafy Hertfordshire, is an association that deals with the scientific conversion of raw wheat into an optimum product for human consumption. Work on flour-milling and bakery research is also done by the Lord Rank Research Centre at High Wycombe, established in 1963 as RHM's principal Research Centre in the UK. At Chorleywood they have perfected the 'Chorleywood bread process', which gained the FMBRA a Queen's Award in the first year of its inauguration, 1966. This research success has enabled more home-produced wheat to be used for British bread, thus helping the UK import balance. The FMBRA has no less than 56 wheat varieties on its own List, which is designed for milling and baking purposes. It contrasts with the twenty-three varieties on the NIAB List[3], of which ten were fully recommended, eight were provisionally recommended, and five were outclassed by later introductions.

The HGCA introduced its own voluntary classification scheme in 1974, which

[3] 1977.

only listed the best milling and bread-making wheat varieties. It created classes 'A' and 'B', and listed in all twenty-five varieties—of which only ten were on the NIAB List. Thus the duplication of these recommendations can only leave the farmer confused.

Malting barley also has its own priority list designed by an offshoot of the Institute of Brewing, known as the Barley Advisory Committee. It has been in existence since 1920, but in 1973, in an effort to highlight for farmers those barley varieties with the greatest malting potential, the committee decided in a spirit of one-upmanship to issue its own 'Recommended List'. The requirements of the brewing industry are such that only a few of the many varieties on offer are suitable, and it included only six varieties in their list, although the NIAB had 26 on their list. This proportion would appear about right, as the malting trade uses 2 million tonnes annually out of a UK average barley harvest of 10 million tonnes. The BAC evolved its recommendations from work carried out in conjunction with the NIAB and from malting and brewing trials after the crops had been harvested. It all adds up to a complicated and perplexingly complex, if overlapping, scene of operations in the world of plant varieties—and this is only one small sector of British farming.

National Seed Development Organisation

'The British tax payer is cashing in on the Government's involvement in plant breeding'.

Edward Long
'The Farmers Weekly', October 1972

'Complementing the success of Maris Huntsman in France is the news that Maris Nimrod has been placed on the Belgian Recommended List.'
NSDO Press Release, 17 September 1973.

The NSDO was created as a commercial company in March 1967, with initial funds provided by the Government of £200,000. Its Chairman and Governing Body are appointed by the Minister of Agriculture, Fisheries and Food, acting jointly with the Secretary of State for Scotland and the Home Secretary. It has since repaid its initial loan, and the financial structure is more conventionally established, with an ordinary share capital of £300,000. HM Government are the only shareholders, and the dividends are payable to the Exchequer.

By 1971–2 its phenomenal commercial success had enabled the initial loan to be fully repaid, and although it would be easy to suggest that the NSDO was on to a winner from the start, its success has been accompanied by a pugnacious marketing drive. True, it inherited years of work from the Plant Breeding Institute but many of those seeds which have appeared since 1967 have been exploited ruthlessly and commercially in the best traditions of big business. It is, however, more than a marketing organization, and does produce its own stocks of seed before they enter the great wide world. The NSDO established itself at

Newton Hall, near Cambridge; this imposing mansion in Queen Anne style had been the home of Socialist peer Lord Walston, but was in fact only built in 1911. Today tarmacked car parks have been laid out where the Edwardian carriages swept up to the stately portals; a factory warehouse in the grounds today would surely have offended the lordly eye; and the seed-cleaning process of basic seeds for multiplication is carried out with sophisticated modern machinery and fork-lift trucks in a motley collection of buildings amid magnificent trees.

The NSDO owns only about 6 hectares, but rents, hires or leases another 290 hectares on which to grow its basic stock of seed. Since the land employed for such a careful procedure must be free of previous cereal cropping, a handy neighbouring vegetable-grower allows it parts of his land to provide a break from his intensive vegetables. On this land it sows cereal crops with a seed rate as low as 41 kilos per hectare. This is about a quarter of the commercial rate which a farmer would sow, but the objective is to multiply the greatest quantity possible from relatively tiny quantity of seed.

In its initial year of operation, 1967–8, the NSDO was responsible for marketing the products of seven of the National Plant Breeding Stations in the UK. The range embraced glasshouse crops, vegetables, many farm crops, and even some from the Royal Botanic Gardens at Kew. Ten years later it was marketing the output of fifteen plant-breeding stations, including one each in Wales and Northern Ireland and two in Scotland. In the initial year 29 crop species was the limit; ten years later it had just about doubled to 56, and in crop varieties the increase has been more dramatic. It grew from 90 varieties to 254 varieties in 1977. In terms of profit, it was stretching towards three-quarters of a million after its first decade.

Such progress has depended upon the continuing output of the plant-breeding stations, and the list seems endless. Since it takes a minimum of twelve years to produce a new cereal variety, and actually nearer fifteen years, the explosion of varieties came in the late 1970s, as the initial revenue that accrued from the 1964 Act was ploughed into development and research. Commercial stations, such as Nickersons at Rothwell on the bleak Lincolnshire wolds, have sought to emulate this multiplication and breeding of new varieties, but although their success is not to be minimized, the State establishments have done better.

Silsoe

'Until the end of the 18th century, agricultural engineering was largely in the hands of craftsmen, and notably that of the village blacksmith. . . . I claim to have a heritage in the mainstream of this history, because for many years my grandfather was an agricultural blacksmith in Suffolk.'

Professor C. J. Moss, Director, NIAE.

Bedfordshire is a county not noted for its good farming, yet at the village of Silsoe, on the A6 about midway between Bedford and Luton, within a single village is established three formidable centres of agricultural progress. The National Institute of Agricultural Engineering came to Silsoe in 1947. The College Farm of the Bedfordshire Farm Institute, Mander College, established itself with an offshoot farm at Silsoe in 1946, and when a National College of Agricultural Engineering was founded in 1960 it came to rest at Silsoe. Silsoe's situation makes for good links with farmers from the more prosperous eastern side of the country, and it is easily accessible from the Midlands and West. Farmers have followed developments with interest, and the village could have become the centre for the Royal Show, now established farther north in Warwickshire.

National Institute of Agricultural Engineering

Some farming institutions are partly administered by Government and partly by farmers' interests, or by the trade bodies, but the NIAE is unashamedly and unadulteratedly part of the Agricultural Research Council, under the wing of the Department of Education and Science, and not of the Ministry of Agriculture. Although the NIAE received support—notably from Oxford University and the RASE—in its initial years, it has become more and more solely a Government-sponsored body.

Its impact upon the agricultural engineering world is difficult to assess, but this is not to decry its achievements. When the Plant Breeding Institute was beavering away to produce new varieties the Plant Varieties and Seeds Act 1964 put into the hands of the Treasury the means to cash in on the results. The NSDO was created as the trading vehicle. The NIAE has no such body to develop the results of its research, and advances in farm mechanization have to be commercially taken up by a private company, and exploited with marketing expertise before they represent any cash sum. Thus, while it is possible to identify the 'Maris' seed varieties with the products of the PBI, there is no such prefix for the NIAE.

The NIAE's work in the field of mechanization has resulted in increased mechanization of British farms. Its work, moreover, has extended to include livestock, which has itself been affected by a mechanical revolution in the handling of its feed and manure. There have also been developments in the technical field of fodder conservation, in ventilation of livestock buildings and in milking-parlour ergonomics, as well as mechanical feeding systems for pigs and solar-radiation. Since the escalation of fuel prices, the NIAE has done important work in assessing energy-saving techniques.

It was used nationally in the ill-fated 'User Testing Scheme', which was ignored by the farmers and disliked by the trade. The NIAE was the piggy in the middle, and suffered a consequent drop in status. It commented blithely on its decease that this demise was the result of a Ministerial decision, but for a short time it had had a positive role. Work in the field of research does not always produce instant, tangible results, and the NIAE had a lack of headline-catching results. It issues no 'Recommended Lists' as does the NIAB.

Although firmly under the wing of the Government, the NIAE, with the Scottish Institute of Agricultural Engineering, is an independent public company limited by guarantee, and without share capital, an anomaly that exists among several Government bodies. The NIAE is in theory owned by the British Society for Research in Agricultural Engineering, and the Government Body is in fact a Board of Directors who administer the Institute. The success of many bodies sprang from the flamboyance of a headline-seeking director, and since 1964 Professor Charles Moss has blown a wind of change through the corridors of agricultural engineering. A short, bespectacled and balding man, Moss was previously in private industry, but his research capabilities were expanded while he was at the Royal Aeronautical Establishment at Farnborough during the War. Moss has used his position to defend the role of the NIAE, and has used the results of its achievements to popularize its image. After the Rothschild Report on the ARC—which castigated its shyness and forced the boffins to face the bright lights—Moss did just that, and has added prestige to his foundation.

Mander College came to Silsoe to lease a farm in 1946, which it purchased outright in 1955, and today there is a teaching block, lecture rooms and work-shop; but the College itself sits by the placid waters of the river Ouse, sixteen kilo-metres away in Bedford. Its pleasant riverside site shimmers in the sunlight, shaded only by the tree-lined banks of the river, but dominated by an eight-storey modern tower block where farmers' sons and daughters from Bedfordshire come to learn their trade.

The National College of Agricultural Engineering was founded in 1960 as the culmination of many years of agitation for the training of agricultural engineers. The impetus came from the AEA and AM I DA (now BAGMA), and other trade organizations who saw a need for highly trained engineers to operate from local dealers on the mechanized farms of Britain. There were doubts whether such training was required, as the necessary skills were normally picked up through apprenticeship schemes, and the national emphasis upon training through the Training Boards did not come into plans until after the 1964 Act. It has altered its emphasis to satisfy the areas of need, and has settled down to both full-time and short courses giving a less detailed skill training, but one that can be amplified on the ground.

The NCAE lives in a glass palace at Silsoe, built in the architectured style of 1960, and is dominated by a pre-cast gallows that hides a chimney. Both the NCAE and the Mander College premises contrast starkly with the magnificence of Wrest Park, with its French château, where the NIAE has now lived since 1947.

The origins of the NIAE go back to May 1919, when the testing and adaption of farm machinery was mooted by the then President of the Board of Agriculture.[4] It was October 1923 before these recommendations bore fruit and

---

[4] R. E. Prothero (later Lord Ernle), a far-sighted agriculturalist politician whose claim to immortality is his *English Farming*.

the Ministry of Agriculture invited Oxford University to set up a 'Farm Engineering Research and Testing Unit'. The following year the University's convocation accepted a decree authorizing the Curators of the University Chest to accept grants from the Ministry, and it opened for business as the Institute of Agricultural Engineering in an office in St Giles, with a small field operating station at Sandford-on-Thames. It was renamed the Institute for Research in Agricultural Engineering in 1932, and moved to larger premises in Park Road, Oxford, two years later. The field station moved firstly to Hampton Poyle, Benson and Long Wittenham, part of St John's College Farm. With the advent and importance of mechanization from 1939 onward the Ministry took close control of this embryonic organization, and it became a branch of the Ministry in 1932. From a staff of twenty-three at Oxford, only twelve went to Askham Bryan in June 1942 to inhabit the recently completed new buildings of the Agricultural College in what was then the West Riding of Yorkshire, standing on a windswept ridge overlooking the Vale of York, and less than eight kilometres from the ancient Roman city itself.

In 1946 the National Agricultural Advisory Service was formed, and the NIAE accepted association in an advisory capacity. The Scottish Institute of Agricultural Engineering was set up in 1946 at Howden, Mid Calder as the then Scottish Machinery Testing Station. It became grant-aided by the Department of Agriculture and Fisheries for Scotland in October 1949, and moved to the Edinburgh Centre of Rural Economy in 1961. The Scottish Institute has concentrated upon potato-crop mechanization, grain-drying, soil-cultivation and the behaviour of farm machinery on the sloping hillsides of Scotland. The NIAE came to Wrest Park in 1946, with a staff which had now grown to 150. It became fully established at Silsoe in July 1948, and the following year it passed its control to the Agricultural Research Council. It has trebled its staff since that time.

Wrest Park, Silsoe, is the most stately home occupied by any of the British farming institutions or organizations. It is a vast château-like mansion, built by the second Earl de Grey in 1836, but on a site whose gardens had been laid out in 1706 by a Duke of Kent, and completed by 'Capability' Lancelot Brown between 1758 and 1760. There are ornamental fountains, formal rides and walks, canals and statues, with the centuries-old trees where peacocks strut and screech beside the exquisite orangery. French gardens open up to a cascade of fountains; this unique home of the NIAE exhibits eighteenth-century affluence and taste.

Inside, where the latest developments of grotesque farm machinery are planned, the image of the eighteenth century is retained. The house was in fact a military hospital in the 1914–18 War, before the estate was broken up on the death in action of the last member of the de Grey family, Lord Lucas. The NIAE has restored much of the original beauty, although it is under the general control of the Department of the Environment. A feature of the interior is the magnificent multi-pattern wood floor of walnut, oak and beech, with a double staircase of bright scarlet carpet and gilded, wrought-iron balustrade. Pastel shades abound. The furniture is white, as are the large square containers which are occupied by brightly blossoming orange trees. Portraits of distinguished aristocratic owners abound, as well as one of Queen Anne, who created Henry de Grey Duke of Kent in 1710. It is house with a long history and, unlike many stately homes, it has found a new and positive role.

25 The Professional Bodies

'Through God's good grace, through strength of English oak,
  We have preserved our face, our throne, our land;
Now with our freedom saved from tyrants' yoke,
  We plant these trees. Remember why they stand.'

Lines on a plaque in Windsor Great Park

The Worshipful Company of Farmers

Within the square mile of the City of London there are 90 Livery Companies. Their origins were as tradesmen's guilds, a sort of medieval trade union defining the various occupations and crafts practised within the city limits. In this respect, since farming was not carried out within this area, it is perhaps not surprising that the Farmers Company is of comparative modern origin, being granted its Livery only in 1952.

It may be almost the oldest profession in the world, but the Aldermen and Sheriffs of the City of London preserved the rights of Livery Companies until modern times.

The Solicitors Company was chartered in 1944, and the Farmers followed eight years later; it is number 80 in the order of precedence, and was followed in 1971 by the Air Pilots and Navigators. But in 1977 a sudden boom occurred, and four Companies were created in an unprecedented single year. They were the Chartered Surveyors, Chartered Accountants, Chartered Secretaries, and Builders Merchants. Others, like the Mercers, Goldsmiths, Apothecaries, Fishmongers and Vintners can claim a history extending over six centuries, yet when there was a vacancy in the crypt of Guildhall for a new stained-glass window the youthful Farmers Company was successful in the ballot.

It owes its formation to the contribution from agriculture to the Red Cross Fund in the 1939–45 War, although the Appeal extended until 1947. Perhaps the news of peace took a long time to reach the countryside. Five red oaks were planted in Windsor Great Park when the Appeal reached £5 million, but when the Agriculture Fund was finally closed a total of £8·5 million had been raised. This was a large sum in 1947, and the King ordered four more oaks to be planted.

After the War the Appeal Committee decided to institute a scheme for training ex-Servicemen in farming. It was intended to be instituted and implemented via the County Agricultural Committees, the Farm Institutes and Agricultural Colleges. But a Government Scheme at the same time, with the same objective, thwarted these ideas. Then the suggestion was made that application to form a

City Livery Company should be pursued. It took from 1947 to 1952 before the dream became a reality, and in 1955 a Charter of Incorporation was granted by the Queen.

The Farmers Company is not a secret society, and membership may be obtained up to the maximum of 300 Liverymen, yet it has few really serious objectives, and is certainly not a quasi-political or pressure body of any kind. It offers no lead in farming matters, and keeps itself very much to itself. Nevertheless, it has instituted an Annual Course in conjunction with Wye College in Kent in the higher aspects of farm management. The Course is open to non-members, was first instituted in 1963, and occupies three weeks of high-powered concentrated effort.

Although the leading personalities in UK agriculture are to be found among the Liverymen, there is nevertheless a solid hard core of 'backwoodsmen' yeoman farmers from the shires. It lunches itself four times a year, usually in the Innholders Hall in tiny College Street, not far from the Thames and Cannon Street Tube Station. The Farmers Company does not have its own ornate Hall to compete with the grandeur of the Goldsmiths or the Fishmongers. Only 35 of the 90 Companies in fact have their own Hall. The Farmers have a valuable city site purchased at a modest price before the property boom, and there is a fund to build one day a 'Farmers Hall', but although this scheme is not dead, it has been put off by escalating building costs and the economic squeeze.

The Company also holds an Annual Banquet, usually in the Mansion House where it entertains the Lord Mayor and Sheriffs in their own home. It seeks at a high level to promote a better understanding between the powerful forces and influence of the City of London, and the more distant farms of Britain

Prince Charles and his sister, Princess Anne, with her husband, Captain Mark Phillips, became Liverymen of the Farmers Company in 1975, and this support for farming is paralleled by their own interest in the farming activities on their own estates. Prince Philip was Grand Master of the Guild of Air Pilots and Air Navigators in 1978, and is also a Livery Member of the Mercers.

The Farmers Livery Company represents a sort of high-class Rotary Club of farming, where the members wine and dine themselves at their quarterly lunches, and in white tie and tails at the Mansion House. They did allow ladies to the Annual Banquet in 1978, but despite the fact that there are many lady farmers, Princess Anne remains the only lady Liveryman of the Farmers Company.

The Farmers Club

'A gathering place for farmers which could also serve as a platform, from which would go out to England news of all that was good in farming.'
Letter promoting a British Farmers Club,
28 May 1841.

It seems incongruous that a Farmers Club should exist among the pavements of

London, but exist it does, and it has a profound influence as a forum for farmers. The Club itself hides behind the tessellated Victorian block known as Whitehall Court, which faces the Thames, and looks out backward into a narrow street, with the monolithic Ministry of Defence building at one end. Just around the corner is Whitehall Place and the Ministry of Agriculture. The Farmers Club, at No. 3, is unremarkable. Next door is the Horseguards Hotel.

Within this building, there were once seventeen London clubs; some of a lesser nature, such as the Fly Fishermen's Club, have now gone. At the end of the street the National Liberal Club still provides a dusty political museum, with Gladstone and Asquith looking down upon the airline girls whose office is now part of the building. It is true that it boasts a magnificent staircase and a unique library, but the Farmers Club just along the street is by contrast warm, chintzy and comfortable.

Here are none of the pretensions of the Reform, Athenaeum or the United Services Clubs, and the oil paintings are of prize-winning pigs, horses and cattle. It does not have the Regency appeal of Boodles, where the talk is of pheasants and fishing. It does not have the political overtones or plush premises of the Carlton, and neither does it cost as much as any of these. In fact, it is among the cheapest London clubs.

The Farmers Club is well separated from the centre of London's Clubland in fashionable St James's. However, the dining-room and terrace overlook the Thames just below the Palace of Westminster, and the food, like the view, is good. The club is situated on the first floor, but there are additional bedrooms on the sixth and seventh floors, and even some in the semi-basement. It is also a hotel for its members, providing rates that are a third of the normal London charges. It moved down to its sunlit rooms in 1944, having occupied a small club-room and office on the seventh floor from 1903. The Club itself was founded in 1844, although it was 1941 before it adopted its crest, which is a central figure of Ceres, goddess of agriculture in the Roman mythology, and counterpart of the Greek Demeter. Ceres was also goddess of corn, whence derives our word Cereal.

There are 5,000 members of the Farmers Club, of which about a third are not farmers, but are connected with agriculture in some fairly direct way. Although some 500 new members are elected every year, a black ball is set against any application which comes from someone without agricultural connections. There are lady farmers, so that there are lady members in their own right. The atmosphere is not exclusively male, nor is it quiet: it buzzes to the hum of farming talk.

Surprisingly, so much farming takes place in London that the Farmers Club provides a home from home, away from the anonymity of a soulless hotel, and although other London clubs have folded almost annually, the Farmers Club prospers. It owes its existence in its present premises largely to a gift of £140,000 from Sir Jack Eastwood in 1970, which secured a long lease on the premises. It is not the preserve of the larger farmer, neither is it dominated by the agro-businessman; and almost half of its members have never been inside it. Members receive the bi-monthly journal which reports the discussion meetings organized; the Farmers Club has always adopted a non-partisan approach to politics; so that each new Minister of Agriculture is invited to address the Club. Since Ministers change fairly frequently, this is a chance to get the measure of a new man. It can be a daunting experience for the Minister, when for the first time he comes face to face with his customers. In 1962, 1,200 farmers came to hear Heath talk about Britain's position within the Common Market; nine years later 700 turned up to hear Geoffrey Rippon talking on the same subject, but this time Britain's accession was nearer.

The Farmers Club Pavilion at Stoneleigh is another feature, while at the annual ball in the Great Room of Grosvenor House 1,200 farmers and their wives sit down on the Tuesday of Smithfield Week each December to a banquet and a dance. Such is the eminence of the Farmers Club that it can attract speakers such as the Archbishop of Canterbury and Prince Charles. An Under-30s Section provides an opportunity for younger farmers to participate in their own discussion meetings and farm walks. The Club fills a unique and influential place in British agriculture, although it does not in any way compete with the roles of the NFU, the CLA, the universities or the Farming Conferences. It manages to be in the vanguard of agricultural thinking, and often provides a platform for the controversial issues of the day. In some respects, more farming progress takes place in these elegant Victorian drawing rooms than in some of the more public high-pressure bodies that embark upon flag-waving exercises.

The annual presidency of the Farmers Club attracts the limelight, but it only lasts one year. The attempt has been made to put a cross section of agriculturalists and farmers into the hot seat, and there has been no opting for 'safe' characters. The following list of more recent Presidents emphasizes the diversity of interests in the Club.

1971 Sir Harold Sanders; ex-Ministry man, university professor and farming author. 'Wise and witty.'
1972 John Harris; publisher—Chairman Agricultural Press Division of IPC, responsible for seven farming journals, Including the *Farmers Weekly*. 'Hard boiled businessman.'
1973 Derek Pearce; farmer from Norfolk—ex General Manager Eastern Counties Farmers Ltd, ex Chairman Farm Buildings Centre. 'Professional smoothness.'
1974 Hew Watt; farmer 333 hectares from Essex—journalist, broadcaster, farming TV personality—Chairman, Apple and Pear Development Board 1973-7. 'Youthful exuberance.'
1975 Charles Coad; farmer from Wiltshire—part owner part tenant of 270 hectares—was Chairman of Oxford Farming Conference in the same year, Governor Royal Agricultural College, Cirencester. 'Cool, calm and confident.'
1976 Roddy Loder-Symonds; partner, Strutt & Parker, in charge of Canterbury office—youngest Chairman at thirty-seven. Stepson Colonel Jack Houghton-Brown, Chairman 1967. Farms 208-hectare Denne Hill Farm, Canterbury. 'Cultured enthusiast.'

1977   Roland Stewart Sandeman; ex-printer—farmer of Ashington Manor, Yeovil—tenant of the Church Commissioners. 'Solid yeoman.'

1978   Anthony Rosen; controversial managing director of Fountain Farming Ltd, much-maligned institutional farming group. 'Entrepreneurial whiz-kid.'

1979   Reg Older; farmer near Ashford, Kent—Chairman Apple and Pear Development Board 1977–present day. Chairman Governors of Wye College. 'Straightforward and dignified.'

The Farm Management Association

'Agriculture is a totally different operation from factory production, and requires an entirely different approach to management problems.'

Prince Philip

'I personally have never been so enthusiastic about a development in British farming as I am over the formation of this Association.'

Sir Emrys Jones, First President FMA, 1965.

It holds its Annual Conference in the draughty Cairn Hotel in bleak Harrogate each dull November; it hardly sparkles, but provides a 99 per cent stag occasion for very serious listening and few light-hearted moments; but then the FMA is a very serious-minded organization, whose members are largely frustrated farmers. They have settled for a Managership as second best, and it shows. There is a strong link in the membership with the lesser lights of ADAS and the academic side of farming—a composition hardly dedicated to raising the roof. Self-employed farmers are scarce among its ranks, and the academic note of the proceedings proclaims the members' purity and disdain of commercial instinct.

The Association finally got off the ground in 1965, but it had been five years since Bob Starling (then Manager of the Duke of Devonshire's Chatsworth Farms) first conceived the idea of forming an association for farm managers. He had been a farm manager for ten years then, and later became Farm Manager for the *Farmer and Stockbreeder*'s own farm in Hertfordshire. He later went back to ducal service as Manager to the Duke of Grafton at Euston, in Norfolk. The *Farmer and Stockbreeder* provided an interest-free loan to cover the cost of a secretary for three years; somehow the FMA never achieved the ambition of its founders—to provide an effective centre for farm management—but it had a full-time permanent secretary—Pearl Jukes—and accepted the invitation of the Midland Bank to share its pavilion at Stoneleigh. In 1978 things came to a head and the FMA merged with the British Institute of Management. The office moved to the BIM, Management House, off Kingsway, in London. By this time its membership had fallen from a maximum of 2,000 to 1,300, although there are some 7,000 full-time farm managers in the UK.

The first Chairman was Derek Pearce, and among the steering committee was John Harris of IPC and Anthony Rosen (both to become Chairmen of the Farmers Club), plus Robert Trow-Smith, Editor of the *Farmer and Stock-*

breeder. One finds the same names peppering the many bodies and associations that control the UK agricultural scene.

The Association of Agriculture

'There is nothing good in the countryside, and if there is, they won't let you have it.'

Cockney boy after visiting a farm.

The Association of Agriculture is an educational charity; it was incorporated in 1947, and has as its patron Earl Mountbatten of Burma. The AA has little connection with farming, but helps in the education of schoolchildren in rural affairs, and is an organization to which insufficient regard has been paid. The farmers are not interested, few are members, and few have ever heard of it.

The AA holds a list of farms where schoolchildren and others can visit, and its headquarters at 78 Buckingham Gate, London, is a national centre furnishing information on every aspect of agriculture and land-use; the customers are lecturers and teachers in colleges and schools. Financial support comes from a variety of charities and trusts, such as the Carnegie and MacRobert Trusts, but the finances are always fraught with uncertainty.

If you hold your Annual One Day Conference at the London School of Economics on a Saturday in November it is hardly surprising that few farmers support it, but the AA's educational role has also become suspect, and farmers may often wonder if it is really on their side, with its emphasis upon opening up the countryside and the problems of food-consumers, rather than those of food-producers.

The objectives of the Association of Agriculture are at least straightforward, and it can define its role clearly, but the Agricultural Development Association (which ceased in 1972, after a chequered career) had lost its definition and its identity. ADA sought to be the link between its customers and the research organizations, but research personnel are proverbially reluctant to disclose their findings before they reach concrete conclusions. ADA wanted to create a link between the scientist and the farmer, something the Agricultural Research Service was forced, against its inclinations, to accept after the Rothschild Report. The Association had relied upon financial assistance from many organizations and large companies with agricultural connections, but since it lacked a definitive role this support was gradually withdrawn, and it sank with little trace.

Royal Agricultural Benevolent Institution

'We have regretfully to announce the deaths of 43 pensioners during the year.'
1975 Annual Report.

The RABI was founded in 1860, and given a Royal Charter in 1935; it exists to dispense assistance to aged farmers and their widows in desperate straits, has its own home, and a block of eight flats in Bury St Edmunds, with nomination rights in a string of homes for the elderly throughout southern England. It covers England and Wales, but has a stronger representation south of the Humber. It is operated by 62 Honorary local Secretaries, who act as collecting agents and stimulate local interest in fund-raising activities. The RABI operates very much with the active co-operation of local and county NFU Secretaries, but it is not part of the NFU: was nearing its first half-century when the NFU was born.

There were over 500 on the pension roll; nearly 100 live in assisted accommodation, some get quarterly grants, and 250 get free TV sets. It has the Queen as its patron, and the Duke of Beaufort as its active President. It has assets of over £2 million, and boasts that it has raised and distributed more than this sum since its inauguration. It has also inherited several farms through legacies, the largest being 416-hectare Caustons Hall, near Sudbury in Suffolk, and it owns over 1,000 hectares of farmland in Essex, Oxfordshire, Worcestershire, Leicestershire, Somerset and Devon.

One would expect the RABI to be supported from within the farming community. This is largely true, yet it appears surprising that the Birmingham Motor Cycle Club has in fact contributed £1,000, while a form of girls at South Hampstead High School in London contributed £140 13s.6d. to buy a cow, after they had learnt in a geography lesson of the severity of the foot-and-mouth epidemic in 1967. It was 'to buy a cow for a farmer whose herd had been slaughtered'. The Motor Cycle connection comes from the many field events which motor-cycle enthusiasts engage upon by permission over rough farmland.

The Royal Institution of Chartered Surveyors

'We have recently been looking at farming in France, Spain and Portugal, and there is little doubt that British average standards of husbandry are far superior.'

Strutt & Parker Annual Report, 1972.

There are in the UK around 5,000 firms of Estate Agents, Auctioneers and Land Agents. They range from those conducting furniture auctions in decrepit sale-rooms to the national, or even international, companies dealing with multi-million office and development properties. There is a ring of public livestock auction markets in every major or minor rural town in Britain, and these help to form a regular source of income to the auctioneering profession.

Estate Agents are also the major way of selling farms, although this only happens in Britain once in every two generations; thus the profession would be living on thin crusts if it relied upon a farm sale and its resultant auction of the stock and machinery. There has, however, been a growing need for professional advice by farmers and landowners to combat the complexities of the planning and development regulations, and in no small measure to plan for tax avoidance. The complicated financial structure of many farming businesses—some quite small—has meant trust deeds, family partnerships, sometimes limited liability companies, and a host of permutations on a central theme of protecting the farm. Together with the farm accountants, the members of the Institute of Chartered Surveyors have themselves become professional tax-dodgers.

There have been major developments in the establishment of departments dealing only with Planning Applications on behalf of landowners, and the personnel are familiar figures in the Local Planning Office; but there has been another major development in the post-War period, in the establishment of highly professional departments of farm management.

Strutt & Parker—one firm only—boast that they are in charge of the farming operations on over 200,000 hectares. The high-class agents have always had a major role on the aristocratic estates, with their dozens of tenant farmers and one small home farm. Their job was to act as a buffer between the landlord and his tenants, but they were also responsible for rent-fixing and the investment on new farm buildings. This role existed happily while the large estates existed, and with the extremely large there was a qualified Resident Land Agent, a figure usually disliked by the tenantry. But in more recent years, even with the escalation of owner/occupation, the farm management connection has increased, and there are still many owners of farms who may be fully engaged in other occupations, but inherited a medium-sized farm. It provides a handsome residence in the country, but they have been content to hand over the actual farming and the bookkeeping problems to a firm of professional advisers.

The Pension Fund and institutional investors, coming into this strange new world, went immediately to the established and experienced firms. This has prevented them from committing too many boobs.

The Royal Institution of Chartered Surveyors as it stands today is an amalgamation of three organizations. It also incorporates The Chartered Land Agents Society and The Chartered Auctioneers and Estate Agents Institute. The merger took place on 8 June 1970, and the RICS resides in a valuable building, 12 Great George Street, which abuts on to Parliament Square. The office was closed in Jubilee Year, and the Queen officially visited the redesigned offices in 1978. The RICS was originally founded in 1868, with a membership of only 200. Today it boasts over 30,000 members working in every country of the world, but with the amalgamation there are in fact over 40,000 professional people entitled to the letters FRICS and ARICS licensed by the Institution as qualified Chartered Surveyors. It was granted its Royal Charter in 1881, only thirteen years after its formation, and the present title dates from 1946.

The Chartered Land Agents Society was formed in 1902, and consisted of Resident Land Agents in large properties. It was granted a Royal Charter in 1929, and by the time of the general merger in 1970 still only had a membership of 1,400, although it had extended itself from Resident Land Agents to a few in the public services and in general practice. The Chartered Auctioneers and Estate

Agents Institute was in fact founded in 1886, two years earlier than the original 'Institution of Surveyors' which formed the foundation of the RICS; but the antecedents of the CAEAI went back to an Institute primarily involved in house purchases in London, which had been formed in 1872, but had embraced the whole country by 1886. It was granted its Royal Charter in 1947.

The movement towards amalgamation started in 1964, but took six more years to come to fruition. They moved together very slowly, each jealously guarding the specialized roles which it was performing, but with the power of Government on such matters as compensation for compulsory acquisition and a gradual tightening of the many laws and regulations involving Planning Applications, it seemed that a national body with more strength could perhaps act as a voice for the profession, and influence legislation before it was enacted and became law.

In its enhanced role of direct farming, it has achieved an inconspicuous but honest solid farming practice without being technical innovators or pioneers.

26 The Trade Organizations

'Let me have no lying; it becomes none but tradesmen.'
William Shakespeare

'In every age and clime we see
Two of a trade can never agree.'
John Gay

The United Kingdom Agricultural Supply Trade Association Limited (UKASTA)

'Joseph, under Pharaoh, stored the grain in the seven plentiful years, and re-distributed it to the buyers in the seven lean years. Thus, he was fulfilling the sort of functions which a modern corn merchant has to fulfil.'
'The History of NACAM', 1967.

Farmers' feelings towards their local corn merchants could be termed a love/hate relationship, with more emphasis upon the hate. There is always a surmise—founded upon outdated traditions—that the merchant is trying to outsmart the farmer, and even though merchants today employ advisory staff to help farmers, the feeling persists that this advice may not be as impartial as that from ADAS. This latent animosity breaks out into open warfare when farmers' corn is contracted forward at a good price, but has dropped on the 'spot' market when delivery finally takes place. The merchant (or compounder) uses magnifying glasses to discover faults, and make deductions under the pretence that the bulk delivery is not up to the standards of the original sample.

To be fair, the merchant today is largely a middleman, or broker, and the vast majority of sales are destined for the few major national compounders; nevertheless, the merchant gets the blame. UKASTA, and its predecessor organizations, have set out to give the merchants a better standing with their farmer customers; although farmers always imagine the merchants to be ganging up against them, they are in fact completely independent small businessmen and compete against each other.

Perhaps UKASTA is best known for its annual harvest predictions. Each year, with the help of collated reports from the whole country, it announces with a fanfare of trumpets its own calculations of the annual UK harvest. This fanfare is blown almost within days of the completion of each harvest, and farmers are always suspicious that rapid assessments of this nature are designed to hold down prices.

UKASTA has, however, broadened its horizons, and pontificates upon the whole range of farming affairs, although it is careful to be pro-farmer. It has called for a strategic plan to maximize UK food production, and to help alleviate the country's economic difficulties, and has taken up the cudgels on behalf of farmers with the Minister of Agriculture over the various crises in the livestock industry. It also has a vested interest in maintaining the number of mouths to be fed on UK farms; declining numbers are poor for trade.

The organization owes its existence to the need for food in the Great War, and was founded as the 'National British and Irish Corn Trade Association' in 1917, as a national organization that could co-ordinate the buying and selling of grain. It retained the title NACAM from 1917 to 1971, when it became the British Association of Grain, Seed, Feed and Agricultural Merchants (BASAM), but six years later, after protracted and sometimes acrimonious discussions, it amalgamated with a sister organization, CAFMNA,[1] to form UKASTA. CAFMNA had a membership of 282, and BASAM one of 1,276, but many merchants were members of both, so that the new organization was launched with a membership of 1,300. With the closure of many local country mills and the take-over of others, the total membership has been declining by about 75 members annually.

The hub of the British corn trade is the Mark Lane Exchange, amid narrow streets in the City of London. NACAM and BASAM had resided at adjacent Cereal House for fifty-eight years, from their inception to 1975, when they were forced out by spiralling local rates, then amounting to £18,000 per year. They went outside the city limits to Whitehall Court in Westminster, where the rates for their new offices were only £5,000. They took a suite of offices on the ground floor in Whitehall Court, beneath the Farmers Club and just around the corner from the Ministry of Agriculture, and launched a new company, BASAM Property Ltd, to which the corn merchants rapidly subscribed.

Once a year they sally forth to Bournemouth, Harrogate or St Andrews in Scotland, for their Annual 'Business Conference'. The delegates are recruited from the higher echelons of the merchanting companies, at managing director or sole proprietor level. There was an insistence upon dinner jackets every evening, and selection of venues with creditable golf courses—but poverty has now set in! The business sessions allow for the golf tournament to take place. About a third of the four hundred participating merchants bring their wives along, these being treated to a separate programme of visits to local stately homes and pottery factories, or other ladylike pursuits. There are no farmers at the UKASTA Conference, and even the farming press pays little attention to it. Nevertheless, a sense of power and importance is engendered by the range of Daimlers in the car-park. The whole affair is coupled with an AGM and Presidential cocktail parties. A humble farmer peeping through the door might be surprised at the acrimony

---

[1] Compound Animal Feeding Stuffs Manufacturers National Association Limited (CAFMNA).

that can develop from time to time. The merchants are at many levels in the business strata, and fiercely competitive.

There is also the Institute of Corn and Agricultural Merchants (ICAM), founded in 1946, which provide facilities within the trade for education and training and the interchange of technical information, and with the UK accession to the EEC, UKASTA and its predecessors have been heavily involved in the small print of the Treaty of Rome, and the new legislation affecting seeds. The advent of metrication also affected corn merchants more than farmers.

Agricultural Engineers Association

'The machinery with which we tend crops and stock repays Britain a thousandfold.'

Sir Henry Plumb.

'We were looked upon as blacksmiths. We didn't get out of that image until the 1960s.'

Captain E. N. Griffith.
(Founder with Arthur Howard of the Howard Machinery Co., formerly Rotary Hocs Ltd).

If UKASTA seems dominated by its annual harvest predictions, then the AEA seems only absorbed in its export figures, which it announces regularly as a criterion of its success; but since 70 per cent of all UK manufactured farm machinery is exported, this is perhaps vital to the members' interests. The headquarters of the Association (which was founded in 1875) is at No. 6 Buckingham Gate, just across the road from the Palace in a building which was once the Rothschild town house. The Council Chamber was formerly the Rothschild ballroom. The Association moved to its present address from Dashwood House, Old Broad Street, during the presidency of Mr Edward Griffith, 1948–1955.

Export sales apart, the AEA is a joint sponsor of the Royal Smithfield Show, and it was instrumental in reviving this after the 1945 war. The tripartite members are the AEA, the Smithfield Club and the Society of Motor Manufacturers and Traders (SMM&T). At the 1949 Show the AEA share of the profits was a modest £63. Two years later it spiralled to £7,000. Presidents come and Presidents go annually, but heading the permanent staff is AEA Director-General Dean Swift (not to be confused with his son, Jonathan Swift, Director-General of the British Agricultural & Garden Machinery Association Ltd (BAGMA), representing the distributors and dealers in tractors, farm machinery and garden equipment in the UK.

Although members of AEA export 70 per cent of their products, the prosperity of home agriculture is a vital factor in the industry's welfare, and accordingly Presidents expound on the wider issues of the day.

In 1974 its President, Alan Rundle, said, 'Farm machinery manufacturers are particularly worried about the difficulties facing livestock and milk-producers.'

The expenditure of British farmers upon new machinery still represents 30 per cent of the industry's income, and an unhealthy agriculture will cut back on its machinery purchases even before cutting its own standards of living. Relations between the AEA and farmers have not always been harmonious, but during the past ten years there has been a series of regular meetings between the AEA and the NFU Machinery Committee. The resulting frank exchange of views has helped close co-operation and mutual understanding between the two organizations, which worked closely together to establish priorities for steel and oil supplies during the crisis which hit industry when it went on to a three-day week. The advent of the 'User-Testing-Scheme' which was launched by the NFU for the assessment of machines and implements set problems for AEA members. However, the scheme suffered through lack of support and finally was faded out. As Robert Trow-Smith wrote in his history of the Association, 'It was unmourned by everyone except a handful of theorists who still refused to acknowledge that it was not possible to produce a comparative assessment of a machine that was valid in all circumstances.' Farm machinery, like fertilizers, is now a part and parcel of modern farming methods, but it has a longer history than is popularly imagined, even though the multiple-horsepower iron beasts of today bear little resemblance to the 'machinery' of early Victorian days.

British Agricultural and Garden Machinery Association Ltd

BAGMA and the AEA, although under the separate direction of the father and son Swift combination (only a tenuous connection to the famous Jonathan Swift who died in 1745) are at pains to point out that as two completely independent organizations they are in no way connected, although they are also not opposed to each other, but carry out different roles. The AEA, with a membership of 230, is the major manufacturers parent body, while BAGMA represents the distributive dealers, and has a membership five times as high, standing at 1,250.

The AEA had been in existence forty-two years before the dealers got together in 1917, with the objective of combating the unfair practices which were prevalent at that time. Farm machinery was also being boosted at home in the food-production campaign of the First World War.

BAGMA was originally called AMTDA (Agricultural Machinery and Tractor Dealers Association), but it changed its name in 1972 in an attempt to keep up with its modern image. It had started a Horticultural Section in 1957, but changed the name of this ten years later to the Garden Machinery Division. With the pedantic obsession of the modern Briton with flowering cherries and pocket gardens, there has been a boom in garden centres.

BAGMA lives in Church Street, Rickmansworth, away from the hubbub and turmoil of London life, and its logo is a cog-wheel bearing the legend 'symbol of service'. In addition to protecting the interests of machinery dealers, it also places great emphasis upon its educational role in attracting and training farm mechanics, and it was a founder member of CLIMMAR, the Confederation of European Farm Machinery Dealers, and has established connections with similar associations in America and South Africa.

National Association of Agricultural Contractors (NAAC).

'A contractor is a man who arrives to bale your hay two days after it was ready.'

With the growing expense of farm machinery, and a reduced labour force, the NAAC has been predicting its own spiralling importance for many years. The golden age of contractors is always around the corner, but never seems to arrive. To farmers the employment of anything but a specialized contractor is an insult, implying that he cannot cope himself. It conjures up the same image of a 'week-end' farmer whose efforts and results are so poor that he must take another job to prevent insolvency. The unreliability of contractors is another factor that gives them a poor image.

Nevertheless, in highly specialized areas, such as land-draining or aerial spraying, contractors have blossomed, although the living in such humdrum jobs as ploughing and cultivations has never been lucrative. The other department which has shown some promise is contract-milking, and several companies in the UK are involved in finding replacement cowmen for periods when the farmer is without a regular hand, or during illness.

The NAAC was formed in 1956, and has a membership of around 450 contractors, though there are none from Northern Ireland. It was an Association born out of the original National Traction Engine Owners and Users Association, formed in the last years of the nineteenth century, with the task of fighting the absurd laws which differed from county to county, setting out licensing regulations for highway travel. At that time the itinerant threshing machines with their steam engines were the most commonplace forerunners of today's high-powered farm contractor. The restrictions on highway regulations seem archaic by today's standards. Bunker plates had to be covered with oblongs, squares, rings, etc., denoting where they could go and where they could not go, but the new age of the motor-car was dawning, and a young lawyer, Joynson Hicks, took up the cudgels on behalf of the Tractor Engine Association. He later became the guiding light in the formation of the Automobile Association.

The NTE continued in its almost moribund form until the escalation of mechanization after 1945, when it lengthened its already cumbersome title to express new expansion, becoming the National Traction Engine and Tractor Association Incorporated, with the pious hope of attracting the more modern contractors into the traditional Contractors Association. The newcomers, however, formed another representative body called the British Agricultural Contractors Association, which covered a wider field, and embraced the new contracting tasks of lime-spreading and liquid fertilizer application. The new organization flourished, while the old one nearly foundered; it was an amalgamation of the two which created the NAAC in 1956.

An internal reconstruction tidied up the organization in 1964, but by 1971 the rebellious members with gardening machinery interests felt they were being ignored, and that they had more affinity with the horticultural industry, so that they formed a breakaway movement. The NAAC Headquarters is at Thornton Heath in Surrey, and it has a telegraphic address 'Agritract, Croydon'. It now has seven divisions within the wide field of contracting represented inside the organization. The original Secretary was W. F. P. Bishop. His place was taken in 1971 by John Castle, a trained animal nutritionist who had been Chief Agricultural Adviser with Levers, but was axed in the Unilever/BOCM-Silcock amalgamation. If his links with machinery seem tenuous, he was once under the wing of that doyen of the farm machinery world Claude Culpin, whose book on farm machinery has been a standard text for over thirty years.

British Agrochemicals Association (BAA)

Producing chemicals is an expensive business, so that it becomes the prerogative of the large industrial company. The BAA has only forty-six members, and they range from ICI, Fisons and Shell to a few minnows like Crop Safe Ltd in Salisbury. It is a self-protection organization, financed by a levy upon its members' sales, and formed to fight a rearguard action against the stranglehold of legislation governing the use of toxic substances.

The BAA has only developed in a relatively minor way. It instituted a certificate of proficiency for spray operators on the farm in 1976, but it operates with a staff of only three, plus a secretary from modern Alembic House on the south side of the Thames. It holds an Annual Dinner in a posh London hotel, and each member company has representatives upon a multitude of committees.

The British Crop Protection Council is another organization geared to the greater understanding of farm chemicals. It instituted a conference on this subject in 1962, which fills the Hotel Metropole at Brighton each November, and has swollen beyond all recognition to some 2,000 people. It has become an international symposium, and concurrent sessions within the Metropole complex present erudite papers on the latest developments in the agrochemical world. Every other year the topic is weeds, while the alternate years deal with pests, thus marking off the different fields of herbicides, insecticides and fungicides. The international aspect of this conference is shown by the national flags on the delegates' lapels, and by the multitude of languages. In this vast throng are to be found no more than half a dozen UK farmers, yet the papers are at a level from which farmers could usefully profit.

Fertiliser Manufacturers Association

'The crops on a field diminish or increase in exact proportion to the diminution or increase of mineral substances conveyed to it in manure.'
                                                                      Justus Von Liebig, 1840.

The crop yields on UK farms have doubled in forty years; wheat at 4·9 tonnes per hectare, barley 4·4 tonnes, potatoes 30·7 tonnes, turnips and swedes 52·5 tonnes[2]. Plant-breeders have upgraded the botanical potential, the agrochemical industry has cleaned up the weeds, pests and diseases, but artificial fertilizer too has played an integral part in this race for crop-increases. The yields show that without them the UK cereal harvest would be 34 per cent lower, or 5 million tonnes, while potatoes would drop by a half.

The import/export deficit on fertilizers in 1975 was £78 million, but the additional crop and milk yields amounted to £500 million—a sixfold increase on the investment—which disproves the theory advanced by the anti-fertilizer lobby that it would be more advantageous to import direct food products.

There has always been an anti-fertilizer lobby amongst the 'back-to-nature' purist pressure groups, led by ex-Prime Minister's daughter Lady Eve Balfour and the Soil Association. But compost-grown vegetables have failed in marketing ventures, due to the higher price and the indifference of the public. If smokers will not give up, despite a Government campaign, food produced with the aid of artificial fertilizer is not going to worry the eating public.

As recorded, the BAA has a membership of 46, but the Fertiliser Manufacturers Association has only 33 members, and some of these are the subsidiaries of major companies. The FMA also resides in Alembic House on the Albert Embankment, and its objectives are the co-ordination of fertilizer statistics and the general protection of its members. It has, in fact, a lesser task to defend itself than do the chemical manufacturers. It was founded in its present form in 1875, the same year that the Agricultural Engineers Association was formed, and it was known in those days as the 'Chemical Manufacturers Association'. The middle years of the nineteenth century had seen the emergence of a new industry in Britain—the manufacture of fertilizers.

Even by the 1850s artificial stimulus to crop-growing was an established fact, for scientific research twenty years before had established the elements necessary for stimulating plant-growth. The marketing of sulphate of ammonia was already being carried out on a considerable scale, and the East Anglian coprolite mines were exploited from 1847, when they were producing 500 tonnes per year, reaching a peak of 250,000 tonnes in 1875. Coprolites, fossilized excreta, had been discovered in the mid-eighteenth century to have a high phosphatic content, but it was only in the nineteenth century that cheaper phosphate rock was imported from North Africa. It is said today that the whole African continent rests upon a foundation of phosphate! By 1870 there were 80 factories producing superphosphate, and the Chemical Manure Manufacturers Association was renamed the Fertiliser Manufacturers Association in 1904.

Britain is not today wholly dependent upon the imports of its fertilizer raw materials; nitrogen comes flowing from the giant plants of ICI, Fisons and Shell, and in 1968 the first British potash mine was discovered and opened at Cleveland, 16 km north of Whitby in North Yorkshire. It has a shaft 1,190 metres deep,

---

[2] MOA 1977 Estimates.

which makes it the deepest in Britain. In 1973 the Moroccan phosphate moguls tried to put a phosphate stranglehold upon the world. The US phosphate mines had been allowed to run down until the Moroccans were in a strong position. They applied shock price increases, and British farmers suffered a sudden escalation in their prices. Yet despite the withdrawal of a subsidy on fertilizers which existed for nearly thirty years, British farmers can still buy artificial fertilizer cheaper than their European counterparts.

The Institute of Agricultural Secretaries

It was during the 1939–45 War that farmers first became overwhelmed by a mass of form-filling and statistical bumph, mainly emanating from the Ministry of Agriculture. It was the shape of things to come. The maze of office work and accountancy procedures grew ever more complex, and became a vital part of farm management. Farming success seemed more and more to depend upon accountancy procedures and financial control as opposed to the market haggling, and handshake contracts.

To cope with this obvious development meant to break into an area where the customers were highly independent, and highly suspicious of any outsiders looking at their accounts: it was a tough and daunting task to convince farmers that they even had any need for a farm secretary. They guarded their secrets jealously, and there was also the suspicion that a travelling secretary, going from farm to farm, could speak out of turn. Nevertheless, it was inevitable that a ring of farm secretaries should become available throughout the country. It is doubtful if more than one in a hundred farmers employ any secretarial assistance even today, but with the growth of this new profession a National Institute of Agricultural Secretaries was registered in 1967. Its objectives were to keep its members up to date with the more complex and ever-growing mountain of farm form-filling, and income tax allowances. (Later, VAT added to their work.)

The Institute's Honorary Secretary was John Birtles, who had formed Multiple Accounting Services in 1965, and a decade later had built up a clientele of 400 farmers, covering over 200,000 hectares. He opened an office at Chipping Norton in Oxfordshire, and another in York in 1973. Accounting machines of computer-like complexity are now situated at the Chipping Norton office, and by a postal service and a monthly accountancy procedure MAS have brought a modicum of financial control to many farms.

Earlier than this, in 1956, Mary Belcher and Mary Collins had set up Farmers Secretarial Service at Devizes. A third partner, Ann Spencer, joined them in 1967. In 1961 Mary Belcher gained national fame by winning a TV *Get Ahead* Competition which sought to discover pioneering young businessmen and women. The money from this competition was used to open the first office in Devizes, and now with 160 farmers and a staff of 20 it has moved from straight secretarial work to providing management accounting services and a wider range of jobs for their farmer customers.

27 The Marketing Boards

Milk Marketing Board

'We do not want the powers of our Milk Boards reduced in any way. That also goes for the Potato Marketing Board and the other Marketing Boards we have in this country.'

Reg Bottini, General Secretary, NUAAW.

'It would be idle to pretend that all the Marketing Boards have been unqualified triumphs.'

The British Genius
(Grosvenor and McMillan, 1973).

The Milk Marketing Board is a producers' organization, set up under the Marketing Act 1932, which was an attempt to help a depressed agricultural industry. It is not an adjunct of Government, although the Ministry of Agriculture appoints three of its eighteen members, but it can hide behind the cloak of Government when the price of retail milk is fixed. This is the only food where the Government actually fixes the price, but the Board has still been attacked for being a monopoly. In a sense it is because it buys, or is under obligation to buy, all the milk that registered dairy farmers in England and Wales produce. It is also very big business, and its turnover in 1977 of £1,031 million was almost as large as that of the UK Ford Motor Company, almost the same as that of Burmah Oil, greater than that of Marks & Spencer, and as large as the combined turnover of Woolworths and Sainsburys. With milk and milk products providing 21 per cent of the income of the total UK national farm, the Milk Marketing Board is a vitally important organization.

There are eight marketing schemes in operation, and one defunct,[1] but four of those schemes are for milk. The others cover potatoes, eggs, wool and hops. The MMB itself only covers England and Wales, while three separate Boards operate in Scotland: the Scottish MMB, with its office in Paisley, the North of Scotland MMB at Inverness and the Aberdeen and District MMB.

The MMB is a producer organization, and milk is not subsidized in the UK. The Board emerged in times of distress, but could in fact be abolished by a

---

[1] The Tomato and Cucumber Marketing Board was wound up in 1969.

democratic vote of dairy producers. The Board Members are elected on a postal ballot which grants one vote for every ten cows; nevertheless, as in other forms of democracy, the voting percentages are not high. For its Regional Members, and its special members, the average vote is around 35 per cent, and when there is no crisis in dairying on the horizon it can drop to as low as 20 per cent. Nevertheless, democracy does work, and in 1975 James Jackson, a member of the MMB for twenty-four years, and its Vice-Chairman, was beaten at the polls by militant Devonshire farmer Wallace Day. It was a 33 per cent poll.

With its HQ at Thames Ditton, near London, and a staff of 8,500, the MMB organizes the purchase of milk from Britain's farmers, and sends it through a chain of communications with the private enterprise wholesale dairies, and thus to the retailers. Some of the milk is collected by MMB tankers, and others by the commercial companies, and in many cases the Board never touches the milk. The price operates under a Government price-fixing system, which arranges the retail price on the doorstep. It makes allowance for retailers' profits, but the crunch comes with the over-supply of milk for liquid consumption, which includes deliveries direct to the housewife, to schools and catering establishments. It has always been in the interests of dairy farmers to boost the intake of liquid milk, which was under two litres per head in 1938, had jumped to three litres by 1950, and has remained steady just below that figure ever since, though the people of Northern Ireland drink more milk than those of England and Wales.

The excess must go into the consumption of butter, cheese, cream and other milk products, which fetch about half the price of liquid milk. Any increase of liquid consumption therefore reduces the amount sold off at a cheaper rate. To capture the best returns for milk products, the MMB has built its own creameries, and now has forty-nine such establishments. Thirteen of these were in operation before 1939, but the bulk have been opened in more recent years. When a drought cuts milk-production, or the industry descends into one of its periodic downward cycles, these creameries often look like milky white elephants, but this is a hazard which also affects the private enterprise companies operating in this field.

In Britain 92 per cent of the housewife's milk is delivered to her doorstep. In Holland 50 per cent arrives this way, but in Denmark, Belgium, France, Germany and Italy the daily pinta delivery is unknown. It is therefore not surprising that in most of those countries, Denmark apart, the consumption of milk by the public is only half that in Britain. The MMB spends £1·6 million annually on television and other advertising. The 'Drinka Pinta' campaign and the commercials on TV—with such gimmicks as the crowning of Dairy Queens and the Annual Milk Race on bicycles around Britain—are all part of the highly successful campaign to sustain milk consumption.

In England and Wales there is one cow for every ten people, and the average-sized dairy herd is 46 cows. In Scotland it is 71 cows, and in Northern Ireland 20, with a grand UK average of 45·6 cows per herd, and dairy farming, although concentrated in Cheshire, Somerset, and Wiltshire, is nevertheless to be found throughout every county in the UK. This does not solve the problems of the MMB in balancing supplies, when the greater quantity is required in the large metropolis, where there are naturally few cows. London depends for part of its supplies on the dairy cows of Cornwall and West Wales, Birmingham gets its milk from Central Wales, and Newcastle is served by Cumbria. About 85 per cent of milk sold on the liquid market goes directly from the dairy farmer to the wholesaler or retailer, 11 per cent passes through country depots and 4 per cent is sold by producer retailers. With the introduction of pasteurized milk and hygienic bottling-plants the day of the local milkman, with his hand cart, his churn and his measure for dispensing into the housewives' milk jugs, has all but gone. In 1945 there were over 50,000 producer /retailers, many of whom were small farmers supplying their own village, and supplementing their living by the profits from retailing. But today there are fewer than 4,000 producer/retailers left, and many of these may in fact only be bottling their milk on the farm of origin, while it is delivered by another operator.

The inequality of production is emphasized by the fact that Wales has one-fifth of the dairy farmers in England and Wales, but supplies only one-tenth of the total milk.

The MMB was not born without considerable criticism, and in its initial years incurred the wrath of that irascible press baron Lord Beaverbrook. He mounted a campaign in the *Daily Express* before 1939, which sought to castigate the new Board on every count. Initial reaction against the Board had come from the producer/retailers, who in the early 1930s at least were able to sell their products. However, it was a time when dairy farmers were being ruthlessly exploited by the wholesalers and retailers: with milk a highly perishable commodity in the days before bulk refrigerators, farmers were often left pouring their milk down the farm drain. This was a tragic waste of highly nutritional food. The MMB brought an instant stability to the market, with a firm promise to buy all that farmers produced, and the monthly milk cheque was the salvation of many more British farmers than are engaged in dairying today. Even today 70,000 monthly statements are dispatched within four days in direct payments to the farmer's bank, while he receives a printed statement of these transactions. At Thames Ditton they have a vast computer to organize this monthly payout.

The MMB lost its powers in 1939. It continued to exercise its role, but under the stringency of wartime Government control. In the aftermath of the War it was April 1954 before it regained its full powers, and in this period there was agitation for the creation of other Boards to emulate it; but the Government was lukewarm, and the failure of the NFU to persuade it to create a Fatstock Marketing Board resulted in the formation of a Fatstock Marketing Corporation Ltd.

In its early days the Board was reviled by many farmers. They called it the 'Mickey Mouse Board'—the 'Milk Muddling Board'—'The Milk Boar', but today it stands as a shining example of organized marketing without monopoly control, or even without price-fixing. The Board makes no profit, and it makes no loss. The dairy farmer gets exactly the amount which the total milk-production has realized in any one month. There is nothing comparable to the MMB in any other nation in the world, and certainly during the negotiations for entry into the EEC its abolition was mooted several times. However, any return to the chaos of the 1930s, or any dismantlement of its peripheral services, such as the operations in A.I., the fleet of lorries, the Low Cost Production Unit which acts as an advisory service to dairy farmers, would be detrimental to milk-distribution. Prices have risen, but milk still represents one of the cheapest forms of food—cheaper today than in 1938, or at any time during the post-War period. In terms of wages, it took 20½ minutes for a working man to earn the price of a litre of milk in 1938. By 1970 this was down to 8½ minutes, but by 1975 it was only taking 5½ minutes.

Sir Richard Trehane

'Richard Trehane is the sort of man who could have become an industrial dictator.'

Stuart Seaton, Editor 'The Farmers Guardian'.

Dick Trehane wanted if anything to be President of the NFU. He became Chairman of the MMB in 1958, and held that position for nineteen years until 1977. He had at that date been a member of the Board for thirty years. In that time he dragged an archaic MMB into the limelight of a rapidly changing society.

Suave, elegant, silver-haired, upright, smooth and with an engaging film-star smile that disguises an impatient, autocratic vein, he became a rock upon which British farmers relied, and Governments trembled. His quiet persuasiveness, accompanied always by the disarming smile, made the MMB a formidable Board in the operation of UK milk-supplies. He also became known as the producers' champion.

Whatever the public image of a farmer might be, Trehane certainly does not match that image, but a farmer he is, and at 180-hectare Hampreston Manor, near Wimborne in Dorset, he has farmed since he took over from his father at the age of twenty-three. A herd of pedigree Friesians, 140 strong, is unique, in that although it was established in 1903—and is thus one of the oldest in the country—since the time of Trehane's birth in 1913 no cow has been introduced from another farm. Thus the purity of the herd remains. But farmer that he is, Trehane nearly became a research worker.

Trehane tells his own story:

> When I left Reading, my father had expected me to go home and assist him on the farm. But, being I suppose, rather an intellectual character, at that point I was frankly, though as I now consider, unreasonably, alarmed at the prospect of what I imagined as mental isolation, even stagnation. By contrast, the academic and research life exerted a strong pull: hence my move to Cambridge.[2]

[2]'Together in Enterprise', The Massey-Ferguson Papers No. 7.

He became a demonstrator in agriculture on the staff of the School of Agriculture, but his mentor at Cambridge said, 'I've known a good many people in research who've left to go into farming, but I've never met anyone in farming who left it to go into research.' Trehane discovered that the isolation and stagnation of Cambridge was worse than farming, and in 1936 he took over Hampreston Manor at the age of twenty-three. As an outspoken rebel, he soon attracted attention, and at the age of thirty-three became a member of the MMB. He was young and impatient, and the Board was peopled by men who sat upon it until they died. His own father, whose seat he took, was the first man ever to retire voluntarily. The story of this impatient young man, who soon attracted attention, meant that his efforts were soon to be fully directed into the affairs of the MMB. What the NFU lost no one will ever know, but his contribution to British agriculture has been recognized by the many honours bestowed upon him.

His successor in 1977 was sixty-year-old Steve Roberts from Shropshire, with 420 hectares and 250 pedigree Friesians. James Jackson of Burnley, Lancashire, had been displaced from the Board in 1975 by Wallace Day from Devon.

Wallace Day

Farming produces surprisingly few rebels. Jack Merricks from Romney Marsh was one whose outspoken leadership in the fight to abolish the Cucumber and Tomato Board was heard. The Farmers Club made him their Chairman, and he resigned in mid-term through a disagreement. Merricks was drowned tragically in a typical exhibition of his unflagging bravery, when he went to the rescue of a small boat in high seas off the South Coast of England. A farming character was lost.

Hew Watt is another whose outspoken comments have placed him in a formidable position, but Wallace Day has been the scourge of the NFU to such an extent that although he had been Chairman of the Devon Branch, and London Council Delegate for seven years (1963–70), he can claim the unique honour of being expelled from the NFU (although three years later his membership was reinstated). He took on the Vice-Chairman of the MMB, James Jackson, and beat him. It was a David *v.* Goliath operation, and although Jackson had been on the Board for twenty-four years, he was democratically ousted; but such are the rewards for public service. It was Day's militant stance and flamboyant character, coupled with an intensive nation-wide campaign, which propelled him to the top of the poll.

Day's background was not all farming. He had secured the tenancy of a small farm near Barnstaple in 1951, and bought it with a 100 per cent mortgage in 1962. With 300 mainly Friesian cows, Day became a full-time dairy farmer. He had served as an Advisory Officer for NAAS in North Devon, and had seen wartime service. He canvassed the Prime Minister, Harold Wilson, and militantly pressed the milk-producers' case. He attended meetings of the House of Commons Expenditure Committee on Trade and Industry in 1974, which constituted a massive public inquiry into all aspects of milk-production. Day's evidence occupied 15 pages of this 170-page detailed inquiry into milk-production.

The Potato Marketing Board

> *'What small potatoes we are, compared with what we might be.'*
> Charles Warner, 1829–1900.

Ostensibly another producer organization, the Potato Marketing Board bears no resemblance to the MMB. It is more of a regulatory organization that seeks—largely unsuccessfully—to balance the supply of potatoes grown in the UK with the housewives' demands. That it fails to achieve this is not its own fault, but as a producer Marketing Board it is much more under the thumb of Government dictates than is the MMB. It is also one of those rare organizations in British agriculture to embrace Scotland.

While the MMB does not seek to control the quantity of milk produced, but promises to buy all of it, the PMB seeks to issue quotas on the hectarage which farmers may grow, and exercises a strict system of fines for those errant farmers who dare exceed their quota. It employs teams of secret inspectors to check up, and in total it receives about a third of a million pounds each year in excess hectarage fines. The sugar-beet hectarage in the UK is also governed by contracts from the British Sugar Corporation, but only the PMB exercises such ruthlessness in forcing adherence to its quota. The objective is to produce sufficient potatoes for the UK populace apart from those new potatoes which may be imported at the start of each season, but with such a fluctuating crop as potatoes the task is an impossible one. The strictness of this system is governed by the Treasury financial support which may have to be called upon to buy surplus potatoes over and above the national needs, in the years of plenty; although they can be used for stock feeding, potatoes, like milk, are a perishable commodity, unlike cereals which can be held over from one year to another.

Since most of the trade is negotiated between farmers and the 3,000 registered wholesalers, the Board does not handle the money, and its support is achieved by a levy system upon the area grown. Farmers have to write out a cheque to the PMB for their potato quota, unlike the MMB who pay the pooled price for milk after the administration costs have been covered. Thus the farmer never sees how much he is paying for the services of the MMB unless he totals up his monthly statements and makes some calculations.

There are 21 members of the PMB; England supplies 7, Scotland 5 and Wales 1, with 4 'Special' members, 3 from England and 1 from Scotland. The Ministry of Agriculture also makes 4 appointments, which are usually of non-participants in the farming industry, who can exercise impartial judgment. The members are elected by a voting system, as with the MMB, but their votes are weighted according to the tonnage grown. The number of votes cast is even more pathetic than the MMB, and most of the Board Members are returned unopposed. In 1975 seven were unopposed, and there was an election for two seats; the following year there was only one election, and eleven members were unopposed. The elections on average take place more often in the Scottish Divisions. The PMB operates from a London address in Hams Crescent, Knightsbridge, and borrows the NFU's Agriculture House for its AGM, at which about 80 farmers are present out of 35,000 potato-growers.

Year	No. of Growers	Area in hectares	Total UK Yield	Average UK Price
1967	50,310	271	6,569	£14.65
1968	48,239	266	6,276	£15.52
1969	45,130	237	5,727	£22.05
1970	43,346	258	6,987	£14.05
1971	42,756	246	6,697	£15.07
1972	40,756	222	6,222	£19.30
1973	38,753	211	6,534	£18.77
1974	36,872	203	6,494	£25.40
1975	35,478	193	4,309	£103.91
1976	34,938	208	4,458	£131.61
1977	35,286	195	N/A	N/A

Source: PMB Annual Reports.

The chart above demonstrates the drop in the number of potato-growers over an eleven-year period, showing a loss of 15,000 farmers, but the third column demonstrates how the area sown has slowly reduced as greater crops have become the norm. These areas are those quota hectarages which the PMB calculates will be required to meet national demands. The low yields in 1975 and 1976 produced a sudden jump in shop prices, and there was a dramatic drop of 20 per cent in sales as customer resistance mounted. This is also demonstrated by the last column, which shows the rapid quadrupling of price between 1974 and 1975, and a further rise in 1976. With a heavier crop in 1977, and lower prices, demand picked up again, but inevitably the consumption is a better regulator than the area planted, whose results cannot be predicted. With greater irrigation and better varieties, there is, however, a general upward trend in yields. In consequence, a smaller area will be required annually.

The chart also shows how a poorer crop in 1969 resulted in a 42 per cent increase in price, while a bumper crop the following year sent prices downward. The Government paid out heavily against the guaranteed 'floor' price in 1971 to the tune of £18 million, and in an endeavour to limit its commitment it dropped the quota hectarage in the succeeding years. This yo-yo pattern of production will always continue, and civil servants will never anticipate it.

The Board was founded in 1933, along with the MMB, but evolved as a new Board in 1955, was subjected to the Agricultural Marketing Act 1958, and was amended again in 1962. Its broad criterion is to 'encourage actively the production, harvesting and sale of a good quality product, and to bring a greater measure of stability to the industry by regulating supplies and improving methods of marketing.' It is this broad outline which has subjected the PMB to considerable criticism. In 1972, John Sainsbury, Chairman of the Sainsbury Group, and a noted anti-PMB critic, said, 'For years I have criticised the operation of the Board, and also the fact that the British housewife suffers from a worse quality of potatoes than any of her opposite numbers in Europe and North America.'

Other critics have added their voice concerning the lack of quality in UK potatoes, but the Board never sees most of the potatoes which farmers grow, and has no quality control, or means at its disposal other than by educating farmers. Like the MMB, it embarks upon publicity to popularize its humble product—but the campaign is a very low-key affair in comparison.

Its Chairman for fifteen years was Scots farmer James Rennie, who was ousted in a dramatic vote at the AGM in November 1973, after a fifteen-year autocratic occupancy of the Chairmanship. He was succeeded by Lincolnshire farmer Geoffrey Grantham, and only seven days after this shake-up James Rennie was killed in a road accident near Edinburgh. The James E. Rennie Awards were instituted in his honour,these being granted annually to enable the winners to undertake a study tour of potato-growing within the Common Market countries.

The Eggs Authority

'When I was appointed Chairman of the Eggs Authority in 1971, I little realised how traumatic would be my experience during the next three and a half years.'

Adrian Collingwood

The placid waters of the MMB and PMB are in direct contrast to the stormy turmoil that has accompanied the chequered career of the Eggs Authority. This resides in pleasant Tunbridge Wells, amid the tree-lined streets and antique shops, but markedly without peace, for it has been locked in mortal combat with its deadly enemy, the British Egg Association, since its inception, it is not liked by egg-producers, and it has been treated to Ministerial indifference. It only survives until a new system of egg marketing is devised.

Technically, the farmer/producers can vote to wind up any of the Marketing Boards, but the Minister also has a right to disband them, and in the case of the ill-fated BEMB (British Egg Marketing Board), that is exactly what he did. The Potato Marketing Board is the odd one out in this group, being only invested with regulatory powers; the others, Eggs, Milk, Hops and Wool, must accept everything that their farmer/producers offer them. It was created in 1971, and given a three-year lease of life, but when 1974 arrived it still survived, amid a welter of criticism, and the indifference of the Minister of Agriculture. It is supported by the levies upon chicks which are hatched, and receives only a small support from the Minister of Agriculture. As the following list shows, egg politics have never been in calm waters.

1923 Linlithgow Report.
1926 Ministry of Agriculture Report.
1929 National Mark Egg Scheme.
1932 Tariffs introduced.
1935 Reorganisation Commission for eggs and poultry.
1924–1937 Northern Ireland marketing system.
1938 Report of Technical Poultry Committee.
1939 Poultry Industry Bill (withdrawn on outbreak of war).
1941–1953 National Egg Distributors Association Ltd (NEDAL). Operated under Ministry of Food to co-ordinate and distribute eggs under rationing.
1947 National Egg Marketing Organisation (NEMO). Buying powers operating in conjunction with NEDAL.
1954 NEDAL (1954) Ltd. Import buying function ceases.
1957–1971 British Egg Marketing Board.
1971 British Egg Marketing Board.
1967 Government Reorganisation Commission for Eggs. Recommended abolition of BEMB and creation of Eggs Authority.
1971 Eggs Authority.
1971 'Dead by 1974.' (*Farmers Weekly*).
1973 'Crunch year.' (*Farmers Weekly*). Pressure to disband the Eggs Authority.
1974 'Find your own cash,' says Godber. Authority continues, egg subsidies phased out.
1975 'Eggs Authority criticised for levy increase.' (FT). Levy rises from £2.84 to £3.01 per 100 chicks sold. BEA says producers going bankrupt, and unable to afford the heavy burden of an expensive statutory body over which it had only partial control. BEA determined to pursue its complete opposition to the Authority.
1977 'Egg producers renew attack on Authority.' (FT). British Poultry Federation attacks Authority. Egg producers representation should be increased. They are not getting their money's worth. Advertising campaign not doing its job.

With milk, the producer/retailers selling direct occupy only a very small part of the outlet, but with eggs it was estimated in 1968 that no less than 40 per cent were not passing through the BEMB. The direct farm-gate sales, or contracts between egg producers and local shops, give an opening to bypass any official Marketing Authority. Sugar beet is an unsaleable commodity until it has been processed into sugar; thus the British Sugar Corporation is the monopoly buyer, with the factory capacity to transform the raw material. The potato-marketing system in no way compares to the problems of eggs, yet the Eggs Authority is second only to the MMB, but without its system of registered producers and its rigid controls. The Eggs Authority rests on an uncomfortable bed without the requisite powers, and without the support of its producers.

The milk advertising campaign has been highly successful, but the Eggs Authority publicity to stimulate the consumption of eggs does not exhibit the same flair. In 1957 the BEMB coined the 'Little Lion' as its stamped symbol of freshness on every egg. This was an unfortunate mistake. A few bad eggs gave the cartoonists an opening to portray the Little Lion with his nose turned up. The

BEMB was on a hiding to nothing, but inexplicably they retained this symbol for ten years.

In 1958 the average British consumption of eggs was 231 per person—but with a sustained publicity campaign it had risen to 263 eggs by 1966. It was not mentioned that between 1955–1956 it rose from 211 to 226—and without an advertising campaign. One need hardly add that lower prices are one of the best inducements.

Within the industry itself the major body is the British Poultry Federation Ltd, which embraces most, but not all, of the multitude of fragmented bodies which represent the various sectors in the poultry world. It was created in 1969 to provide a co-ordinated body to speak for the industry. There are also many other bodies:

> National Association of Poultry Packers Ltd
> British Chicken Association Ltd
> (now combined as the British Poultry Meat Association).
> British Egg Association, formed 1961.
> National Egg Packers Association Ltd
> Poultry Stock Association Ltd
> (now merged with the Hatcheries to become the British Poultry Breeders and Hatcheries Association).
> British Turkey Federation Ltd, formed 1953.
> Duck Producers Association.
> Poultry Industry Conference Ltd
> National Federation of Wholesale Poultry Merchants.
> National Egg Producers Retailers Association.

On some issues the BPF has been able to speak with a united voice. It made joint representations to the Brambell Committee on its investigations into intensive, battery-kept hens, and the Swann Report on antibiotics, the fowl-pest vaccination policy, and in the campaign to fight the EEC edict that traditional farm-fresh poultry (New York Dressed) would not be allowed after 1981. But the Eggs Authority remains its implacable enemy.

British Wool Marketing Board

> *'In the EEC, wool is classified as an industrial raw material, not as an agricultural product.'*
>
> NEDO Report, *Sheep and Wool*, May 1974
>
> *'The Board is a completely commercial enterprise based upon financial opportunism.'*
>
> S. R. Blackley, Managing Director
> and Secretary of the Wool Board, 1974

The wool clip to a sheep-farmer, amounting on average to only some 400 kilos per flock, is a bonus, a side issue, just as the price of calves is only a small part of the dairy farmer's income, with his one calf per year to sell. Wool as an adjunct to the production of lamb and mutton comes into the same category; nevertheless, its importance must not be minimized, and at times it has provided a substantial part of the sheep-farmer's income. The secret has been the Wool Board.

Unlike its fellow members in milk, hops and potatoes, the Wool Board only came into existence in 1950, just as the Korean War had stimulated a boom in wool prices. These booms in wool have been a feature of our times, and in Australia and New Zealand, for instance, they have a deeper and more profound effect upon farmers' fortunes. Although prices rocketed in 1951–2, they declined thereafter, first swiftly and then steadily. The direction was always downward, but during the next twenty-five years the Wool Board achieved a remarkably steady price for its customers. The secret was in its monopoly powers.

It is a Government-sponsored Board with elected producer members and Government nominees, and its control has been exercised through the vagaries of the annual wool clip. Wool is a commodity which varies considerably, and there are over three hundred grades of it. Before 1939 there were also three hundred merchants to buy it, but this number has declined to only thirty-five. The strength of the Wool Board is in matching wool grades to each other, and presenting concise quality lots to the buyers, but it has also achieved stability by holding off the market and only selling when better prices arrived.

It has also bought its way into some of the merchanting companies; the North of England Wools Ltd at Bradford is a 75 per cent subsidiary of the Wool Board, and the largest single buyer in the UK. With the advent of synthetic fibres such as polyester and acrylic, the demand for wool has sunk, yet it still maintains a strong position in many homes, and will undoubtedly never completely fade. All farmers with more than four sheep are bound to sell their wool to the Wool Marketing Board, and there have been few problems with its performance in the past. It operates from Kew Bridge House at Brentford, up-river from the grime of central London, and near Kew Gardens.

The Hops Marketing Board

'Did you ever taste beer?' 'I had a sip of it once,' said the small servant. 'Here's a state of things!' cried Mr. Swiveller. . . 'She never tasted it–it can't be tasted in a sip!'

Charles Dickens

'Those who drink beer will think beer.'
Washington Irving

Unsung though the Hops Marketing Board is, and overshadowed by the Milk Marketing Board, it has several claims to fame. It was in fact created in 1932, ahead of the mighty MMB itself, it exercises a monopoly control, it is immune from the Restrictive Trade Practices Act, and as such it provides a sheltered market for its producers—even though growing hops in the UK is small beer indeed.

The Board extracts a levy operated on a quota system to its 400-plus farmer growers; a declining number since there were 660 in 1969, and hops provide self-sufficiency, and more, for the UK brewing industry. Kent, with its picturesque oast-houses, is the hop industry's centre, and the area has declined to 6,000 hectares, with isolated pockets away from its main centre.

It has the most impressive buildings of any of the Marketing Boards. Central Buildings in Southwark Street, London, are an example of some of the better relics of Victoriana to survive the bulldozer. They were built in 1866, and have a façade surrounded by iron columns and narrow arches. They were once the Hop Exchange. The Hops Board also has a warehouse and laboratories at Paddock Wood, near the centre of the hop-growing area in Kent.

British Sugar Corporation

'Whatever the outcome, the stock market has already picked out the Cinderella from the Ugly Sisters. Should the rest of us agree with Prince Charming's judgement?
The British Sugar Corporation is the darling (Cinderella at the Ball) of the dealers . . . by contrast, Tate & Lyle and Manbre & Garton are looked upon as the Ugly Sisters.'

Peter Wainwright, 'Daily Mail', 3 September 1973

'Britain's sugar supply has shown a much changing pattern since the first shipments came from the fledgling colonies in the Caribbean some 350 years ago in the days of Charles I and Cromwell.'

19th (and last) Annual Report: Sugar Board, 1976.

Sugar beet produces only 1·5 per cent of the total income of UK farmers, and it occupies roughly the same area as potatoes. Yet it is concentrated around the seventeen factories of the BSC, of which fifteen are in the east of England and two in the Midlands. As such, it presents a highly important farm crop in those areas where its growth is suitable, and provides a greater measure of farm income than the statistics would display.

Sugar beet is not grown in the south of England or in Wales, while since the closure of the Cupar Factory in Scotland it is not grown there either. It has become a political hot potato, with the advent of the EEC and the changing emphasis upon Britain's sugar-supplies with the phasing out of the Australian quota. As a commodity it is subsidized the world over, and the UK Government long paid over the odds under the Commonwealth Sugar Agreement (which ceased in 1974), to sustain the economies of such countries as Jamaica, Mauritius and Barbados.

It has become an important crop in East Anglia in the drier areas, where dairying is less popular, and now it is to the arable farmer what the milk cheque is to the milk-producer. Its importance in the UK dates from the first sugar beet factory, which was built at Cantley in Norfolk in 1921, but after a rapid expansion as processing factories were built it stabilized to become an important crop grown under contract on a strict quota basis. Its importance could not grow under the arrangements for International Sugar Agreements, and it was not until 1974, under the EEC, that a programme of expansion was embarked upon.

Despite its late introduction as a farm crop, sugar beet has long been known. Experiments in 1747 by a German chemist succeeded in producing sugar from it, although it was over half a century later when Napoleon granted State assistance for the cultivation of sugar beet during the Napoleonic Wars. One of the first attempts at a home-grown sugar industry was a factory near Maldon in Essex, built in 1832. Another at Lavenham, Suffolk, in 1868 was built, but failed. It took until after the First World War to build the first modern factory, and to create a new industry for Britain, and a new crop for British farms. Within the four years from 1924 to 1927, fourteen of the existing seventeen factories were completed, and by 1928 eighteen factories had been built. In 1936 they were co-ordinated under a public company with Government support: the British Sugar Corporation.

The original sugar beet factories had been established with Government aid, but the British Sugar Corporation had gone to the money market for its continuing expansion programme, and the Government has not taken up its share options; thus the stake has now whittled down to around 25 per cent. It has become an independent company, with three Government-appointed Directors upon its Board, including the Chairman. The death-knell to the Scottish beet industry was sounded in 1971, when Government support was withheld from a small and ailing factory, although it was worth £1 million per annum to Scottish farmers. Government subsidies to shipbuilding in Scotland continued, and the Scottish farmers were angry. The closure was part of reorganization which two years later manifested itself in an expansion programme of the remaining seventeen factories, but this was all allied to the intense complications of sugar politics.

Britain's sugar supplies were represented, pre Common Market days, by a 30–70 per cent market split, the 30 per cent being supplied from home-grown sugar beet, and the remainder from sugar-cane, which was largely refined in the UK by two companies, Tate & Lyle with 55 per cent of the market, and Manbre & Garton with the remaining 15 per cent. Although the International Sugar Agreement allowed the EEC to import cane-sugar from the developing countries, a proportion of Britain's sugar came from Australia—and Australia could not still be considered a 'developing' country in the mid-1970s. This shortfall was an obvious direction in which the British sugar beet grower could expand, and where the British Sugar Corporation could enlarge its factory capacity; but the cane-sugar refining companies saw massive loss of jobs and closures, and Sir Ian Lyle (famous for his Mr Cube Campaign against sugar-nationalization in the 1950s) had to embark upon a new campaign. The workers marched on Westminster, and at the same time a sudden escalation in world sugar-prices threw the market into confusion, and made the housewife short of sugar. The EEC countries, particularly France, were anxious to take up the shortfall from the Australian supplies themselves, and Peart negotiated with the EEC for this quantity to be provided by UK farmers. The politics of sugar are emotional, and stem from a support for the Negro cane-growers in the Equatorial regions. Politics may be emotional, but economics are not, and unfortunately the political and emotional aspects of the case took precedence.

Rumours of a merger between the BSC, Tate & Lyle and Manbre & Garton resulted in a takeover bid which reduced the trio to a duo, leaving the BSC and Tate & Lyle.

UK farmers' prices were part of the Annual Price Review negotiated between the Government and the NFU, with the BSC only left to foot the bill, but the intricacies of sugar were more profound, and as part of the package of the decontrol of food, and the transition to free world market supplies and prices—covered and safe-guarded by International Trade Agreements after 1954—the Sugar Board was constituted on 15 October 1956, starting its operations on 1 January 1957. Its objective was to operate the Commonwealth Sugar Agreement, and to take the place of Government in trading Common-wealth sugar into the UK market. Quotas from various Commonwealth countries were arranged, and when South Africa left the Commonwealth in 1961 her quota was phased out in the three successive years. Rhodesia lost her quota when Ian Smith declared UDI, and St Vincent ceased exporting sugar-cane in 1960, St Lucia in 1963 and Antigua in 1972. The spoils were shared out by the remaining countries.

With the signing of the Treaty of Rome, and a new situation in sugar-supplies, the work of the Sugar Board was finished. It was disbanded in 1976 but had achieved a useful role during its nineteen-year life.

While UK farmers in the beet-growing areas had for many years been irked by the restrictions upon their beet area, the call for expansion after 1974 coincided with the two hot, dry summers of 1975 and 1976, coupled with delays in raising prices to keep pace with inflated costs. From being the golden crop for arable farmers it became the Cinderella.

BSC employs 5,500 personnel, which is 3,000 less than the Milk Marketing Board, and its steady profit level escalated in 1976 to £14·3 million (nearly double the previous year). Embarrassed, the BSC had to issue a statement to all its employees, and to farmers, explaining why it had made such a large profit, when farmers were crying out that their prices were too low. In Eire the Irish Sugar Company carries out the same function as the BSC in the UK, but it also has major interests in food-packaging and other diversified handling industries.

Meat and Livestock Commission

'The NFU is a good deal less critical of the MLC than the wholesale and retail meat trade.'

'British Farmer and Stockbreeder', 26 May 1973

The MLC is not a marketing body; it has no trading powers. It is not a regulatory body, and has no powers for that. In essence it seems to have little reason for existence except that it copes with an erstwhile untidy list of obligatory duties previously carried out by a multitude of bodies. It is a trade- and farmer-financed body that in fact carries out many tasks for the primary benefit of farmers producing beef, mutton or pork. It carries out several other duties, some of which the Government has adroitly hived off, and for which it no longer foots the bill.

If the MLC was abolished ADAS could continue the advisory work, while the Agricultural Research Council—to which the MLC already contributes, with grants to the Meat Research Institute at Norwich—could continue the research work undertaken by the Commission. The British Farm Produce Council could take over the publicity machine which boosts British meat; the local authorities have lost legislative control over slaughterhouses, but could resume these powers, while they already share with the police responsibilities in any epidemic situation. The Centre for European Studies at Wye could monitor cattle trends on the Continent. The multifarious roles of the MLC could be reassigned without undue disruption. However, it is a neat and tidy situation at present.

The Commission was set up by Peart in 1967, acting upon the Report of the Verdin Committee; its Commissioners are appointed by the Minister, and its office is at Milton Keynes New Town. It is supported on a levy basis, equally between farmers and wholesalers, and the Government contributes for agency work carried out on its behalf. It has a low-key history which has been strongly lacking in criticism, despite the fact that at its initiation the NFU loudly deplored its toothlessness. Perhaps as the wholesale trade is paying half the cost of boosting the farmer's meat products, it is best to keep quiet.

Its range of activities include carcass classification and livestock testing, and it embraced the now defunct Pig Industry Development Association (PIDA). In its short history it has provided a sinecure within the patronage of the current Minister, both for its influential Chairmen and for its Commissioners. Sir Rex Cohen, banker and financier, was its original Chairman from 1967 to January 1972. He was succeeded by Peter Coleclough, industrialist and managing director of the Howard Rotavator Company. In October 1974 George Howard, owner of a stately home, Castle Howard, and a landowner, became its Chairman, to be succeeded in September 1977 by Wally Johnstone, managing director of ICI Plant Protection Division. At least, the last three Chairmen have had some connection with farming.

Home-Grown Cereals Authority

'In planning our future, our principal job is to improve the marketing of home-grown cereals.'

W. D. Scott, Chairman HGCA.

If the MLC, as a toothless wonder, seems to serve little purpose by its existence, then changing circumstances have obscured any direction in which the HGCA might seem to be going. It originated in 1965 as one of the first 'new broom' organizations to be set up by the incoming Minister, Fred Peart. It took over the vacuum created by the gradual decontrol of cereal deficiency payments, although the Ministry continued to cling to its job of annually paying out these sums to farmers. The HGCA was set up to create a more orderly system.

The problem with cereal-growing is that the harvest all comes in a rush, but consumption exists throughout the twelve months of the year. In the post-War era in France, and similarly in Australia, co-operatives have set up vast, centralized storage facilities to enable them to cope with the massive influx of grain within a few short weeks. The difference in the UK is that grain-storage exists on the farms where it is grown; various Government grants towards the building of grain silos have encouraged this on-the-farm storage system. But it needed a disincentive scheme to prevent farmers dumping all their grain on to the market in August–September.

The Ministry have operated a scheme of deficiency payments, calculating the exact price of all grain marketed within five specified periods which divided up the year. As the months progressed away from the harvest the guaranteed minimum prices grew greater, and the deficiency payment was the amount by which the actual calculated market prices fell short of the guaranteed minimum. It was a system that was dying on its feet, and the HGCA was born to take this marketing responsibility away from the Ministry, and to simplify the Ministerial application of an involved system.

It instituted a new system of forward contracting, by which HGCA bonuses were paid when forward contracts, on a monthly basis, were registered, and its objective of creating more organized marketing if anything benefited the merchants rather than the farmers, who were thus precluded from gambling on the open market because their grain had already been contracted forward. Grain not contracted did not receive an HGCA storage bonus.

The scheme was financed in equal proportions by the Treasury and the farmers by a deduction from the overall deficiency payments; thus its true cost to an individual farmer was heavily disguised. The HGCA took over the Treasury commitment, and although at first merchants did not contribute, after 1974 (when a hurried revised financial structure had to be evolved), the merchants paid 25 per cent of the HGCA costs, and collected another 25 per cent from the 'second buyer'. Farmers continued to meet half its expenses.

The system had some merits, and was workable until the price of grain suddenly escalated as the Russians became major world buyers in 1972.

Suddenly grain prices went through the roof, and shot above the guaranteed minimum prices, thus removing any necessity for Government deficiency payments. It was relieved of an expenditure item—but there was no method of collecting the HGCA levies, and in 1974 a new system was brought into operation, with its divided responsibilities to raise the cash. The main point at issue should have been that the HGCA no longer had any role to fulfil—market forces on a free world basis were determining violent fluctuations, but since farmers had by this time erected massive storage capacity on their own farms, they would obviously want to utilize this storage and market their grain in a traditional pattern. Even if it was all to be sold at harvest-time, the merchants could always hire the farmer's storage facilities. The HGCA continues to exist, and now produces statistics showing world trends and reports on market prices; it is composed a membership of five independent members, nine farmers and nine merchants. One suspects it is still the merchants who derive the greatest benefit from its continued existence.

Agricultural Training Board

'The ATB has now become agriculturally respectable, widely accepted, and subject to few or none of the criticisms initially levelled against it.'
'British Farmer and Stockbreeder', 10 June 1972

It started life as the 'Agricultural, Horticultural and Forestry Industry Training Board', dropped the long-winded title in favour of the more simple 'Agricultural Training Board', left forestry training out of its syllabus, accepted self-employed farmers, was violently rejected by the farmers at the outset, but vigorously defended by them six years later when the Government wanted to abolish it; instituted massive court proceedings against farmers who refused to pay its levies, lost its case, is now financed by the Government, and has slowly become acceptable to the farming community.

It was the Conservative Industrial Training Act 1964 which set up the edifice of Training Boards throughout industry. The Agricultural Training Board was the fifteenth to be set up of a total embracing all industries, which eventually amounted to twenty-seven similar Boards. It was a Conservative Act which established the principles, but it was a Socialist Minister of Labour who two years later bore the brunt of the widespread animosity towards many of the Training Boards. The plush, overburdened hierarchy which had been set up had to be paid for by the industries concerned, and they considered the levies an exorbitant additional charge upon their businesses. The situation with the ATB was even more complex.

Initially, it appointed as Chairman Basil Neame, a farmer from Faversham in Kent, and a former Chairman of the National Agricultural Apprenticeship Council, an NFU Council Delegate, and a man with experience in agricultural education and farm management. The original Board consisted of an equal number of employer and employee members, with additional representatives from the Agricultural Colleges. Its problem was that before a levy could be collected notices had to be served upon farmer employers, and the forms which required farmers to declare the number of workers they employed were largely ignored. The Board followed this by arbitrary demands, which again were ignored. The ATB had proposed a levy of £6 per head on farm-workers for the year ending 31 August 1968, but a Government grant of £450,000 was quickly made, and the levy demand was reduced from £6 to £3. It was not enough, however, to stop a mass desertion from the ranks, and farmers in their thousands refused to pay. They were reluctant to allow their men time off to embark upon training courses when there was a job to do on the farm, and the workers, with pride in their own professionalism, did not take kindly to the idea of training. The NUAAW fought for many years for a new classification of farm-workers as 'craftsmen', with a series of tests to be accomplished and a certificate to be given. This designation rates a wage increase commensurate with its status in the official wages orders, but disappointingly only very few farm-workers took the exam to become craftsmen. They considered that they were already skilled craftsmen; in most cases their wages were above the minimum prescribed, and this kind of feeling led to the united hostility towards the ATB.

The original headquarters of the ATB was at Bourne House, 34 Beckenham Road, Beckenham, Kent, and it was the neighbouring Bromley County Court which was inundated by the summonses which were issued to farmers. On 9 December 1969 an Appeal Court upheld the Bromley County Court decision of 30 July 1969, which had decided against the ATB, and in favour of two 'guinea-pig' farmers who had refused to pay their levies. The issue turned upon the Assessment Notices which had been sent out for the 1967–8 levy. The issue turned upon the later letter informing the farmers of their rights of appeal; it transpired that many of these had not arrived, and despite the ATB plea that the job had been done by a sensitive micro-switch on a machine, the Court witnessed a test run and discovered that the machine was indeed inaccurate. It was a narrow legalistic point, but it emphasized the ATB's bureaucratic approach. By this time, however, the Government was aware of the inherent hostility of farmers, and the NFU had been making counter-proposals.

An Agriculture Bill had been published by the Government on 29 October 1969, proposing that in future the expenses of the Training Board should be financed by the Government, but taken out of the total sum granted under the agricultural support system of the Annual Review. In February 1972, with another Conservative Government in power, new proposals were published in the light of the lessons learnt in the previous eight years. A new Training Services Agency to control all industrial training was proposed, and the NFU and the farmers who had bitterly criticized the ATB suddenly found that, whatever its failings, it would be a loss if agriculture was lumped under this new Agency. They fought a campaign to stave off this amalgamation, and for the ATB to retain its independence. The other development which the NFU had pressed for was that self-employed farmers—who after all were indirectly financing the whole operation—should be allowed to participate in the grants and training schemes. It made a case that agriculture had special needs, and should come under the wing of the Ministry of Agriculture. In December 1972 the ATB won its fight to remain outside the Training Services Agency. All the other pleas were met, and the ATB embarked upon a more placid course for the future. Forestry training ceased to be within its scope after 31 August 1971, and now self-employed farmers could participate. In 1975 the area of participants was further widened to embrace landscape gardeners, producer-retailing of eggs and dairy produce, poultry-meat production and egg-packing. It was a wider spectrum, and covered half a million potential customers. Nevertheless, the broadening of training courses and the scope of instruction only adds up to an additional £8 per head for all those eligible for instruction.

The new entrance scheme has slowly grown, and the range of on-farm courses has given it practical expression of conditions in the field. Nevertheless, there still remains an overlapping of functions, with the instruction procedures of new machinery which commercial companies design for operators, and the multitide of other avenues of instruction, training and advice.

The ATB has not been free of all criticism since that time. In 1976 Sir George Huckle—its second Chairman, who succeeded Neame—defended a survey on the needs of supervisory staff on farms at the farm foreman level. The ATB had diagnosed a need for this facet of farm training, but in an industry where the labour force is equal on a one for one basis with the employers, and there are few farms with more than two employees on their books, the need for supervisory training must be of minimal application only.

Processers and Growers Research Organisation

'There was an old person of Dean
Who dined on one pea and one bean;
*   For he said, 'More than that,*
*   Would make me too fat,'*
That cautious old person of Dean.
            Edward Lear

The PGRO is an independent research station situated on the Great North Road, 56 kilometres north of Cambridge, 13 kilometres west of Peterborough, in the heart of eastern arable England. It is financed by a system of voluntary levies calculated on a modest scale, and is supported by only a handful of farmers among its subscribers. A few local merchants, and the large canning companies such as Batchelors, Bird's Eye, Findus, Ross, Smedley-HP and Cadbury-Schweppes, form the bulk of its support. Despite its UK orientation, it also has members in sixteen other countries, but is very much a small brother to the NIAB, with its 5,000 'fellows'. It gets little Government support, other than on a customer basis, but has good liaison with some of the ARC establishments—

notably the John Innes Institute in Scotland, where they also specialize in the development of peas and vegetables. Despite its smallness, its reputation in the industry is high, and the list of its achievements is formidable, although its operations are small within the UK agricultural context.

Prior to 1970 the UK was principally an importer of dried peas to supplement housewives' demands. Both the USA and Holland were the principal sources of imported peas, but since 1970 production in the UK has expanded, with some handsome if unexpected price escalations. One might imagine a necessity to balance supplies from imports, yet there has been an ever-increasing export of UK peas, particularly to the fastidious Japanese, where the UK has ousted the Dutch as the principal supplier. In the face of this competition the Dutch pea crop has been reduced drastically, and they now import dried peas from the UK. This is an unsung story of progress, arising from the diligent encouragement of private merchants seeking new outlets, coupled with developments in pea-growing which have included such revolutionary advances as the evolvement of the new 'leafless' peas.

Baked beans have become a staple British food, being imported from the USA, where they are known as navy beans, coming from a small area in Michigan near the Great Lakes. Navy beans are reputedly so called because they were instrumental in saving the lives of a group of US Marines who were shipwrecked on a deserted island, with only cans of baked beans for survival. The PGRO instituted trials of navy beans in the UK, with the obvious objective of obtaining a share of this vast market. After several years, in the early 1970s, the project was finally abandoned.

The PGRO has changed its name three times, and changed its home. It started in 1944, when a group of interested farmers, processors and merchants formed the Home Grown Threshed Peas Joint Committee, with an office in the centre of Peterborough. With the advent of cans into British homes, and the expansion of vining peas made possible by the invention of mobile machines to operate in the fields, there was an expansion of pea-consumption; and in 1956 the original organization changed its name to the Pea Growing Research Organisation, incorporated as a limited company. At this time it moved from central Peterborough to a site just south of the city, and took over a moribund Mushroom Research Station at Yaxley. These premises became too small with the wider development of research and the expansion of the crop. In 1963 the PGRO had widened its role to include other vegetables and fruit, but it took ten years to change the name, cleverly, to Processors and Growers Research Organisation, thus perpetuating the same initials. In 1967 it left the old Mushroom premises and moved to Thornhaugh on the A1, where the trial grounds and laboratories had more room for expansion. Next door is the RASE's Demonstration Farm at Sacrewell.

There is also a British Edible Pulse Association composed of canners and merchants who have joined together to promote British peas as a greater force in the market-place. This co-operates with the PGRO in the development of new strains, the most avant-garde development having been the introduction of new 'leafless' peas which represent a botanical triumph. The South is also beginning to copy the erstwhile North of England prerogative of mushy peas—the dried split and skinned peas which are tinned, and which may yet become a staple British food, to rival baked beans as the only vegetable which can be consumed on its own as the major constituent of an average meal.

28 The Exotics

The world of cattle-breeding

'Because half a dozen grasshoppers under a fern make the field ring with their importunate chink, whilst thousands of great cattle, reposed beneath the shadow of the British Oak, chew the cud and are silent, pray do not imagine that those who make the noise are the only inhabitants of the field.'

Edmund Burke

The world of pedigree animal-breeding is dominated by the Herd Book Societies, whose aim in life is not to be political or commercial pressure groups, but rather the detailed compilation of geneological charts, and adherence to the principles of genetic improvement. These so-called 'improvements' may be a change of direction to popularize a breed, such as Bakewell's work in the eighteenth century to upgrade the British Longhorn (then the national breed) from a beef animal into more dual-purpose lines. There are still 17 national cattle breeds, 9 pig breeds, and 32 varieties of sheep, plus the influx and blood infusion of the Continental 'exotics' which have formed a dramatic and exciting phase in Britain's cattle evolution since 1965, when the first commercial importation of the French Charolais arrived.

In Britain there were 216 million animals at the 1976 MoA Census. Thus there are four times more animals than human inhabitants, although the humans are compressed into 11 per cent of the land area, while nearly 60 per cent of the farm animals are chickens. The number of pigs is only slightly greater than the number of dogs, and no one has attempted to count the cat population.

After the dominance of the Longhorn, its place was taken for 150 years by the Shorthorn, which spread from its home in Lincolnshire, but Britain had a multitude of other breeds, many of which are now extinct, or exist only in modest numbers. As the British scene has been overshadowed by the Continental importations, so British national breeds have become dominant in faraway parts of the world. In 1817 Herefords went to the United States, then to Australia in 1839 and Argentine and Uruguay in 1858. By 1943 there were three times more Herefords in the USA than all other pure beef breeds together. The beef Shorthorns and Aberdeen Angus went to the Argentine in 1876, and although by 1920 there were only 20 Angus-breeders in the Argentine, there were 600 by 1945.

But although this exodus has taken place, the dominant British breed today is the Friesian, which is not British at all.

The oldest breed in Britain is probably the Welsh Black, which may date from pre-Roman times. It had a spread of horns of over a metre, like the curly-coated but brown Scottish Highland; the better land in South Wales having produced a large animal that is ferocious-looking but docile. There were two Herd Societies, a North and South, and despite the antiquity of the breed, the Welsh Black Cattle Society was founded in 1873. A breakaway group of North Welsh farmers formed another society between 1882 and 1904, when they came back into the fold. Hereford-breeders saw a similar example, with the Hereford Herd Book Society being formed in 1878, and the Hereford Cattle Breeders Association in existence from 1884 to 1901, when it was absorbed by the parent body. The antiquity of British national breeds is indisputable, but the Herd Book Societies were largely of late-Victorian origin. They nearly all exist today, and the centenary of many of them has been in the 1970s.

The Friesian cow with its black-and-white markings has become immortalized in paint and canvas as the epitome of the typically British cow. It occupies 81 per cent of the breed distribution of cows in England and Wales, takes 88 per cent of those in Northern Ireland, but comprises only 28 per cent of Scottish cows. It originates from an importation of Friesian Holstein cattle from Holland in 1914, almost on the day that war was declared; but the Friesian Herd Book Society had been created three years earlier, and there were already in Britain many 'Dutch' cattle, black and white, which had been imported before 1892, when Government restrictions were imposed. It was rumoured that before that date as many as 80,000 had arrived in one year, a sign of the affluence in some quarters after the Industrial Revolution, and the commencement of the milk-drinking habit in Britain. Despite the concentration of milk-production into fewer hands, the British Friesian Cattle Society has held and increased its membership to a total of over 14,000 members. It does include the republic of Ireland within its orbit. It has a grand, almost palatial, national headquarters at Scotsbridge House, Rickmansworth, which has been criticized by its members for its grandeur. The National Pig Breeders Association had a membership of 10,000 in 1955, but has slumped to about 3,000 today. The National Sheep Association saw an even sharper decline, and with 20,000 sheep-farmers in Britain, only 1,000 are prepared to pay the membership fee.

The Herd Book Societies were formed for the vigorous defence of their individual breeds, and to sustain and perpetuate their merits. They reached the crossroads in the late 1970s, when it became recognized that there might be some advantages in dual crossing; this diluted the pedigree blood, but kept up the viability of an animal, and increased its potential. This stemmed from the commercialization which had only manifested itself through the organization of Annual Pedigree Sales, but which began to prove the requirements of the producing farmer, or consuming public. At the Smithfield Show for several years the prime championship carcass Awards had been given to animals which were sometimes even double crosses. It was a mark that the infusion of new blood was producing better animals—and the newly imported Continentals were already figuring in the prize lists.

The importation of the 'exotics'

In 1953 an importation of 103 Swedish Landrace pigs was made into Britain. In less than an hour sales records which had stood for thirty years were broken. Fifteen hundred farmers had turned up for the sale at the Peterborough Auction Ring, and the Swedish pigs on sale were soon taken up to help combat pig-farmers' difficulties in producing bacon competitively against their traditional enemies, the Danes. The moment was ripe for the infusion of new blood, but the extent of this infusion took everyone by surprise. Within two years the Landrace breed was second only to the traditional Large White in numbers.

This illustrated the crying need of British breeders for new lines to develop, British farmers being the last people to fall for expensive gimmicks. The Landrace is now almost as British as the British themselves. Strangely, it was only the Swedish Landrace which was imported, and although a scheme was put forward for an importation of Danish Landrace in 1973 it was questioned by the pig-breeders themselves, after the Ministry had authorized 200 head from Danish herds. The scheme was later limited to 20 Danish pigs, then with per-suasion from the British Landrace Pig Society, dropped completely. Some Norwegian Landrace have, however, been imported. The enthusiasm with which the Landrace pigs were integrated into British herds was an omen for the massive influx of Continental cattle breeds that was to come twenty years later.

In 1961 there was an importation of 26 Charolais cattle destined for the Milk Marketing Board for trials. These were the first of a new breed into England, and the results were good. The pressure built up for a foundation stock importation, but it was to be four years before this happened, when in November 1965 200 heifers and 19 bulls came into Plymouth Harbour from Brest. After 28 days in quarantine on the other side of the Channel, they faced another 28 days in a converted Admiralty warehouse at Devonport, and the C-in-C at Plymouth, Vice-Admiral Sir Fitzroy Talbot, drew lots for the allocation of these heifers to members of the already created British Charolais Cattle Society.

The stringent veterinary precautions emphasized the reluctance of British Governments to allow new cattle strains into Britain, which had been, and continues to be, a floating quarantine station for the world, with its natural barrier of isolation from the more disease-prone mainland of Europe. Britain's health record is world-renowned, and the Government of the time determined it should so remain, but as the Charolais cattle gradually multiplied and spread across the country their characteristics of liveweight gain were impressive, to say the least. There were some difficulties at calving time due to the large frame of these chunky-looking animals with the teddy-bear coats. But they illustrated that an infusion of new breeds could add immeasurably to British livestock strains. This was not to denigrate Brittish cattle, but was a measure of the changing public taste for less fat which these generally larger animals could provide at a younger age. The Continental farmers too had seen that they had something for which many areas of the world were crying out.

On 4 August 1971 Jim Prior in the House of Commons announced that the Government intended to 'liberalize' their policy on the importation of breeding stock, although he warned that it could only take place while stringent veterinary control remained. In March 1972 a Committee was established to monitor the imports of breeding livestock and to allocate licences to several Continental breeds. By that time there were already applications relating to twenty-six breeds from eleven countries. It was to be a flood which needed careful control. The new panel was chaired by Professor O. G. Williams, Agricultural Director of Fisons, a past Regional Director of the National Agricultural Advisory Service, and also an Adviser to the New Zealand Government. The remaining six members of the panel were practical farmers, except one, whose expertise in the field was sufficient credibility. It set to work on a massive task.

The flow becomes a torrent

'Now that the period when an Import Permit was almost a licence to print money has passed, there will be fewer requests to bring in fresh breeds with fewer numbers of cattle involved.'

W. Longrigg, RASE 'Journal'

In the four years 1972–6 eleven new breeds of cattle arrived from the Continent. Murray Greys from Australia, Black and White cattle from Holland and Canada, Texel sheep from France, Flemish sheep from the Netherlands. Not only was the leash relaxed, but the excitement of new and often unpronounceable names appeared all too suddenly upon the British scene. No time was given for a proper assessment of the potential of these new animals. It became a rat-race, and those fortunate farmers who acquired some of the original importation stock could sleep happily in the knowledge that they were coining money. The imported cattle were expensive, but the offspring repaid for the outlay. It was an ever-increasing spiral that could not last. The Murray Greys from Australia, for instance, had cost the British farmers £3,500 each, including a £500 air ticket. It required supreme optimism to expect to recoup these amounts, and eventually the bubble burst. This emphasized that the massive importations had been for the wrong reasons. The new breeds were:

The Simmental. The most popular breed in Europe, with 35 million coming from several countries; the UK imports are from West Germany, Austria and Switzerland. A yellowish-brown coat, with a white head, and the progeny colour-marked with the white face of a Hereford, though the yellowish-brown coat contrasts with the deep red of the latter. It is a dual-purpose animal, but was introduced into Britain primarily as a beef-producer. The Simmental originated from the Simme Valley in Switzerland, and it had been exported since the middle of the nineteenth century to upgrade cattle in many neighbouring countries. There are now four main types, situated in Switzerland, Austria, Germany and France.

The Limousin. The Limousin breed originated from the province of that name in West-Central France, and is a rich golden-red in colour, with a lighter tan under the belly. A beef breed with a reputation for early calving, the total carcass weight of a Limousin cross is slightly less than with other breeds such as the Charolais or Simmental cross.

The Maine Anjou. Coming from Brittany in France, this has a red or red and white coat, and looks like a roan, although the purists favour smaller patches of white. Labelled as a dual-purpose animal, the beef qualities exceed the milking potential.

The Blonde D'Aquitaine. Originating from some English beef Shorthorns which were introduced into the Quercy region of France, it has a diverse background of other breeds, and is blonde in colour, with no other coloration permissible, although the legs and belly are usually a lighter shade. It is a beef breed, with little milking potential.

The Gelbvieh. An importation from Germany, where it originated in the Lower Central Area, it was bred from local breeds improved in the seventeenth century by crossing Simmental and Brown Swiss. The coat colour varies from cream to yellow, and this animal has a more useful milk-yield, but is still essentially a beef animal.

The Braunvieh. Known as the Brown Swiss, this is one of the oldest breeds in Europe, and has been kept pure for over a thousand years. A short-horned animal, it is of medium size and has a single-coloured beige-brown coat, the darker shades being preferred.

The Meuse-Rhine-Issel. An imported dairy cow from Holland, with an ancestry related to that of the Dutch Friesians, but in this case resulting in a red and white animal instead of a black and white one. The calves are well suited to veal-production, and are about six pounds heavier at birth than the Friesian. It compares favourably with the high-yielding Friesians for milk-production, and is the only new breed to come from Holland.

The Chianina. Almost the largest animals to be found in Europe, the Chianina have a pure-bred history going back nearly two thousand years. When one recipient was asked how it had been kept pure so long, he retorted, 'No other breed of bull was tall enough to serve the cows,' demonstrating the height of these magnificent animals. The breed is predominant in central west Italy, and there are four types. The coat-colour is pure white, with a long head and well-developed shoulders. It has enormous potential for beef-production.

The Romagnola. Another introduction from Italy, where its home is in the North-East, on widely varying terrain. The coat-colour is grey, and although similar to the Chianina, it is originally shorter, and the cows give better milk-yields.

The Marchigiana. Marchigiana cattle were first crossed with the Chianina, and then with the Romagnola. It is found in central east Italy, and also in the southern regions. The coat is short grey or white-haired, but a distinctive head silhouette and black rings around its eyes makes this animal less pretty than many others. It is primarily a beef animal.

Additional to these have been minor importations of Piedmontese from Italy, Pinzgaver and Rotbunte from Germany. But the importing of the Murray Greys from Australia perhaps produced one of the strangest new animals to roam on British meadows and hills.

The Murray Greys. Most of the Continental breeds which came into Britain had been hiding in the valleys of Europe for centuries, and had often developed unique characteristics. As such they burst upon an unsuspecting world with obvious potential for UK farmers' beef-breeding. The Herefords and Angus were fully exploited, and the dual-purpose Red Polls and Shorthorns in decline, while the Ayrshire was the only other useful milking cow, but losing its popularity to the Friesian. The Guernsey and Jersey provided the small market for high cream content, and other breeds such as the Sussex, Red Devon and Lincoln were proving useful crosses for beef-breeding. All in all, there was a watershed in the development of British cattle-breeding. The Continental 'exotics' arrived, and will undoubtedly provide the foundation bloodstock of an influx that will reverberate down the centuries. But the importation of Murray Greys did not fall into that category.

They are of modern evolution, even in Australia, where the Murray Grey Breed Society was only formed in 1962. The breed dates from 1905 with a cross between a British Shorthorn cow and an Angus bull; but for forty years there was a thread of grey in their coats, and six years before their importation in 1973 they had been displayed as Australian carcasses at Smithfield Market. They topped the bill, and took all the Awards. Such was the euphoria surrounding the Continental imports that in 1973 no less than three groups of potential importers were knocking at the door of the Ministry of Agriculture. A Murray Grey Beef Cattle Society of Great Britain was formed, and another named the Murray Grey Cattle Society attracted 70 members, while some Australians themselves made application to export these cattle to the UK. This application was later withdrawn, but in August 1973 the first Murray Greys were released from quarantine near Manchester Airport. They consisted of 44 heifers and 5 bulls; three of these new cattle went to Wales, and 12 to Scotland. The remainder stayed in England, but were divided between 15 farmers. It represented another new breed for British fields, but was in fact a homecoming for two of Britain's oldest original national breeds.

Although these new importations have had a profound effect upon bringing British cattle-breeding methods up to a higher pitch of efficiency, the importation into the UK has not been entirely a one-way trade. As the Murray

Greys came back to Britain, so, ten years after the first Charolais imports, it was announced that a British breeder was exporting semen for artificial insemination back to France again. New Zealand has 50 pure breeds of sheep, over 300 cross-bred types of ewe, and its highly developed sheep industry, yet it has been shopping in Britain; experimental animals have been bought for a closed flock at Ruakura Agricultural Research Station, North Island. Thus the world becomes a smaller place all the time.

British Cattle Breeders Club

A 'Bull-Breeding Course' was held at Cambridge in January 1947, organized by Dr John (later Sir John) Hammond, with the support of George Odlum. Its object was to introduce breeders and stockmen to the scientist behind their empirical work. As a result of this, the British Cattle Breeders Club was founded that year. It started with the link between those on the ground and those in the laboratory, but unlike the Agricultural Development Association which had the same objectives but became defunct, the British Cattle Breeders Club continues. In the early years the accent was upon dairy cattle, and the Club became an arena of passionate argument as to the relative merits of respective breeds. The entire venture could have failed if this had degenerated into mere tit-for-tat among the advocates of various breeds, but suddenly beef became important and the debates wider.

The Club started in 1947 at Cambridge, and continued to have a January Conference there until 1953, when it decided to move around the country. Between 1954 and 1965 it moved around regional centres, but came back to the impressive University Arms Hotel in 1966, and has remained there ever since. Its membership is small but dedicated, and in the early 1960s there were 150 attending the Annual Conference; a number which had doubled ten years later. It is slightly top-heavy with the scientists, but a recent estimate shows that there is now an almost equal balance in its membership of research pioneers and farmers. It is solely concerned with genetic improvements, and plays no public role in flag-waving for the industry.

29 Boosting the Farming Image

'The cod fish lays ten thousand eggs,
The homely hen lays one.
The cod fish never cackles
To tell you what she's done.
And so we scorn the cod fish,
While the humble hen we prize,
Which only goes to show you
That it pays to advertise.'

'It Pays to Advertise.'

With the majority of the British people living in the smoke-filled towns, absorbed with the troubles in the motor industry, the grime of steelworks or the roar of traffic, there is still nevertheless an obsessive interest in all things appertaining to farming and the countryside. This is shown by the popularity of the Archers on radio, and Emmerdale Farm on TV. The public enjoy the countryside, and despite the Industrial Revolution, still regard themselves as an agrarian nation.

Participation is a more difficult matter, but at times during the year farmers go on parade; the ring of Agricultural Shows have their meretricious aspect. But interspersed with the shopping arcades are the prize-winning animals, the gaudy-looking tractors and the bowler hats. Communications between the public and the farmers are boosted also by the insidious advertising campaigns. TV space and newspaper advertisements proclaim the benefits of eating British eggs, milk and meat. Authors, journalists and public personalities produce a galaxy of material emphasizing the nostalgic and romantic aspects of traditional farming. Almost every local newspaper has its farming page, partly as a sop to a small readership, but also educative to the wider, interested public. Communications are good.

Within the farming industry itself the communication between farmers exists at mundane, social levels, but more intensively at the wealth of Annual Farming Conferences, lectures and practical demonstrations. If there are debates about the application of new techniques, then there are also furious debates about the broad policy lines, and the political implications which permeate the industry. No longer can the farmer live in isolation, and the integration of the industry into a highly complex society has made him only too aware of his responsibility to keep well informed. The British farming press is a fine example of a technical press that is highly competitive, authoritative, impartial, and is more responsible than many other sectors of the publishing world.

Royal Agricultural Society of England

> *'Practise with Science'.*
> Motto of the RASE.

The RASE could well be described as the mother of English farming, whose guardian role is to minister to and protect her fledgling baby. It acts unobtrusively, but comes to the rescue when the baby is in trouble, aiding the Farm Buildings Centre or acting quickly to preserve the British Agricultural Export Council. It gently points the way, and curbs the wild tantrums of the heavy-handed father of farming—the Ministry of Agriculture.

Its family consists of three sons and two daughters, with an ever-widening circle of grandchildren, nephews and nieces. The energetic, tycoon-like son, who wants to go places in the world, is the National Farmers Union. The second, quieter and more dignified son is the CLA, while the third son, the NUAAW, is inclined to be rebellious at times. The two daughters are the Farmers Club and the Worshipful Company of Farmers, both demure and beautiful girls, who will never leave home. The grandchildren are Marketing Boards, Herd Societies and Co-Operative Marketing Companies, and the nephews and nieces can be seen in the trade bodies representing the farm-machinery makers, the chemical, fertilizer and corn merchants. This is an ever-expanding family, but once a year the ageing grandmother has her own birthday party, when all the family make a duty-journey to her gently undulating home only ten kilometres from bustling industrial Coventry, but a vast distance in time and atmosphere. Here the RASE has its seat.

National Agricultural Centre

> *'The Society has now been at Stoneleigh for ten years, and the National Agricultural Centre is no longer a dream, but a reality.'*
> Duke of Northumberland,
> Chairman of RASE Council, 17 November 1972.

In its original concept, the formation of the RASE in 1838 set out to promote the interests of British farming, and raise its standards. This applied to livestock-breeding, to new developments in machinery (even at that date!) and to the promotion of any other useful trends which came to its notice. Such a policy was best achieved by holding an Annual Show, and the first was held at Oxford in 1839. (The academic balance was redressed by a resort to Cambridge the following year). At that time the RASE Council had among its members two dukes, five earls, one marquess, two barons, five baronets and twenty-five MPs. By 1970 there was one duke, one earl, five barons, two baronets and only one MP; obviously the blood had been diluted.

The RASE continued its peripatetic existence, holding its Annual Show, and Queen Victoria was its President when the Royal came to Windsor in 1889. It was at Windsor, from 1903–5, that the RASE, tired of its wanderings around the country, settled down on a permanent exhibition showground at Park Royal. Despite royal patronage, this proved a disaster; the first year's attendance was 65,000, but by the third year this had slumped to only 24,000. Eight years previously at Manchester attendance had topped 218,000. This serious decline in its fortunes almost brought it to its knees. Not for fifty-five years, until 1960, was the Royal Show held (at Cambridge) for two consecutive years, and again attendances slumped. During this period the wandering County Shows had been forced to opt for centralized permanent sites as the only hope of survival—the costs of transportation from year to year, and the increasing difficulty of finding suitable sites, as the aristocratic mansions were pulled down and the parks ploughed, put the whole business of show organization into jeopardy. The Royal was in a greater cleft stick than the Counties, as it had no roots of its own, but in the early 1960s, and despite the falling attendances at Cambridge, the search commenced for a permanent site; it was announced that from 1963 onward the Royal Show would continue to be held at a little-known village near Kenilworth in Warwickshire. As a final 'stag-night' fling, steps were first retraced to Newcastle, which had seen the highest attendance ever in 1956, when nearly a quarter of a million people turned up at the gates. The two years at Cambridge had produced only 186,000 attendance figures.

There were other examples to follow. The Yorkshire Agricultural Society had purchased the first permanent showground in the UK in 1951, when it paid £22,380 for a sloping site on the outskirts of Harrogate. Debts had mounted, and in 1971 it was forced to sell part of this to adjacent residential development, but nevertheless it had been a good investment. The Royal Highland Show had established itself on a permanent site at Ingliston in 1958, and the first show was held two years later. The RASE looked at the possibilities of remaining itinerant and 'borrowing' the ring of existing permanent sites that were becoming established, but few of these were large enough to meet the minimum 250-hectare requirement for the show and its attendant car-parks. A search began which, despite the central location of London for the Smithfield Show, concentrated upon the Midlands. A show held in early July could afford to be in the countryside, but apart from the area of the site itself, the adjacent road system had to be sufficiently flexible to provide several entrances, and in general not too far from the motorway network which would bring farmers from all over England. The choice of Stoneleigh resulted in few farmers being more than three travelling hours away.

Stoneleigh Abbey was owned by Lord Leigh, whose family had had it for many years, and he negotiated a lease with the RASE for seven years. It was to be a proving time, a make-or-break period. The Stoneleigh ground had the requisite circle of access roads around it, and a pleasant tree-lined aspect of rolling countryside with a large, virtually flat area for the erection of the tents and portable buildings which accompanied every English summer Agricultural Show. The lands of Stoneleigh Abbey had been cultivated by monks of the Cistercian Order, who had settled there before the year 1200. This part of Warwickshire had been heavily wooded, and the Doomsday Book records there was adequate feeding for '2,000 swine' in the woodlands, from which wild honey was also collected. The Abbey survives today; in the Middle Ages the Stoneleigh tenant farmers stimulated their farming by the proximity of Coventry, even then a rapidly expanding and industrial town. They sent their produce to the markets, and farming has not changed since that time.

It was an inauspicious baptism for the new permanent home of the Royal Show when in 1963 it not only rained heavily during the Show, but the exhibition of pigs was cancelled by an outbreak of swine fever. However, the number of stands went up, as did the vital gate-money from the attendance. Before the seven years had been completed the RASE made up their mind to rest at Stoneleigh permanently, and a 99-year lease from Lord Leigh was obtained. It gave the impetus for a more permanent establishment, a National Agricultural Centre.

The time and effort of organizing a show that lasted only four days was an obvious stumbling-block in the way of the erection of permanent and expensive buildings. A National Agricultural Centre, that could be used all the year round, therefore took shape in embryo. The RASE itself removed its offices from 35 Belgrave Square to Stoneleigh; the Young Farmers Clubs and various Herd Book Societies moved too. The banks spent large sums on prestigious buildings, and an air of permanence started to become apparent. An appeal for £1·5 million was launched, and the money was subscribed.

Stoneleigh became an address with some meaning; livestock demonstration units in the form of small farms were established. They were strictly for demonstration purposes, and not for research. Nevertheless, the performance of animals at the NAC soon became a regular feature in the farming reports. Visitors came in small numbers, but at the Annual July Show each year a gradual development of permanent buildings was noticed.

The concept of a National Agricultural Centre dates from 1967, but it was to be five years before the idea really caught on. During that time the first sods had been cut for the National Exhibition Centre, Britain's first modern venue for large-scale trade fairs, at Bickenhill, not thirty kilometres from Stoneleigh. The National Exhibition Centre had been mooted by Birmingham Chamber of Commerce in 1970, and in 1973 the then Prime Minister, Heath, formally launched the project. Its area is 130 hectares, against the RASE 250-hectare Stoneleigh site. It seemed a waste of resources to spend £20 million on another Exhibition Site, when the RASE was going painfully slowly with its own plans due to financial stringencies. In 1972 a new post was created of 'Chief Executive', and a previous director of Cunard, barrister, civil servant and magazine editor was appointed. He was John Hearth, and his task was to take an overall look at the strategy and development of the Royal Showground into the National Agricultural Centre.

His appointment was greeted with some scepticism. His friends suggested he had landed a job with a four-day week, and the *British Farmer and Stockbreeder* had a headline 'What will he do?', adding that this new appointment was (a) because the RASE itself did not know where it was going or (b) was not aware of modern business management, and had hired a management expert to do the job for it. It was not an appointment that was widely welcomed, and Hearth came in over the head of Christopher Dadd, who had been the Agricultural Director of the Show since 1963, and had seen the Show into the Stoneleigh site. Dadd retired in 1978, but before that his partnership with Hearth worked, and the latter's appointment brought a new crescendo of activity. As a non-agriculturalist, with no knowledge of farming, he was impartial, but it was not roses all the way.

To critics of the concept of an NAC Hearth replied, 'There is no real doubt as to our prime objective—to make Stoneleigh the communications centre for English agriculture.' He took six months from his appointment in February 1972 to assess the potential, and in September announced further changes and a shake-up of the administration, as well as a new positive policy of attracting non-farming events, so that the Stoneleigh Showground could be utilized in the off-season periods of the year. It took courage to commence the 320-seat Conference Hall (costing £100,000), when the cash was not in the bank, but despite some wet Shows the crowds came rolling in, and with cash receipts rising the money for expansion became available. A collection of events based upon the Stoneleigh ground gradually evolved, but they were not always successful. In 1972 the revived National Dairy Show made its debut at Stoneleigh, but the RASE charged a high rent and the following year the Show went to the Yorkshire Showground at Harrogate, coming back to Stoneleigh again in 1974. The National Grassland Demonstration organized by Shellstar took place at Stoneleigh in 1972, an action-packed demonstration with a specialized theme. The following year the RASE launched a Sheep Fair; it attracted more sheep than visitors, but the society persisted with other farmer demonstrations and fairs in the succeeding years, continuing implacably to try to popularize Stoneleigh as a centre for the greater cultural knowledge of farmers. It remained a centre of farmers for farmers by farmers until an Annual 'Town and Country Fair' was inaugurated to bring in the urban crowds. Twelve Dog Shows and three Caravan Rallies added to the full exploitation of the Showground potential.

In a flood now, many national farming organizations closed up their office blocks and moved to Stoneleigh. The trek had begun, and in 1976 alone six new permanent buildings were erected. By this time there were 15 kilometres of permanent roads, 6½ kilometres of water mains, 29 kilometres of water services, 6 electricity substations and enough services to cope with a town of 100,000 people. During Royal Show week there are 550 telephone lines, but the Royal Pavilion itself remains a wooden structure that was taken down and re-erected on many sites through its wandering days; somehow it is still more in keeping with the image of an English summer Royal Show.

The Royal Show

For all its general motherly role in British agriculture and its preoccupation with developing Stoneleigh as the NAC, the Annual Royal Show is nevertheless still the centrepiece of the RASE. It is the high spot in the farmer's social calendar, and is placed seasonally in early July, before the farming scene shifts to a preoccupation with the harvest, when farmers go into purdah.

As a glittering social occasion, it attracts the dark suits and the ladies' hats, but it is still a hard business occasion, with an emphasis upon farm machinery and the exhibition of pedigree animals. The bowler hats of yesteryear have all but disappeared from the Royal, although they persist as part of the uniform at the local County Shows throughout the shires. It is a curious mixture of dedicated farmers, landed aristocrats, the ever-swelling crowds of farm workers and urban townspeople.

Discounting football crowds and sporting attractions, Henley Regatta and the Badminton Horse Trials, the combined Agricultural Shows attract more poeple annually. In fact, the attendances total approximately 3 million people, and the marquees, grandstands, massed bands and rosette-covered champions have become part of the annual summer tourist itinerary. At the Royal Show the bedecked humans often exhibit more rosettes and emblems on their lapels than the cattle have rosettes on their faces.

Average attendances

Royal Show	200,000
Smithfield Show	60,000
Game Fair	78,000
Dairy Show	17,000
Ideal Home Exhibition	680,000
Motofair	401,000
(Motor Show 1965)	660,000
Boat Show	270,000
Chelsea Flower Show	160,000
Crufts	55,000

Flevohof

The NAC has set out to provide a focal-point for British farmers, with an all-the-year-round centre for education, demonstration and instruction, with discussion and debate thrown in. Only at the Royal Show itself, and at some of the peripheral events, are the public welcomed through the gates. It does not set out to provide an insight into farming for an ignorant public. But at Flevohof, 120 kilometres north-east of Amsterdam, and on land which was beneath the Zuider Zee some years previously, the Dutch have set out to provide a 'model farm' where townspeople can view constructively what goes on down on the farm.

A private-enterprise scheme, unsupported by Government money, its attendance figures have been over a million per year, and in the picturesque waterside restaurant, and the landscape area of woods, hills and lakes, the Dutch have set out to make Flevohof an attraction for the urban population, and a day out in the country. It is a 145-hectare site, which cost originally about £2 million, and was contributed by a combined consortium of farming organizations. The main buildings house a dairy unit, a pig unit, chickens and heated glasshouses growing tomatoes, cucumbers, lettucs and melon. Exhibition Halls demonstrate mushrooms growing, eggs being laid, cows being milked, and even calves being born. There is no parallel to the extent and success of Flevohof anywhere in the world, and the NAC does not pretend to emulate it. It was officially opened by Princess Beatrix in May 1971.

Farming Shows—the international scene

In Britain many of the ancient Agricultural Shows have adopted a candy-floss image to bring in the crowds and sustain the gate money. It has been an exercise in survival, and there have been many casualties. In the world scene, the large Agricultural Shows have done the same; with the Sydney Show and the Paris Show in particular ensconced in the centres of those cities and attracting annually over a million people. There the agricultural element has been diluted to create a vast concourse, almost a national gala week.

The Calgary Stampede exhibits the truly rural atmosphere of a holiday fair, while in Canada the Toronto World Fair has a strong agricultural bias, with the merit of being the only show to concentrate upon prize-winning samples of farm produce (as opposed to prize-winning animals). However, it takes place largely indoors at the Toronto Exhibition site in cold November, and is a show which attracts the townspeople and the children. It also has vast indoor Exhibition Halls, utilized for events linked only tenuously to farming.

The Royal Showground at Stoneleigh is probably the largest Showground in the world. The Sydney Show takes place on 30 hectares in Sydney itself, attracts 1·25 million people in its nine days and eleven nights, and stays open until 11 pm every evening. It is aimed as a spectacle for the people of Sydney, the largest city in a continent which rests heavily on its agriculture. Farmers have competitive classes drawn from regional areas, which is something unknown in the UK, but it is a popular show.

Paris in the springtime is dominated by the Paris Show, which takes place in the permanent Salon International de l'Agriculture at the Porte de Versailles, one of the southern gateways to ancient Paris, where a vast Exhibition Centre of national proportions has been established. It is bisected by two roads which are elevated above the crowds. For a city Exhibition Centre it is large, covering 38 hectares, but this does not compare with the 250 hectares at Stoneleigh. Eighty per cent of the Exhibition Site is occupied by vast Exhibition Halls, each of which would make Earl's Court or Olympia look small. The Show itself lasts eight days, and cleverly the French open on a Sunday, thus drawing the weekend crowds twice. The Paris exhibition is not an agricultural show; it is the Ideal Home Exhibition, Horse of the Year Show, Camping Exhibition, Boat Show, Crufts, Smithfield Show and a few others all rolled into one. It is true that the section devoted to farm machinery in the Palais Sud is itself larger than Earl's Court, and displays machinery in the open air on the adjacent tarmac. It has a greater concentration and a more comprehensive display of farm machinery than does the Smithfield Show, which itself shows in a comprehensive and business-like fashion the latest designs in farm machinery.

However, the machinery aspect is in some ways kite-flying; many of the machines on display are prototypes which may be said to be testing the market reaction. Many of them will never be put into universal production. The Show originated as an Agricultural Machinery Show in 1922, under the title SIMA (Salon International de la Machine Agricole), but in 1964 the SIA evolved another show on a broader basis, and the two combined to make this one vast show. There is a carnival atmosphere in the aroma of cooked cheese from the Food Hall, the musical background and the tinkling cowbells of the giant Continental cattle, the Aubrac, the Deep Red Maine Anjou or the multi-coloured straps of the Brune. Cattle and horses, people and ponies—the Paris Show is a spectacle and a carnival on its own, unique to the French, and yet vastly different from the more brash exhibitionism to be seen in Sydney.

Berlin Green Week lasts ten days, and the beleaguered city, with no farms, has established a giant annual binge. The Show is financed jointly by the City of Berlin and the German NFU; there are other food fairs in Germany, the most notable being at Munich and Cologne. One in six of the three million inhabitants of divided Berlin pass through the doors of the Berlin Show. The Show today is the descendant of a pre-War Berlin Agricultural Show, when its average attendance was about 40,000 people. Today half a million throng to this annual feast and there are only 2,700 hectares in the whole of modern Berlin. Its post-War origins were a defiant attempt by the Americans to display to the Russians over the Wall that Berlin could proudly hold up the notice 'Business as Usual', the Show having strong business connections inasmuch as West Germany imports a good deal of food. British participation in the Berlin Green Week started in 1966, when the then Board of Trade supported an exhibit, but three years later the British withdrew and only a feeble Union Jack has been waved since, although it has become usual for the UK Minister of Agriculture to visit the Show every year.

The heavy aroma of German sausages fills the air, coupled with the music blaring forth from every stand, but there are some live animals, and in a hall about the quarter of the size of Earl's Court there are sheep grazing on real imported grass; a strange contrast to the urban surroundings.

East Germany holds its Annual Leipzig Fair in the spring, which has attracted exhibitors from more than sixty countries. It is a display of farm machinery from the Comecon countries, but in West Germany there is also the DLG, a nomadic machinery show held only every two years at such centres as Cologne (1970), Hanover (1972), and Düsseldorf (1974). It vies with the Paris Show as the largest European Machinery Exhibition, and one whose interest has grown for British farmers, who arrive in organized parties. Being nomadic, it looks for a centre with permanent Exhibition Halls, and is normally held at the end of May. It lasts for eight days, twice the length of the Royal Show.

To describe the Italian Verona Machinery Show as 'up and coming' is an insult, as the 'International Agricultural and Animal Farming Fair' held near the medieval town of Verona in Northern Italy has an ancestry that stretches back before 1900, although a combined Agricultural Machinery Section was only created in 1947, and in 1968 an Exhibition of 'New Agricultural Techniques' was also incorporated to attract a wider interest. It is held largely out of doors in early March in the week following the Paris Show, and in an international avenue countries ranging from Russia to the Argentine are to be found. Britain as an exhibitor takes only a modicum of interest.

The autumn Italian Machinery Show staged at Bologna, and called the EIMA, originated in 1968 in a fine modern Exhibition Centre at Bologna. Planned as a biennial event, pressure by the Italian machinery manufacturers persuaded the organizers to make it an annual affair, and support is on a wider basis and from more countries than those which support the Verona Show. It was a Spartan affair in its early days, and was a pipsqueak newcomer against the stately Verona. It seems all set to become Italy's premier Farm Machinery Show.

In Holland the Dutch Machinery Show known as the RAI is held in one of the magnificent Exhibition Halls in Amsterdam, where the paint shines on both the building and the new tractors. It brightens up the early January days, which are its normal place in the International Calendar, but in May the Dutch go to the Liempde Show, which offers a continuous demonstration in practical terms, and a static display of farm machinery tastefully laid out.

In Spain the Zaragoza Show only opened its doors in 1968, and is a technical machinery fair coupled with a conference. It only lasts for three days.

The Tel Aviv Show is a four-day event, which has attracted more interest of international repute since it opened its doors to the world in 1973. It is held on the Tel Aviv Fair Ground, and despite the arid nature of Israel, it has agricultural machinery companies which exhibit at this Show. It occurs every two years, and in 1973 there was also instituted an International Conference on the control of water-resources in Haifa, irrigation and desalination being vitally important to the Israelis.

In Africa the Nairobi Show is the largest, and has a week-long run. It is basically a microcosm of Kenyan farm and industrial life, but emphasizes the growing importance of agriculture to Kenya. In 1976 it assumed a wider importance and was renamed the 'Nairobi International Show', attracting 12 International Pavilions with 200 foreign firms. The UK Pavilion won first prize.

In South America the São Paulo International Food and Technology Exhibition is Brazil's contribution to the world scene of farm shows, but here there is an emphasis upon agricultural aviation—the tractors of the air—and the whole spectrum of farm production is covered, right to the processing industries and the Brazilian supermarkets.

The movement to internationalize the Royal Show stems from 1972 onward, although there had been five overseas countries exhibiting in 1971, and 100 nations were represented by the overseas attendance figures. The French had been the first to mount an all-out effort to display their national cattle breeds, but at the last moment in 1972 the Germans decided to spend £15,000 on a trade stand, and upset many UK firms by obtaining a prime site near the Royal Enclosure. The same year Canada, New Zealand and the Arab Sheikdom of Abu Dhabi also joined the throng. By 1976 eleven countries were mounting trade stands, some of them in permanent buildings, and the throng of overseas visitors numbered nearly 6,000, or 8 per cent of the total attendance. An International Pavilion was built in time for the 1976 Show, and the emphasis on creating an international atmosphere has continued.

It has not been roses all the way through, and in 1971 no less than 83 exhibitors, including such large companies as Fords, International Harvester, British Leyland, New Holland, David Brown and John Deere, withdrew from the Royal Show. The costs of showing had become staggering, and these companies seriously questioned the benefits. The following year there were grass patches where some of these had been; others came in to swell the numbers, but with the major machinery companies gone it was a serious blow to the RASE. They came back later, but not all of them, Leyland and New Holland returning in 1976. Massey-Ferguson had taken up the vacated space of British Leyland, and had extended their Royal Show stand to massive proportions, but in 1975 RHM decided to change their policy and closed down their permanent building. It later became the English Restaurant, but RHM declared they would increase their sponsorship and investment in the NAC Dairy Unit. Thus, the advantages of an all-the-year-round involvement outweigh the benefits from a four-day show.

In 1972 the Royal Show opened on a Monday, but, retaining its four-day run, closed on the Friday. Initially it was not a success, there was conflict between stockmen who wanted to get their animals home by the following weekend. In 1977 the RASE abruptly announced that it would open on the Sunday in 1978 as a preview day for the local population. It quickly withdrew this announcement after heated and acrimonious comment from many of the machinery and stock exhibitors, who refused to arrive on a Saturday, ready to open shop on the Sunday. By this time the RASE had been embarrassed by a crowd of 90,000

Britain's beef-production is not insignificant, even when compared with that of the Argentine. Above is an example of one of the traditional beef breeds with its owner, former Minister of Agriculture Jim Prior, on his Suffolk farm. Below is a specimen of the new European breeds that have arrived on the British scene—a Charolais Champion exhibited at the Three Counties Show, Malvern *Photos The Ministry of Agriculture (Crown copyright reserved); 'The Farmers Weekly'*

Breeding developments of sheep and pigs: above, a crossbred sow, Fastback 323, and below, three shearling rams on Mr Coburn's Gloucestershire farm
Photos 'Big Farm Management'

The new Ministry Permanent Stand at the Stoneleigh Showground of the RASE (opened in 1977). It is symbolic of the town which has grown up at the National Agricultural Centre *Photo The Ministry of Agriculture. Crown copyright reserved*

Barclays Bank was among the first to erect a permanent building at Stoneleigh, and it gained an architectural award *Photo Barclays Bank*

The *Farmers Weekly* keeps mud on its boots with its own ring of farms. Here is Cowbyers Farm, in northern Durham

Photo 'The Farmers Weekly'

which had arrived on the Wednesday in 1976, and were seeking to extend the Show. (The Smithfield Show, however, runs from Monday to Friday every year.)

Royal Show visitors

	%
Farmers	34
Farm Managers	2
Farm workers	4
Farm machinery people	6
Teaching or advisory farm work	3
Ancillary employment to farming	10
Retired but connected	1
Overseas visitors	2
Unconnected to agriculture	38
	100

Source: *Survey of Visitors: Royal Show,* 1971.

Additionally, it was revealed that 32 per cent of the Royal Show crowds are women. This emphasizes its place as a social occasion, as well as the involvement of women in practical farming tasks, or even as farmers themselves. On the other hand, at the Smithfield Show there is hardly a lady in sight; it is a more businesslike show. The RASE revealed in the 1971 Survey, and confirmed it in later surveys, that it was in fact attracting the cream of British farming, and that the farmer visitors held in their hands nearly half the total farmland of England, something that the Sydney Show, despite its vast, thronging crowds, could never hope to emulate.

The Smithfield Show

'As the threat of the cleaver loomed, there came the sudden emotional claim that the champion was "too beautiful to die", and it reached beyond farming circles.

The man from the Reading abattoir was finally persuaded to relent his hold. Thousands cheered, without knowing quite why, and the champion was spared.'

Jack Sarl, 'The Farmers Weekly', 29 November 1974.

It is an odd mixture of cattle and combines, sheep and standholders, pigs and people, but there are no mass bands, no parachutists, and no horses. More incongruous surroundings for such an event as a cattle and machinery show in the heart of London, with not a tree in sight, would be hard to imagine. It is a national rather than an international affair, and attracts only a quarter of the crowds that turn out for the mighty Royal at Stoneleigh in the summer. Despite its domestic rather than international atmosphere, one cynic has been heard to say,[1] 'The main reason for having the Exhibition appears to be for overseas

[1] *Agricultural Machinery Journal,* December 1973. 'Management View'.

visitors to see and order what is available from British manufacturers, and for British visitors to see and order what is available from overseas manufacturers. After which they all go and pat the cattle and sheep.'

The vicissitudes of livestock farming have rarely been exemplified by the Smithfield turnout, but the world of breeding champions is far removed from the everyday world of commerce and erratic local markets, for Smithfield is a meat show, and it is the quality of the dead carcass that is important. This is not to deny that special electric sockets are installed for the hair-driers which put the final waves on the coats of the animals, and the fine hair-dos on these curly coats would do justice to the most professional hairdresser in the land. As a picture of sheer beauty there is nothing to excel the line-up of cattle at the Smithfield.

Judging these animals on the hoof was a traditional part of the Smithfield procedure, but it was subject to the criticism that you did not always know what was beneath the skin, and in any case, the judge's idea of a championship beast might not always correspond with the butcher's discoveries with his knife. In fact, it rarely did, but in the early 1970s points were given at last for the carcass quality.

'Any more for the Cow Show?' cry the London clippies as horny-handed, ruddy-faced farmers throng to the murky Earl's Court Road in dull December each year. The disdain of the farmers for anyone who thinks that a beef animal is a cow is heavily disguised in passive snorts of indifference. The farmers are certainly more critical in their professional appraisal of the cattle merits. The Royal Show deals in pedigree breeds and scorns mongrels, but the Smithfield positively revels in cross-bred animals; the 1975 champion was a Charolais-Aberdeen Angus-Shorthorn cross, while for good measure Lulu broke the rules as the first not so dainty female to take the supreme championship of the Show in nine years.

Covered with rosettes, subjected to the TV lighting, acclaimed and awarded, the champion of the Show each year is auctioned, and in the 1960s there was no rule that it must be slaughtered; thus in the quotation above the champion that year, Barnoldby Orange Miss, the heroine of the drama in Jack Sarl's quotation, was saved from the butcher's block and lived to commence a breeding life. Nowadays the champion is bought by Pricerite or Dewhurst's.

Smithfield is not much frequented by the ladies, although the first lady judge was appointed for the 1977 Show. Though attendance at the Royal Show is on an ever-diminishing scale , the Smithfield attracts a good attendance from the Home Counties, though with good-quality beef the specialized prerogative of the expert Scottish farmer, many London hotels ring with Scottish tongues during Smithfield week.

Said the *Farmers Weekly*:[2]

> There is a lot that is illogical about the annual rush of blood to the head which stirs stockmen in far corners of the kingdom and sends them to the big fatstock show in London.

[2] 10 December 1971.

This is where the exercise of traditional, yet mysterious, skills is recompensed by the award of highly-priced rosettes required at this time of the year to round off butchers shop decorations.

The Smithfield Show is run by a triumvirate, one being the Royal Smithfield Club (which was formed on 17 December 1798, and was known at that time as the Smithfield Cattle and Sheep Society). It is also under the auspices of the Agricultural Engineers Association, who worked hard to re-establish it after the period in outer darkness 1939–45. At least it has a considerable vested interest in the machinery section of the Show. The last member of the trio is the Society of Motor Manufacturers and Traders (SMMT), which ironically does not include tractors under its wing, but has a strong hold over the lettings at Earl's Court. As the principal architect behind each show is Gerry Kunz (son of pianist Charlie), who organizes the Motor Show, Racing Car Show, etc., the SMMT do have an interest in the Smithfield Show. Each organization designates its Chairmen in order. The Smithfield Club is the oldest of these bodies, and the modern Smithfield Show—greatly changed—dates from 1799 and the Smithfield Market, a long way from Earl's Court, where the first Show was held at Wootton's Livery Stables in Dolphin Yard, Smithfield. But the Smithfield butchers are one of the oldest trades practising in the city of London, and the Worshipful Company of Butchers has an antiquity which extends beyond the records, is one of the seven oldest of London's Livery Companies, and there was possibly a Butcher's Hall in A.D.975. The derivation of 'Smithfield' comes from a smooth-field, where Friday markets were held as early as A.D. 1174. It was also a place of public execution by burning at the stake, and was used as a tournament area in medieval times. The Smithfield Market was confirmed by a Charter of 1400; thus its antiquity is indisputable.

From the first Show in Dolphin Yard it moved to Sadler's Wells in 1806, where no doubt the heavy footsteps of the great oxen were in contrast to the ballerinas that were to come. It remained at Sadler's Wells until 1839, although it had almost become defunct in the depression following the Napoleonic Wars; but in 1839 it moved to the Horse Bazaar in Baker Street, and five years later a flurry of excitement preceded its accolade of respectability   the arrival of the young Queen Victoria.

In 1862 it moved to the newly built Agricultural Hall at Islington, and remained there until 1947, with breaks during the two Great Wars. It has remained at Earl's Court ever since, though its permanency was in doubt when the redevelopment of Earl's Court was mooted.

The future of London as an Exhibition Centre has never been sufficiently considered, and the opening of the National Exhibition Centre near Birmingham has done nothing to alleviate the problem. Not only UK nationals but overseas visitors want to come to the capital for the major exhibitions, but neither Olympia nor Earl's Court is large enough on its own. The impossibility of closing one and expanding the other has been a talking-point for many years; a big new show arena was mooted at Hillingdon in 1972, and plans for the rationalization of the 12 hectares occupied by Olympia and Earl's Court were made. The Smithfield Show was given its marching orders, and sought a new venue. With planners' indecision and escalating costs, despite the elaborate plans that had been drawn up reprieve was granted to the Smithfield Show, and a refurbishing job done at Earl's Court. In the discussions the farmers opted firmly to remain in London. Maybe the attraction of the shops for their wives had some bearing on the matter.

The problems of accommodating this Show in the constricted space of Earl's Court have resulted in open warfare between the vested interests of the livestock people (represented by the Smithfield Club) and the machinery exhibitors (represented by the AEA). Prior to 1947 there were virtually no machines at the Show, and long history as a Butchers' Show for the exhibition of meat for the Christmas trade was of paramount importance; but since the 'resurrection' in 1947 was partly the result of AEA pressure and participation, the machines have been gently ousting the cattle and jostling for the space. In 1971 twenty machinery companies were turned away for lack of space; in 1976 forty were turned away; and despite an extra 1,858 square metres of floor space in 1977, fifty companies could not exhibit for lack of stand space. Although a large contingent of interested cattle, sheep- and pig-men make up part of the Smithfield crowds, it is the machinery avenues which throng with people, and the business announced by the companies is considerable. It may be accidental, but the Show comes at a time when the harvest has been completed and there is a chance to assess the new machinery requirements for the coming year. It often also provides a barometer of farmers' confidence, and has sometimes provided surprises in the enthusiasm with which farmers have ordered new machinery. Nevertheless, the battle Cattle v. Combines remains, and Richard Lee[3] wrote:

> Smithfield has been fobbing off would-be exhibitors for years with the 'shortage of space' plea, yet half the ground floor is occupied by a butchers show! It is not a new suggestion that the animals and machines should part company . . . one exhibitor was complaining that his Smithfield space allocation would not accommodate his one main exhibit—unless he cut the draw bar off!
>
> Would-be exhibitors who can't get into Smithfield have been hinting darkly for some time that the animals are a good excuse to keep the current 'Club' highly selective.
>
> If there is anything in that suspicion, it should be said at once that adult exhibition practise is now way above that sort of schoolboy game.

The Smithfield Show brings more farmers into London than any other event; for the AGM of the NFU is only attended by Council Delegates, and the other agricultural events are held around the country. On occasions the Londoners get a treat when a pig breaks loose, or when a steer ran amok down the Earl's Court Road, chased by its attendants and the police.

[3] *Agricultural Machinery Journal*, October 1974.

The County Shows

The English summer scene would not be complete without its Rose Shows, Regattas, Varsity Matches, Cricket Tours, Boat Race, strawberries and cream, and Agricultural Shows. Many of them have become a frivolous by-product of the farming world, dominated by fun-fairs, shopping avenues, children's ponies and motor-car stands. A true agricultural background is hard to discover. and the origins of the organizing societies—many of which stretch back to the eighteenth century, and were instituted for the development and spread of new farming techniques—have largely disappeared.

The changed outlook of the County Shows is a result of the struggle for survival; by bringing in the 'lower classes', many have boosted their gate money, and ensured a continuous run during what might have been a slump in show-going. In the process there have been amalgamations among the proudest shires to form new consortia; just as the new map of England has abolished the ancient county boundaries, the grouping of the farming Shows has done the same. Many counties have remained aloof but have curbed their costs by the establishment of permanent showgrounds; any attempts to transform these into centres of county farming have largely failed. The movement towards a permanent site was created with the objective of building a small town and attracting other activities, such as caravan rallies, vintage-car shows and sporting events, throughout the year to utilize the permanent halls and fixed stadiums which were part of the original plan, but which in many cases have not transpired. It has been a story of immense change, coupled with financial perils.

In the process some farming shows with a long history have succumbed; the Royal Lancashire kept its head above water while its showground was near holiday-filled Blackpool, but after moving to Ribby Hall, Kirkham, it finally failed. The Oxfordshire and the Cheshire have also disappeared; in general, one County Show has disappeared or become amalgamated with others every year.

The East of England Show is a typical example. It resulted from a meeting on 12 May 1967, chaired by former Olympic hurdler and stately home-owner the Marquess of Exeter (previously Lord Burghley). From this stemmed a show that was to replace five others. These were the Bedfordshire (formed 1801), Cambridgeshire and Isle of Ely (1863), Huntingdonshire (1837), Peterborough (1797) and Northamptonshire (1848). With a permanent showground just off the A1 near Peterborough, the East of England has become one of the major shows of the British Isles; farther east the Royal Norfolk, Suffolk and Essex—forming the historical East Anglia—retain their individual County Shows annually. The East of England has also been joined by the Long Sutton and District Agricultural and Horticultural Society; originally formed in 1837, this was absorbed into the East of England in January 1969. A month later the Societies of Peterborough and Huntingdonshire merged to form one Agricultural Society, known as the Peterborough and Huntingdonshire Agricultural Society. The following year Cambridge and Isle of Ely Agricultural Society merged with the new Peterborough and Huntingdonshire, and the 'East of England Agricultural Society' had been created. The Bedfordshire merged in 1971, and the Northamptonshire in 1972; thus not only have the local County Shows become defunct, but the original ancient Societies which ran them have also lost their identity. A piece of England has gone with them.

The Three Counties, with its Showground at Malvern, is an amalgamation of the Herefordshire, Worcester and Gloucester County Agricultural Societies, but its history of amalgamating goes back further. It was in 1894 that the Worcester Chamber of Agriculture and the Herefordshire Agricultural Society joined together, and in 1922 the Gloucestershire Agricultural Society came into the fold. The South of England, with its attractive Showground at Ardingly in Sussex, incorporates the Royal Richmond (Surrey) Horse Show and the Tunbridge Wells and Sussex County Agricultural Societies.

The Bath and West has even earlier origins; it is probably the oldest surviving Agricultural Show, with a history going back to 1777, but it is not the result of a series of mergers. Originally it covered the counties of Somerset, Wiltshire, Gloucester and Dorset, while the City and County of Bristol were added later, and Hereford soon followed. The Society in those days covered Berkshire, Hampshire, Devon and Cornwall, and was a peripatetic show. In 1790 the title was altered to the Bath and West of England Society, and in 1868 it amalgamated with the Southern Counties Agricultural Association. Its territory thus extended along the south coast from Kent to Cornwall, and up to Oxford and Gloucester. Its present title is the Bath and West and Southern Counties Society, a name which evolved in 1890. It has become a major attraction at its Shepton Mallet Showground, and attracts attendenaces close to 100,000 annually. For its bi-centenary Show in 1977 it extended itself to a five-day show, beating the Royal and the Royal Highland, which only extended to four days. The majority of shows are a two-day event, which traditionally give the farmers the first day and the farm-workers the second. With pricing structures which make the first day expensive, this traditional if somewhat outdated outlook still persists.

Traditionally, the County Show was a beer-swilling orgy at which the corn merchants provided the free booze, but with show-going expenses spiralling, many national and local companies withdrew from it in the early 1960s. A ruling by Callaghan when Chancellor of the Exchequer that entertainment expenses could no longer be deducted for income-tax purposes was a death-knell to many shows, but the writing had already been on the wall as the local merchants had vied with each other to provide ever more resplendent hospitality. In the 1960s the shows took a knock, but despite the withdrawal of the Ministry of Agriculture from every local show in 1972, and the withdrawal of BOCM/ Silcock Ltd from 1973 onwards the Shows have revived. Organizing an outdoor event in England can be hazardous, even with the backing of a 'pluvious' insurance policy, but examination of the trends reveals that a traditional wet summer is not the prime cause of lower attendance figures: inexplicably, if there are record crowds at one County Show then it seems to be copied throughout the country. Perhaps a greater degree of investigation into the moods of the show-going public might reveal that the massive attractions of the Household Cavalry or the Red Devils have brought in the townspeople, while the farming element is encouraged by its relative state of prosperity—and the 1970s, despite various livestock crises, proved more prosperous.

Bringing in the outsiders was always a difficult problem with mid-week shows; and the vast majority of shows still do adhere to the middle of the week. The Essex Show was the first to violate this tradition when it plumped for Friday/Saturday, and advertised itself as a family event. You could not have a family event at mid-week during term-time.

In 1974 the Royal Cornwall gambled £75,000 by extending from a two-day to a three-day show, despite a roaring gale which blew down a marquee just before it opened on the Wadebridge Ground. Since that time they have built a vast, steel-framed livestock 'palace'. This has been another feature which only a few of the County Shows have achieved. At Malvern the Three Counties has built a stone and steel building at a cost of £67,000. The Royal Welsh at Builth Wells built a new Exhibition Hall in 1972; this is known as Clwyd Hall, and was contributed by the farmer counties of Denbigh and Flint. It was part of the policy of attracting all-the-year-round events. At Ingliston the Royal Highland Show-ground adjacent to Edinburgh (Turnhouse) Airport, bought in 1957 as a permanent showground, has announced plans for a £5 million Conference and Exhibition Centre, and at Bingley Hall, the picturesque showground of the Staffordshire County Show, there is perhaps the most modern permanent complex, which is in fact large enough to house some of the national events, farming or otherwise, which the Show Societies hope to attract.

The advantages of owning the Showground as an appreciating asset have given the Societies a solid financial base, even though this is uncashable, and the annual show receipts must help to balance the books; the Great Yorkshire Agricultural Society was offered £1 million for its ground adjacent to Harrogate. It refused this sum for these 104 hectares, but it did sell three hectares for a useful sum which kept it out of the red.

The pilgrimage of the Agricultural Societies in the 1970s has been along an uncertain path to an unknown destination. They have survived, while changing their image beyond all recognition. Nevertheless, they remain a happy part of the English summer season, a tourist attraction and a shop window for prize-winning animals, and a means for the general non-farming public to learn a little more about this intricate industry.

A National Dairy Event

Once upon a time there was an Annual Dairy Show at Olympia, which took place at the end of October, while the Motor Show was drawing its crowds to Earl's Court. Both have undergone a transformation, but that of the Dairy Show has been the greater. Motor-cars have become a part of our way of life, but so is drinking milk. Does this remove the need for an annual exhibition to boost the product?

The Royal Association of British Dairy Farmers was founded on 24 October 1876 as the British Dairy Farmers Association. It organized a Dairy Show at the Royal Agricultural Hall, Islington, from 1878 until 1937, by which time the accommodation had become so overcrowded that the Diamond Jubilee Show was scheduled for the newly constructed Earl's Court. The Show was halted by the War, and in 1947 re-established itself at Olympia. Twenty-three years later, in 1970, it was in dire straits: it cost £65,000 to mount, and it was losing money. The farmers were not coming, attendance and interest was waning, and the RABDF cancelled its show. It was resurrected again in 1972 at the Stoneleigh National Agricultural Centre without the gloss and polish of its predecessors. Gone were the goats, the pigs, the poultry and the pigeons. There were no spectacular grand ring parades, but a solid, down-to-earth exhibition of dairy cattle with competitive classes, and a good display of dairy machinery. It had taken on a business-like appearance, and had dropped the title 'Dairy Show' in favour of the lesser 'Dairy Farming Event'.

Undoubtedly feeling that the beef people were stealing the limelight, at the ever-strengthening Smithfield Show, the Dairy Authorities sought to provide their own Annual Event or Show, but the excuse for it seems feeble. There are Dairy Cow Classes at the Royal Show, plus the Breed Societies Annual Show and Sales, and there is an opportunity to view dairy machinery at either the Royal Show or one of the County Events. The Event's steady, if uninspiring, record prior to its demise in 1970, and the low-key event revived two years later, seems to point to little enthusiasm for this occasion. Nevertheless, it represents a date on the annual farming calendar.

The slackening of interest in the County Shows is due partly to the proliferation of specialized farming events in the post-War years. These concentrate upon particular crops or animals, and draw their audience from the true specialists. The Annual Sugar Beet Demonstrations arranged by the British Sugar Corporation, and itinerant, take place on one farm in both spring and autumn. The first event gives an opportunity to see machinery in action at the drilling and early stages of the crop and in the autumn the same farmers return to the same farm to see the same crop and to watch it being harvested by one of a dozen different methods. It is a prime example of the new breed of farming shows, and has been copied by the Potato Marketing Board with their own brand of Annual Potato Demonstrations.

As early as 1955, the *Farmers Weekly* recognized, with journalistic perception, the need for specialized events, and instituted what has become the National Drainage Demonstration; moving around the country to new sites each year, this exhibits the highly technical and expensive drainage machinery, and illustrates the benefits of good drainage to the soil of Britain. Despite a massive boost to the laying of pipes for underground drainage systems during the Second World War, and a continuing emphasis ever since—stimulated by good Government grants—the job of draining Britain's farmland is like painting the Forth Bridge. The *Farmers Weekly* has extended its sponsorship with the inauguration of a 'Pig-Day' in 1968 and a 'Meat From Grass' Exhibition in 1973, which after a few wanderings settled down at the resplendent Bingley Hall of the Staffordshire Agricultural Society.

Fisons introduced an Annual Display under the ungainly title 'Spreaders-in-Action', when they set out to attract the manufacturers of fertilizer-spreaders to demonstrate the effectiveness of their machines on the same site. Eventually the manufacturers became worried that their machines might suffer in a highly competitive event, and that greater sophistication was producing more accurate displacement of fertilizer—from the bag to the ground—so Fisons opted to make this a two-yearly event. Shellstar (now UKF), the other fertilizer group, countered with a 'National Grassland Demonstration' (NGD), which set out to illustrate the benefits of fertilizer treatment upon Britain's largest farm crop—grass—which was also one of its most neglected. It later became established at the National Agricultural Centre at Stoneleigh.

BOCM-Silcock annually organize what is now termed a 'European Poultry Fair' at their Stoke Mandeville Farm, near Aylesbury in Buckinghamshire. It was commenced in 1965, and is the only event which brings together the poultry industry. The original Poultry Show was annually held in London at the same time as the Dairy Show.

Of a different nature is the World Ploughing Match, which was held in 1971 at Nynehead in Somerset. It was a financial disaster, and bankrupted the hosts, the 21-year-old British Ploughing Association, but two years later with new financial backing—some ironically donated by a French tyre company—the British Society of Ploughmen was created. It continues an annual British Ploughing Competition in the great traditions of the furrow-drawing matches or even the great Sheep Fairs that were held at Woburn Abbey in the eighteenth century, and provided the forerunners for today's National Farming Events. Another development has been the surprising rise of the 'Power-in-Action' Demonstration organized by the little-known East Suffolk Farm Machinery Club, and held on warm East Anglian soil at the Otley Farm Institute annually. It has provided an opportunity for tractor manufacturers to prove the reliability of their machines. Operating in a totally different way again is the Annual Doe Show, organized by Essex machinery dealers Ernest Doe and Sons Ltd, who withdrew from participation in their own Annual County Show to provide a vast collection of new machinery for their customers at their own works and farm. It draws attendance from many parts of the country, and is symptomatic of the new sales drive and rethinking of the companies involved in agriculture.

Oxford Farming Conference

'Successive Oxford Farming Conference audiences have exhibited a masochistic desire to worry themselves sick over the changes, the pressures, the challenges. Reading the title lists of past Conferences could lead to an interesting analysis of the psychology of that important sub species—the Oxford farmer.'

Henry Fell, opening the 1973 Oxford Farming Conference.

Look down Oxford High on any morning in early January, and you will see heavily muffled, brown-suited and cloth-capped farmers in small groups, wending their way towards the Town Hall. The Oxford Farming Conference, held in the first days of January each year, is about to commence. One goes up the stone steps and into Oxford's municipal pride and joy, with its ornate ceilings, oil paintings and vast amphitheatre, where the organ stares benignly down on the dedicated sons of the soil. If the accommodation is Spartan, the ornate ceiling a long way away, and the hall vast, then it is no worse than the old Oxford Playhouse where it all began, and where on more than one freezing January morning even well-clad farmers wrapped themselves in huge rugs.

The Town Hall is devoid of comfort and of extra-mural lobbies for the sort of animated discussions which should occupy the splinter groups at any Conference. You are forced to listen to the platform—there is nowhere else to go—and as the year dawns Oxford gets down to its serious business. It is a unique conference that sponsors itself, seems only to listen to itself, and might be said only to exist for itself. True, the ripples spread into the farming world, but few farmers have ever been to the Oxford Farming Conference.

This is not to suggest that it is poorly attended; on the contrary, the faithful turn up regularly, but since they are the same eight hundred people each year, one imagines them to be a particular breed of farmer who finds himself in tune with the radical thinking there. Is it progressive philosophy, radicalism, a sounding board or a crank's platform? Oxford is all of these, and none of these. It goes its own sweet way, organized by Mike Soper, that indefatigable bastion of farming thought within the University of Oxford, but its Chairman and Committee are chosen by those who attend the AGM on the second evening. There is no membership, ensuring that new thinking is for ever paramount.
yet is democratic, and one of the few rules restricts the tenure of Committee membership ensuring that new thinking is for ever paramount.

You can imagine a plea to nationalize farmland being greeted with polite silence, or even a mild clap, though in the more rational light of day those same participants would tomorrow fight tooth and nail against such a proposal. Attendance was originally banned to Ministry of Agriculture officers, although the Ministry has relented in the 1970s, and senior civil servants have actually delivered papers. Does it choose to take place at an inconvenient time for the boys of Cirencester's Royal Agricultural College not far away, or does the Royal choose to open its term in time to prevent its students becoming tainted? It has swung between the mundane and the highbrow, and back to the centre, but has never failed annually to present the challenge of the times. First-day speakers are world names, and deliver world-ranging papers; second-day papers come from a series of practical farmers on the same theme as on the first day, but with a muddy-booted approach. Each year they succeed in dragging into the limelight modest farmers with a story to tell, and the list through the years has included the best yeomen in the land.

It started in 1936 in a get-together sponsored by the Oxford School of Rural Economy, the Institute for Research in Agricultural Engineering and the Agricultural Economics Institute of Oxford University. Its first Conference was entitled 'Oxford Conference on Mechanisation in Mixed Farming', and three pre-War Conferences were held. It had sprung from the Harper Adams Power Farming Club, which had been formed in 1936, and its emphasis was upon the mechanization of farming. In 1951 it was resurrected with a philosophy of progressive if radical thinking, and strangely it was a guarantee by the capitalist Ford Motor Company which put up financial backing that enabled the 1951 Conference to take place; the guarantee was never called upon.

If the talk is red-hot the temperature is usually cool, but not perhaps as cool as the accommodation in Worcester College where the majority of the farmers stay; only the affluent ones manage the Randolph Hotel, where the pre-Conference Dinner sets the scene with an industrialist pontificating upon agriculture, usually with a set speech written by his secretary.

Power Farming Conference

Oxford is 99 per cent farmers, with a small representation from the NUAAW and only a minor sprinkling of others, but the Power Farming Conference, first held in February 1951 at Harrogate, attracts only 40 per cent farmers. The remainder consist of 28 per cent farm-machinery manufacturers, for whom this is perhaps an opportunity to meet customers, 12 per cent machinery dealers, and 20 per cent representatives from the other influential bodies to be found in agriculture, such as ADAS and the big banks. In its heyday Oxford attracted an unmanageable 1,000 people. The Power Farming Conference also reached these figures when it was free, but now a charge is made by its sponsors the numbers have reduced to a hard core of just over 300. After nearly three decades discussing the advances of farm machinery it must become somewhat repetitive; certainly the original stimulus of 1951 does not apply today.

Despite a fee or Conference charge, it costs its sponsors, the Agricultural Press Division of IPC, a considerable subsidy to continue this Conference. It was initiated by D. N. McHardy, and convened by Sir Richard Haddon, but jointly sponsored by two farming magazines, *Power Farming* and *The Farmer and Stockbreeder*. Today it is sponsored by *Power Farming*. After nineteen Conferences it widened its scope from an examination of innovatory machines to a broader outlook at the farming scene, but this is no Oxford; the politics of agriculture rarely sully its lips, and nomadic though it is, the best attendances always came from the South of England. Despite the efforts of the Government with hotel subsidies, and the pressure of the British Tourist Board, there is a dearth of suitable Conference towns in the UK. The major political conferences are held chiefly in Eastbourne, Brighton or Blackpool, and discounting London, the range of other centres is restricted. The Power Farming Conference travelled around until it settled at the Royal Bath Hotel in sunny Bournemouth—which is perhaps one of the better places in Britain in early February—and it has remained there since 1974. It has twice been cancelled; once it was postponed on the death of King George VI in 1952, but cancelled during the petrol-rationing Suez Crisis in 1957, and again (as with so many other dates on the farming calendar) during the foot-and-mouth epidemic in 1968. The organizing committee has a minority of farmers on it, but the Chairmanship alternates between a member of the machinery trade and a farmer. A man from the Ministry, Dennis Willows, took the hot seat in 1976. It is a mark of the co-operation at all levels that civil servants have in more recent years taken an active part in leading the industry.

30 The Media

The Times	'Read by the people who run the country.'
Daily Mirror	'Read by the people who think they run the country.'
Guardian	'Read by the people who think they ought to run the country.'
Daily Mail	'Read by the wives of the people who run the country.'
Financial Times	'Read by the people who own the country.'
Daily Express	'Read by the people who think the country ought to be run as it used to be run.'
Daily Telegraph	'Read by the people who think it is run as it used to be run.'
Morning Star	'Read by the people who think the country ought to be run by another country.'
The Sun	'Read by the people who don't give a damn who runs the country.'

If British politics should ever witness the birth of a farmer's party, it would start with the inbuilt advantage of a quasi-political farming press that is extremely non-partisan. Largely written by left-wing journalists for an inherently traditional Tory readership, it delves deeply into the political effects upon farming fortunes, but owes allegiance to no political party, and with careful abandon attacks everybody. This is not to suggest that the farming press is irresponsible; on the contrary, it is highly responsible, if sometimes dull and tedious. It is a technical press in the best sense of the word, dedicated to the rapid dissemination of farming news, and there always seems an abundance of crises to report, or new developments to analyse.

At the last count, there were 126 farming magazines or publications listed,[1] but if this seems an inordinate weight of paper read by farmers, it compares favourably with the 189 publications that circulate within the medical fraternity. The reason for such figures is not so much the dissemination and distribution of knowledge as the revenue from advertisers who have sensed a valuable market. The disparity between the farming and medical worlds emphasizes the vast purchasing power, through their prescriptions, of doctors. The circulation figures of these magazines, both farming and medical, do not rate among the highest in the national stakes, where the women's magazines rival even the greatest daily newspapers.

The *Farmers Weekly* dominates the farming scene, but it has several challengers, and the scene is an ever changing one, with new titles being launched in rapid succession.

[1] *British Rate and Data*. (Brad.)

Launched	Publication	Publisher
1970	*Agrifind*	George Wardrop
1971	*Agricultural Supply Industry*	Verabrite Ltd (Diane Montague)
1971	*Big Farm Management*	Thomson Organisation
1972	*Euro-Farm Business*	Farm Businesses Ltd (Clifford Selly and Laurence Gould)
1972	*Farm Contractor*	Anthony Collier
1973	*Anglian Farmer* (became *English Farmer,* 1977)	Lincolnshire Standard Group
1975	*The Farmer*	Lincolnshire Standard Group
1975	*Farming Industry*	Verabrite Ltd. (Diane Montague)
1977	*Big Farm Weekly*	Thomson Organisation
1977	*What's New in Farming?*	Morgan-Grampian
1977	*Fish Farming*	IPC

Such an influx of newcomers has not been accompanied by a corresponding demise, although some of those listed above, like *Agrifind,* have been wound up, *The Farmer* only lasted for a year, *Livestock International* has been sold to *World Crops* and *English Farmer* is restricted mainly to East Anglia. The advent of controlled-circulation magazines such as *Arable Farming,* which was launched as a paid paper in 1967, but with an unsatisfactory sales record went on to free circulation among selected designated farmers in 1974, is a phenomenon of modern publishing which seems to succeed.

Besides the technical farming press, the weight of farming news published by the national media is disproportionate to the 2 per cent of the population actively involved in farming, and in a highly industrial country the coverage of farming news by the open channels of communication is certainly higher than would be expected. Both radio and TV accord farming news-items in their regular broadcasts, and there are specialized farming programmes on BBC radio or TV seven days a week. No other section gets such treatment. The national dailies since the War have given farming a good coverage, although this is now changing, with 'food' rather than farming being the main interest. The number of specialized farming reports is diminishing, and in local weekly newspapers the farming page has been a traditional feature, and farming has been well served by regional daily papers.

In spite of this weight of activity, there is a dearth of farming books. Gone is that champion of the farming novel A. G. Street, and changing fashions have ousted the countryside novels, largely written in incomprehensible dialect. This is not to deny the success of the James Herriot series on the life of a Yorkshire vet travelling the farms, but today there is no outstanding farming novelist in the Street tradition.

Perhaps British farming is epitomized today by Derbyshire farmer Ted Moult, with his agile brain and quick wit, replacing A. G. Street and Ralph Wightman in their 'Any Questions'. Within the technical farming media, there is a galaxy of down-to-earth farmers, such as Norfolk farmer David Richardson, with his rich but articulate Norfolk tongue, his hosting of TV and radio programmes, and a prodigious output of written material. Hampshire farmer John Cherrington, a banker's son but a farmer nonetheless, keeps the *Financial Times* on the straight and narrow with his pugnacious and perceptive commentary. Somerset farmer Michael Clark brings a fruity countryside atmosphere to the Saturday morning BBC 'On Your Farm' programme, and Essex farmer Hew Watt contributes to various radio and TV programmes. In the local field, the weekly farming column in many provincial newspapers is given an earthy flavour by the contributions of a local farmer, interpreting current problems to an interested public. But the majority of the influential men and women behind the scenes of the farming press have little if any farming background, though they know more about farming than most farmers, have travelled more widely, and are more up to date. There are farmers who write, but few writers who farm; among the latter Clifford Selly, formerly Agricultural Correspondent of the *Observer*, made the transition from Fleet Street into practical farming in Hertfordshire. Paul Attlee left the *Farmers Weekly* to farm a 29-hectare holding in Cornwall in 1964, and the editor of the *British Farmer and Stockbreeder*, Monty Keen, has a small farm with pigs at Pentlow on the Essex/Suffolk border.

The most influential position in British agricultural journalism (once occupied by Sir Anthony Hurd, MP for Newbury) is the agricultural niche on *The Times*, which was taken over in recent years by Leonard Amey, who graduated from a provincial daily newspaper at Ipswich. His successor, Hugh Clayton, was an internal promotion and the emphasis has changed—in line with the trend in the national Press to a greater preoccupation with the consumer and food-production. The esteem in which *The Times* is held is perhaps traditional, as opposed to the more modern image of *The Financial Times*. In the farming coverage of UK daily newspapers, the largest space given to farming appears in the latter. The *F.T.* has recognized that farming is big business and its daily half-page feature 'Farming and Raw Materials', gives as much space to agriculture and food as it does to the fortunes of copper and zinc, coffee and soya beans. It does accord farming its rightful place as an industry within the UK, and with its succession of farmers who write, it supplies the best daily news coverage of agriculture. Tristram Beresford, who farms on the chalkland of Salisbury Plain, was its agricultural correspondent for fourteen years from 1949 to 1963, when John Cherrington took over the slot. The *Daily Express* has given farming a good press—perhaps due to Beaverbrook's Scottish farming ancestry, and his farming interests in the South-West, though since the paper has predominantly a readership of urban housewives it emphasized for years the part farming played in the country's economy. After the retirement of Alexander Kenworthy in 1977, no successor was appointed, and farming is now part of the paper's consumer affairs coverage. The *Daily Mail* has had a 'Farm Mail' column for over twenty years, contributed originally by Alan Exley, followed by John Winter and Peter Bullen, but it gives only a compressed section on some aspects of farming news. Nevertheless, farming has its platform in a newspaper that has become almost a ladies' magazine. The *Telegraph* and *Guardian* also have full-time farming journalists on their staff, and Yorkshire farmer Claud Scott has contributed a weekly column to the *Telegraph* for nearly 30 years. It started by accident, when in the immediate post-War period an ex-soldier with whom he had served asked him to write a piece for his newspaper. He was a member of the Berry family, and Colonel Scott started a hobby-career that was to last many years.

'The Archers'

> *'No-one at that time could possibly have forecast the impact it was to make as a permanent ingredient of sound broadcasting, and that at its peak, before the introduction of television, it would attract a regular audience of well over ten million listeners here in Great Britain.'*
>
>   '"The Archers, a Slice of my Life"' (Godfrey Baseley, 1971)

The brain-child of Godfrey Baseley, the son of a village butcher at Alvechurch in Worcestershire, *The Archers* was to become part of the British way of life, has contributed in a most outstanding way to bridging the gulf between town and country, and has given the farming industry a unique platform. Baseley's programme was sub-titled 'An Everyday Story of Country Folk' when it started in January 1950. It filled the teatime slot on BBC radio, and was the successor of *Dick Barton—Special Agent*, which had been a suspense-filled popular programme, with Dick, Snowy and Jock left suspended on a cliff-hanging ending at each programme. A new programme about the sleepy affairs of an English village would still need suspense. This was before the brash days of eroticism, and love in the hay-loft would not do. Suspense was needed; would the listening public rally to the goings-on in the cowshed? Godfrey Baseley takes up the story[2]:

> The very first situation was one of anxiety about the birth of a calf. Dan Archer had to leave his farm worker, Simon, to look after the birth because he had to attend an important Farmers Union meeting in Borchester.
> The scene was set in the farmyard with Dan and Simon looking over the half door of a loose box at the cow.
> There was a low 'moo' from the cow, then Dan said,
> 'Well, Simon, what do you think?'
> And Simon replied,
> 'Ah, well—'er might and 'er might not.'
> In just those two lines we laid the foundation of thousands of scenes and situations where anxiety, doubt and suspense have all played their part.

Five years after its debut, when Brookfield Farm, Dan and Doris Archer, Walter Gabriel and The Bull had become part of Britain's national heritage, the BBC dropped a dramatic bombshell. Into this everyday story of cows and sheep, farming and village life, they dropped a sudden and horrific event even more suspense-filled and interest-laden than anything Dick Barton had ever done—they killed off Grace Archer.

In the annals of the BBC it still ranks as the most famous fictional death when

[2]Godfrey Baseley, *The Archers* (Sidgwick & Jackson, 1971).

in September 1955, the young Grace Archer, a bride of only five months, was dragged from a blazing stable and died in her husband's arms. It had the biggest impact on listeners in the history of the Archers up to that time, and ever since. It was front-page news in every newspaper the following day, and treated as a national disaster. Women wept in the streets, house-blinds were pulled down as a mark of respect, and the BBC was swamped with flowers and wreaths, and even money for the bereaved of Ambridge.

Secrecy had prevailed, and the script for that day was only written that morning; even the actress, Ysanne Churchman, did not know before the afternoon recording. She came back into the Archers in another role sixteen years later as Mary Pound. There was a sequel to this dramatic exit, when at the 25th birthday of the Archers the BBC discovered that this dramatic scene had been edited out of its archives, which by that time had accumulated 14 million words. In 1975 they re-enacted the scene again, with the same actress, and the same Philip Archer—Norman Painting, who later received mention in the Royal Honours List for playing the part for twenty-five years non-stop.

Ambridge was linked to the real Worcestershire village of Inkberrow, but in 1977 it moved its fictional location to Ashdon-under-Hill, a short distance away, where the leading farmer happened to be Fred Archer, the author of several countryside books, and member of a family well known in that area. A feature of the Archers has been that it has kept abreast of the times, and Godfrey Baseley himself has given praise to the team of script-writers who have sustained the interest. It even has an Agricultural Advisory Panel which strives to present an authentic image, yet continue the suspense. It went through a period of resembling *Coronation Street*, but with perceptiveness found a new role and retained its listenership.

Its objective is 'An Everyday Story of Country Folk', but it seeks to boost farming and even to act in an advisory capacity to farmers themselves; indeed, there is little cardboard about the Archers, and it still rings true to the most hard bitten and dedicated farmer in the country. It remains the most potent, if subtle, publicity weapon the farming community or the NFU could ever wish to achieve.

In the first 25 years of the Archers, 250 characters cropped up in the series, the cows at Brookfield Farm were milked 26,000 times, there were 20,000 cups of tea drunk, and 12,000 pints of beer drawn at the Bull. Dan Archer represents the archetypal farmer; he is a Tory, and outraged Labour MPs in 1965 by commenting upon the Budget proposals to end tax-free entertainment. He has suffered all the natural disasters that affect farmers. In 1957 one of his cows got a tin stuck on its muzzle; in 1973 a stray dog caused his sheep to abort; Jolly, the bull calf, died from lead-poisoning, and Dan himself strained his back lifting a gate post. He has cut his hand on a circular saw, fractured his leg on the binder, and developed a slipped disc. He fell over chasing a poacher, and has been crushed by a cow. Yet he still represents the best picture of a typical farmer that fiction can provide. There is, of course, nothing fictional about *The Archers*. To millions of people it is real life.

BBC

The Government is for the people;
The BBC is for the people.
Therefore the BBC must be for the Government.'

Lord Reith, First Director-General, BBC.

Monday morning starts with the weekly *Farming Week*, which is transmitted by rotation from Norwich, Bristol, Leeds, Cardiff and Aberdeen, and comes on the air before 6.30 a.m., usually followed by the religious *Thought for the Day*. On the remaining days of the week the programme is entitled *Farming Today*, and covers the fatstock and grain prices, with some short bursts of farming news items and comments. On Saturday morning, a little later (at 7.10 a.m.), comes the weekly half-hour *On Your Farm*, produced in Birmingham by Anthony Parkin. It started in August 1964, and although Norfolk farmer David Richardson was involved from the early days, Somerset farmer Michael Clark started broadcasting in his heavily accented West Country tones in 1969.

Scotland has its *Farming Journal*, a ten-minute magazine from Monday to Friday, at 12.45 p.m., certainly a more hospitable time of day; *Farming Today in Wales*, produced in Cardiff, is an early morning starter, but *Ulster Farm* is a weekly magazine programme broadcast at lunch-time on Fridays. Additional to the regional farming programmes on both BBC and IBC is the broadcast from London in the BBC World Service, where three times a week is broadcast a farming programme of thirty-minute duration. *Farming World* is heard in Australia, the Pacific Islands and throughout Africa and America. It covers features and talks about the UK farming scene.

The BBC's network of farming programmes all started in 1929, when fatstock prices were included following the shipping forecasts, but in October 1934 came the first regular farming feature, and on Thursday evenings John Morgan, agricultural correspondent of the *Daily Herald*, gave a series of talks basically designed to help farmers through what was a period of depression. Farming was a popular subject, even before Munich. The new farming gospel of such people as Stapledon and Boutflour had to be propagated, and radio was an ideal vehicle.

With the wartime emphasis upon food-production, there was a boost to the farming programmes, and a more vital interest in the subject of producing food from local farms. *Backs to the Land* was a wartime lunch programme for farmers, and was followed by *Five to One on the Land*, a short lunch-time farming broadcast which it was hoped farmers would hear in their kitchens. It dealt with such topical subjects as trying to persuade farmers to drop their prejudices against employing women on farms.

From these small beginnings has evolved a sophisticated series of farming programmes, and the BBC has an Agricultural Advisory Committee, whose membership changes frequently. It is estimated that about one million people hear the 6.30 a.m. early-morning *Farming Today* programme, and Lady Wilson during her stay at 10 Downing Street said, 'I turn on to Radio 4 as soon as I get up at about 6.30, and always listen with at least half an ear to part of "Farming Today", so I'm quite well up with the price of cabbages.'

A report by the BBC Central Agricultural Advisory Committee on the future of broadcasting, August 1975, said that when the weekly *On Your Farm* programme was discontinued as a regional repeat at 12.30 p.m. on Wednesdays (the previous Saturday morning programme), the BBC lost 200,000 agricultural listerners. But the listenership of the farming programmes extends beyond the farming community.

Emmerdale Farm

The BBC has not attempted to rival the success of *The Archers* on TV; it has been left to ITV Yorkshire Television to create a famous farming family for the visual media. In 1972 it launched a daily programme on the goings-on at fictitious Emmerdale Farm and the Sugden family. Unlike radio, a real farm is required for the shots, and the farm chosen was that of Arthur Peel, deep in the Yorkshire Dales and a few kilometres from the television studios in Leeds. Its real identity and the location of its character-filled village are supposed to be a secret, but nevertheless 'Beckindale' is eagerly sought by addicts and hero-worshippers who have discovered the Peel Farm, and inundated the place with gawping sightseers. Arthur Peel has been forced to lock his gates at weekends to protect his privacy. The success of *Emmerdale Farm* surprised even its instigators, and it commands a 70 per cent viewing rating, higher than any other programme shown at that particular time of day, it is watched by an estimated 300,000 viewers in Yorkshire alone. The Woolpack pub and the village shop have become famous; even the offertory box in the village church has been filled with £50 a week by tourists. Producer Bob Cardona was himself surprised at its success, and he commented:

> Farmers are up to their eyes in mud in all weathers for seven days a week, and umpteen hours a day milking cows, but they love their job.
>
> Yet these people in the towns who go to their warm offices at orderly hours and return to the centrally heated homes in the evening actually envy the farming profession.

Emmerdale, like *The Archers*, succeeds because of its simplicity. There is no exploitation of violence or sex, and the scripts aim to portray country life as an honest, hard-working, if sometimes simple, occupation. Ironically, the real Beckindale is surrounded by hills, and the villagers cannot receive TV.

The Guild of Agricultural Journalists

A doctor, once qualified and becoming a member of the BMA, remains a member of this after his retirement; a Chartered Surveyor is entitled to use the initials RICS for life; but a member of the Guild of Agricultural Journalists is only entitled to full membership while he remains an active participant in the realms of farming journalism, and it must be in a full-time role.

The Guild has a system of 'second class citizens' known as Associates, and gentlemen from the public relations industry or from other aspects of publicizing farming in various commercial capacities are put into the 'Associate' class. A member who once attains full status will lose this status automatically once he changes jobs and is no longer occupied in full-time agricultural journalism. At least the audio section of the media is recognized as being equal to the written word.

The Guild exists to promote the high ideals of journalism, whatever the general public may think about journalists and the inaccuracies of the Press. It is not an employment agency, and rarely circulates, even to its own members, vacancies which may be occurring. Nevertheless, there is a vast changeover in the journalistic profession as ambitious men and women jockey for new jobs along the promotional ladder.

Its main functions are a harvest service annually in the historic St Bride's Church, tucked away behind the humming activity of Fleet Street, and there is a spring lunch at the International Press Centre nearby, but it has dropped the Annual Cocktail Party at the Royal Show in July. It has just over 300 members, and there is a strict ratio of 55 per cent full-time active journalists to 45 per cent associates, although despite mutterings from the Associate Members this ratio is not carried on to its governing council.

To further journalistic standards, there are the Perkins engines Awards and the Fisons Awards granted annually for the best selection of published material. In 1978 came a broader competition for the best 'Communicator of the Year' to embrace the wider spectrum of the media, and to break the stranglehold of puritanism which is symbolic of the Guild's functions and objectives. Its emblem is on the tie which members may obtain in various hues, and shows the quill pen and wheat ear crossed. This happily covers its objectives and motives.

'Farmers Weekly'

'Grove Farm, Tring, Hertfordshire, was Farmers Weekly's first practical stake in the industry. We bought the 270 acres of chalky loam for £30,000, lock, stock and barrel, in 1943'

'Farmers Weekly', 31 March 1972.

The *Farmers Weekly* is more of a farming institution than a magazine. It dominates the scene, and has become known as a responsible organ which faithfully portrays the industry. If it becomes dull and tedious at times, or tends to be over-technical, its defence is that farming is a technical business. It plays down the disruptions and rows within farming, and does not seek to be a newspaper. The *Farmers Weekly* was once in competition with the *Farmer and Stockbreeder*, which was very much its senior, being founded in 1889, while the

Farmers Weekly was only launched in 1934. The difference between the two magazines was that the 'Weekly' was considered a better-class paper than the 'Stockbreeder'; one was orientated towards the arable farmers, and the other, as its title implied, to the smaller livestock men. It might be cynical to observe that the only difference between them was that the 'Weekly' had its 'small-ads' at the front, and the 'Stockbreeder' had them at the back. Eventually the two papers became owned by IPC, and in 1971 the 'Stockbreeder' was axed, and reappeared under a new guise (merged with the NFU's *British Farmer*), with a controlled circulation, and only fortnightly. It left the 'Weekly' in a paramount position.

There are two other weekly farming publications, but so far they have made little impact upon the circulation figures of the *Farmers Weekly*. The *Farmers Guardian*, part of the United Newspapers Group, was launched in 1958 to fill a gap in the more northern counties of England, with a weekly newspaper, giving the political and practical news with some feature articles. Stuart Seaton was its first Assistant Editor, and took over the hot seat in 1962. It started with a circulation of 16,000, and has doubled this in the intervening period.

The *Farmers Guardian* maintains a strong accent upon livestock matters as a natural product of the region it serves. It has spread from its base at Preston, and has slipped into Gloucestershire, but does not extend to Lincolnshire or East Anglia. A Friday newspaper delivered by the newsagent, it has also sponsored a Poultry Fair as part of the now defunct Royal Lancashire Show, but it is no competitor to the *Farmers Weekly*. On the other hand, *Big Farm Weekly*, launched in 1977, as an easy-to-read national weekly farm business newspaper, emanates from London, and aims at the top end of the readership of the *Farmers Weekly*. It is a controlled circulation paper for large farmers with 125 hectares of crop and grass or 100 beef cattle, 80 dairy cows, 500 breeding ewes, or large pig herds. It is delivered at the convenience of the Post Office, and does not always arrive before the weekend. With these small pinpricks, the *Farmers Weekly* can rest assured that its position will not diminish.

Paid		Free	
Farmers Weekly	130,000	British Farmer and	
The Countryman	69,000	Stockbreeder	140,000
Country Life	43,000	Modern Farmer	41,000
Scottish Farmer	32,000	English Farmer	25,000
Farmers Guardian	31,500	Livestock Farming	25,000
Dairy Farmer	27,500	Big Farm Weekly	23,000
The Field	25,000	Big Farm Management	22,000
Power Farming	22,000	Arable Farmer	17,000
Poultry World	9,500		

The *Farmers Weekly* was the child of an unlikely duo of press barons, Lords Beaverbrook and Rothermere, but Beaverbrook soon bought out his competitor press baron; in 1937 he sold it to the Hulton Press, which had just launched *Picture Post*. It must have come hard to Lord Beaverbrook to sell it, and many years later he attempted to launch another farming paper called *Farming Express*. It was launched on an anti Common Market platform in 1960, and ceased publication in 1965, when Beaverbrook had been dead a year. The Hulton Press was acquired by Odhams in 1959, and absorbed by the Mirror Group in 1961. A subdivision of farm journals was created; at the same time Associated Iliffe Press had also built up a collection of farming journals, and when the Mirror Group took over Associated in 1958 further mergers resulted; ten years later Agricultural Press was created as a division within the new company. The ramifications of big business have resulted in the Mirror Group coming under the umbrella of Reed International, later to become IPC, which at the last count had a total staff of 84,000 people. Agricultural Press Ltd controls seven of the major farming publications.

The 'Farmers Weekly' farms

In an effort to identify itself with the farming community, the *Farmers Weekly* in 1943 established its first farm, where it could study farming fortunes and problems for itself, and present the facts in the magazine. This one farm has grown to seven, representing a broad spectrum of UK farming interests and divisions, and ranging from Scotland and Wales to an arable farm in Eastern England. It attempted to buy a farm in France when Britain joined the Common Market in the early 1970s, but discovered that the French had rules about foreigners buying farms.

Grove Farm was the first of the *Farmers Weekly* farms, and is situated at Tring in Hertfordshire. Here farming has gone on amid the pressures of urban surroundings, and in 1954 some off-hand land was separated to create Bulbourne Farm as a concentrated 70-cow intensive dairy unit. In 1968 the *Farmers Weekly* pioneered the ill-fated 600-cow Asclin Cotel, an experiment in mass milk-production on a vast scale which never got off the ground in Britain. In this experiment they had placed Grove Farm at the disposal of the Cotel for fodder-production, but afterwards it went on to a simple arable system; later sheep were introduced, but the changing scene and changing pattern of farming at Grove Farm has been symptomatic of the everlasting search for new and more profitable farming system. In 1976 it added another 46 hectares, amalgamated Grove and Bulbourne and went all arable, calling it Marshcroft Farm. Fortunately, *Farmers Weekly* could afford the losses which have been incurred better than many private farmers.

Broadley Farm, set amid the hills just inside South Wales near Abergavenny in the Black Mountains, with only 31 hectares, was bought in 1959 to examine the problems of a family struggling for survival from a small unit on highly marginal land. Twelve years later the magazine claimed to have found at last a successful formula, but it had been a traumatic experience. The Hereford suckler cows developed copper and cobalt deficiencies, suckler calves refused to thrive, sheep were intensified, but did not thrive either, and deep-litter poultry were scrapped after an abortive attempt to integrate them into the farming system. In the end a system of intensive calf-rearing, store-cattle production, fat-lamb and seed-potato production seems to have filled the bill for this marginal farm. The following year tenancy was taken of a farm in Durham, Cowbyers Farm. This was a large hill farm of 486 hectares; certainly the problems of hill farmers were learnt, and in 1966 to complete the spectrum of the farming activities the tenancy was acquired of a large arable farm on the Marquess of Exeter's estate near Stamford in Lincolnshire, and another farm, East Brackland, near Callander, was taken in partnership with the landlords, the Moray Estates Development Co., who kept a 25 per cent share in the farm business. This was a highly experimental operation on a large farm in Scotland, but it emphasized that the financial structure behind the landlord/tenant system was becoming a vital feature for younger farmers entering the industry. Finally, in 1976, came Conrick, another Scottish farm where the objective is to concentrate upon the problems of dairy farming. The *Farmers Weekly* summed up its own attitude towards this involvement in farming:[3]

> Since "Farmers Weekly" began farming on its own in 1943, our policy has been to identify dilemmas which were common to substantial groups of farming people, and then to examine them in a public, practical way. At Bulbourne and Broadley, we have looked at the continuing problems of the small, single-family unit. At Cowbyers, we have sought a profit formula for beef and lamb on a hard hill farm. At Easton Lodge, we have pitted our resources and our wits against poor soils, low rainfalls and modern big farm rentals. Now, we intend to take up the cause of the marginal producer of milk.
>
> Our search for a suitable place on which to do so has led to the purchase this week of the farm of Conrick, near Sanquhar in the Scottish borders.

'British Farmer and Stockbreeder'

The largest circulating farming journal going to all NFU members free, the BF & SB, was the result of an amalgamation of the oldest farming magazine with *British Farmer*, the official organ of the NFU. One wonders if the amalgamation would have taken place if the Stockbreeder and the Weekly were under individual ownership, but they had come under the same roof after a series of take-overs and mergers, and the decision to axe the Stockbreeder was undoubtedly taken with a view of strengthening the *Farmers Weekly*. It happened that at the same time the rather pathetic *British Farmer*, published by the NFU, was in dire straits, and in March 1971 the reborn *British Farmer and Stockbreeder* appeared. With a controlled circulation, and a guaranteed

[3] 24 September 1976.

market, it certainly reaches the furthest corners of England and Wales (the Scottish NFU has its own organ, the *Scottish Farming Leader*, formerly known as *Farming Leader*). However, since it is a fortnightly publication, the new enterprise has never been the serious threat to the *Farmers Weekly* which it might have been, its free distribution resulting in a declining circulation for the latter. It cannot keep up with news that is two weeks old, and the lack of continuity with rapidly changing market prices means that it is not a serious competitor.

The BF & SB goes back to the foundation in 1832 of the *Mark Lane Express*, and although it acquired its title in 1889, there are claims that it bases its line of descent from another paper founded in 1843. During this time, before its demise and rebirth in 1971, it absorbed the *Agricultural Gazette* in 1925, a magazine that itself dated from 1844, and in 1938 it absorbed *Farm Field and Fireside*.

The new magazine was launched during a postal strike, and it has suffered from distribution problems. Bob Trow-Smith was its Editor until November 1972, when he was succeeded by Monty Keen, who had been employed as Parliamentary Secretary to the NFU until he resigned to take up farming at the age of forty-four. He retained his small pig farm, but among the agricultural editors and journalists there are few with practical farming experience. The *British Farmer and Stockbreeder* acts as a noticeboard for the NFU, and is part of its highly geared publicity machine, but it tries to present an independent line of thinking.

'Power Farming'

Another of the IPC Group, *Power Farming*, is a glossy monthly magazine that started with the boost for mechanization on farms in wartime June 1941, and has developed into a highly technical magazine peppered with intricate drawings of the internal mechanism of highly sophisticated gear-boxes, transmission devices and hydraulic operations. Its circulation in farming terms is not large, but its adherents are enthusiastic specialists at all levels of farm size.

It was founded independently by D. N. McHardy, a former machinery correspondent of *Farmer and Stockbreeder*, and was in 1941 launched as the official organ of the Tractor Users Association, now absorbed into the NAAC. McHardy was both publisher and editor, and he had an office in London, but it was printed in Reading. Early in 1944 the Tractor Users Association was wound up, but the paper continued, and shortly afterwards 'British Power Farming Clubs' became the rage, to be followed in 1948 by the 'Irish Power Farming Clubs'. In that year the journal was published in Dublin, but the head office remained near London. There was a two-day 'Power Farming Club' Rally in London in 1948, and an Irish one the following year. From this evolved the National Power Farming Conference.

McHardy died in 1957, having had sold his magazine to Associated Iliffe Press Ltd in July 1950, but having remained its Editor. At his death the title was changed to *Practical Power Farming*; it was changed again in June 1965 to its current title, although in 1969 it absorbed *Farm Mechanisation* and *Buildings*, established in 1946 by Temple Press Ltd. After McHardy died George Wardrop became its Editor for five years, when Stanley Farmer succeeded him, and in 1974 Ted Fellows, previously Technical Editor of the *British Farmer and Stock-breeder*, took over the Editorship.

Also in the IPC basket, and now removed—with all the other IPC farm papers—from dusty Fleet Street to an inelegant tower block at Sutton in Surrey, is the *Poultry World*, first published under this title in 1908. It sprang from the old *Fanciers Gazette*, and had been launched by Frederick Carl. It came into the IPC Group through its take-over of Associated Iliffe Press, but had been acquired by Iliffe in 1931. Its sister journal *Poultry Farmer* was absorbed after the merger.

Another specialized journal which circulates among machinery dealers is *Agricultural Machinery Journal*, launched in 1946 by Captain R. L. Carey, who sold it within a year. It became a monthly in 1950, and later merged with *Farm Implement and Machinery Review*.

More farming magazines

'The farming press in the UK has no equal in the world. It may not have the colour and the wealth of publications of its nearest rival, the farming press of the USA, but it has the edge in originality and readability.'
Philip Hassall, 'Big Farm Management', May 1971

'The press lives by disclosures.'
'The Times', 1851.

There is a plethora of farming news and developments every day; while the hard-pressed farmer tries to find time to keep up to date, the farming press also strives manfully to cover and record all that goes on. There are some concise news sheets with bare facts and little comment. One such is *Agricultural Supply Industry*, and its sister paper, *Farming Industry*. The first named is the 'Pink Un' of the agricultural ancillary industries, a small sheet, newspaper-style, produced by Diane Montague with the help of an assistant and her mother, from a small office in Beak Street, London. Small magazines have been launched by entrepreneurs as individuals, and in 1964 *Beef and Sheep Farming* appeared. It is now known as *Livestock Farming*, and was the brain-child of Alan Exley, who had been for five years agricultural correspondent on the *Daily Mail*, had been anchor man of Southern TV *Farm in the South*, Editor of the ill-fated Beaverbrook weekly *Farming Express*, and had also farmed for ten years, while doing other jobs.

Exley sold his baby in 1973 to Morgan-Grampian Ltd, but not before he had changed the format to include dairy farming from 1970 onward. Morgan-Grampian was first registered in 1929 as Morgan Brothers (Publishers) Ltd, but added the suffix in 1967. As a specialist in magazine publishing, it became the subject of a Monopolies Commission Inquiry in 1973, when it proposed to dispose of 18 local newspapers in Kent and Sussex to Westminster Press Ltd (largely owned by Lord Cowdray), through his S. Pearson & Sons Ltd (owning among others merchant bankers Lazard Brothers, and the *Financial Times*). M-G purchased *Livestock Farming* in 1973, and appointed Marcus Oliver as Editor. Its foray into farming continued in October 1977, with the launching of *What's New In Farming*?

From Ipswich radiates the publications of Farming Press Ltd, which include three magazines and an off-shoot producing a long list of technical books on aspects of farming. *Dairy Farmer* was launched in 1929 by a private company called Dairy Farmer Ltd, which later became Associated Agricultural Publications. Taken over in 1958 by Bradbury Agnew, a family company with its origins in the Agnew family in Northamptonshire, it was taken over again in 1968 by United Newspapers Ltd, of which Farming Press Ltd is a subsidiary. In 1953 it launched *Pig Farmer* and in 1967 *Arable Farming*, which later became *Arable Farmer*. Also in this company is the ageless *Punch*, and *Farmers Guardian*, launched in 1958 with its office at Preston.

The evolvement of magazine titles and their changing emphasis is well illustrated by the example of *Big Farm Management*, an ungainly title which has somehow managed to stick. It is the latter-day successor of *Sporting and Dramatic Life*, a glossy in the image of *The Tatler*, later changed to *Farm and Country*, and in 1967 changed to a controlled circulation journal going into the homes of larger farmers with over 125 hectares as a free, if glossy, magazine. For the first time it aimed at the most valuable section of the farming market, those with a large enough buying capacity to attract the advertisers. By the end of its first year it had registered 11,000 farmers, and in 1971 broke away from the old image with a new title—*Big Farm Management*. By 1977 it had gathered into its net 22,000 large farmers, accounting for around 50 per cent of the industry's market capacity. Edited by Philip Hassall until April 1978, when George Mac-Phearson took over, and owned by the Thomson Organization, it was a foray into farming that was quite outside the normal scope of that bluff Canadian Lord Thomson, who magnanimously bought *The Times*, and lost a fortune sustaining it, but revelled in the image which it created for himself. In 1977 Thomson launched *Big Farm Weekly*, edited by Derek Fraser, with Philip Hassall as Managing Editor of the duo, for the same readership as the monthly *Big Farm Management*, with the aim of providing the big farm with a complete package of news and technical information.

Mergers, take-overs, amalgamations, reorganizations, rationalizations, have all played their part in projecting a rapidly changing scene of the farming media, and it has been engendered by the highly volatile and unpredictable swings of the publishing world. Farmers have been subjected to a bombardment of free magazines, mostly of a high calibre, dropping unannounced through their letter-boxes. The advent of the controlled-circulation publication ensures that its circulation can be directed at a specific group of people and the advertiser can be assured that his product-news is being faced by his potential customers. Perhaps almost surprisingly amid this welter of weekly and monthlies, those which farmers pay for still exist, but at least it allows the discriminating reader to take his pick. In the variety of the farming press in the UK, there is certainly something for everybody—and who said that farmers did not read anything?

Index

By RICHARD RAPER

Notes
1. The alphabetical arrangement is word by word.
2. Entries in *italics* refer to newspapers, magazines and books.
3. Entries on Laws and Acts of Parliament are grouped together under Legislation, for user convenience.

Index

By RICHARD RAPER

Notes
1. The alphabetical arrangement is word by word.
2. Entries in *italics* refer to newspapers, magazines and books.
3. Entries on Laws and Acts of Parliament are grouped together under Legislation, for user convenience.